PROCESSES IN TECHNICAL WRITING

PROCESSES IN TECHNICAL WRITING

David A. McMurrey
Austin Community College
IBM Corporation

MACMILLAN PUBLISHING COMPANY
New York
COLLIER MACMILLAN PUBLISHERS
London

Copyright © 1988, Macmillan Publishing Company,
a division of Macmillan, Inc.

Printed in the United States of America

All rights reserved. No part of this book may be reproduced or
transmitted in any form or by any means, electronic or mechanical,
including photocopying, recording, or any information storage and
retrieval system, without permission in writing from the Publisher.

Macmillan Publishing Company
866 Third Avenue, New York, New York 10022

Collier Macmillan Canada, Inc.

Library of Congress Cataloging-in-Publication Data

McMurrey, David A.
  Processes in technical writing.

  Includes index.
  1. Technical writing.   I. Title.
T11.M3683 1988   808'.0666   87-11231
ISBN 0-02-379700-2

Printing: 1 2 3 4 5 6 7   Year: 8 9 0 1 2 3 4

ISBN 0-02-379700-2

Preface

The word *processes* in the title of this book, written for introductory courses in technical and professional writing, should tell you much about its approach and organization. In this book, the process approach to technical-writing instruction means:

- Focusing on the way we get to the finished written product, not just on the details of that product.
- Understanding and practicing the typical steps in report writing.
- Studying the difficult or often overlooked steps such as audience analysis and revision.
- Understanding how most writing projects force us to make small—and sometimes large—changes in our writing process in order to meet the needs of a specific audience, purpose, and subject matter.

This book identifies the most important and the most common processes in technical writing and the typical steps within those processes. Then, using a system of specific instructions (called *steps* in this text), discussion, and examples, the book guides students through these processes as they prepare reports, articles, letters, and resumes. These key processes include:

- Writing descriptions, process and causal discussions, comparisons, definitions, classifications, introductions, conclusions, and summaries (abstracts).
- Writing business letters, resumes, informational reports, progress reports, proposals, feasibility reports, instructions, and popular science articles.
- Preparing and delivering oral reports and visual aids to accompany them.
- Analyzing audiences and adapting technical discussions to specific audiences.
- Planning, creating, and incorporating graphic aids.
- Revising sentences and paragraphs in technical prose.

- Selecting, narrowing, and outlining a technical report topic.
- Finding information for technical reports both in and out of libraries.
- Taking notes for technical reports: quoting, paraphrasing, and summarizing.
- Handling the physical production and binding of reports.
- Collaborating on technical report projects.

Organization of the Chapters

Following the Introduction, which offers a definition of technical writing, this book contains five parts:

Part I. Shows how to write process and causal discussions, descriptions, definitions, comparisons, introductions, conclusions, and summaries (abstracts).

Part II. Shows how to analyze audiences, adapt technical discussions to specific audiences, find ways to make difficult technical concepts easier to understand, plan and create graphic and textual aids, and revise paragraphs and sentences.

Part III. Shows the main phases in preparing reports: selecting and narrowing topics, outlining, finding library and nonlibrary information, taking notes, drafting, revising and proofreading, and final packaging of reports.

Part IV. Shows how to write common types of business letters, resumes, informational reports, progress reports, feasibility reports, proposals, instructions and popular science articles, as well as how to prepare and deliver oral reports.

Part V. Provides a group of appendices on different ways to document reports, sentence patterns and elements, paragraph patterns and elements, usage and punctuation rules, rules for numbers in text, copyeditor's and instructor's symbols, and terms used in this book.

These parts of the book and the chapters within them are designed to be as flexible and adaptable as possible to meet your teaching needs:

- If you prefer to start with practice writing, Part I chapters will be your starting point.
- If you prefer to dive into the applications and return to the practice-writing chapters when need be, Part IV chapters can easily be assigned first.
- If you prefer to focus on such skills as audience analysis, graphic aids, and revision techniques at the beginning of the semester, you can assign Part II chapters first.
- If you prefer to focus early on the phases in preparing technical reports—the topic selection, narrowing, outlining, information-gathering phases, for example—you can begin with the chapters in Part III.

The book's organization does not force you to adopt a particular arrangement of units, nor should it cause you to modify the syllabus you have been using. You may be interested in looking at the sample syllabi included in the Instructor's Manual. These will give you some ideas on different ways the chapters of this book can be used.

Features of This Book

Within this book, you'll find a number of features to help you teach technical writing, enable your students to learn more effectively, and provide innovative classroom activities and writing projects.

The Steps and the Worksheets. Scanning the pages of this book, you will immediately spot one of its key features: the blue-lettered steps that punctuate the text of each of the main chapters.

Here's how the steps work. As students begin reading, they are also beginning work on their assignment. As they read the text and come to a step, they stop and do the planning or writing activity it requests. The step is based on the discussion and examples they have just seen. They continue in this way until they reach the end of the chapter or section. By then, they have considered, planned, and gathered information sufficient to write the assignment. At that point, they have been through key steps in a particular process of technical writing.

The steps can help students plan their writing tasks thoroughly. Furthermore, these steps help students remember what they've read when they begin their writing assignment. But more importantly, the steps carry an underlying message that a complex activity such as writing must be approached in a systematic, step-by-step manner.

The steps refer to *worksheets*, which can be any system you or your students choose: a notebook or notecards are generally best.

Translating Technical Discussions. Chapter 5, "Translating Technical Prose," should be of particular interest in your technical writing class. The second half of this chapter presents techniques for translating difficult technical concepts into understandable prose. The exercises at the end of this chapter include the following classroom activities:

- Explaining a complex technical subject to a nonspecialist.
- Rewriting highly technical passages so that they can be understood by the nonspecialist.
- Identifying translation techniques used in well-translated technical discussions.

Collaborative Writing. In the Introduction, you'll find suggestions on collaborative writing in technical-writing courses. Students can team up to write their practice assignments or their semester reports. If they do, they gain valuable experience in the way technical writing is commonly done in business, industrial, and governmental settings.

The suggestions for collaborative technical-report writing sketch ways to set up the individual writing teams, monitor individual team members' work, devise schedules for the report projects, and allot work in such a way that all team members do their share of writing.

Models and Examples. This book has hundreds of examples—some of them high-tech, others quite familiar. Many of the examples come directly from student technical writers' own work; others have been selected and edited such that they are in keeping with what you might reasonably expect from students.

Chapters 1 to 3 and Chapters 12 to 14, the key practice and applications chapters, contain *models*. These are extended examples that should give your students an idea of what their own writing for these assignments should resemble.

Technical Writing in Everyday Life. Throughout this book you'll find that many of the examples, topic suggestions, and exercises deal with personal and community concerns: a citywide program for recycling aluminum, newspaper, glass, and metal; community gardens on unused city property for apartment-bound gardeners; a system of bike lanes on city streets; and municipal ball parks on city-owned property. Report projects like these show that good technical writing can be a force in the improvement of our civic and personal lives, as well as a tool for our large-scale business and government concerns.

Today's Issues. You'll also note that many of the examples, models, exercises, and topic suggestions involve current issues about which there is a technical side:

Heart transplants	Laser technology in medicine
Nuclear warefare	Plastics in automobiles
Wind and solar power	Space exploration
Nuclear power	The greenhouse effect
New technology for diabetics	High-tech agriculture
Electronic publishing	Salt water purification
Mass transportation alternatives	Robotics in manufacturing
Advanced oil recovery techniques	Computer speech recognition systems

This book encourages students to explore these and other exciting areas of technological change and to be undaunted by the apparent impenetrability of some technical information. With topics like these about which to think, read, and write, technical writing can be one of the best courses in a student's college career.

Popular Science Writing. The last main writing chapter urges students to try their hand at writing and publishing popular science articles on technical subjects. In the popular science article, the primary concern is to convey the excitement that comes with the exploration of the technical world. While the technical report is more a challenge to be accurate, complete, and thorough, the popular science article is a challenge to your students to make technical discussions lively, entertaining, and even exhilarating to read.

Instructor's Manual. Accompanying this book is an instructor's manual that contains suggestions for using the part and chapters of the book, sample syllabi showing various ways to assign chapters and writing projects during a semester, suggestions for classroom activities and writing assignments, and a diagnostic test on common grammar, usage, punctuation, and spelling problems.

Acknowledgments

This book is dedicated to my son, Patrick, and his mom, Phoebe Jane. Also, I must express my thanks to Douglas Day for his help and support, to Kay Nichols for her expert assistance on Chapter 9, to Lynn Hanson (Williamsport Area Community College), Kathryn Roosa Weisinger (San Jacinto Junior College), and M. Sue Campman (Tri-State University) for review and helpful suggestions on many of the chapters, to Tucker Jones and Vicky Horbovetz at Macmillan for their guidance and help in getting this book into its finished form, to Aliza Greenblatt, production superviser, Holly Reid McLaughlin and Alma Orenstein, designers, and Eben Ludlow for his support and confidence in this project. And, of course, I would like to thank the following colleagues for their thorough and useful comments in the development of this text: David J. Amante, *University of North Carolina at Charlotte*; Russell Briggs, *Kalamazoo Valley Community College*; Robert W. Gentry, *Texas State Technical Institute*; Scott P. Sanders, *University of New Mexico*; Pearl Saunders, *St. Louis Community College*; Barbara Smith, *Alderson-Broaddus College*; Arthur A. Wagner, *Macomb Community College*; and Dennis L. Williams, *Central Texas College*.

Brief Contents

INTRODUCTION **Technical Writing and Writing Processes**   1

PART I **Designing and Writing the Basic Report Components**   23

CHAPTER 1 **Process and Causal Discussions**   28
         2 **Description and Comparisons**   72
         3 **Extended Definitions and Classification**   115
         4 **Introductions, Conclusions, and Summaries**   162

PART II **Writing Readable Technical Discussions**   201

CHAPTER 5 **Translating Technical Discussions**   204
         6 **Constructing Graphic and Textual Aids**   236
         7 **Strategies for Revising Paragraphs and Sentences**   279

PART III **Gathering, Organizing, and Reporting Technical Information**   321

CHAPTER 8 **Planning Reports: Invention, Narrowing, and Outlining**   324
         9 **Finding Information for Reports: Library and Nonlibrary Sources**   361
        10 **Developing Reports: Notes, Drafts, and Final Packaging**   395

PART IV   **Processes for Correspondence, Reports, and Articles**   439

CHAPTER 11   **Corresponding with Business and Professional Associates**   443
12   **Designing and Writing Informational Reports**   490
13   **Writing Effective Instructions**   541
14   **Designing Proposals and Feasibility Reports**   580
15   **Writing Popular Science Articles**   620
16   **Preparing and Delivering Oral Reports**   657

PART V   **A Technical Writer's Handbook**   679

APPENDIX A   **Common Systems for Documenting Reports**   681
B   **Basic Patterns and Elements of the Sentence**   691
C   **Basic Patterns and Elements of the Paragraph**   702
D   **Common Conventions in Standard Written English**   725
E   **Instructors' Correction Symbols and Copy Editors' Marks**   773
F   **Glossary of Terms Used in This Book**   780

Index

Detailed Contents

INTRODUCTION **Technical Writing and Writing Processes** 1

Technical Writing and Technical Writers 2
   What Is Technical Writing? 2 / Who Are Technical Writers? 12 / What
   Skills Do Technical Writers Need? 14 / Why Is Technical Writing
   Important? 15
Using This Book 16
   Organization of the Five Parts 16 / The Steps and the Worksheets 18 /
   The Process: A Key Concept 19
Collaborating on Technical Reports 19
   Collaborating on Practice Reports 20 / Collaborating on Full-Length
   Reports 20 / Setting Up a Schedule 22

PART I **Designing and Writing the Basic Report Components** 23

CHAPTER 1 **Process and Causal Discussions** 28
   Chapter Objectives 29
   Process Discussions 29
      Types of Process Discussion 30 / Locating Process Areas in Report
      Projects 35 / Dividing the Process into Steps 37 / Discussing the
      Steps 37 / Determining Length for Process Discussions 42
   Causal Discussions 45
      Types of Causal Discussion 46 / Locating Causal Areas in Report
      Projects 49 / Identifying the Situation, Causes, and Effects 49 / Discussing

the Causes and Effects   51 / Determining Length for Causal
Discussions   54

Developing and Completing Process and Causal Discussions   58
Adjusting the Discussion to the Audience   58 / Special Sections   59 /
Headings and Lists   60 / Graphic Aids   61 / Revising and Finishing Process
and Causal Discussions   61
EXERCISES   62
MODELS   65

CHAPTER **2**   **Descriptions and Comparisons**   **72**

Chapter Objectives   73
Descriptions   73
Types of Description   74 / Locating Descriptive Areas in Report
Projects   75 / Identifying the Parts or Characteristics   79 / Discussing Parts
or Characteristics   80 / Sources of Information for Descriptions   82 /
Determining Length for Descriptions   83
Comparisons   86
Types of Comparisons   86 / Locating Comparative Areas in Report
Projects   89 / Identifying Points of Comparison and Criteria   90 / Selecting
a Pattern of Organization   90 / Discussing Differences and Similarities   92 /
An Information-Gathering Strategy for Comparisons   94 / Sources of
Information for Comparisons   94 / Determining Length for
Comparisons   97
Developing and Completing Descriptions and Comparisons   100
Adjusting the Discussion to the Audience   100 / Special Sections   101 /
Headings and Lists   102 / Graphic Aids   102 / Revising and Finishing
Descriptions and Comparisons   103
EXERCISES   103
MODELS   106

CHAPTER **3**   **Extended Definitions and
                  Classifications**   **115**

Chapter Objectives   116
Definitions   116
Locating Definition Areas in Report Projects   117 / Choosing the Sources
of Definition   118 / Combining and Organizing the Sources of
Definition   121 / Writing Formal Sentence Definitions   124 / Adding Short
Definitions of Other Terms   127 / Sources of Information for
Definitions   130 / Determining Length for Extended Definitions   133
Classifications   136
Locating Areas in Reports for Classification   138 / Identifying Classes and
the Principle of Classification   139 / Discussing the Classes   140 / Sources
of Information for Classifications   142 / Determining Length for
Classifications   144
Developing and Completing Definitions and Classifications   147
Adjusting the Discussion to the Audience   148 / Special Sections   148 /

Headings and Lists   149 / Graphic Aids   149 / Revising and Finishing
Definitions and Classifications   149
EXERCISES   150
MODELS   154

CHAPTER 4   **Introductions, Conclusions,
and Summaries**   162

Chapter Objectives   162
Introductions   163
Elements of Report Introductions   163 / Elements of Section
Introductions   171
Conclusions   175
Summaries   175 / Conclusions   178 / Recommendations   180 /
Afterwords   180
Summaries (**Abstracts**)   184
Two Types of Summaries   184 / Selecting Important Information   193 /
Condensing Important Information   197
EXERCISES   199

PART II   **Writing Readable Technical
Discussions**   201

CHAPTER 5   **Translating Technical Discussions**   204

Chapter Objectives   205
Analyzing the Report Audience   206
Steps for Analyzing Audiences   206 / Using an Audience Analysis   216
Translating Technical Discussions   216
Definitions of Unfamiliar Terms   217 / Comparisons to Familiar
Things   217 / Elaborating the Process   219 / Providing Descriptive
Detail   219 / Providing Examples and Applications   219 / Shorter
Sentences   220 / The "In-Other-Words" Technique   224 / Posing
Rhetorical Questions   225 / Explaining the Importance of a Topic   227 /
Providing Historical Background   229 / Reviewing Theoretical
Background   230 / Providing the Human Perspective   231 / Combining the
Translating Techniques   232
EXERCISES   235

CHAPTER 6   **Constructing Graphic and
Textual Aids**   236

Chapter Objectives   237
Graphic Aids   237
Graphic Aids for Physical Things   238 / Graphic Aids for Numbers   238 /
Graphic Aids for Key Concepts   248 / Graphic Aids for Words   251 /
Planning and Developing Graphic Aids   251

Textual Aids   257
Headings   257 / Titles   267 / Tables of Contents   268 / Lists of Figures or
Illustrations   270 / Lists   270 / Pagination   272 / Title Page   273 / Cover
Label   273 / Glossary and List of Symbols or Abbreviations   273
EXERCISES   275

CHAPTER 7   **Strategies for Revising Paragraphs
and Sentences**   **279**

Chapter Objectives   280
Revising Paragraphs   281
Topic Sentences   282 / Paragraph Organization   285 / Paragraph
Coherence   288 / Paragraph Development   295 / Paragraph Length   299
Revising Sentences   304
Overnominalization   304 / Redundant Words and Phrases   305 / Weak
Pronouns   307 / Weak Use of the *Be* Verb   308 / Problems with the
Passive Voice   309 / Expletive Problems   309 / Predication Problems   310 /
Awkwardly Phrased Sentences   310 / Sentence Length   312 / Problems
with Grammar, Usage, and Punctuation   312
EXERCISES   314

PART III   **Gathering, Organizing, and Reporting
Technical Information**   321

CHAPTER 8   **Planning Reports: Invention,
Narrowing, and Outlining**   **324**

Chapter Objectives   325
Overview of Technical Reports   325
Informational Reports   325 / Feasibility Reports   326 / Instructions   326
Finding a Subject for the Technical Report   326
Major, Future Courses, and Textbooks   327 / Instructors' Ideas and Topic
Lists   327 / Magazines, Journals, and Periodical Indexes   329 / Career
Plans, Interviews, and Current Work   329 / Ideas for Local
Improvements   330 / Problems   330
Analyzing Your Report's Audience and Purpose   331
The Invention or Brainstorming Stage   331
Narrowing Report Subjects   336
The Outlining Stage   338
Exploratory Reading   339 / Arranging the Parts of the Outline   339 /
Elaborating the Rough Outline   344
Finishing the Outline   347
Comparing the Outline to the Rough Draft   347 / Eliminating One-Item
Outline Entries   352 / Adjusting Items in the Outline   352 / Checking for

Parallel Phrasing   356 / Making Outlines Self-Explanatory   356 / Adjusting the Graphics   356
EXERCISES AND MODEL   356

CHAPTER 9   **Finding Information for Reports: Library and Nonlibrary Sources**   361

Chapter Objectives   362
Developing a Research Strategy   362
Broad Categories of Information Sources   362 / Specific Categories of Information Sources   363 / Selecting Information Sources   363 / Finding the Right Subject Headings   367 / Bibliography Cards   368 / Selecting Books, Articles, and Reports   368
Finding Information in Libraries   368
Finding Books   369 / Finding Articles   372 / Finding Reference Works   376 / Finding Government Documents   380 / Finding Trade and Association Literature   383 / Using Computerized Information Retrieval   386
Sources of Information Outside the Library   388
Site Inspections and Measurements   388 / Calculations   388 / Business Literature   389 / Interviews   389 / Surveys and Questionnaires   390 / Governmental Sources   390 / Letters of Inquiry   392 / A Note on Collecting Nonlibrary Information   393
EXERCISES   394

CHAPTER 10   **Developing Reports: Notes, Rough Drafts, and Final Packaging**   395

Chapter Objectives   396
The Traditional Note-Taking System   396
Developing the Rough Outline   397 / Information on the Bibliography Cards   397 / Information on the Notecards   398 / Methods of Recording Information on Notecards   400 / Updating the Outline   412 / Final Stages in the Note-Taking Process   415 / Other Systems of Note Taking   417
Rough Drafting   418
Preparations   418 / Sample Rough Draft with Notecards   420
Revising   425
Planning a Revision Strategy   426 / Identifying Potential Problem Areas   429 / Grouping the Problem Categories   429 / Problem-Spotting Strategies   430
Final Packaging of the Report   430
Typing the Final Copy   431 / Taping in Illustrations   434 / Proofreading the Final Typed Copy   434 / Making a Good Photocopy   435 / Binding the Report   435 / Attaching the Cover Label   436
EXERCISES   436

PART IV   Processes for Correspondence, Reports, and Articles   439

CHAPTER 11   **Corresponding with Business and Professional Associates**   **443**

Chapter Objectives   444
Common Types of Business Letters   445
Inquiry Letters   445 / Letters of Complaint and Adjustment   447 / Order Letters   449 / Query Letters for Publishing   452 / Application Letters   454
Resumes   459
Gathering the Information   459 / Designing the Resume Format   462 / Drafting and Finishing the Resume   470
Components and Formats for Business Correspondence   473
Components of Business Correspondence   473 / Business-Letter Formats   476 / Memoranda   477
Tips on Writing Business Letters and Memos   479
Finishing Business Letters and Memos   486
Revising   486 / Final Packaging: Originals and Photocopies   486
EXERCISES   487

CHAPTER 12   **Designing and Writing Informational Reports**   **490**

Chapter Objectives   491
Progress Reports   493
Reasons for Progress Reports   493 / Ideas for Progress Reports   493 / Timing and Format of Progress Reports   493 / Organizational Patterns for Progress Reports   494 / Gathering Information for Progress Reports   496 / Other Parts of Progress Reports   498
Primary-Research Reports   499
Problem or Question   502 / Purpose, Objectives, and Scope   502 / Review of Literature   502 / Materials, Equipment, and Facilities   505 / Methods and Procedures   505 / Results or Findings   505 / Discussion, Conclusions, and Recommendations   505
Technical-Background Reports   506
Finding a Report Topic   510 / Analyzing or Creating a Report Situation   510 / Narrowing the Report Topic   510 / Developing a Rough Outline   512 / Determining the Kinds of Writing Needed   512 / Identifying Sources of Information   512 / Gathering Information and Taking Notes   513
Other Informational Reports   514
Site-Inspection and Field-Trip Reports   514 / Work Estimates   514 / Survey Results   519 / Minutes of Meetings   521

Finishing Informational Reports   523
EXERCISES   524
MODELS   525

CHAPTER 13   **Writing Effective Instructions**   **541**

Chapter Objectives   542
Preparing to Write Instructions   542
Finding a Topic   542 / Identifying the Audience   543 / Narrowing the
Topic   543 / Locating Information Sources   543
Identifying the Elements of the Procedure   544
End Product   544 / Tools   545 / Resources   546 / Steps   547
Planning Your Instructions   547
Simple Instructions   547 / Complex Instructions   547 / Organization   553
Identifying and Explaining the Individual Steps   553
Supplementary Sections   557
Equipment and Materials   557 / Related Theory and Principles of
Operation   560 / Guidelines, Cautions, and Warnings   560 /
Troubleshooting and Maintenance Charts   562 / Introductions   563
Graphic and Textual Aids for Instructions   564
Illustrations   565 / Textual Aids   569
Finishing Instructions   571
Testing Your Written Instructions   572
EXERCISES   573
MODELS

CHAPTER 14   **Designing Proposals and
Feasibility Reports**   **580**

Chapter Objectives   581
Proposals   582
Ideas for Proposals   582 / Types of Proposals   583 / Parts of
Proposals   584
Feasibility Reports   590
Ideas for Feasibility Reports   591 / Phases in a Feasibility Study   592
Finishing Proposals and Feasibility Reports   599
EXERCISES   600
MODELS

CHAPTER 15   **Writing Popular Science Articles**   **620**

Chapter Objectives   621
Types of Popular Science Articles   621
How-To Articles   622 / Reviews   625 / Retrospectives   626 / Travelogs
and Personal Accounts   627
Preparing to Write the Article   628
Finding Ideas for Articles   628 / Finding and Analyzing the Right
Magazine   628 / Other Preparations   631

Characteristics of Popular Science Articles 631
Interest-Grabbing Titles 631 / Narrative Style 632 / Personalities and
Dialogue 632 / Pacing and Density of Technical Detail 632 / Pervading
Mood of Excitement 634 / Exploring the Potential of the Subject 634 /
Attractive Graphics 637
Strategies for Openers 637
Question, Problem, or Mystery 638 / Striking Fact 638 / Unusual or
Humorous Phrasing 639 / Opening Definition 639 / Striking
Quotation 640 / Introductory Anecdote 640 / Prose-Poetry
Openers 640 / Attacking on a Commonly Accepted Idea 640 / Common
Ground with the Reader 641
Ways to End Articles 641
Summary Quotation 643 / Quotation with Supplementary Comment 643 /
Concluding Anecdote 643 / Prose-Poetry Endings 645 / Striking or
Important Fact or Idea 645 / Other Suggestions for Endings 645
Final Stages of Writing Popular Science Articles 646
Writing Query Letters and Cover Letters 647
Stages in the Publishing Process 649
Thinking about Yourself as a Writer 651
EXERCISES 651
MODEL

CHAPTER 16 **Preparing and Delivering
Oral Reports** **657**
Chapter Objectives 658
Functions of Oral Reports 658
Ideas for Oral Reports 658
Preparing the Oral Report 659
Script Approach 660 / Outline Approach 660 / Cue-Card
Approach 661 / Extemporaneous Approach 663
The Oral Delivery 663
Rate of Delivery 663 / Enunciation 664 / Volume 664 / Pauses 664 /
Eye Contact 664 / Posture and Gestures 664
Designing the Verbal and Visual Aids 665
Verbal Signposts 665 / Visual Aids 667
Introductions and Conclusions to Oral Reports 670
Evaluating Oral Reports 674
EXERCISES 676
MODEL

PART V **A Technical Writer's Handbook** 679

APPENDIX A **Common Systems for Documenting
Reports** **681**
The Name-Year System 683
The Number System 684

The Works-Cited System   686
Citing Government Documents and Other Sources   688

APPENDIX **B**   **Basic Patterns and Elements
of the Sentence**   **691**

Basic Sentence Patterns   692
   Subject + Intransitive Verb   692 / Subject + Linking Verb + Subject
   Complement   692 / Subject + Transitive Verb + Direct Object   692 /
   Subject + Transitive Verb + Indirect Object + Direct Object   692 /
   Subject + Transitive Verb + Direct Object + Objective Complement   692 /
   Passive Voice Construction   693 / Sentence Types   693
Basic Parts of the Sentence   694
Parts of Speech and Other Sentence Elements   695
   Nouns and Pronouns   695 / Verbs   696 / Adjectives and Adverbs   698 /
   Conjunctions   698 / Phrases and Clauses   699

APPENDIX **C**   **Basic Patterns and Elements
of the Paragraph**   **702**

Topic Sentences   703
   Main-Point Topic Sentences   703 / Placeholder Topic Sentences   704 /
   Topic-Reference Sentences   704 / Listing Topic Sentences   704
Levels of Detail in Paragraphs   704
   Coordinate Detail   705 / Subordinate Detail   706
Types of Development in Paragraphs   708
Common Patterns of Paragraph Organization   711
   Spatial Organization   711 / Chronological Organization   711 / Inductive
   Pattern of Organization   711 / Deductive Pattern of Organization   714 /
   Rhetorical Patterns of Organization   714
Coherence and Transitions in Paragraphs   715
   Transitional Words and Phrases   717 / Repetition of Important Words and
   Phrases   718 / Combining, Paralleling, and Rephrasing Sentences   718 /
   Rearrangement of Whole Sentences   719 / Transitional Sentences   720 /
   Transitional Paragraphs   721

APPENDIX **D**   **Common Conventions in Standard
Written English**   **725**

Structural Problems   726
   Fragments   726 / Run-ons and Comma Splices   727 / Parallelism   728 /
   Modifier Problems   728
Usage Problems   730
   Principal Parts of Verbs   730 / Agreement   731 / Pronoun Case   737 /
   Adjectives and Adverbs   738 / Glossary of Other Usage Problems   740
Graphics Problems   742
   Commas   742 / Semicolons   745 / Colons   747 / Dashes   748 /
   Hyphens   750 / Apostrophes   751 / Quotation Marks, Brackets, and

Ellipsis Points   752 / Underlining and Italics   755 / Parentheses   756 /
Capital Letters   757

Diction: The Use of Words   760

Precision with the Meaning of Words   760 / Concrete and Abstract
Words   760 / Formal and Informal (Slang) Words   761 / Neutral and
Slanted Words   762 / Cliches   763

Spelling   764

Homonyms   764 / Doubled Internal Consonants   765 / Internal Syllables
or Letters   765 / Words Ending in *-ance* and *-able*   765 / Words Ending in
-cede, *-seed*, and *-sede*   766 / The Silent *-e* Rule   766 / Words Ending in *-ie*
and *-ei*   766 / Doubling Consonants   766 / Words Ending in *-y*   766

Handling Numbers, Abbreviations, and Symbols   766

APPENDIX **E**   **Instructors' Correction Symbols and
Copy Editors' Marks**   773

APPENDIX **F**   **Glossary of Terms Used in This Book**   780

Index   I-1

Introduction: Technical Writing and Writing Processes

Technical Writing and Technical Writers
What Is Technical Writing?
Who Are Technical Writers?
What Skills Do Technical Writers Need?
Why Is Technical Writing Important?

Using This Book
Organization of the Five Parts
The Steps and the Worksheets
The Process: A Key Concept
Collaborating on Technical Reports
Collaborating on Practice Reports
Collaborating on Full-Length Reports
Setting Up a Schedule

This book and your technical-writing course, if you are enrolled in one, introduce you to a field that has been rapidly gaining importance in recent years. You may find technical writing one of the most important and rewarding courses you'll ever take—and, possibly, one of the most challenging and enjoyable.

Technical writing is the kind of writing people use to do their jobs: it enables them to construct, repair, and operate things; report accidents; propose new projects; and report their evaluations of equipment or programs—the basic day-to-day concerns of scientists, engineers, and other technical people. If you are involved in any technical field—auto mechanics, electronics, computers, medicine, nursing, agriculture, environmental issues, community planning—technical writing can be an important and useful tool for you.

With its increasing importance, technical writing offers a growing number of job opportunities. However, you should know that technical-writing skills are becoming increasingly important in many different occupations. It is surprising how many people in so many different occupations must write and how important that writing is to their careers, to the organizations they're associated with, to their professions, and to society in general. Technical writing is something you may well end up doing no matter what field of work you enter.

What's causing technical writing to become so important? One answer is the explosion of technology occurring all around us. There has been more technological change in the past 100 years than in all the rest of human history. But how does that information get communicated? Often, people prepare reports, manuals, guides, and other written materials to do the job. In other words, it takes technical writing—and plenty of it. And, as more and more new technology ends up in the hands of ordinary people who are not specialists or experts, a special kind of technical writing is needed—one that communicates effectively to people with no background in a technical field. And perhaps this kind of technical writing—for the beginner or nonspecialist—is the most important of all.

Technical Writing and Technical Writers

Consider some of the characteristics of technical writing, some of the people who work as technical writers, some examples of this kind of writing, and some of the reasons why technical writing is so important.

What Is Technical Writing?

On first hearing about technical writing, it may sound like highly technical, advanced scientific material written by and for experts and specialists only. Actually, that is only a part of technical writing; much of it is intended instead for nonspecialists. Technical writing plays a primary role in enabling people—all kinds of people with all kinds of backgrounds—to learn about new technology. Good technical writing must communicate as effectively with nonspecialists as with specialists—if not more so. Therefore, think of technical writing in broad terms: as *practical written communication* used routinely by business and professional people to convey technical information to a variety of audiences.

Some of the characteristics of technical writing include the following.

• *Technical content*. Obviously, technical writing contains technical subject matter. But that does not necessarily mean that only experts and specialists can read it. See Figure I–1 for two example excerpts of technical writing on computers that contain generally the same subject matter: one is simple and basic; the other, very detailed and specialized.

The heart of any computing system is the central processing unit, or cpu. This component controls the operation of the entire system, performs the arithmetic and logic operations, and stores instructions and data. Such instructions and data are typically stored in a high-speed memory unit using a binary representation. The control unit fetches these instructions from memory, decodes them, and causes the system to execute the operations indicated by the instructions. Those

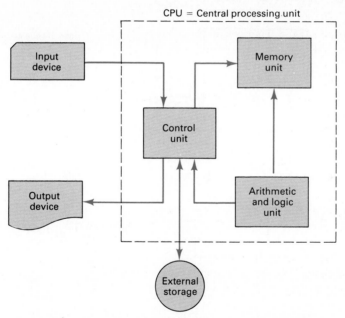

FIGURE I–1a. Major components of a computer system

Larry Nyhoff and Sanford Leestma, <u>Problem Solving with FORTRAN 77</u> (New York: Macmillan, 1983), 12.

(continued)

FIGURE I–1. Excerpts of technical writing
Reprinted from Microprocessor/Microprogramming Handbook (No. 785), copyright 1975 by TAB Books Inc., Blue Ridge Summit, PA 17214.

operations that are arithmetical or logical in nature are carried out using the special registers and circuits of the arithmetic-logic unit.

Instructions, data, and computed results must be transmitted between the user and the cpu. There are a large number of input/output devices designed for this purpose that are in use today, such as card readers, remote terminals, punched tape readers, optical scanners, voice input devices, and high-speed printers. The function of each of these input/output devices is to convert information from an external form understandable to the user to electrical pulses decodable by the cpu and vice versa.

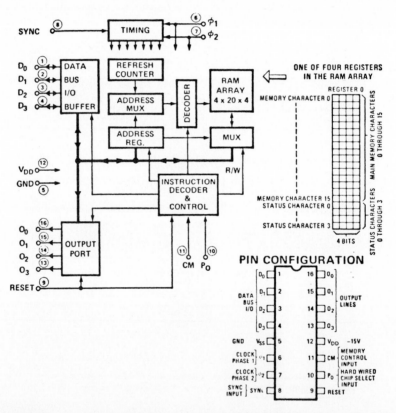

FIGURE I–1b. Detailed block diagram of 4004 CPU (Courtesy of Intel) Brice Ward, <u>Microprocessor/Microprogramming Handbook</u> (Blue Ridge Summit, Pa.: TAB Books, 1975), 78–80.

FIGURE I–1. (cont.)

<u>Address Register and Incrementer</u>. The address register (right side of Figure I–1b) is a dynamic RAM array of 4 × 12 bits. It contains one level used to store the 12-bit instruction address (program counter) and three levels used as a stack for subroutine calls. The stack address is provided by the effective address counter and by the refresh counter, and it is multiplexed to the decoder. The address, when read, is stored in an address buffer and is demultiplexed to the internal bus during subcycles A(1), A(2), and A(3) in three 4-bit nibbles. The address is incremented by a 4-bit, carry-look-ahead circuit (address incrementer) after each 4-bit nibble is sent out on the data bus. The incremented address is transferred back to the address buffer and finally written back into the address register.

FIGURE I–1. (cont.)

• *Aimed at a specific audience.* All technical writing is designed or adapted for specific audiences—some who are experts, others who are beginners. Whoever the audience is, the technical report, manual, or article must be written with that audience's specific needs and background firmly in mind. When nonspecialists are the readers, that means no technical digressions only specialists would understand and plenty of careful explanation of difficult concepts. When specialists are the readers, that means avoiding simple, introductory discussions. (See Chapter 5 for step-by-step procedures on identifying and analyzing report audiences and adapting your discussion according to their needs.) Here are some examples of specific audiences:

Beginning computer hobbyists learning to use graphics software

Experienced legal secretaries just learning computerized word processing

Voters in a bond election wanting to know more about nuclear power plants

Research scientists interested in increasing the memory capacity of computer chips

Agricultural researchers studying ways to control the Southern pine beetle or the fire ant

Advanced COBOL programmers reading up on new functions added to the language

Mechanical engineers trying to learn the basics of hemodialysis for a clinic construction project

Coastal residents concerned about the impact of the construction of an offshore dock for supertankers

Medical experts researching ways to facilitate insulin intake for diabetics

Experienced medical technologists looking up troubleshooting

Automechanics needing information on automatic transmission overhaul	information on intensive care unit equipment

- *Figures, illustrations, tables.* Browsing through technical articles, reports, and books, you'll also see an abundance of illustrations (photographs, drawings, and diagrams) and tables and graphs. That makes sense: technical reports often show people how to do things or how things are structured—much of which must be shown in illustrations. Also, technical reports must often convey volumes of data. Often, the best way to do that is through tables, charts, graphs, and the like. Figure I–2 is an example of an illustration and a table in technical writing. (See Chapter 6, "Constructing Graphic and Textual Aids," for step-by-step procedures on incorporating illustrations into reports).

- *Specialized terminology.* In technical prose you'll also see plenty of specialized terms—the jargon of the field the report is about. For specialist and expert audiences, this terminology probably won't be defined; the intended readers should already know it. However, for beginners and nonspecialists, the terminology should be carefully defined. Figure I–3 is an example in which the writer assumes a knowledge of certain terms among the readers (see Chapter 3, "Definitions and Classifications," and Chapter 5, "Translating Technical Discussions for Varied Audiences," for step-by-step methods on defining technical terms in your reports and articles).

- *Importance of format.* In technical writing, format is also quite important. This includes such details as headings, illustrations, binding, quality of the typed copy, the title page, the table of contents, lists of figures, and abstracts. (See Chapters 6 and 10 for some of the most common ways to prepare these report elements). In planning the format of their reports, writers ask themselves questions like these:

Should abbreviations be used in the report?
Where should the list of abbreviations and symbols be placed in the report?
Should the report contain a glossary?
How should the fourth-level headings be designed?
Should certain lists be bulleted or numbered?
Should the report be bound with a three-ring binder, a spiral wiring, or something else?
How should special cautionary or warning material be presented so that it will stand out?
Which type style and margins should be used?

- *Report-writing situation.* Unlike college essays, term papers, and magazine articles, most technical reports originate in specific business or professional situations. Consider the following examples.

An engineer needs to know about hemodialysis to win a contract on a proposed hemodialysis unit at a nearby hospital.

A financial officer needs information on conversion of biomass to energy to evaluate a loan application from a local farmer interested in starting such an enterprise.

Representatives of the petroleum industry must prepare a report for coastal residents and officials opposing construction of an offshore oil-loading dock for supertankers.

Captured Atmospheres: The Giant Planets

An atmosphere that has simply been captured from the solar nebula should have a composition that reflects the elemental composition of the Sun itself (Table I–2a).

TABLE I–2a.   Solar abundances
of the elements*

Element	Value**
H	2.66×10^4
He	$1.8 \ \times 10^3$
O	18.0
C	11.0
Ne	2.6
N	2.3
Mg	1.1
Si	1.0
Fe	0.9
S	0.5
Ar	0.11

*The abundance of silicon is made equal to 1.0, and the list is arbitrarily terminated at argon. **The units indicate numbers of atoms on a scale normalized to silicon (that is, for each silicon atom, there are 18 oxygen atoms).

Jupiter and Saturn. The two planets in the solar system that are generally considered to have atmospheres of this type are Jupiter and Saturn.

Tobias C. Owen, "Origin of Planetary Atmospheres," McGraw-Hill Encyclopedia of Science and Technology: Yearbook (1984), 2. Reprinted with permission.

Exterior uses. On the 757 and 767, exterior applications of advanced composites are numerous, including elevators, rudders, spoilers,

(Continued)

FIGURE I–2.   Illustrations and tables in technical writing

ailerons, flaps, engine cowling components, fairings, landing gear doors, and the radome. Composite materials can generally be defined as a mixture of two dissimilar materials to enhance the properties of the individual components.... Figure I–2a schematically locates the advanced composites applications on the 757 model. Approximately 3340 lb (1515 kg) of graphite, Kelvar, and hybrid materials are used, resulting in a weight savings of approximately 1490 lb (675 kg).

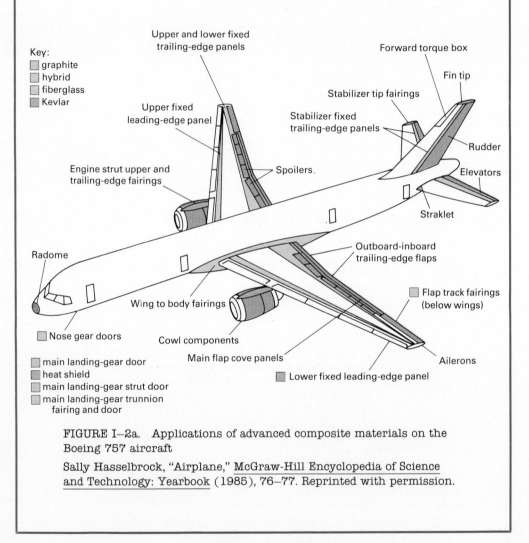

FIGURE I–2a. Applications of advanced composite materials on the Boeing 757 aircraft

Sally Hasselbrock, "Airplane," McGraw-Hill Encyclopedia of Science and Technology: Yearbook (1985), 76–77. Reprinted with permission.

FIGURE I–2. (cont.)

Videodisk. Laser videodisk is the most exciting of the new visual media. It has rich potential since it employs a random-access technique. Available videodisks store single-frame television images in the form of analog FM-encoded TV signals. These are decoded and played back by using a low-power laser. Future optical disks will be memory systems rather than frame storage devices. However, because of the enormous quantities of digital data they will be capable of storing in binary form, the creation of all-digital image archives will be their prime application.

These kinds of picture data bases in digital format are impractical with present technologies because of the enormous amount of data contained in images. As an example, the number of ASCII characters in a standard office document in 8½ × 11 in. (216 × 279 mm) format is about 3840 characters. This page could be transmitted over a 9600-baud phone line connection in 3.4 seconds. The same page in a digital scanned format would take 3,800,000 bits of storage, or 475,000 characters. This data would require 63 seconds of transmission time. A color picture would have four or five times the amount of information.

David H. Goodstein, "Electronic Publishing," McGraw-Hill Encyclopedia of Science and Technology: Yearbook (1984), 60. Reprinted with permission.

FIGURE I–3. Specialized terminology in technical writing

An engineer needs a feasibility study of computer-aided design equipment to decide whether to use it in her firm.

• *Numbers, abbreviations, formulas, equations, and symbols.* Because technical subject matter so often involves such details as dimensions, statistics, and frequencies, it's common to see technical reports laden with specific numerical values, symbols special to the field, and abbreviations. Figure I–4 presents some examples.

• *Process and descriptive writing.* Common too in technical writing are discussions of processes (events, routines, procedures) and descriptions (the physical aspects of things, places, or people). Much of technical writing is concerned with new or current technologies, specifically their structure and components (description) and their operation and maintenance (processes). (See Figure I–5.)

El Chichon

In late March and early April of 1982, a sequence of three major pyroclastic eruptions took place in southeastern Mexico at El Chichon volcano.... The eruptions were relatively small in volume, involving only about 0.07 mi^3 (0.3 km^3) of andesitic magma. They were extraordinary, however, in that the magma was unusually rich in sulfur. The large magmatic sulfur content was expressed mineralogically by 1 vol % crystals of anhydrite (CaSO$_4$), an uncommon igneous mineral, in the 1982 pumices.... The large sulfur content of the magma also produced an unusually large stratospheric cloud consisting principally of micrometer-sized droplets of H$_2$SO$_4$, which may significantly influence the Earth's climate in coming years.

FIGURE I—4a.   New crater left by the eruption as it appeared in June 1982 (photograph by Wendell A. Duffield, U.S. Geological Survey)

Surprisingly, El Chichon was not known to geologists until 1928, when it was first described by F. K. G. Mullerried. It is a small

FIGURE I—4. Numbers, abbreviations, and symbols in technical writing

composite volcano, 2.5 × 3 mi (4 × 5 km) in diameter, and rests on a Jurassic-to-Miocene sequence of carbonates, lutites, arenites, and evaporites. These sediments have been deformed into northwest-trending anticlines. Before the recent eruptions, the summit of El Chichon (4430 ft or 1350 km) was marked by a central dome filling an elliptical crater 6200 × 3000 ft (1900 × 900 m).

James Luhr, "Volcano" McGraw-Hill Encyclopedia of Science and Technology: Yearbook (1985), 458. Reprinted with permission.

FIGURE I–4.   (cont.)

Boiling-water reactor (BWR). A BWR assembly for a design produces about 3580 MW thermal and 1220 MW net electrical power. The reactor vessel is 238 in. (6.05 m) in inside diameter, 5.7 in. (14.5 cm) thick, and about 71 ft. (21.6 m) in height. The active height of the core containing the fuel assemblies is 148 in. (3.76 m). Each fuel assembly contains 63 fuel rods, and 732 fuel assemblies are used. The diameter of the fuel rod is 0.493 in. (12.5 mm). The reactor is controlled by the cruciform-shaped control rods moving up from the bottom of the reactor in spaces between the fuel assemblies (177 control rods are provided). The water coolant is circulated up through the fuel assemblies by 20 jet pumps at about 70 atm (7 MPa), and boiling occurs within the core. The steam is fed through four 26-in. diameter (66 cm) steam lines to the turbine.

H. S. Isbin, "Nuclear Power," McGraw-Hill Encyclopedia of Science and Technology (1977), 223G. Reprinted with permission.

FIGURE I–5.   Examples of description and process discussion in technical writing

Who Are Technical Writers?

Technical writers are potentially anybody and everybody: They aren't just the full-timers in large corporations who make their living by writing reports and manuals; they are also individuals whose jobs are primarily to design, develop, investigate, evaluate, research, test, and analyze. People who construct, operate, or repair things also do their share of technical writing. When you study technical writing, therefore, you're not necessarily training for a specific occupation but for an integral part of any occupation.

Among people who do a great deal of technical writing, however, you can find these types.

• *Full-time technical writers.* Some technical writers work full-time and have the title of "technical writer." Their backgrounds vary widely: some come from technical areas, some have been journalists or English teachers, and, more recently, some are graduates of technical-communications programs where technical-writing skills are taught. They are not necessarily experts on the things they write about. Instead, they rely on design and function "specification" documents that the specialists provide and on meetings and conferences with these people to ensure the accuracy of their written work.

What kinds of companies hire full-time technical writers? Here are some examples:

Computer manufacturers
Software-development companies
Underwater-diving-equipment manufacturers
Petroleum-drilling and -exploration equipment makers
Medical-equipment manufacturers
Consumer-appliance (microwave ovens, food processors, etc.) manufacturers
Farm-machinery manufacturers
Automobile and automotive-parts manufacturers

• *Part-time technical writers.* Many technical specialists also serve as technical writers. Technical writing is only a part—but an important part—of their job. For example, product designers and developers must describe their creations so that others can evaluate or implement them. In small software-development shops the developer of a graphics tool or a spreadsheet program may have to write the user's guide to her creation as well. Accident investigators often must write descriptive reports of the accidents and damage they observe and assess.

• *Free-lance technical writers.* Some technical writers work full- or part-time at their profession but not with any particular company or organization. Instead, they are self-employed, working by the contract. During one six-month period they may be writing a user's guide for a software company and during another six-month period, reference materials on sophisticated logging equipment for a petroleum company.

• *Consultant technical writers.* Other technical writers do consulting for organizations seeking their professional advice. Personnel and management consultants are typically paid to visit companies, identify problems, and find solutions for those problems. Their work appears in the form of reports. For example, engineers typically consult on lighting and air-conditioning problems and convey their findings and recommendations in technical reports.

• *Journalistic technical writers.* Some technical writers are primarily journalists who make part or even all of their living writing about technical and scientific matters for magazines and newspapers. The job of translating technical language and concepts for the ordinary reader falls most heavily upon these technical writers: they must find a way to make technical information not only understandable but interesting, stimulating, and even enjoyable. Most often journalistic technical writers produce popular science articles, which are discussed in Chapter 16. This sort of technical writer is not necessarily an expert or specialist either.

Here are some example magazine-article topics involving journalistic technical writing.

New capabilities and applications for robotics
Voyager's reports on Saturn: new discoveries, new questions
Computer hackers: the trouble they cause
Generating electricity on the farm
The building of the Golden Gate Bridge
Using fractals to study natural patterns
Magnetic fields in the human body
New devices for diabetics

• *Nonoccupational technical writers.* One final group of technical writers write about technical subjects for reasons having little or nothing to do with occupation. Instead, they write out of a concern for the welfare of the communities they live in. In this way, technical writing serves not only careers and organizations but social interests and needs as well. You can use technical writing as a powerful tool to influence your community or to promote improvements in your community. For example, have you voted in bond elections on nuclear power plants? The information you used to make your voting decision came through politically oriented technical writing—technical writing especially geared to promote understanding of technology among nonspecialist citizens.

Here are some additional examples of how technical writing can play a role in the life and well-being of a community.

A report on building bicycle lanes in the city: feasibility, routes, costs, safety provisions, benefits
A project to plant trees, shrubs, and flowers in parks, esplanades, sidewalks: costs, construction, plant varieties, locations, beautification of the city
A proposed city recycling program: facilities, revenues, procedures for recycling, citizen involvement
A volunteer project to build softball and baseball fields on unused city-owned property
A report on simple construction that would make it easier for members of the senior-citizens center to get to a nearby park
A plan to start a community gardens project for apartment dwellers on unused city-owned property

What Skills Do Technical Writers Need?

To be an effective technical writer, you don't necessarily need lots of training and experience in a technical field. In fact, in many ways, it's best not to be an expert. Many fine technical writers have journalism, English, or other humanities backgrounds. These people are new to the fields they write about and can usually write more effectively for nonspecialist readers because of that fact. These writers with nontechnical backgrounds tend to take much less for granted among their readers. But there are some basic skills you do need as a technical writer, including the following.

• *An openness to new knowledge.* Be ready to learn new systems, new equipment, new procedures, and new concepts—and enjoy that learning process. You can't let yourself be intimidated by the brave new world of science and technology. It also helps to be a fast learner. For example, a technical writer in data processing may have only a few months to acquaint herself with a new programming language, text editor, or graphics tool before writing.

• *Attention to technical detail and accuracy.* Because technical documents explain how to construct, operate, or repair equipment; because they evaluate technical projects; and because they report on problems, accidents, or other situations, you must provide the right kinds of details and make sure that the details are accurate. Inaccurate, inadequate, or unclear technical information can lead to damaged equipment, physical injury or loss of life, financial losses, or unsuccessful projects.

Remember that it is through technical writing that medical people know how to operate life-saving and life-maintaining emergency-care and intensive-care equipment. Through technical writing, designs and other plans for nuclear power plants, dams, bridges, and aircraft are transmitted. Through technical writing, communities choose alternatives for traffic control, waste-water treatment, and generation of electricity—alternatives that can either save or cost citizens millions of dollars.

• *Sensitivity to the intended audience's needs and background.* You must have or develop a knack for understanding the readers' situation, for putting yourself in their shoes. If, for example, you are writing instructions, you must be able to imagine yourself as one of your readers—a reader with ordinary intelligence and ability—and provide exactly the steps and explanation that the reader needs and in appropriate, clear language.

• *Concern for proper and consistent format.* As a technical writer, you must also be concerned about the format of the reports and articles you write. Many companies have well-defined guidelines on spacing, margins, fonts, headings, illustrations, and components of reports (such as title page, table of contents, and abstracts). Some even publish their style requirements. Even if you have no established format guidelines to follow, it's your job to know the standard report formats and to follow them. This means keeping up with the design characteristics of various kinds of reports.

• *Care in producing the final bound copy.* You must also take great care with the final packaging of your report—that is, the final typed copy, its binding, the inserted illustrations, and other finishing touches. The best of reports can lose much of their impact if they make a bad first impression—for example, if the typing, illustrating, photocopying, and binding are poorly done. People often pay lots of money to have reports written; they often spend lots of time studying reports. Messy, hastily, or carelessly produced reports can cause problems for their writers; on the other hand, well-designed, well-prepared reports can do much for these writers' careers.

• *Appreciation for clear, simple language.* As a technical writer, you must have or develop a feel for the simplest and most economical way of saying things. You must have or develop an ear for awkwardly phrased sentences that have a clumsy, confusing lurch to them. And you must have or develop a knack for fixing sentences that are wordy, inflated, or awkward.

• *Patience.* At so many stages in technical-report writing you must be able to grit your teeth through delays and other frustrations. For example, you may have a hard time finding good information in the library, you may struggle with a rough draft, or you may face a demand for extensive revisions. All of these situations— and many more—will seriously test your patience.

Perhaps the greatest test of patience will occur if you collaborate on a technical report, as so many professional technical writers do. As a technical writer, you must constantly work with people, verifying the information you've recorded, making sure that the right people can understand it, getting new information and updating what you already have. You must be able to take criticism of your written work and to defend your work tactfully when you don't agree with certain revision suggestions.

• *Good sense of organization, good work habits, and the ability to carry out long-term projects.* Technical writing projects are usually lengthy efforts lasting months and months. Usually they represent an enormous amount of work. Therefore, it's important to know how to organize yourself for a long project and make steady progress, know where and how your information is stored, lose or forget nothing as the weeks go by, never get into a panic-stricken rush, handle every detail of the project carefully, and finish the project on time.

Why Is Technical Writing Important?

By now it should be clear why technical writing is important, but here is a review of some of the main reasons.

• Technical writing enables people to construct, operate, repair, or maintain equipment. Think of how much complex equipment there is in our world and how much it is changing. All of it must have users' manuals, guides, and other reference materials to be of any use.

• Technical writing enables people to understand the principles or theories behind complex technologies or phenomena—for example, integrated circuits, microprocessors, nuclear reactors, the greenhouse effect, Alzheimer's disease, sickle-cell anemia, acid rain, or earthquakes.

• Technical writing enables people to share their new technical ideas with others—to propose new products, new ways of doing things, and new ways of under-standing things. Do you have an idea for a paper-feed device that makes paper handling in a photocopying machine more efficient and prevents paper jams? Great! Put it in a report so that the right people can find out about it—and find out about you.

• Technical writing enables people to evaluate the technical, financial, or social worth of new ideas. Think of the amount of information to present in reports evaluating different plans for traffic control, generation of electricity, or waste treat-ment and disposal. Without clear organization and effective graphic aids, particu-larly tables, charts, and graphs, such reports can be almost unreadable—a sea of uncontrolled and unorganized facts.

• Technical writing also provides records of events that have a scientific or tech-nical element to them. Damage from airline crashes, large fires, hurricanes, or earth-quakes, or the occurrence of unusual natural phenomena like El Niño all get documented in technical reports and ensuring the preservation of knowledge about such events and enabling their further study.

• Technical writing enables people to present technical ideas that have potential for personal or community benefit or to present technical information on potential harm to individuals and to communities. Do you have an idea for shrubbery that could be planted in those planter boxes on Main Street, the ones that nothing ever seems to grow in? Great! Put it in a technical report and take it to city planners. Are you worried that city reliance on coal to produce electricity is harming the environment or that nuclear power is dangerous? Write a report, an article, or a letter to the city's newspaper editor. Do you think recycling might be a good source of revenue for the city? Explain it in a report and take it downtown.

Using This Book

This book is designed a bit differently from other writing textbooks you may have used in the past. Use the following discussion to familiarize yourself with this book's organization and contents.

Organization of the Five Parts

You can use the chapters in this book in almost any order that you need them. If, for example, you are in the middle of a report on industrial uses of robots and need information on how Japanese industry is currently using robots, use Chapter 9 to find out how to locate that information. If you can't remember what's usually the best way to set up a comparison, go to Chapter 2. The contents of the five parts of this book are organized this way:

Part I. Designing and Writing the Basic Report Components
This part of the book gives you a chance to practice writing some of the basic components of reports such as process and causal discussions, de-

scriptions, comparisons, and extended definitions. You get a good foundation for writing full-length reports.

Part II. Writing Readable Technical Discussions

This part shows you various ways to make your reports more readable and understandable. These techniques include analyzing your audience and writing specifically for its level of understanding and for its needs; using "translating" strategies to help your audience understand difficult technical concepts; creating illustrations and tables that further clarify discussions; and making the paragraphs and sentences read more smoothly, coherently, and concisely.

Part III. Gathering, Organizing, and Reporting Technical Information

This part of the book takes you step by step through the main phases in writing a technical report. You get a close look at strategies or methods for finding a report topic, brainstorming it, outlining, locating information on a topic, taking notes on that information, rough drafting, revising and editing, and putting the edited draft in a professional-looking final package.

Part IV. Processes for Correspondence, Reports, and Articles

This part builds on all of the chapters that precede it. It shows you the main applications of technical writing, the various kinds of reports, proposals, and articles in which you use technical-writing skills. Part IV chapters define these applications, explain their purpose, show you their typical organizational patterns, present examples and models of these applications, and provide you with step-by-step methods for constructing them.

Part V. A Technical Writer's Handbook

This part is a handbook for your questions on how to document a report (footnotes, bibliography, references, or other such systems), what certain grammatical terms mean, how to correct certain errors in usage and punctuation, and what certain terminology on paragraph structure means.

You can find more information on how to use the five parts of this book in the short introductions at the beginning of each of the parts.

The book is organized so that you can start at practically either end—Part I or Part IV—depending on whether you want to practice some of the basics of technical writing or dive right into a full-length technical report.

• *The practice approach.* Use Part I to write practice process and causal discussions, descriptions, and comparisons, and then move on to Part II to learn techniques to make your Part I practice writing more readable and understandable. (In your practice phase, however, use Part III chapters for help in finding a topic, brainstorming, narrowing, outlining, note taking, rough drafting, editing, and final packaging.)

• *The final-report approach.* Begin with the main applications chapters in Part IV if you want to plunge right into a big report project. Part IV chapters direct you back to discussion in Parts I, II, and III when you need help. For example, if you need certain information in the library, you are directed to Chapter 9 for help in finding it. If you suddenly realize you don't know how to do an audience analysis, Chapter 5 is there waiting for you with a detailed step-by-step method.

The Steps and the Worksheets

Throughout the following pages you'll notice one of the most important features of this book: the steps printed in color. Most of these steps refer to something called a worksheet, i.e., a set of planning notes you keep as you read and make decisions about your report project.

Use these steps and worksheets to guide yourself through the phases of writing a report; do the steps and make notes on your worksheet as you read the chapters, rather than afterwards. That way you won't forget to do important steps, and you'll have the makings of a well-organized, well-planned report, section of a report, letter, or article once you finish a chapter.

Here are some suggestions for following the steps in this book and keeping worksheets.

1. First, skim the whole chapter to get an overview of what you'll be doing. Pay particular attention to how the steps fit together.
2. Also, skim the section "Technical Background Reports" in Chapter 12 to get an idea about how all of the steps in the first ten chapters (Parts I, II, and III) fit together in the typical technical-writing project.
3. Write the information requested in each step as soon as you come to it within the chapter. Don't wait to do all of the steps at the end of the chapter.
4. Write the information requested in each step on worksheets, which are simply notes that you make as you follow the steps and prepare to write. Since you may be keeping worksheets over a number of weeks, consider using a notebook to centralize your worksheets.
5. In certain chapters some of the steps direct you to go to other chapters and to read the discussion and follow the steps there. Depending on the work you're doing and your instructor's advice, you can either go to these other chapters or save them for another time.
6. If you find that a step does not apply to what you're doing, explain that in your worksheet and move on.
7. If you don't understand what's being asked of you in a particular step, skip that step for the moment, continue reading, and come back to it later.
8. Be thorough in your responses to the steps, but don't worry about such things as legibility or grammar. These worksheets are your notes on your report project; they should make your job of report preparation thorough and more effective.
9. If you believe that a step important to your own report project is missing, make it up yourself, insert it in this book, and take notes on it on your worksheet as normal. (And let me—the author of this book—know about it.)
10. When you've finished the steps in a chapter, you should have a good set of notes to write with. For an example excerpt from a set of notes from a worksheet, see page 26.

The Process: A Key Concept

Basic to this book is the concept of the process and the steps that make up a process. When you take on a complex activity like technical-report writing, you want to treat it as a process and divide that process up into its most important steps, that is, groups of related actions. Then, you look closely at the actions involved in each of those steps and practice each one separately.

Approaching technical writing this way is no different from practicing any other skill. In tennis, for example, you practice individual strokes so that you can use them better when game time comes. In choral singing you practice difficult passages (of the Hallelujah Chorus in Handel's *Messiah*, for example) until you get them right. The same is the case with technical writing: you need to practice the important phases. Then when it comes time to write a full-length report, each of these phases won't seem so overwhelming (understanding your technical subject matter and expressing it in writing may be overwhelming enough!).

Collaborating on Technical Reports

As mentioned earlier, many technical reports are written collaboratively—by a team of people. These people divide the various responsibilities.

- Some members gather the report information.
- Others design the layout and format of the report.
- Others do the actual writing.
- Still others create the illustrations and produce the finished copy.

Some report-writing teams divide the responsibilities according to their individual members' areas of expertise. For example:

- One member may know about the actual uses of a technology.
- Another may know the design and theory behind the technology.
- Still others may know the financial and legal implications.

In business, industrial, and government situations, technical writers often are not experts in the report subject matter, or at least not at the beginning of the report project. They get their information from the technical experts on the project—the designers, developers, technicians, skilled operators, and other such specialists. The process of producing a team-written report works generally this way:

1. The technical experts convey their information to the writer in various ways—through design notes or rough sketches of how they think the report should be written and through conferences, meetings, and other personal communications.
2. The writer takes this information and produces a rough draft from it, according to the needs and background of the audience.
3. The team members then review that rough draft with the writer, looking for problems in technical accuracy and completeness.
4. The writer makes the needed changes, and the review process begins again.

You may want to write a report as a member of a team for several reasons. Some report projects are just too big for one person. You can gain good practical experience for the team report writing you may do later in your career. Also, it's often nice to have some comrades during a long report project.

Collaborating on Practice Reports

Here are some ideas on how to organize a team effort on the practice writing assignments in Part I. In these steps *you* choose a subject to write on and gather the necessary information, and then *your team member* does the actual writing—with your help, of course.

1. Find someone with different interests and background and pick a topic for him or her to write the practice assignment (process, description, comparison, and so forth) on. Make sure your team member does not know much about the topic you chose. (Your team member will do the same for you.)
2. After you read the Part I chapter and do some preliminary reading and investigating, meet with your team member to develop outlines for your writing assignments.
3. With your outlines prepared, begin gathering information on your subject. Use any kind of note-taking technique you wish, but make sure it is agreeable to your writer.
4. When both of you have gathered the necessary information, trade that information with each other, explain anything about it as necessary, and go off to write each other's assignment. (Call or meet with each other whenever necessary if there are problems with the information you've given each other.)
5. When you've both written rough drafts, exchange them, and work with each other to make any necessary changes.

Collaborating on Full-Length Reports

In longer report projects you'll need much more planning and meeting to collaborate successfully. Consider following the suggested plan sketched here.

1. Choose team members with a variety of backgrounds, experiences, interests, and skills.
2. Meet to choose a report topic and to determine the audience, purpose, and type of report you want to write.
3. Have each member of your team keep a journal of some kind on his or her work during the report-writing project. Keep notes on the dates you work on the report, the amount of time you spend, and the kind of work you do.
4. After some preliminary reading and investigating, meet again to brainstorm on your report subject. In the same or a later meeting, describe as specifically as you can the audience of your report, and then narrow the report subject accordingly.
5. Have each member of the team create as detailed an outline as possible, and

then meet again to compare outlines and work together to develop one outline everybody agrees on.

6. Meet to discuss how to divide the work load involved in writing the report. If you are taking a technical-writing course, divide the work so that every team member gets to write a portion of the report.

7. Meet to plan your information search and to decide who is going to gather what information. Then, decide how to gather the information you need to find (through, for example, some form of note taking).

8. As you gather information, remember to keep a record in your journal on the amount of time you spend, and meet occasionally with team members to discuss how the information-gathering phase is going.

9. When all of your team members have finished gathering information, meet again to update the outline and to discuss how to write the rough draft. At this point

   • Exchange notes and write rough-draft sections of the report using each other's information (to simulate the typical technical-writing situation).
   or
   • Use the information you have gathered yourself to write rough drafts for the sections of the report you're responsible for.

10. When the drafts are written, make copies of your own section for the other members, have everyone exchange their copies, put together a complete draft, discuss potential problems in the drafts or in the report as a whole, and begin the revising and editing phase.

11. On your own now, read through the complete draft, marking problems and making changes that will improve the report. In particular, watch for problems with

   • consistency in tone or style
   • transitions between main sections written by different team members
   • cross-references to sections or figures
   • consistency in the terminology you use
   • sections that need to be translated into nontechnical language for the intended audience of the report
   • areas needing additional graphic or textual aids.

12. Meet again and exchange marked-up copies, review other team members' comments, and then discuss how you are going to make changes. Then make needed changes to your part of the report that cannot be made in the meeting.

13. When you have made revisions to your part of the report, repeat the revising-and-editing cycle (return to step 10). Go through the cycle again as long as unresolved problems in the report remain.

14. When you finally have a revised rough draft that everyone agrees on, begin the production phase of your report work: the final typing, creating and taping in of the illustrations, proofreading, and binding. If anyone has done more than his share, try to equalize the production work. If you "team type" the report, make sure to use the same type style, margins, spacing, paper, and so on.

Setting Up a Schedule

With such a complex schedule, such a big project, and such a long period of time, your report-writing team will need to devise a schedule to make sure you get the report finished on time. Here's an example:

Date of meeting	Purpose of meeting	Work for next meeting (on your own)
9–4	Choose team members of the report-writing team.	Think about report-topic possibilities.
9–6	Decide on report topic, type of report, and audience.	Think about how to handle the report.
9–7	Brainstorm the report topic, describe the audience, and narrow the topic.	Create a rough outline of the report.
9–11	Compare outlines and develop one everyone agrees upon.	Think about which information sources to use.
9–13	Divide the information-gathering work, and decide on a system to collect information.	Begin gathering information.
——	Meet regularly to discuss how your work is going.	List problems or questions for the group to consider.
10–16	Complete the information gathering and update the outline.	
10–18	Prepare to write rough-draft sections of the report.	Write rough drafts of the sections of the report.
10–25	Copy and exchange rough-draft sections of the report; discuss potential problems.	Read the complete rough draft and make changes or comments.
11–1	Copy and exchange marked-up copies of the report and discuss changes.	Make any necessary, additional changes.
——	Repeat the revising-and-editing cycle again as necessary.	
11–27	Divide the report-production work.	Do your part of the production work.
12–12	Submit the report (on time!).	Get some rest.
12–13	Celebrate!	

PART I

Designing and Writing the Basic Report Components

Chapter **1.** **Process and Causal Discussions**

Chapter **2.** **Descriptions and Comparisons**

Chapter **3.** **Definitions and Classifications**

Chapter **4.** **Introductions, Conclusions, and Summaries**

Introduction

The main purpose of these first four chapters is to give you an understanding of the most commonly used *contents* and *patterns of organization* in technical writing—or, to put it another way, the most commonly used kinds of writing. Process discussion (Chapter 1) and description (Chapter 2), for example, make up much of the content of technical reports. Discussion of causes and effects (Chapter 1) is quite important too. Practicing these heavily used kinds of writing—getting used to their contents and their organizational patterns—gives you some basic tools with which to build effective technical reports.

A key concept in these first chapters is the *expandability* of these report components: for example, you can describe part of a mechanism in only a portion of a sentence; you can take a full sentence to describe it; you can take an entire paragraph to describe that one part; or you can take a whole section—a number of paragraphs—to describe that same part. (See Figure I–1.)

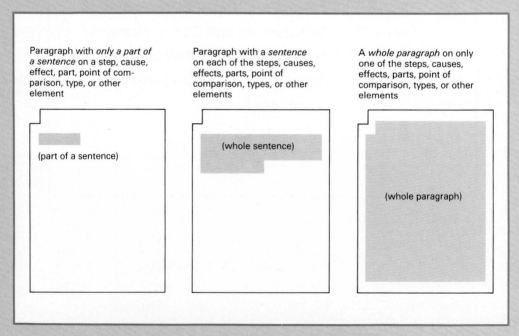

Paragraph with *only a part of a sentence* on a step, cause, effect, part, point of comparison, type, or other element

(part of a sentence)

Paragraph with a *sentence* on each of the steps, causes, effects, parts, point of comparison, types, or other elements

(whole sentence)

A *whole paragraph* on only one of the steps, causes, effects, parts, point of comparison, types, or other elements

(whole paragraph)

FIGURE I–1. Expanding report components

Using the Chapters of Part I

You can use the chapters of Part I in two basic ways.

• *Practice writing.* If you are new to technical writing, you may need some time to practice the basics. Most technical-writing courses begin with practice on description or process discussions and, only later, launch into full-length technical reports. The chapters of Part I are designed to give you plenty of experience with the basic building blocks of technical reports.

• *Report planning and writing.* The chapters of Part I are also designed to help you plan and write the sections of technical reports. Each chapter gives you pointers on how to locate areas within your report project requiring a specific kind of writing. And, once you locate areas where, for example, description is needed, you can then follow the steps in the Part I chapter or use that chapter for review.

Using Other Chapters for Additional Information

Of course, understanding the kinds of writing commonly used in technical reports is not everything. As a technical writer, you must also be concerned with invention, audience analysis, narrowing, outlining, information gathering, graphic and textual aids, revision, and final packaging. Detailed discussion and step-by-step procedures for these skills are provided in the chapters of Parts II and III. However, the point of these first four chapters is to concentrate on the content and organization and not to worry so much with the other phases in technical-report writing.

If you do want more on some of these additional phases, the design of this book makes it easy for you to go to the chapters where they are covered, read the discussion, follow the steps there, and then return to the chapter you started from here in Part I. Here are some examples of how you can use other chapters in this book to supplement your work in Part I.

Using Other Chapters to Supplement Part I	*Chapter*
To set up an introduction and a conclusion for an extended definition	4
To find out how to make your technical description understandable to nonspecialists	5
To incorporate illustrations, graphs, and tables into a practice description	6
To find information (from either library or nonlibrary sources) with which to write your process discussion	9
To find out about an organized way to gather information for your extended definition	10

Worksheet for the Practice Description

Step 1A. Going to do a description of the flat-plate solar collector—
the basic component of most solar heating systems. It traps solar
energy and heats the water circulating through it in coolant
pipes. The water is then used for general household heating
purposes or for hot water.

Step 2A. It's going to be both an external and internal
description—how it looks from the outside and what its parts are
on the inside. Also, mainly a description by parts—although a
description of characteristics may be necessary later in the paper
(can't tell right now).

Step 3A. Main parts of the flat-plate solar collector:
   transparent cover
   absorber plate
   coolant tubes
   box construction
   insulation

Step 4A. Sources of description include:
   shape: long rectangular box shape; looks like a large window
   dimensions: cover plates—2 cm thick; doubled with 5 cm
            between
            absorber 1 × 3 m; 2.2 cm thick
            coolant tubes—1 cm diam.
            insulation—6 cm thick
            frame—1.5 cm thick
   materials: cover plates—glass or plastic
            absorber—black enameled aluminum
            frame (box)—fiberglassed plywood
   attachment: coolant tubes welded on absorber underside . . .

FIGURE 1—2. Example excerpt from a worksheet

As you can see, the chapters of this book are set up in a modular way: that is, you can use chapters in almost any order or combination according to your needs in order to write a report, article, or letter.

Filling Out the Worksheets

To get the most out of these four chapters—in fact, the most out of every chapter in this book—you should be at work on a writing project as you read the chapter. For example, if you must write a process discussion, start reading Chapter 1: every time one of the steps (printed in color) asks you to write something on your worksheet, stop and do that step in the process. It's better to do the planning while the chapter discussion is fresh in your mind than to wait and forget some of the key steps.

For example, steps in Chapter 2 ask you to explain various things about the mechanism you're describing on your worksheet. As you come to each step in your reading, stop, figure out what the parts are, go look them up in a reference book if necessary, and then write something like what appears in Figure I–2 on your worksheet.

If you are uncertain how to do a step, continue reading the chapter and come back to it later. The order of the steps in each chapter is not always necessarily fixed.

When you come to the end of the steps in a chapter, you should be ready to produce a well-organized, well-planned piece of technical writing. The steps in these chapters should have guided you in thinking through the important aspects of your writing project.

CHAPTER 1

Process and
Causal Discussions

Chapter Objectives
Process Discussions
  Types of Process Discussion
  Locating Process Areas in Report
    Projects
  Dividing the Process into Steps
  Discussing the Steps
  Determining Length for Process
    Discussions
Causal Discussions
  Types of Causal Discussion
  Locating Causal Areas in Report
    Projects
  Identifying the Situation, Causes,
    and Effects
  Discussing the Causes and Effects
  Determining Length for Causal
    Discussions

**Developing and Completing Process
  and Causal Discussions**
  Adjusting the Discussion to the
    Audience
  Special Sections
  Headings and Lists
  Graphic Aids
  Revising and Finishing Process and
    Causal Discussions
Exercises
Models
  1–1. The Cardiac Cycle (extended
    noninstructional process
    discussion)
  1–2. Technique for Taking Blood
    Pressure (extended instructional
    process discussion)
  1–3. Immediate Effects of a Nuclear
    Attack (extended effects causal
    discussion)

─────────────── *Chapter Objectives* ───────────────

After you read this chapter, study the examples, work the steps, and do the practice writing, you should be able to:

- Define process discussion and causal discussion.
- Spot areas in report projects requiring process and causal discussion.
- Recognize the different types of process and causal discussions.
- Identify the steps of the process to be narrated, or the causes and effects to be discussed.
- Organize process and causal discussions by a sequence of steps, causes, or effects, either in a single paragraph or in a section.
- Use the right kinds of supplementary discussion in process and causal discussions.
- Use the right kinds of supplementary sections in process narrations.

This is the first of four chapters that show you patterns of organization and content that are often used in technical writing. In this chapter you'll read about *process discussion* and *causal discussion*—two of the most heavily used kinds of writing in technical reports. The two appear here together in the same chapter because they often appear together in technical reports.

You can either start here with the first section on processes or skip over to the next section on causes and effects; but be sure to use the last section, "Developing and Completing Process and Causal Discussions." (Steps specifically for process discussions end with "A"; those for causal discussions end with "B.")

───

Process Discussions

In technical writing, process discussion is one of the most important kinds of prose: people need to know how things happen, how to operate things, and how to perform certain actions. A *narration* tells how something occurs over a period of time. A *process* is an event or set of events that can be performed or that occurs regularly or repeatedly. The words *procedure* and *routine* are closely related. When you "narrate" a "process," you explain how to do something, how something works, or how something occurs.

Examples of processes include the simplest of activities, actions people perform every day:

Washing the dishes	Doing the laundry
Brushing your teeth	Making a cup of coffee
Feeding the cat	Driving to work

Processes also include such activities as these:

Changing a flat tire	Making a pizza
Grafting a fruit tree	Performing open-heart surgery
Overhauling an automobile engine	Writing a computer program in Pascal

Technical reports narrate such processes as the following:

> Hazardous-waste processing and disposal
> The events hypothesized in the theory of the Big Bang
> Electricity generation in a photovoltaic cell
> Application of dopants and etchants in integrated-circuitry manufacture
> Techniques in soil analysis
> Oceanic surveying
> Parallel processing in computers
> Weather-forecasting techniques
> Hurricane path tracking and predicting
> Synthesizing the human voice with the computer
> Speech recognition in computers
> Operation of a pick-and-place robot
> Computerized vision: how robots can "see"
> Data transmission through fiber optics
> Data transmission through communications satellites
> Laser eye surgery
> Household energy-conservation measures
> Diagnosis with computerized tomography

When you discuss processes, you characteristically use such words as the following:

Steps	Stages
Phases	Periods
Moments	

STEP 1A.   On your worksheet, briefly describe the process discussion that you plan to write about. If you need more information on process discussions, read the rest of this section and return to this step. (If you are thinking about collaborating with someone else on your process discussion, see "Collaborating on Technical Reports," in the Introduction for ideas and suggestions.)

Types of Process Discussion

To get a better understanding of processes, consider some of the different types of processes.

Instructional Processes.   Often, process discussions are concerned with how something is done or performed by people. They provide specific (or, sometimes, general) instructions on the construction, operation, maintenance, or repair of something. Such discussions can be specific or general. Specific process discussions of human-controlled events, or *instructions,* tell exactly how to do something. Look at the example in Figure 1–1.

A general instructional process discussion, on the other hand, conveys a general sense of how people do things or how things happen. It is often for nonspecialist readers who are curious about technical matters but who are not going to perform the processes themselves. See the example in Figure 1–2.

Enlarging

To enlarge a photograph from a negative, you must position and focus your enlarger, trim your photographic paper, and then expose the paper. To begin these procedures, turn the safelight on inside the darkroom. Pull out a sheet of photographic paper, and cut it to the size you want. Next, adjust the easel on the baseboard of the enlarger to the size of the paper you have just cut. Put the paper in the easel, and revolve the red ring of the enlarger until it is positioned directly beneath the lens (Figure 1–1a). Now, turn the enlarger on, and place the negative in the carrier section of the enlarger. Loosen the head adjustment knob, and move the head of the enlarger up and down on its post until the projected image fills the surface of the paper.

FIGURE 1–1a.   Components of an enlarger.

Once you have the image positioned correctly, tighten the head adjustment knob. Next . . .

FIGURE 1–1.   Example of an instructional process

In the direct freezing method used to remove salt from seawater, the water itself acts as the refrigerant. In this process, there are essentially four steps: pressurization and evaporation, freezing, separation, and discharge of the briny portion of the seawater. The process begins as seawater enters a heat exchanger that cools the incoming water. This cooled seawater then enters the crystallizer, or freezing tower, which is kept at a pressure of 3 to 4 mm Hg, equivalent to about 0.005 atmospheres. As the water is sprayed into the crystallizer, evaporation occurs because of this lower pressure. Since

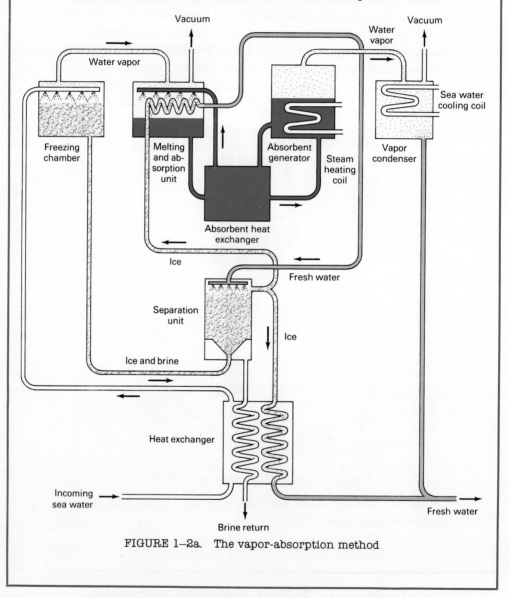

FIGURE 1–2a.   The vapor-absorption method

FIGURE 1–2.   Excerpt from a general process discussion

heat energy is used up as a liquid evaporates, the temperature in
the crystallizer drops to a range from $-1.9°$ C to $-3.8°$ C. (See Figure
1–2a.)

This temperature drop causes most of the water to freeze. The
conversion of the water to ice in the crystallizer, in turn, provides the
heat needed for evaporation. Once the crystallization process has
produced a fine slush, the mixture of ice crystals and brine can be
separated. For this purpose, the countercurrent washing method, in
which the ice crystals rise against a stream of fresh water that
cleanses the crystals of their brine coating, is employed.

After this separation phase ...

FIGURE I–2.   (cont.)

This example conveys a general idea of how one method converts seawater into
fresh water; it could not be used to either construct a desalination plant or operate
one.

Noninstructional Processes.   Some process narrations do not provide instructions; they focus instead on events generally not under the control of humans, on
such natural or mechanical phenomena as

Formation of lightning, snow,
    hurricanes, cold fronts, tornadoes
Pollination of a flower
Automatic operations of a
    photocopier or a computer

Gestation of a human embryo
Occurrence of supernova, black
    holes, red giants, or white dwarfs

This type of process discussion explains the workings of such mechanisms as

Automobile batteries
Telephones
Microwave ovens

Light bulbs
Televisions
Stereo receivers

This type of process discussion can also be general or specific. In the first example
in Figure 1–3 you get a quick overview of diabetes, whereas in the second, you get
a detailed view at the cellular level.

Historical Events.   Process-oriented discussions of historical events are not exactly a separate type because they overlap the two preceding types. Historical events
may or may not be entirely under the control of humans. The space-shuttle missions,
the lunar landing, or open-heart surgery are in large part. The eruption of Mount
St. Helens, the partial meltdown at Three-Mile Island, or the destruction caused by
Hurricane Agnes are generally not. Also, the word *process* refers to actions or events
that are repeatable. Historical events (despite the old saying) in general are one-

General Process Discussion

Diabetes mellitis occurs when the body's cells are unable to obtain
or utilize adequate amounts of the hormone insulin. Insulin is secreted
by special cells, called beta cells, that are found in certain cell groups,
the islets of Langerhans, in the pancreas. When insulin is present in
the bloodstream, it normally enables the body cells to absorb and
metabolize the sugar glucose, a major constituent of carbohydrate
foods. In most diabetics, the amount of insulin in the blood is higher
than in normal people, but the effectiveness of the hormone is
impaired, either by the presence of insulin antagonists or by tissue
resistance to the hormone's action. Furthermore, the release of insulin
from the pancreas after eating is delayed in diabetics.

Specific, Detailed Process Discussion

The initial interaction of insulin with its target cells occurs at the
cell surface, through specific receptors in the cell's plasma membrane.
Insulin receptors have been identified on almost all cells of vertebrate
species. Insulin binding to its receptor is rapid, saturable, and
reversible. There is a high degree of specificity of the receptor for
insulin since it has a stronger attraction for insulin than other
hormones and substances, since it binds insulin in preference to other
hormones and substances, and since its interaction with insulin
results in the known specific biological effects of that hormone. The
number of specific cellular insulin receptors appears to be regulated,
at least in part, by insulin itself. Studies suggest that the plasma-
insulin concentration inversely regulates the number of insulin
receptors, a phenomenon known as down regulation.

The insulin receptor enables a cell to recognize insulin in the blood,
to bind it, and to form an insulin-receptor complex. The insulin-
receptor complex then somehow activates or triggers an orderly
sequence of events throughout the cell, which culminates in a
multiplicity of biological responses among which are glucose uptake
and metabolism.

FIGURE 1—3. General and specific process discussion

time occurrences, but they have processes associated with them. For example, the eruption of Mount St. Helens occurred only once, but volcanic eruptions have occurred and will occur again many times. Still, historical events can be discussed in a step-by-step manner as can the other types of processes. Process narrations of historical events can be included in technical reports in two ways:

- An entire report can narrate the historical event in all its technical detail.
- A section of a report can discuss the historical event as helpful, informative background.

Reports often have sections that discuss important dates, events, discoveries, and people associated with the topic. An example of a technically oriented discussion of a historical event appears in Figure 1–4.

STEP 2A.   On your worksheet, explain which type of process discussion you are going to write, who the audience is, and why that audience needs the process discussion.

Locating Process Areas in Report Projects

At the start of your work on any technical report, you should decide whether process discussion might be used in it. Make a list of all the processes and events that are related to your topic, and then decide which ones you must discuss in your report. Here are some examples:

Report topic	Subtopics for Process Discussion
Solar devices for the average home	How solar collectors and their related components work Planning the angle of inclination of a solar panel Calculating costs and savings of a solar water heater Calculating the necessary size of an array of solar panels
Acid rain	The chemical process by which acid rain is formed How acid rain is transported
Cathode-ray tube (CRT)	How images are produced on a CRT How color is produced on a CRT Adjusting color and brightness Assembly-language programs for different colors
New insulin-injection devices for diabetics	How each of the new devices works The role of insulin in metabolism How the pancreas works Traditional methods of diabetes control

STEP 3A.   On your worksheet, list the processes in your report topic that you may need to explain, and indicate the type of process for each.

In March 1981, the orbital vehicle Columbia (OV 102) successfully completed integration testing at Kennedy Space Center. Installation of the thermal protection system had been completed with roll-out in November 1980 to the Vertical Assembly Building for mating with the other elements of the shuttle vehicle. The development flight test program of the Space Transportation System (STS) consists of four orbital flights, of which the first two, STS 1 and STS 2, were launched in 1981.

STS 1

The terminal countdown for the initial attempt to launch STS 1 was conducted April 1, 1981. The countdown proceeded normally until T minus 20 min when the orbiter general-purpose computers (GPCs) were scheduled for transition from the ground mode to the flight mode. The launch was held for the maximum time and scrubbed when the four primary GPCs would not provide the correct timing for the backup flight system GPC. Analysis and testing indicated that the primary set of GPCs had provided incorrect timing to the backup flight system at initialization.

Ascent.　Lift-off from the Kennedy Space Center, Launch Pad 39A, occurred at 07:00:03.9 EST on April 12, 1981, with John W. Young and Robert L. Crippen as crew members. With both solid-fuel rocket boosters (SRBs) and all three main engines delivering sea-level rated thrust, the space shuttle vehicle lifted vertically off the launch pad until the tower structure was safely cleared. Next, a pitchover and roll maneuver placed the Columbia on its correct launch azimuth heading to achieve the desired orbital inclination of 40.3°. The vehicle was flown through the high-dynamic-pressure region, during which programmed main engine throttling down to a 65% power level and electron deflection schedules were successfully implemented to maintain acceptable structural load margins during first-stage ascent. The SRBs burned out approximately 1 s early and separated 2 min 11 s after lift-off, with all separation constraints satisfied with comfortable margins. The first-stage trajectory lofted high, resulting in SRB burnout approximately 3000 m higher than predicted.

Aaron Cohen, "Space Shuttle," McGraw-Hill Yearbook (1982–1983), 431. Reprinted with permission.

FIGURE 1—4.　Example of a technical historical discussion

Dividing the Process into Steps

When you write a process discussion—whether it's a single paragraph or a whole report—one of the most important tasks is to divide the process into its main steps, phases, stages, or periods.

A *step* is one action or event (or a group of related ones) that is performed or that occurs in the process. Consider a simple process such as making coffee with a drip coffee pot. Such an activity involves the following steps, each of which actually represents a group of actions:

Steps	*Individual Actions (Step 1)*
1. Boiling the water ⟶	a. Finding the kettle and taking it to the sink
2. Rinsing the coffee pot and the basket	b. Turning on the water and rinsing out the kettle
3. Measuring in the new coffee	c. Filling up the kettle to the desired amount
4. Pouring in the boiling water	d. Turning off the water and walking to the stove
	e. Placing the kettle on a burner
	f. Turning on the burner
	g. Waiting for the water to boil

Obviously, no one needs to be told all these specific actions; the example shows that a step usually stands for a group of related specific actions or events. A more conceptual illustration of the role of steps within processes and actions within steps appears in Figure 1–5.

STEP 4A.   On your worksheet, make a numbered list of the steps that are involved in the process you are reporting on. (If you are not sure about the steps yet, do some introductory reading on your process, using Chapter 9 as a guide.)

Discussing the Steps

After you identify the main steps, you must discuss those steps, explaining what happens in each one or how each one is performed. In some cases, you'll need additional, supplementary information—either sentences or whole paragraphs—to make the steps easier to understand.

Process Sentences.   A paragraph that explains a process can easily be identified: it is usually loaded with *process sentences,* sentences that explain specific bits of action. Some examples appear in Figure 1–6. An action or event is at the heart of each of these sentences. You write sentences like these in order to explain a process. Identify the individual process sentences within the process paragraph in Figure 1–7. Only sentences 1 and 4 do not directly present a step. Typically, paragraphs that narrate processes contain other kinds of sentences, called *supplementary* sentences.

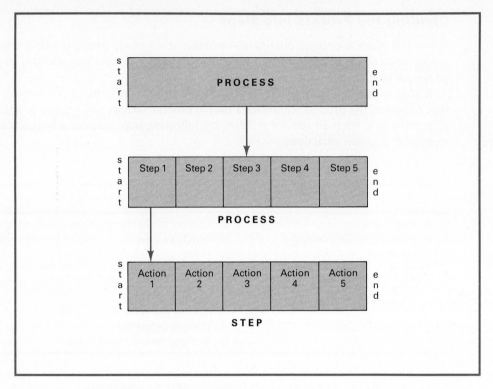

FIGURE 1—5.   Dividing a process into steps and a step into actions

Supplementary sentences and sections. Supplementary information helps make the discussion of the process clearer by adding useful detail. You normally supply supplementary sentences almost without thinking, but when you have written about a process, review your draft to see if any additional supplementary discussion is needed.

• *Description.* In process discussions, description often helps you to visualize the object before or after each step or at the end of the whole process.

> Once an accident has occurred, a number of systems (all of which were functioning in the Three Mile Island accident) immediately add water and remove heat to terminate the progress of the damage. In a typical reactor, there are eight separate pipes and fourteen independent sources--pumps and tanks--for adding water to the reactor vessel.

• *Definitions.* Be ready to define any word or phrase that may not be familiar to your particular audience.

Processes controlled by humans	Processes not controlled by humans
Loosen the head adjustment knob, and move the head of the enlarger up and down on its post until the projected image fills the surface of the paper.	As cleavage proceeds, the adhesion of the blastomeres to one another increases, and they arrange themselves into a true epithelium.
After completion of the secure-type landfill, a two-foot clay cover, followed by six inches of soil for vegetation is placed on top of the landfill.	As the condensing region of a developing star grows, so does its gravitational influence, and more and more material is thus attracted to it.
The third step for a potential investor is to follow his selected commodity daily and to chart its high, low, and closing prices.	The slope of a cold-front surface becomes increasingly exaggerated, reaching an order of slope of 1 in 40 to 1 in 80 (meaning that the slope rises 1 foot vertically for every 40 or 80 feet of horizontal distance).
In the special cinematographic technique known as the "glass-shot," a large sheet of glass is mounted in front of the camera, and an artist paints the desired image upon portions of the glass.	In normal adults, the enzyme methyltransferase is produced by a regulator gene along the DNA template and acts as a repressor by binding to the operator section of the operon to prevent the binding of the polymerase.

FIGURE 1—6. Examples of process sentences

It is generally believed that planetary nebulae are a normal stage that occurs late in the evolution of single stars with masses between 1 and 4 M$\odot$. A planetary nebulae is a cloud of interstellar gas, mainly hydrogen, ionized by a hot star, which eventually produces planets and suns.

• *Equipment and supplies needed.* If you are writing instructions, you may need to explain the tools or materials needed to perform an individual step.

1. In most computerized speech-recognition systems, the following pattern of events occurs. 2. A microphone picks up sound and converts the sound waves into analog voltage signals. 3. Each signal then goes into an analog-to-digital converter, which samples the signal at about 10,000 times per second, slices it into intervals, and converts the samples into pattern sets. 4. In other words, the speech signal is cut up into small parts, and each part is assigned either the number "1" or the number "0" depending on the characteristics of the signal in that specific part. 5. The signal then passes through a data filter where all unimportant sound waves including noise are eliminated. 6. The digital pattern sets are then compared to others in the computer's memory for close match-ups.

FIGURE 1—7. Example process paragraph

The first step in determining who owns a property's mineral rights is to obtain a Tobin map. A Tobin map contains the names of counties, maps of boundary lines and roads, and lists of the names of surface owners. Use the Tobin map to locate the county in which the property is located, and then make a trip to that county's courthouse.

• *Cause-effect or purpose sentences.* Consider whether explaining the reason for certain things or the causes or effects of a certain event or action would contribute to your readers' understanding of the process.

Immediately after the detonation of an air-burst nuclear weapon, violent winds blow radially out from ground zero, and, a short time later, afterwards blow back inward toward ground zero. The winds created by a nuclear explosion can destroy lightweight walls, flag poles, antennas, powerlines, bridgespans, and parked vehicles. The winds can impel heavy and sharp objects with tremendous force, thus converting everyday materials into sharp objects.

• *Comparisons.* Comparisons to similar things, events, or actions also help readers through particularly difficult sections of process discussions.

> In a surface-burst nuclear weapon, the fireball in its rapid, initial
> growth touches the surface of the earth where it vaporizes a consider-
> able amount of rock, soil, and other material located in the area. <u>An
> important difference between a surface-burst and an air-burst nuclear
> weapon is that after the surface-burst detonation the radioactive cloud
> is much more heavily loaded with debris.</u>

• *Cautionary sentences.* Instructions often contain sentences that warn or urge
readers to do or not to do things a certain way. Such sentences, closely related to
cause-effect sentences, emphasize the problems or dangers of improperly performed
actions.

> To load the revolver, the cylinder must be swung out by pushing
> forward on the thumb piece and by applying a little pressure on the
> right side of the cylinder. <u>Note: The cylinder should not be flipped out
> sharply because this can cause the crane to be bent, throwing the
> cylinder out of timing</u>.

• *Substep discussions.* Sometimes, the process discussion may be so long that
dividing some of the main steps into substeps helps make the discussion easier to
follow.

> The first phase in the development of a new individual organism
> involves the ripening of the egg and the formation of the spermatozoa.
> The second is fertilization, which involves a number of rather
> independent biological and physiological processes. <u>First, the sperma-
> tozoa must be brought into proximity with the egg. Next, the
> spermatozoa must find the egg and penetrate into the egg cytoplasm.
> Finally, the egg is activated and begins developing</u>. The third phase
> of development is the period of cleavage.

For longer process discussions ("extended" process discussions, which will be
discussed in the next section), supplementary paragraphs are often needed. In these
paragraphs, you discuss such things as:

Description of objects involved or used in the process
Equipment and materials needed to perform instructions
Related theory or principles of operation
Guidelines or cautions

These supplementary sections are discussed thoroughly in Chapter 13. For some
examples, see models 1 and 2 at the end of this chapter:

• In Model 1 the discussion of the chambers of the heart prepares you to understand the basic cardiac cycle.

- In Model 2 the description of the sphygmomanometer prepares you for instructions on taking blood-pressure readings.

STEP 5A.   On your worksheet, list types of supplementary sentences (or supplementary paragraphs, if you are writing a longer process discussion) you think you need in your process discussion and briefly describe their content and purpose.

Determining Length for Process Discussions

Once you've figured out the type of process discussion you're writing, identified its steps, and identified the supplementary discussion to use in it, you're ready to decide how long your process discussion should be—whether it should be a single-paragraph or an extended discussion. Usually, your understanding of the audience and of the purpose and need for the process discussion will help you decide on its length.

Short process discussions.   An example of a paragraph-length process discussion appears in Figure 1–8. Notice that the first sentence defines the process; the second

Mitosis is the process of cell duplication, during which one cell gives rise to two identical daughter cells.	definition of the process
The process consists of four main phases: prophase, metaphase, anaphase, and telophase.	list of the main steps
In prophase, the genetic material thickens and coils into chromosomes, the nucleolus disappears, and a group of fibers begins to form a spindle.	step 1
In metaphase, the chromosomes duplicate themselves and line up along the midline of the cell.	step 2
The halves are known as chromatids.	supplementary sentence; definition
In anaphase, the chromatids are pulled at opposite ends of the cell by the spindle fibers. At this point, the cytoplasm of the mother cell divides to form two daughter cells, each with the number and kind of chromosomes the mother cell had.	step 3
In telophase, the daughter cells begin to function on their own, once their nucleus membranes and nucleoloys reform.	step 4

FIGURE 1–8.   Short process discussion

lists the steps; and each of the following sentences discusses an individual step. Notice also the supplementary sentence toward the end of the paragraph.

Extended process discussions.   If you write a number of paragraphs on a process, you have an *extended* process discussion. Typically, in such writing you discuss each step in a separate paragraph. Supplementary sections (one or more paragraphs) come before or after the step paragraphs and provide important, additional detail to aid in understanding or performing the process. This chapter focuses on writing the steps; see Chapter 13, "Instructions" for more on supplementary sections.

In an extended process discussion, you expand the explanation of steps from individual sentences to groups of sentences, or paragraphs. A conceptual diagram of how the discussion of a step can be expanded appears in Figure 1–9.

The extended approach obviously gives you much more room to explain the process in detail. Figure 1–10 shows an excerpt of the extended approach to process discussion; it concerns the process of mitosis again, but this time, the whole paragraph focuses on the prophase period of mitosis.

STEP 6A.   On your worksheet, explain whether your process discussion will be a single-paragraph or an extended discussion and why. If it is extended, explain which of the supplementary sections you think your process discussion needs and why. Now, go to the appropriate group of steps from the following list.

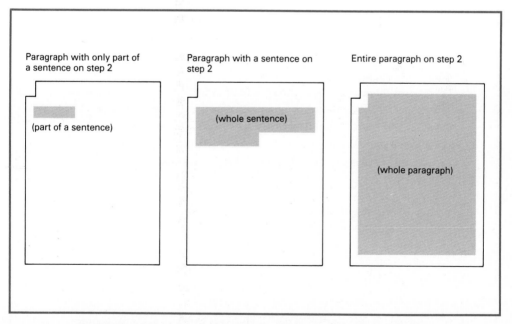

Paragraph with only part of a sentence on step 2

(part of a sentence)

Paragraph with a sentence on step 2

(whole sentence)

Entire paragraph on step 2

(whole paragraph)

FIGURE 1–9.   Expanding the discussion of a single step from a part of a sentence to an entire paragraph or group of paragraphs

Single sentence listing all steps

A certain amount of time elapses before the visible events of mitosis begin. These consist of four successive, not sharply separated stages: prophase, metaphase, anaphase, and telophase.

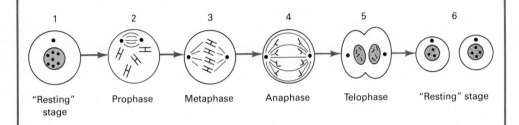

FIGURE 1–10a.   Mitosis summary

Whole paragraph on one step

By the time *prophase* occurs … the centriole, just outside the nucleus in the cells of Metazoa and most Protista, has already divided. During prophase, daughter centrioles then behave as if they repelled each other and migrate toward opposite sides of the cell nucleus. Concurrently, portions of the cytoplasm transform the fine gel fibrils (or microtubules). Some of these radiate away from each centriole like the spokes of a wheel and form so-called asters. Other gel fibrils develop between the two centrioles and produce a spindle, with a spindle pole marked at each end by the centriole. In Metaphyta centrioles are absent and asters do not form. However, spindles do develop.

Paul B. Weisz, The Science of Biology (New York: McGraw-Hill, 1971), 460–61. Reprinted with permission.

FIGURE 1–10.   Extended discussion of one step

Substeps for Short Process Discussions

If you write a short process discussion (only one or two paragraphs), your job is fairly simple. And, if you've done the steps to this point, you can do the following:

1. Gather information about the process, if necessary (using the steps in Chapter 9, if you need to find library information).
2. Write one or more sentences explaining each step.
3. Write several introductory sentences that
   a. Define the process or explain its purpose or importance.
   b. List the steps in the process (that is, provide an overview).
4. Review your paragraph to see if supplementary sentences are needed.
5. Write a concluding sentence or two, if necessary, for your process paragraph.
6. Go on to the section "Developing and Completing Process and Causal Discussions" for the finish-up work there.

Substeps for Extended Process Discussions

If you write an extended process discussion (several paragraphs), your job is rather similar to writing a short process discussion:

1. Gather information about the process, if necessary (using the steps in Chapter 9, if you need to find library information).
2. Write a paragraph explaining each step (there may be some simple, minor steps that can be grouped within one paragraph, however).
3. Write an introductory paragraph that
   a. Defines the process or explains its purpose or importance.
   b. Lists the steps in the process (that is, provides an overview).
   c. Provides other necessary introductory information.
4. Review your paragraphs to see if supplementary paragraphs (for example, paragraphs on equipment and materials needed, on theory or principles of operation, or guidelines) are needed.
5. Write a concluding paragraph for your extended process discussion, if necessary.
6. Go on to the section "Developing and Completing Process and Causal Discussions" for the finish-up work there.

Causal Discussions

In some technical reports you'll find a kind of discussion that focuses on causes and effects—called here *causal discussions*. Basically, they explain the following:

- What brought about a situation, problem, or accident
- What will happen if a certain situation or problem continues
- What changes will occur if a certain plan or action is taken
- How a certain problem or situation can be avoided

- What the advantages, benefits, or disadvantages of an action or object are
- What one or more potential solutions to a problem are.

Before you write a causal discussion, you must do a causal analysis, in other words, investigate the causes or effects, or both, of a situation.

Causal and process discussions are often hard to distinguish because they both occur over time and because steps in a process often involve causes and effects. The distinction depends on your purpose: process discussions are primarily concerned with *how* an event occurs; causal discussions, with *why* an event occurs. Here are some contrasting examples:

Subject	Process Discussion	Causal Discussion
Lightning	How to safeguard home appliances from lightning	What natural phenomena cause lightning
Instruction writing	How to set up understandable instructions	What causes instructions to be unclear
Acquisition of language by children	How to help children learn language more rapidly	Why certain children learn language more rapidly
Growing tomatoes	How to plant and care for tomatoes	Reasons why some tomato plants are less productive
Air conditioning	How cool air is produced by conventional systems	Why your air conditioning is costing you more this summer

STEP 1B.   On your worksheet, briefly describe the situation about which you want to write a causal discussion. If you are not sure about causal discussions yet, read the next section and come back to this step. (If you are thinking about collaborating with someone else on your causal discussion, see the section on "Collaborating on Technical Reports" in the Introduction for ideas and suggestions.)

Types of Causal Discussions

Causal discussions can vary in the following ways:

- What number and combination of causes or effects (or both) are discussed.
- Whether multiple causes or multiple effects occur more or less (a) simultaneously, (b) alternatively, or (c) sequentially.
- Whether the causes or effects (or both) occur in the past, present, or future.
- Whether the discussion requires sentence-, paragraph-, or section-length treatment.

The diagrams in Figure 1–11 illustrate the main types of causal discussions.

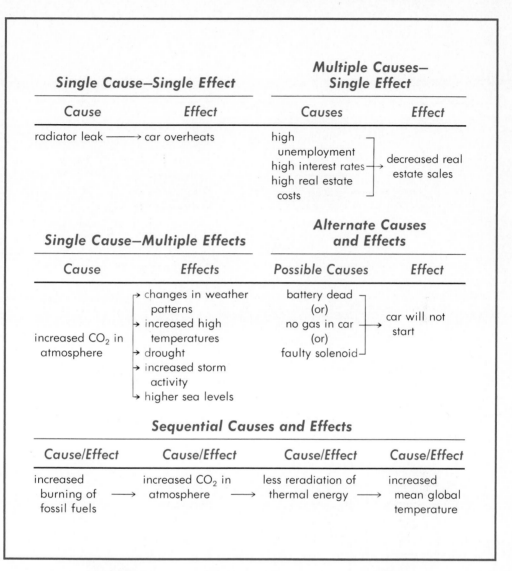

FIGURE 1—11. Different types of cause-and-effect relationships

A more conceptual way of looking at these causal relationships is shown in Figure 1–12.

STEP 2B.   On your worksheet describe the type of causal discussion you are going to write, and explain who the audience is and why that audience needs the causal discussion.

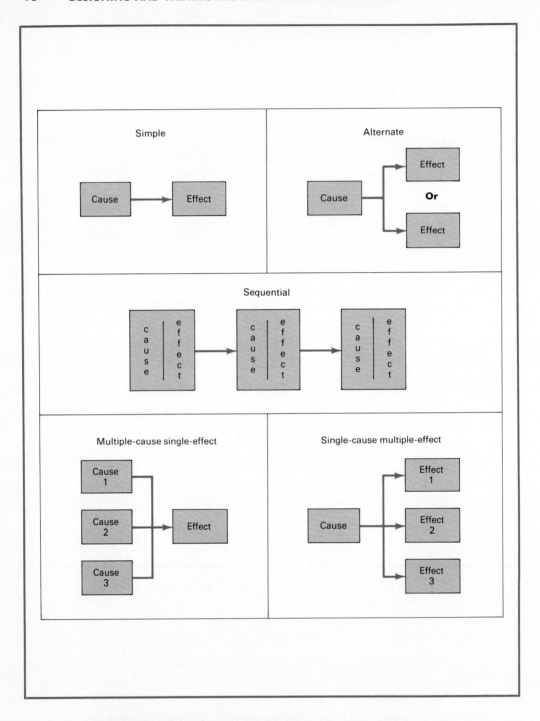

FIGURE 1–12.   Conceptual diagrams of (a) simple, (b) alternate, (c) sequential, (d) multiple-cause single-effect, and (e) single-cause multiple-effect relationships

Locating Causal Areas in Report Projects

Whenever you begin a report project, think about the causes and effects related to your topic that might require discussion. If your report focuses on why certain things happen, what's going to happen because of certain conditions, why a certain problem exists, or how it can be solved, then your report must have causal discussion in it. Here are some examples of report topics:

Report Topic	Subtopics for Causal Discussion
Solar devices for the average home	Factors that have made solar generation of energy feasible Reasons for solar energy's recent rise in popularity Problems with certain design features on solar devices Potential savings from solar generation of electricity
Acid rain	Main industrial contributors to the acid-rain problem Effects of acid rain on vegetation Effects of acid rain on cities Problems with determining the sources and causes of acid rain The future if the acid-rain problem is not addressed Why the acid-rain problem is going to be difficult to control governmentally
New insulin-injection devices for diabetics	Problems with traditional means of diabetes control Effects of an insulin deficit Causes of diabetes Long-term effects of diabetes Problems with the new devices Advantages of the new devices

STEP 3B.   On your worksheet, list the situations in your report topic about which you may need to explain causes or effects, and indicate the type of causal discussion process for each.

Identifying the Situation, Causes, and Effects

When you begin work on a causal discussion, your first job is to identify the situation whose causes or effects (or both) you want to discuss. Here are some examples of situations:

Rising housing prices locally
Lack of jobs in a particular occupation
Someone's increased blood pressure

Increased interest rates
Sudden increase in a particular major
A recent natural catastrophe

Once you've identified the situation, the next step is to determine whether to discuss the causes, effects, or both.

Increased local housing prices	What have been the *causes*?
Lack of jobs in an occupation	What will be the *effects* on people locally?
Decreasing costs of computers	What *caused* this, and what will be the *consequences*?

There may be only a *single* cause or effect, *multiple* causes or effects, or *alternate* causes or effects:

Single Effect	*Causes*
Increased blood pressure	Too much salt in the diet
	Not enough exercise
	Overweight
	Stress at the job

Single Cause	*Effects*
Osteomalacia	Moderate-to-severe bone pain
	Pathological fractures
	Demineralization and pseudofractures
	Epiphyses not closing normally
	Elevated serum alkaline phosphatase
	Low blood calcium levels

Single Cause	*Single Effect*
Ineffectiveness or absence of vitamin D	Osteomalacia

Multiple Causes	*Single Effect*
Uncertainty of oil supply, 1973–1982 Threefold oil-price increase U.S. economic recession (1975)	Decreased U.S. energy consumption, 1973–1982

Once you've determined the causes and effects, you can discuss them in a single paragraph or in several paragraphs. In the example in Figure 1–13, causes and effects are handled in a single paragraph.

In Figure 1–13, the first sentence states the basic cause and effect: the trapping of solar radiation in the earth's atmosphere (cause) leads to a warming of the earth and its atmosphere (effect). The rest of the paragraph goes into the details of that causal relationship. Figure 1–14 covers several effects of the medical problem (the cause), osteomalacia. Figure 1–15 illustrates *sequential* causes and effects: how one effect can turn into a cause in its own right and then produce its own effect, which in turn becomes a cause and then produces its own effect. Figure 1–16 shows *alternate* effects that result from *alternate* causes. A simpler example of this idea is this: if it is clear this morning, I'll ride my bicycle; if it's cloudy, I'll take the bus.

In the "natural" greenhouse effect, less solar radiation is reflected back out of the earth's atmosphere than is absorbed by it, a process that causes higher mean temperatures within earth's atmosphere. Specifically, 65 percent of solar radiation is retained by the earth and its atmosphere. Of that amount, 18 percent is absorbed by the atmosphere, and 47 percent is absorbed by the earth's surface. With radiative equilibrium, that is, a state in which incoming solar radiation matches outgoing thermal radiation from the earth, the mean global temperature would be $-20°$ C. Instead, the mean global temperature is $14°$ C. The difference of $34°$ C is the result of the natural greenhouse effect in which the earth traps most of the longwave radiation that enters its atmosphere. This trapping effect occurs largely because of minor constituents in the earth's atmosphere, mainly carbon dioxide and water vapor. The constituents block out a large portion of the 30 to 50 micron range of wavelengths, the infrared portion of the electromagnetic spectrum, within which excess thermal energy must be radiated back into space. Water vapor is a strong absorber of radiation over the entire thermal spectrum except in the 8 to 18 micron interval. CO_2 absorption retains excess thermal energy in the 12 to 18 micron interval. The earth therefore is constrained to radiate its excess thermal energy in the small range of 8 to 12 microns. This increased absorption and retention of solar energy results in an overall warming of the earth-atmosphere system.

FIGURE 1–13.   A single-cause single-effect relationship

STEP 4B.   On your worksheet, list the causes or effects (or both) of the situation you are writing about.

Discussing the Causes and Effects

At this point, you're ready to think about which kinds of discussion to use.

• *Reasons.* One of the main purposes of causal discussion is to explain *why* certain things happen. You identify such reasons with words like "because" and "since." Here are some simple examples:

Situation or Event (Effect)	*Reason (Cause)*

My car would not start today *because the battery was dead.*
The company's benefit policy for adoptive parents *came about largely through the efforts of one man.*

One of the pathological processes that also occurs in patients with renal disease is called osteomalacia. The condition is an abnormality of bone occurring where there is a normal growth of the protein matrix, the framework substance on which calcium crystals are deposited, but where the deposition of bone crystals is defective because vitamin D is either absent or ineffective. The manifestations of the process include moderate-to-severe bone pain and the development of pathologic fractures. In adults, X-rays show demineralization and, rarely, pseudofractures, while in children, there are epiphyses that fail to close normally. The serum alkaline phosphatase of individuals suffering from osteomalacia is usually elevated. Blood calcium levels are often low, but not universally. Such hypocalcemia is a potent stimulus toward parathyroid hyperplasia, and, if the latter is sufficient, excessive bone resorption may occur with restoration of serum calcium toward normal.

FIGURE 1—14.   A single-cause multiple-effects relationship

As the climate becomes warmer as a result of the greenhouse effect, a number of positive feedback mechanisms tend to exacerbate the problem. Elevated global temperatures decrease the solubility of CO_2 in the oceans. Therefore, as temperature increases, the oceans release more CO_2 into the atmosphere, which causes still more increase in temperature. Also, with the increase in temperature, relative humidity, which is the measure of the amount of water vapor in the atmosphere, is also increased. This effect is known as the greenhouse water-vapor coupling. At the same time this process occurs, the vapor pressure of water is raised; the result is more water vapor in the atmosphere, which causes more greenhouse effect, which raises temperature even higher, which again increases water vapor in the atmosphere. These positive feedback mechanisms approximately double the sensitivity of surface temperature to a change in the amount of energy absorbed by the earth.

FIGURE 1—15.   A sequential causes-and-effects relationship

Early in the development of radar, a technique called <u>sequential lobing</u> came into use. Instead of pointing directly at the target, the radar beam, or lobe, pointed slightly to one side, then to the other, the action occurring very rapidly. Figure 1–16a illustrates elevation sequential lobing. In the figure, U is the upper position and L the lower position. If the target is exactly on the axis of lobing, known as the <u>crossover axis</u>, the echoes are equal.

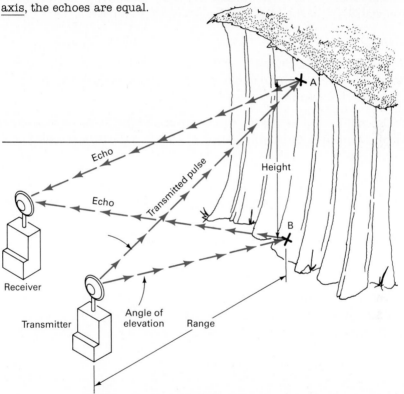

FIGURE 1–16a.   Elevation sequential lobing

If the target is not on the crossover axis, the echoes are not equal. If the target is below the crossover axis, the L echo would still be stronger than the U echo, and the difference (U minus L) is called a <u>difference</u> or <u>error signal</u>. In the example, the error would be negative, indicating the target is below the axis.

William P. Hand and Gerald Williams, <u>Basic Electronics: Components, Devices, and Circuits</u> (New York: Macmillan, 1980), 292.

FIGURE 1–16.   **Alternate causes and effects**

• *Results*. Another main purpose of causal discussions is to explain what happens as a result of certain situations or events.

Situation or Event (Cause)   *Result (Effect)*

The team's star player is in a slump, *and they've been losing a lot of games as a result.*
My car wouldn't start this morning; *therefore, I was late to work.*

• *Implied causes and effects*. Quite often in causal discussions, the causes and effects are implied; in other words, there is no "because," "since," or "therefore" to emphasize the cause or effect. Here are a few examples:

Situation or Event (Cause)   *Result (Effect)*

It rained hard all night; *the next morning, the creeks were far out of their banks.*
When you apply nitrogen to tomatoes, *you'll be surprised how much greener the foliage becomes in a few days.*

• *Description*. To discuss the effects of something, you often use description. For example, a report on the eruption of Mount St. Helens would also describe the damage (effects) it caused, as shown in Figure 1–17.

STEP 5B.   On your worksheet identify the types of supplementary discussion you think you'll need in your causal discussion, and briefly describe their contents.

Determining Length for Causal Discussions

If you know the type of causal discussion you're writing and have identified its situation, causes, and effects, you're ready to decide its length—whether it should be only a few or many paragraphs. Your audience's need for the causal discussion and your purpose in writing it should help you decide.

Short causal discussions.   Shown in Figure 1–18 is a one-paragraph causal discussion. Notice that after the first sentence, which overviews the causal situation and indicates that a discussion of the individual effects is to come, the rest of the paragraph discusses one effect per sentence.

Extended causal discussions.   If you write a number of paragraphs on a causal situation, you have an *extended* causal discussion. Typically, paragraph breaks occur where the discussion moves from one cause or effect (or groups of them) to another; in other words, one cause or effect per paragraph. A conceptual illustration of this idea is presented in Figure 1–19. The paragraph in Figure 1–20 focuses entirely on a single cause, leaving the discussion of other causes or the effects to subsequent paragraphs.

STEP 6B.   On your worksheet, explain whether your causal discussion is a single-paragraph or an extended discussion and why. Now, go on to the appropriate group of steps from the following list.

Cataclysmic eruption.   Mount St. Helen's first magmatic eruption in 1980, on Sunday, May 18, was sudden, violent, and disastrous. At 8:32 A.M., an earthquake of about magnitude 5 jolted the volcano. The earthquake caused a large part of the upper north flank of the volcano to break loose along a steep fracture and begin to slide downslope rapidly. The massive rockslide exposed a steep new rock face. Water from within the volcano flashed to steam--removal of the rockslide slab from the flank had depressurized or "uncorked" the underlying high-pressure system of magma and surrounding rocks. A laterally directed eruption cloud burst from the steep rock face exposed by the rockslide, and a vertical cloud rose from the summit crater. Within 30 s a second huge slide broke loose, and the laterally directed eruption expanded to involve and hide much of the north flank of the volcano.

More slides followed, and the succession of slides formed a series of huge avalanches of hot rock debris that swept into the North Fork Toutle River valley. One avalanche raced up and over the 300- to 400-m-high ridge north of the North Fork into the next valley. Another traveled more than 20 km down the North Fork valley, and still another plunged into Spirit Lake, temporarily forcing lake water up onto the sides of adjacent ridges. The deposits of the debris avalanches made a fill as much as 200 m thick in the North Fork Toutle valley and dammed many streams tributary to that valley.

Donald R. Mullineaux, "Volcano," McGraw-Hill Encyclopedia of Science and Technology: Yearbook (1982–83), 32–33. Reprinted with permission.

FIGURE 1–17. Description used within discussion of effects

Substeps for Short Causal Discussions

If you write a short causal discussion (only one or two paragraphs), your job is fairly simple. And, if you've done the steps to this point, you can do the following:

1. Gather information about the causal situation, if necessary (using the steps in Chapter 9, if you need to find library information).
2. Describe the situation whose causes or effects you are writing about.
3. Write one or more sentences explaining each of the causes or effects.

Some scientists argue that the concentration of carbon dioxide in the atmosphere will have doubled by the year 2020 and will bring disastrous climatic changes. If they are right, we can expect an increase in mean global temperature of about 3° to 5° C, with an increase of 12° C at the poles. There will also be widespread changes in local weather patterns, with record high temperatures and droughts like those of the 1930s becoming commonplace. Increased tropical storm activity will also be observed; with warmer temperatures, hurricanes will be able to penetrate much farther north. As a result of higher polar temperatures, there will be a dramatic increase in the sea level, as much as 15 to 25 feet in the next 100 years.

overview (changes)

effect 1

effect 2

effect 3

effect 4

FIGURE 1–18. Short causal discussion

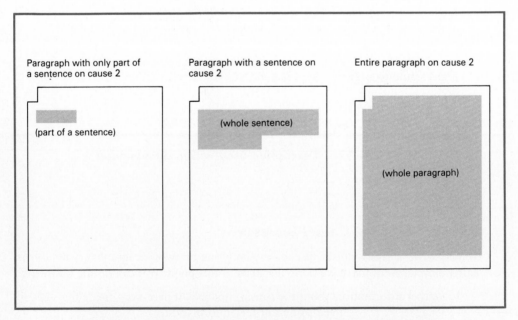

Paragraph with only part of a sentence on cause 2

(part of a sentence)

Paragraph with a sentence on cause 2

(whole sentence)

Entire paragraph on cause 2

(whole paragraph)

FIGURE 1–19. Expanding the discussion of a single cause or effect from part of a sentence to an entire paragraph

CO_2 from Fossil Fuels

One of the greatest contributors to increased carbon dioxide in the atmosphere is the use of fossil fuels. Since the advent of the Industrial Revolution, about 154.4 gigatons (where one G ton equals one billion tons) of carbon have been added to the atmosphere. Of that amount, about 27 percent, or 45 G tons, was produced from 1970 to 1978.

Overall, the use of carbon-based fuels has increased at an exponential rate of 4.3 percent per year from 1860 to the mid-1970s. (See Table 1–20a.)

TABLE 1–20a.   Carbon Released into
the Atmosphere*

Year	Carbon Added
1950	1.63
1960	2.16
1970	3.96
1975	4.87
1978	5.62

*Estimated carbon added to the atmosphere by the burning of fuels (G tons per year).

Reprinted with permission from Gordon J. MacDonald's *The Long-Term Impacts of Increasing Atmospheric Carbon Dioxide Levels*, Copyright 1982 by Ballinger Publishing Company, p. 113.

High energy costs could help slow this use of fossil fuels, although no significant reduction in demand has yet been observed. Industrialized countries may be able to reduce their use of fossil fuels for energy production by using clean energy sources such as solar or nuclear. However, a growing world population will place heavy pressure for increased energy use, especially in developing countries. Even while the United States is projected to reduce its contribution from 27 percent to 8 percent; the amount produced by the developing regions in the same time will more than triple.

FIGURE 1–20.   An extended causal discussion focusing on a single cause

4. Write several introductory sentences that
    a. Provide an overview of the situation, causes, and effects.
    b. List the causes and effects (that is, provide an overview).
5. Review your paragraph to see if supplementary sentences are needed.
6. Check to see if a concluding sentence or two is necessary to your short causal discussion.
7. Go on to the section "Developing and Completing Process and Causal Discussions" for the finish-up work there.

Substeps for Extended Causal Discussions

If you write an extended causal discussion (several paragraphs), your job is similar to writing a short causal discussion:

1. Gather information about the causal situation, if necessary (using the steps in Chapter 9, if you need to find library information).
2. Describe the situation whose causes or effects you are writing about.
3. Write one or more paragraphs explaining each cause or effect.
4. Write an introductory paragraph that
    a. Provides an overview of the situation, causes, and effects.
    b. Lists the causes and effects (that is, provides an overview).
    c. Provides any other necessary introductory information needed.
5. Write a concluding paragraph for your extended causal discussion, if necessary.
6. Go on to the section "Developing and Completing Process and Causal Discussions" for the finish-up work there.

Developing and Completing Process and Causal Discussions

Your most important goal in this chapter is to practice writing process and causal discussions. But other skills are important in developing such discussions: analyzing the audience, creating graphic and textual aids (illustrations, tables, charts, headings, and tables of contents), and revising. These skills are covered in detail in Part II. All you need at the moment, however, is probably just a brief overview.

Adjusting the Discussion to the Audience

Next to knowing your technical subject matter well and reporting it accurately, one of the most important concerns in technical writing is to analyze your readers carefully and to adjust your writing to their level of understanding and to their needs or interests. Chapter 5 shows you a step-by-step way of doing this. For the moment, however, keep these strategies in mind:

- Identify as specifically as possible *who* your readers are and *why* they want to read your report.

- Identify your readers' background: the *knowledge* and *capabilities* they already possess, and those they don't possess.
- Provide *general* or *specific* discussion of technical concepts according to the readers' background and interests.
- For nonspecialist readers, *translate* technical information (see the techniques in Chapter 5, if necessary) so that they can understand your discussion.

STEP 7.   On your worksheet write a brief description of your audience, its members' backgrounds, and their interest in your discussion. Make two separate lists, one for topics you must cover, and one for topics you can omit. Also, list terms you may have to define for your readers.

Special Sections

If you are writing an *extended* process or causal discussion, one that is at least several paragraphs long, you'll need an introduction and conclusion as well as possibly other sections.

Ideas and guidelines for introductions are covered in detail in Chapter 4; however, for processes keep these ideas in mind:

- Be sure to list the steps in the introduction.
- If necessary, define the process and explain its importance.
- Discuss any special conditions or special knowledge required in performing the process.

For introductions to causal discussions, keep these ideas in mind:

- Be sure to list in the introduction the causes or effects (or both) that you'll be discussing.
- If you don't plan to have a separate paragraph or section for it in the body of the discussion, explain in the introduction the situation whose causes or effects you are discussing.

Ideas and guidelines for conclusions are also covered in detail in Chapter 4; however, for processes keep these possibilities in mind:

- Summarize the steps if they are lengthy and complex.
- Describe the end result, or product, of the process.
- Discuss the future or the implications of the process.
- Conclude with cautionary or guidelines discussion.
- End by taking readers through one cycle in the operation.
- Provide a general overview of the advantages or disadvantages associated with the process.
- Discuss applications (actual day-to-day uses) of the process.

For conclusions to causal discussions, keep these possibilities in mind:

- If you discuss a problem (a group of effects or causes), conclude with possible solutions.

- If you discuss a group of causes, discuss their long-term effects in the conclusion.
- If you discuss a current problem, conclude with an exploration of the causes that brought it about.

For examples of most of these ideas for conclusions, see Chapter 4.

Instructions often have these additional sections (which are described and illustrated in Chapter 13 in detail):

- *Equipment and materials.* This section lists and, in some cases, describes the equipment and materials required in certain instructions.
- *Cautions and guidelines.* A cautionary section discusses precautions to take to ensure the success of the instructions or the safety of those performing them.
- *Troubleshooting aids.* This section explains the corrective actions to take in various common problem situations.
- *Theoretical background or principles of operation.* In some instructions, explanation of theory or principles of operation helps readers understand the basis of what they are doing.

An important type of causal discussion reports the results of primary research (for example, an experiment or a survey). Called here a *primary research report*, it often has these additional sections (which are described and illustrated in detail in Chapter 12):

- *Problem or question.* This section explains the problem that the primary research is intended to answer or explore.
- *Review of the literature.* This section summarizes what is already known about the problem as contained in books, reports, and articles.
- *Materials, equipment, and facilities.* This section describes the things you use to carry out the primary research.
- *Methods and procedures.* This section explains the steps you took in carrying out the primary research.
- *Results or findings.* This section summarizes the information you collected in your primary research.
- *Conclusions, implications, and recommendations.* This section draws conclusions based on the collected information, discusses implications for future research, and makes recommendations concerning actions to take.

STEP 8.   If you are writing an *extended* discussion, list on your worksheet the special sections you think are needed, and explain why they are needed. (If you need more information on introductions and conclusions, see Chapter 4.)

Headings and Lists

Headings are the titles and subtitles you see in some of the examples and models in this chapter. Headings are discussed in detail in Chapter 6; but for the moment, study how headings are used in this chapter and try your hand at designing your own. Also, here are a few tips:

- If you spend a paragraph or more discussing individual steps, causes, or effects, make a heading for each.
- If you have other kinds of sections, for example, one for equipment and materials, make headings for them as well.

Listing, numbering, or bulleting things, either within sentences or in vertical arrangements, is a good way to emphasize important points or to itemize things in an easily readable format.

- If you have a list of steps, number each step and separate the steps.
- If you have a set of important points to present, use a bulleted vertical list.

See Chapter 6 for a detailed discussion of lists.

STEP 9.   On your worksheet make a list of the headings for your *extended* process or causal discussion, and describe areas of your discussion where listing might be useful. (For more on headings, see Chapter 6.)

Graphic Aids

Review the graphic aids (drawings, diagrams, flowcharts, tables, and graphs) used in the examples and models in this and other chapters, and decide which kinds your practice process or causal discussion needs. Chapter 6 covers graphic aids in detail, but for the moment, here are a few suggestions:

- For each graphic aid, include a number and a title (see the examples in this chapter).
- Discuss and interpret your graphic aids for your readers.
- Include source information if you borrow your graphic aid from another book, report, or article.

STEP 10.   On your worksheet list the types of graphic aids you think may be needed in your discussion, and briefly describe their contents. (For a detailed discussion of graphic aids, see Chapter 6.)

Revising and Finishing Process and Causal Discussions

While your main goal in this chapter is to practice the organizational patterns and typical contents of process and causal discussions, you may want to practice revising and doing other finishing touches now. Step-by-step strategies for revising are discussed in Chapter 7, tips on proofreading are covered in Chapter 10, and final "packaging" suggestions are covered in Chapter 10. If you plan to study these chapters later, keep these tips in mind:

- Make sure that you've discussed the steps, causes, or effects one at a time, in separate sentences, paragraphs, or groups of paragraphs.

- Make sure that your discussion is clear and understandable to the specific audience you are writing for.
- Make sure that things are easy to find in your discussion: use headings and lists, for example, to ensure this.
- Neatly type your practice process or causal discussion.
- Use scissors and tape to insert your illustrations, and photocopy the whole discussion on a good-quality machine.

STEP 11.   Use the preceding suggestions to revise your process or causal discussion. (If you want more detailed information or revising, proofreading, and final packaging, see Chapter 7 and Chapter 10.)

EXERCISES

1. Use the following lists to help you get started on finding a topic for a process discussion.

   Explain how one of the following works:

light bulb	diesel engine	rheostat
CRT	circuit breaker	thermostat
telephone	carburetor	kiln
radio	microprocessor	any photographic device
food processor	air conditioner	refrigerator
solar device	rocket engines	internal combustion
loudspeaker	maser/laser	engine
battery	lightswitch	rotary engine
organ of the body	television	auto brakes
auto transmission	computer	electric motor
photovoltaic cell	audio recorder	sewing machine
camera	video recorder	any device with digital
microwave oven	stereo	readout
catalytic converter	X-ray machine	

   Explain how one of the following natural or mechanical processes occurs:

corrosion	nuclear reaction	hurricanes
photosynthesis	digestion of food	tornadoes
formation of diamonds	osmosis	continental drift
seeing	satellite transmission	lightning
hearing	electricity	hail
fermentation	bird migration	snow
cancer	formation of oil	rain
cardiac problems	earthquakes	thunder

   Explain how to do one of the following:

exploring for oil and gas	changing a flat tire	grafting a fruit tree
adjusting a carburetor	fixing a leaky faucet	making wine or beer
adjusting valves on an auto	starting a small business	pruning a tree
measuring blood pressure	wallpapering a room	filling out IRS forms

handling your own divorce	surveying property	laying floor tile
reading simple blueprints	using a word	paving a driveway
restoring furniture	processor	adopting a child
welding	writing a simple	tuning a piano
cutting diamonds	computer program	navigating by the stars
scuba diving	changing oil in a car	blowing glass
book printing or	baking bread	predicting weather
binding	sheetrocking a room	making ceramics
selecting and growing	speed reading	growing bean sprouts
houseplants	growing grapes	playing an electronic game

Explain how some specific process occurs or is performed in one of the following fields (or some other that you are interested in):

biology	electrical engineering	astronomy
microbiology	chemical engineering	law
zoology	petroleum engineering	business
geology	automotive engineering	architecture
chemistry	economics	acoustical engineering
physics	sociology	mechanical engineering
agriculture	psychology	architectural
medicine	education	engineering
nursing	meteorology	management

2. Study the following narration of a process that should be familiar to you, identify the steps, identify the specific actions that make up each step, and list them on a sheet of paper.

Frying an egg is one of the easier tasks in cooking. There are, however, a number of details you must make sure of: these include preparing the pan, breaking the egg, and knowing when to remove the egg from the heat. First, you must prepare your pan by oiling it in some way. Butter, cooking oil, and bacon grease are commonly used. If you have just fried bacon, pour off the excess grease into a jar, and leave only a thin layer in the pan. Remember not to pour the grease down the drain, or you'll soon have a problem. Part of the preparation of the pan also involves getting the pan to the right heat. If you have just fried bacon, let it cool a few minutes. If you are starting with an unused pan, let it heat up a few minutes. The next step in frying an egg calls for some amount of dexterity. Break the egg so that no bits of the shell fall into the pan. If you want the yolks to remain intact, break the egg very close to the surface of the pan. If you do not care about the yolks, just break away. The final step in frying an egg involves knowing when to take the egg off the heat. If you like your eggs "over easy," take the egg off rather early, before any browning begins to appear. If you like your eggs "over hard," you'll leave it on much longer. But with over-hard cooked eggs, always check by peeking on the underside of the egg to make sure it is not burning. Once you've mastered egg frying, you'll be ready to move on to omelets.

3. Identify the main steps of any three of the following familiar processes, and list them on a sheet of paper.

putting on a shirt	starting the car	throwing a dart
shaving	changing diapers	making a kite
mixing a drink	jogging	making orange juice
mowing the yard	shining your shoes	sharpening a pencil
brushing your teeth	washing dishes	using the telephone
playing a record	sunbathing	smoking a pipe
using a dictionary	raking leaves	tuning in a radio
putting on a tie	waxing the floor	filling an ink pen

watering plants	combing your hair	throwing a ball
catching the bus	riding a bicycle	sweeping the floor
planting seeds	doing the laundry	typing
swimming	studying for an exam	flying a kite

4. Make a photocopy of a relatively short process discussion, and do the following:
   a. Identify the type of process and the type of process narration.
   b. Identify the elements in the introduction and label them on your copy.
   c. Identify supplementary sentences used during the discussion of the steps and label them accordingly.
   d. Label any sentence or paragraph that provides additional information such as theory, principles of operation, guidelines, or equipment and materials.
   e. Identify and label the type of conclusion used.
   f. Explain what audience level the process has been written for.

5. Consider the following list of general report projects; choose any three; and explain (a) where process discussion will be needed, (b) why it will be needed, and (c) which kinds of process discussion will be needed.

Plans for an addition to a house	Proposal for city bike lanes
Recommendation to develop a nearby area	Plans to rezone certain areas of the city
Request for a loan to start a small business	Proposal to purchase word processors for secretaries in the firm
Report on the need for a new high school	Plans to close off a street downtown for a crafts fair
Proposal to begin citywide recycling	Plans to start selling a product in a new area
Proposal to relocate the business or open a new store in another area	

6. Consider the following topic ideas for causal discussion:

sneezing	colds	lightning
ulcers	headaches	thunder
shin splints	any cancer	northern lights
pneumonia	tooth decay	tornadoes
mental problems	criminal behavior	hurricanes
albinism	genetic mutations	earthquakes
inflation	economic depression	hail
any economic event	any economic phenomenon	snow
corrosion	acid rain	sunspots
any natural event	any natural phenomenon	"El Niño"
red color of Mars	rings of Saturn	cloudiness of Venus
any health problem	radiation	any disease

7. Study the following paragraph on a familiar causal discussion, and label the specific causal sentences according to whether they explain (a) a cause, (b) an effect, or (c) both.

This morning I got up at my usual hour, took a shower, had breakfast, got dressed, and headed out to my car to drive to work. Because the battery cables on my car were corroded, however, my car wouldn't start. I ran back into the house to call my boss. She said I ought to buy a new battery. I said that I didn't have enough money to buy a new battery. I explained to her that I had not had a raise in several years. She sighed and told me to jump start the battery and get to work as soon as possible. I went back out and hooked my battery up to the one in my wife's car. My car started right up. Finally, I was all set to head for work. As

I shifted into first and took off, I immediately noticed a clumping noise and a bouncing motion. The right rear tire was flat. I hadn't even mentioned the poor state of my tires to my boss!

8. Select one of the following familiar topics, and list the potential causes, effects, or both as indicated by the phrasing of the topic.

a bad headache
an increase in your rent
the baby won't stop
  crying

cold
a high grade on an exam
a big raise or promotion
  at work

no money in the
  checking account
an upset victory by
  your favorite team

9. Select one of the report projects listed in Exercise 5, and list the cause-effect situations that you might have to discuss if you were writing the report.

10. Make a photocopy of an extended causal discussion, and do the following:
   a. Identify the main causes, effects, or both that are discussed.
   b. Identify whether their relationship is simultaneous, sequential, or alternative.
   c. Outline the discussion showing the causes and effects in relation to the paragraphs.
   d. Explain for what level of audience the discussion is written.

Model 1–1: The Cardiac Cycle
(extended noninstructional process discussion)

To understand the cardiac cycle, the set of actions that the heart performs repeatedly to keep us alive, consider first the structure of the human heart.

The Chambers of the Heart. The human heart is divided by a series of partitions, called septa, into four chambers, which segregate the blood at different stages in the pumping cycle. The lower two are ventricles, thick-walled pumping chambers that receive blood from the upper chambers and drive it into the arteries by a series of contractions known as heartbeats. The upper two, called atria (or, sometimes, auricles), are thin-walled reservoirs that readily distend to collect blood that pours in from the veins between beats.

The left and right sides of the heart, each consisting of an atrium and a ventricle, are isolated from each other. The right side receives oxygen-poor blood from the body tissues and distributes it to the body tissues. The left ventricle is, by far, the thickest and heaviest chamber of the heart, reflecting its great work in delivering blood to the systemic circulation; its usual thickness is under one-half inch.

The Cardiac Cycle. The sequence of events producing each heartbeat is known as the cardiac cycle. During the cycle, each of the four chambers goes through a contraction, called the systole, and a relaxation, called the diastole. In the first phase of the cycle both atria contract, the right first, followed almost instantly by the left. This contraction fills the relaxed ventricles with blood. Then the ventricles contract, repelling their blood in a powerful surge. As they do so, the atria relax and are filled once again by the veins. This cycle lasts, on the average, six-sevenths of a second. The process is represented in Figure 1.

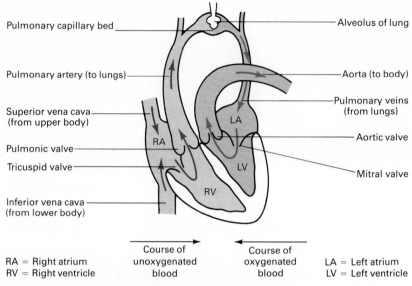

RA = Right atrium
RV = Right ventricle

Course of unoxygenated blood

Course of oxygenated blood

LA = Left atrium
LV = Left ventricle

FIGURE 1.   The chambers of the heart and the cardiac cycle

The pressure created by the heart's contraction varies from point to point in the heart and great vessels. Blood returning from the right atrium through veins is under a relatively low pressure of about 1 or 2 mm Hg. The right ventricle, which sends blood to the lungs, boosts the pressure to about 20 mm Hg during systole. Blood returning to the left atrium is once again at a low pressure, rising with contraction to 3 or 4 mm Hg. The left ventricle delivers blood to the body with considerable force. It raises the pressure to about 120 mm Hg with contraction, the same as the pressure in the arteries of the body. Between beats, the flow of blood into the capillaries lowers the pressure in the arteries to about 80 mm Hg. It is these last two pressures, systolic and diastolic, taken together, that doctors generally call "blood pressure." Thus a typical "normal" pressure might be 120/80.

Model 1–2:   Technique for Taking Blood Pressure
(extended instructional process discussion)

To measure blood pressure, a device known as a sphygmomanometer and a stethoscope are needed. A part of the sphygmomanometer is the cuff, a rubber bag that can be filled with air. It is usually covered with cloth and has two rubber tubes attached to it. One serves as the attachment for the rubber bulb that blows up the cuff. The other tube is attached to a manometer indicating the pressure of the air within the cuff. There are two types of sphygmomanometers: the aneroid manometer (see Figure 1), which has a calibrated dial with a needle pointer; and the sphygmomanometer with the mercury-filled tube. Blood-pressure cuffs come in six different sizes to accommodate different size people.

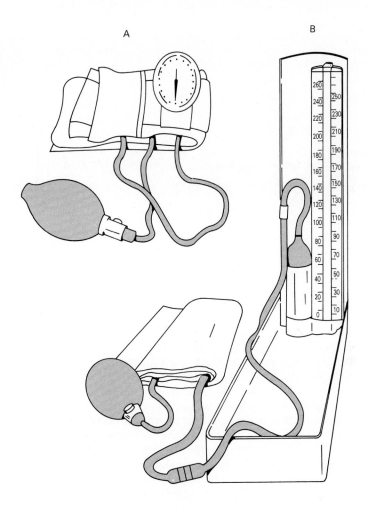

FIGURE 1.   The standard sphygmomanometer

Taking a blood-pressure reading involves two important phases: measuring the pressure accurately, and then interpreting it correctly.

Measuring blood pressure.   To take blood pressure, follow these procedures (see Figure 2):

1. The patient should be as comfortable as possible, his arm free and slightly flexed at the elbow, his brachial artery approximately at heart level. Center the inflatable bag over the brachial artery on the inside of the arm. Its lower border should be about 2.5 cm above the antecubital crease. Secure the cuff snugly.

FIGURE 2.   Using the sphygmomanometer

2. Inflate the cuff to about 40 mm Hg above the level at which the radial pulse disappears. Lower the cuff pressure slowly until the radial pulse is again detectable. This is the palpatory systolic pressure and helps you avoid being misled by an auscultatory gap.
3. Place a stethoscope firmly, but without undue pressure, over the brachial artery in the antecubital space. This point is usually found just medial to the biceps tendon. The stethoscope should touch neither cuff nor clothing. Inflate the cuff again, to about 30 mm Hg above the palpatory systolic pressure. Then deflate the cuff slowly, allowing the pressure to drop at a rate of about 3 mm Hg per second. Note the level at which you hear the sounds of at least two consecutive beats. This is the systolic pressure.
4. Continue to lower the pressure slowly until the sounds become suddenly muffled. This point is the most reliable measure of diastolic pressure, although usually somewhat above that found by intra-arterial measurement.
5. Continue decreasing the pressure and note the point at which all sounds disappear. Record all three points, for example, 120/80/70. When using a mercury sphygmomanometer, make all readings at eye level with the meniscus.
6. Blood pressure should be taken in both arms, at least when evaluating the patient initially. Normally there may be a difference in pressure of 5 mm Hg, sometimes up to 10 mm Hg. Subsequent readings should be made on the arm with the higher pressure. Figure 3 provides a guide for evaluating blood-pressure readings.

180	/	90	/	80
Systolic pressure		First diastolic pressure (muffled)		Second diastolic pressure (ceased)
140	/	—	/	0
Systolic pressure		First diastolic pressure (muffling not heard)		Second diastolic pressure (cessation not heard)

FIGURE 3. Recording blood-pressure readings

Interpreting Blood-Pressure Readings. Blood pressure is the measure of the pressure of the blood as it pulsates through the arteries. Because the blood moves in waves, there are two blood-pressure measures: the systolic pressure, which is the pressure of the blood as a result of contraction of the ventricles, that is, the pressure at the height of the blood wave; and a diastolic pressure, which is the pressure when the ventricles are at rest. Diastolic pressure, then, is the lowest pressure and is present at all times within the arteries. Blood pressure is measured in millimeters of mercury (mm Hg).

Normal pressure varies according to age, as shown in Figure 4. Pressures of adults that are above 160 mm Hg systolic and/or 100 mm Hg diastolic are referred to as hypertensive. Pressures below 100 systolic are considered hypotensive.

Age	Normal Blood Pressure Systolic	Diastolic
Newborn	50	—
1 month	60	—
6 months	70	—
1 year	95	65
6 years	100	65
10 years	110	65
16 years	120	65 (mean measures)
Adult	110–140	60–80
Elderly	110–140 or slightly higher	60–80 or slightly higher

FIGURE 4. Variations in blood pressure by age

Model 1–3: Immediate Effects of a Nuclear Attack*
(extended causal discussion: effects)

The yield of a nuclear weapon is usually described in terms of the quantity of the chemical explosive required to release an equivalent amount of energy; a nuclear weapon is said to have the power of kilotons (thousands of tons) and of megatons (millions of tons) of TNT. A standard bomb in today's arsenal is one of 20 megatons. One of the most devastating immediate effects of a nuclear bomb is the fireball, which produces (1) the thermal pulse and (2) the blast wave.

As the fireball from a nuclear explosion expands, energy is absorbed in the form of X-rays by the surrounding air, and the air reradiates a portion of that energy into the environment in the form of the thermal pulse. The fireball also sends out a blast wave in all directions. Expanding as large as 3 miles in diameter, the fireball pulverizes and then vaporizes all that it engulfs.

Thermal Pulse.   When the thermal pulse is emitted, searing heat ignites everything flammable and starts to melt windows, cars, buses, lampposts, and everything made of metal or glass. People in the street immediately catch on fire and are shortly reduced to charred corpses. The thermal pulse of a 1-megaton bomb lasts for about 10 seconds and can cause second-degree burns in exposed human beings at a distance of 9½ miles, or in an area of more than 280 square miles; that of a 20-megaton bomb lasts for about 20 seconds and can produce the same consequences at a distance of 28 miles, or in an area of 2,460 square miles. Such burns caused by the pulse over half the body result in serious shock and are likely to be fatal unless promptly treated. Thermal pulse can ignite newspapers at 2 miles in a 12.5-kiloton weapon and at 25 miles in a 20-megaton weapon.

The thermal pulse gets weaker as it travels outward because of absorption by the atmosphere as well as by geometrical spreading. The attenuation depends on atmospheric conditions; it is greatest in haze or fog. The intense visible light can cause temporary "flashblindness" in anyone who is looking in the direction of the explosion. A person whose eyes are focusing directly on the fireball will suffer serious retinal damage and possibly permanent blindness.

Blast Wave.   The mechanical motions of a nuclear explosion are analogous to those of a tidal wave. The blast wave is literally a wall of compressed air. As it passes, structures are exposed to a nearly instantaneous rise in the local atmospheric pressure and may be crushed. Following the shock front are strong winds analogous to the water currents that follow a moving ocean wave. The forces resulting from these winds may also lead to the collapse of structures in the target area. Depending on their shape and construction, buildings may be vulnerable either to the blast wave or to the winds that follow it, or to both (see Figure 1).

Peak over pressure	Effects	Distance to which effects are felt[a]
20 psi[b]	Multistory reinforced concrete buildings demolished; winds, 500 miles per hour.	1.8 miles
10 psi	Most factories and commercial buildings collapsed; small wood and brick residences destroyed; winds, 300 miles per hour.	2.7 miles

Peak over pressure	Effects	Distance to which effects are felt[a]
5 psi	Unreinforced brick and wood houses destroyed; heavier construction severely damaged; winds, 160 miles per hour.	4 miles
2 psi	Moderate damage to houses (wall frames cracked, severe damage to roofs, interior walls knocked down); people injured by flying glass and debris; winds, about 60 miles per hour.	7–8 miles

[a]One-megaton burst at 6000 feet.
[b]Pounds per square inch.

FIGURE 1.   Effects of blast from a nuclear explosion

Source: Leo Sartori, "The Effects of Nuclear Weapons," Physics Today (March, 1983), 37. Reprinted with permission.

The blast wave of a 1-megaton bomb can flatten or severely damage all but the strongest buildings within a radius of 4½ miles, and that of a 20-megaton bomb can do the same within a radius of 12 miles. The walls, roofs, and floors of any building that has not been flattened would be collapsed, and the people and furniture inside swept out into the street. The blast wave of a sizeable nuclear weapon endures for several seconds. People of course would be picked up and hurled away from the blast along with the rest of the debris. As far away as 10 miles from ground zero, pieces of glass and other sharp objects would be hurled about by the blast at lethal velocities. At a distance of 2 miles or so from ground zero, winds would reach 400 miles per hour. The 400-mile-per-hour wind would die down after a few seconds and then blow in the reverse direction with diminished intensity (1:34–37).

Literature Cited
1. Sartori, Leo. "The Effects of Nuclear Weapons." Physics Today. March 1983, pp. 32–41.
2. Schell, Jonathan. "Effects of Nuclear Holocaust." New Yorker. February 1, 1982, p. 47.
3. Stern, Daniel. "Electromagnetic Pulse: The Uncertain Certainty." Bulletin of the Atomic Scientists. March 1983, pp. 52–56.

*From Blake Jan, A Republic of Insects and Grass: Report on the Aftermath of Nuclear War (Austin: Univ. of Texas, 1984).

CHAPTER 2

Descriptions and Comparisons

Chapter Objectives
Descriptions
   Types of Description
   Locating Descriptive Areas in Report
      Projects
   Identifying the Parts or Characteristics
   Discussing Parts or Characteristics
   Sources of Information for Descriptions
   Determining Length for Descriptions
Comparisons
   Types of Comparisons
   Locating Comparative Areas in Report
      Projects
   Identifying Points of Comparison and
      Criteria
   Selecting a Pattern of Organization
   Discussing Differences and
      Similarities
   An Information-Gathering Strategy for
      Comparison
   Sources of Information for
      Comparisons
   Determining Length for Comparisons

Developing and Completing
   Descriptions and Comparisons
   Adjusting the Discussion to the
      Audience
   Special Sections
   Headings and Lists
   Graphic Aids
   Revising and Finishing Descriptions
      and Comparisons
Exercises
Models
  2–1. A Standard Automobile
      Alternator (extended description
      by parts)
  2–2. A Comparison of the
      Pressurized-Water Reactor and
      the Boiling-Water Reactor
      (extended point-by-point
      informative comparison)
  2–3. Evaluation of Five Wind-Powered
      Electrical Systems (extended
      point-by-point evaluative
      comparison)

───────────────── *Chapter Objectives* ─────────────────

After you read this chapter, study the examples, work the steps, and do the practice writing, you should be able to:

- Recognize description and comparison in reports.
- Spot areas in report projects requiring description or comparison.
- Recognize the different types of description and comparison.
- Identify the parts or characteristics of the object to be described, or the points to be used to compare two or more things.
- Organize descriptions and comparisons by a sequence of parts, components, or points of comparison either in single paragraphs or whole sections.
- Use the right kinds of supplementary discussion in descriptions and comparisons.

In this chapter, you'll learn about two more important tools in technical writing: *description* and *comparison*. In many ways, description is as important a tool as is process discussion, covered in the preceding chapter. The two together are the real workhorses in technical reports. Quite often in technical reports, description is used when two or more things are compared; that's why comparison is here in this chapter with description.

You can start with either the section on description or with the section on comparisons, but, in either case, finish up with the final section, "Developing and Completing Descriptions and Comparisons." (Steps specifically for descriptions end with "A"; those for comparisons end with "B".)

Descriptions

In technical writing, description enables experts to review plans on a mechanism to make sure they are sound and technicians (construction, maintenance, or repair people) to do their work on the mechanism. It enables uninformed purchasers, investors, or individuals who will be affected by the mechanism to know generally how the thing looks and how it works. It also enables curious, interested readers to understand the mechanism, even if they are not concerned about purchase, technological soundness, construction, maintenance, or repair.

Description is as common in technical writing as process discussion and often supplements it. When you describe a person, place, or thing, it is as if you capture it in a photograph of words, using any appropriate combination of the following sources:

size	color	subparts
shape	texture	depth
height	location	contents
weight	attachment of the parts	materials

A descriptive sentence of an artificial heart mechanism, for example, might read like this:

An implantable pacemaker consists of a miniaturized pulse generator encased in materials compatible with the human body such as epoxy with a covering of silicone rubber.

Descriptive sentences on a flat-plate solar collector might read this way:

> In this flat-plate solar collector, the absorber is a 1-meter by 3-meter steel sheet of 2.2 mm thickness containing 1 cm diameter coolant tubes 10 cm apart.
>
> In a flat-plate solar collector, a black plate is covered by one or more transparent cover plates of glass or plastics, and the sides and bottom of the box are insulated.

The first example discusses subparts and materials; the second, dimensions and materials; the third, colors, texture, materials, and shape.

Descriptive sentences are often used with process sentences (how something occurs or is made or done) and narrative sentences (stories about real or fictional events). The following sentences tell about a process:

> Special selective coatings are used on the surface of the metallic absorber in the solar collector in order to absorb incident sunlight and retard reradiation of infrared heat, allowing the collecting surface to reach higher temperatures.
>
> In a solar heating system, the sunlight strikes the absorber and heats up the water passing through the tubing, which is then piped to an underground thermal storage tank.

Notice that neither of these two sentences gives much visual detail, but instead both explain how the solar collector operates. Description often, however, gets mixed in the same sentence with process narration:

> In a flate-plate solar collector, sunlight is taken in by the transparent cover, usually opaque plastic or glass of some 2-mm thickness, and is transmitted to the absorber beneath it, which is typically a 1-meter by 3-meter steel sheet of 2.2-mm thickness painted black and rigged with 1-cm diameter coolant tubes that transfer the heat to the building or storage tank. The purpose of the thermal storage tank is to store the heat trapped in the solar collector panels for later heating use.

STEP 1A.   On your worksheet, briefly explain the object, mechanism, or place you want to describe. See Exercise 1 at the end of this chapter for suggestions. (If you are thinking about collaborating with someone else on your description, see "Collaborating on Technical Reports" in the Introduction for ideas and suggestions.)

Types of Description

Generally, the kind of description you write depends on at least three things:

- Whether it is an *external* or *internal* description.
- Whether the object or mechanism is described by *parts* or by *characteristics*.
- Whether it is a relatively *general* or *specific* description.

When you plan a description, you must make a decision about each of these categories.

External or Internal Descriptions.   Consider whether your description should be an external or internal description, or both. An *external* description of a photocopier would give us the dimensions of the machine and describe the moving parts the operator uses, the buttons and their functions, the display features, and so on. An *internal* description of a photocopier, on the other hand, would discuss the main functioning parts inside the machine, the parts that enable it to make copies. An example in which both kinds of description are at work appears in Figure 2–1.

The description in Figure 2–1 is mostly internal, although the first section on the zinc can is mainly external. Also, you can see that this description is quite detailed, providing specifications on size and materials. A more general treatment would summarize the location and function of the major parts in no more than a paragraph.

Descriptions by Parts and Characteristics.   Consider also whether your description should be arranged by parts or by characteristics. This choice depends on the nature of the object you are describing. Many things divide easily into *parts* or *components*. A pencil, for example, is composed of a lead, a wooden barrel, an eraser, and a metal connector. The human ear is composed of the auricle, auditory canal, tympanic membrane, malleus, incus, semicircular canals, cochlea, stapes, eustachean tube, and auditory nerve.

However, some things must be described (or can only be described) by *characteristics*. For example, if you propose certain vacant lots as sites for softball fields, you would discuss such things as location, square areas, vegetation and structures on the sites, and the contours of the terrain that might require landscaping. These are characteristics. Take a look at the two example descriptions in Figure 2–2.

Figure 2–3 provides a conceptual illustration of the difference between description by parts and description by characteristics.

STEP 2A.   On your worksheet briefly explain which type of description you are going to write (general or specific, external or internal, and parts or characteristics), who the audience is, and why that audience needs the description.

Locating Descriptive Areas in Report Projects

Three ways to locate areas in your report where description might be needed are the following:

- Make a list of the objects, mechanisms, places, or even people that you may have to discuss.
- Consider the various subtopics related to your report, make a list of them, and try to imagine if any of them has something about it that can be described.
- Take a long look at as detailed a version of your outline as you can create, and again try to imagine areas for description.

Major Parts of the Dry Cell Battery

The typical dry cell battery consists of a zinc can, a carbon electrode, the core, the top and bottom collars, the top seal, and an insulated metal shell.

The Zinc Can

The zinc can of a D-size dry cell battery is of course made of zinc, a relatively soft, shiny, malleable metal. The can is made by capping one end of a seamless cylinder that is about 5.5 centimeters long and about 3 centimeters in diameter. The bottom cap, a circular piece of zinc cut to a diameter that fits the inside diameter of the cylinder, mounts flush with the end of the cylinder and is secured by some form of liquid solder. The wall thickness of the cylinder and cap generally ranges between 0.25 and 0.5 millimeters. This zinc can serves as the container for the battery.

Carbon Electrode

The carbon electrode appears black, rough, and slightly porous. It is composed of finely divided carbon and magnesium dioxide molecules pressed around a small-diameter carbon rod that resembles a small, long black nail. The entire electrode is approximately 5.5 centimeters long and has an outside diameter of about 0.5 centimeters.

The Core

The core of the battery surrounds the carbon electrode and fills the zinc can. The core consists of two parts, the paste electrolyte and the depolarizing mixture.

The Paste Electrolyte.   The paste electrolyte is a clear, high-viscosity fluid composed of zinc chloride ($ZnCl_2$) and ammonium chloride (NH_4Cl). High viscosity simply means that the paste is very thick and almost rubbery. The electrolyte coats the inside of the zinc can with a thickness of about 2 millimeters.

The Depolarizing Mixture.   The depolarizing mixture fills in the rest of the zinc can. This mixture has a silver color and is made up of fine granules of manganese dioxide, carbon powder, ammonium chloride, zinc chloride, and water. It has a consistency similar to that of wet sand.

[Other parts—the description continues.]

FIGURE 2–1.   External and internal technical descriptions

Description by Characteristics

Site Three is a 6-acre area located in the southwest quadrant of the city on Ramsey Boulevard between Tenth and Fifteenth Streets. It is a generally square area, with one side ending in a railroad embankment and the opposite, at Ramsey Boulevard. There are eleven mature oak and elm trees on the site, only one of which will have to be removed to build the park. The rest of the vegetation is low scrub brush and weeds. For some number of years, a nearby construction firm had dumped its rubbish from building projects in the northwest quarter of the site. A dilapidated barn from the time when the site was part of a farm occupies the northeast quarter. The site is generally level, with a gradual incline toward Ramsey Boulevard. Some landscaping will be required to relocate a natural drainage ditch running through the middle of the site and to build up several low areas where stagnant water accumulates during rainy periods. Of course the area where the infield will be located will have to be built up a good deal more.

Part-by-Part Description

A typical flat-plate solar collector consists of transparent cover plates, a black-painted metallic absorber, coolant tubes, a wooden frame box into which these parts fit, and insulation between the parts and the box itself, as shown in Figure 2–2a.

The transparent cover plates are either glass or plastic of some 2 centimeters thickness, doubled with an intervening air space of 5 centimeters to create a heat-trapping effect. The absorber is a black-enameled, 2.2-centimeters-thick, 1- by 3-meter-square aluminum sheet. The coolant tubes, 1 centimeter in diameter, are welded on the underside of the absorber and transfer the incoming solar radiation into the system for heating purposes. The fiberglass insulation is about 6 centimeters thick on the bottom and on the sides of the collector. The wooden frame in which all this is housed is fiberglassed 1.5-centimeter-thick plywood.

(continued)

FIGURE 2–2. Technical description by parts and characteristics

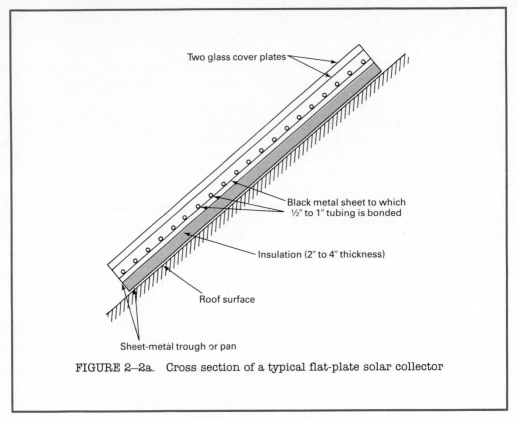

Two glass cover plates

Black metal sheet to which ½″ to 1″ tubing is bonded

Insulation (2″ to 4″ thickness)

Roof surface

Sheet-metal trough or pan

FIGURE 2–2a.   Cross section of a typical flat-plate solar collector

FIGURE 2–2.   (cont.)

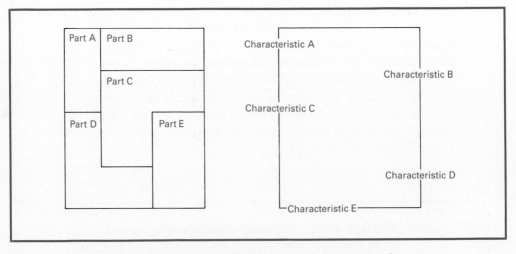

Part A   Part B

Part C

Part D   Part E

Characteristic A

Characteristic B

Characteristic C

Characteristic D

Characteristic E

FIGURE 2–3.   Conceptual diagram of description by parts and description by characteristics

Use these three techniques to review your report-writing project for areas in which description is needed. Here are some examples:

Report Subject	Subtopics for Description
Solar heating system	System components
	The house in which they are installed
	Modifications to the house
Municipal softball fields	The proposed sites (vacant, unused city property)
	Vegetation on the sites
	Structures existing on the sites
	The proposed field, fences, bleachers
Offshore oil-rig explosion	The oil rig before the explosion
	Parts of the rig that malfunctioned
	The explosion and fire
	Equipment used to control the fire
	Resulting damage to the rig
	Resulting oil spill and coastal damage

STEP 3A.   On your worksheet, list the objects or mechanisms related to your report topic that you may need to describe, and indicate the type of description for each.

Identifying the Parts or Characteristics

Whether you describe an object by its parts or by its characteristics depends on that object and on your purposes in writing the description. When you identify those parts or characteristics, the organization—or outline—of the description is almost complete.

Parts.   When you plan a description, try making a list of the main parts of the mechanism you want to write about. For example:

Parts of a Flat-Plate Solar Collector	Parts of a Dry Cell Battery
transparent cover plates	zinc can
absorber	carbon electrode
tubing	core
wooden frame box	paste electrolyte
insulation	depolarizing mixture

Characteristics.   You may find, however, that dividing the mechanism into parts does not do the job for you, either because of your purpose in writing the description or because of the mechanism itself. In that case, make a list of the important characteristics. For example:

Characteristics of Proposed Softball-Field Sites	*Characteristics of an Industrial Robot*
location	materials in construction
square area	purchase and
terrain	maintenance costs
vegetation	configuration
structures on the site	workspace
drainage considerations	payload
accessibility	safety considerations
roads	
utilities	

Subparts and Subcharacteristics.   In some cases, there may be so much detail concerning a part or characteristic that you must divide once again, creating subparts or subcharacteristics. Notice in the preceding examples that the core of the dry cell battery has two subparts (the paste electrolyte and the depolarizing mixture) and that the accessibility of the softball-field sites has two subcharacteristics (roads and utilities).

STEP 4A.   On your worksheet, list the parts or characteristics of the thing you are describing. If you need more information to do this, go to "Sources of Information for Descriptions" in this chapter and return when you are through.

Discussing Parts or Characteristics

Once you've identified the parts or characteristics of the mechanism, consider the sources of description that should be used as well as the supplementary information.

Sources of Description.   Use the following list as a checklist to make sure you include all the sources relevant to the object or mechanism you are describing.

• *Color.* Ask yourself whether the color of the object should be described, and then add this information to your description.

> In a telescope Mars usually appears as a bright reddish disk marked by complex, semi-permanent dark regions and variable white polar caps. In general, surface albedo features are not visible on photographs taken in violet and ultraviolet light because of decreasing contrast between the light and dark regions at these shorter wavelengths.

• *Shape.* You can indicate the shape of an object by (a) comparing it to some geometrical shape, or (b) comparing it to some familiar object.

The typical pressurized-water-type nuclear reactor uses enriched uranium as its fuel, a natural uranium with refined U-235 added, formed into long metallic plates or bars coated with some other metal—aluminum or zirconium—to protect against corrosion.

• *Dimensions*. Much description requires discussion of dimensions such as height, width, thickness, length, depth, and area. The purpose of your description determines how precise this information should be.

A silicon chip is a piece of almost pure silicon, usually less than one centimeter square and a half a millimeter thick.

• *Materials*. Your description may also need to discuss the materials your object or mechanism is made of: for example, steel, plastic, aluminum, or cardboard.

A silicon chip contains hundreds of thousands of microminiature electronic circuit components, mainly transistors, packed and interconnected in layers beneath the surface. On the surface of the chip there is a grid of thin metallic strips; these are the electrical connections via wires to the outside world. When sold commercially, the chips are usually packaged in plastic.

• *Texture and finish*. Details on texture and finish may also help readers understand or visualize the object or mechanism. Texture refers to how rough or smooth something is; finish, how bright, shiny, dull, or glossy it is.

• *Location, arrangement, and attachment of parts*. Most technical descriptions must explain how the parts are attached to each other (are they glued, nailed, screwed, bolted, welded, soldered?) and how they are arranged (are they on top of, inside of, near to, far from each other?).

The long metallic bars used as fuel in PWR nuclear reactors are welded together in a box shape to form the fuel. The fuel element is located in the core of the reactor, where there are control rods, made of cadmium or hafnium, to soak up neutrons, which regulate the reaction. Surrounding this fuel element and the control rods is water under high pressure so that at its normal operating temperature of 600°F it remains liquid.

• *Contents or ingredients*. The object or mechanism may have certain contents or ingredients that should be discussed in the description. Ask yourself whether your audience needs information on these internal aspects of the object.

The Martian atmosphere is thin, with a surface pressure of 7–10 millibars (700–1000 Pa), averaging 8 Mb (800 Pa), less than 1% of the pressure at the Earth's surface. Martian atmosphere is principally composed of carbon dioxide; but it contains nitrogen, oxygen, argon, and traces of water—all totaling no more than 5%. The clouds on Mars are formed of carbon dioxide and ice.

• *Associated noises and odors*. Some characteristic noise (a loud bang, a muffled roar, a squeek) or some characteristic odor (a pungent, acrid, lemony, stale smell, for example) may be associated with the object or mechanism you are describing. Include this information also if readers need it.

The preceding list shows you only the most common sources and may help to get you thinking about others such as the length of time associated with use of a mechanism, its age, its durability, its cost, or references to temperatures or frequencies associated with the mechanism.

Supplementary Sentences and Sections.   Supplementary sentences and sections add additional, useful information to a description but are not description in themselves. Check your description to see whether supplementary information like the following commonly used kinds might help.

* *Process discussion.* Process sentences are often used to supplement descriptions:

The jacket of the standard diskette has a center hole corresponding to the center hole in the diskette, but it is larger, measuring 1⅜ inches in diameter. *The drive hub clamps onto this center hole and rotates the diskette, thus enabling data to be read to or from the diskette.*

* *Definitions.* Be ready to define any word or phrase that may not be familiar to the audience reading your description:

Along the left edge of the standard diskette is a small rectangular notch, measuring ¼ inch long by ⅛ inch deep. This is called the write-protect notch, and it can be covered with a write-protect tab. *A write-protect tab is a simple adhesive tab that prevents the diskette drive from writing (recording) data on the diskette.*

* *Classification.* Quite often in descriptions an object or some part of it is discussed in terms of the class or category of things it belongs to:

Every computer must have some means of storing data—a storage device. For microcomputers, there are *two basic types: "floppy" diskettes, which are small, convenient and portable; and "fixed" or "hard" disks, which are an actual fixed component of the microcomputer, capable of storing great amounts of data.*

* *Comparisons.* Quite often objects being described or their parts are compared to other things—often, to familiar things:

The Victor computer's standard capacity, per disk, is 606K bytes, *which is almost twice that offered by most other computers.* However, the Victor's standard diskette drives are single sided, *while other machines typically use double-sided drives.*

STEP 5A.   List on your practice worksheet which sources of description and which kinds of supplementary information you may need to use in your technical description.

Sources of Information for Descriptions

If you are not sure about terminology for the object or mechanism you are describing, consult a reference book such as

McGraw-Hill Encyclopedia of Science and Technology
Van Nostrand's Scientific Encyclopedia

Consider checking one or two of the more general encyclopedias such as

Encyclopedia Britannica
Encyclopedia Americana

More specific ones include the following:

The Encyclopedia of How It Works
How Do They Do That? Wonders of the Modern World Explained
Man and Machines
The Way Things Work: An Illustrated Encyclopedia of Technology
What's What: A Visual Glossary of the Physical World

What's What is a particularly useful resource; it provides diagrams of common mechanisms along with labels for the main parts.

If these don't help, either ask help from a librarian, or turn to the section on finding reference books in Chapter 9. The specialized encyclopedias, handbooks, and dictionaries discussed there may have the information you need. If all these strategies fail, you can find an expert to help you, or you can label the parts of what you are describing "Part A," "Part B," and so on.

STEP 6A.   On your worksheet, list the sources of information you use to get information for your description. If you need even more information than is available from the sources just listed, read Chapter 9 and follow the steps there.

Determining Length for Descriptions

At this point in the chapter you're ready to decide on the length of your description—whether it should be a short description (only a paragraph or two) or an extended description. The audience of the description, its need for the description, and your own purpose in writing it will help you make this decision.

Short Descriptions.   In single-paragraph descriptions, each part or characteristic is described in a sentence or two. Obviously, short descriptions don't allow you much room to go into detail about an object or mechanism. An example is provided in Figure 2–4.

Extended Descriptions.   In extended descriptions each part or characteristic can be described in a number of sentences—for example, in a whole paragraph or even a group of paragraphs. This approach gives you plenty of room to describe in great detail. An example of an extended description appears in Figure 2–5.

As you can see from these examples, descriptions are expandable: from only part of a sentence, they can be expanded into whole sentences, whole paragraphs, and even groups of paragraphs. This expandability is represented in Figure 2–6.

The major parts of the ASEA IRb-60 include   overview of the parts
(1) the base, (2) the lower arm, (3) the upper
arm, and (4) the wrist. The base consists of the   part 1
pedestal, the resolver, the tachogenerator, the dc
motor, the body, and the gearbox. The lower   part 2
arm measures 140 mm and is controlled by the
drive unit in the body. The upper arm measures   part 3
650 mm and enables the robot to manipulate the
materials that it is working on. The wrist,   part 4
mounted to the upper arm, provides turning and
tilting motion almost like that of a human
wrist. It consists of a drive unit with a dc motor.
These parts enable the ASEA IRb-60 to do
welding and other kinds of work with metal
parts.

FIGURE 2—4.   Short description (part-by-part)

STEP 7A.   On your worksheet explain whether your description will be short or extended and why. Now, go to the appropriate group of steps that follow.

Substeps for Short Descriptions

If you write a short description (only one or two paragraphs), your job is fairly simple. And, if you've done the steps to this point, you can do the following:

1. Gather information about the object or mechanism, if necessary (using the steps in Chapter 9, if you need to find library information).
2. Write one or more sentences explaining each part or characteristic.
3. Write several introductory sentences that
   a. Define the object or mechanism or explain its purpose or importance.
   b. List the parts or characteristics (that is, provide an overview).
4. Write a concluding sentence or two, if necessary, for your descriptive paragraph.
5. Go on to the section "Developing and Completing Descriptions and Comparisons" for the finish-up work there.

Substeps for Extended Descriptions

If you write an extended description (several paragraphs), your job is rather similar to writing a short description:

Robots are designed to have a wide range of specifications so that a prospective user can match the features of a robot to the needs of the job.

Configuration.   The first three links of the manipulator can be designed to join and move in various ways. They can form a rectangular or cartesian configuration; a cylindrical configuration; a spherical or polar configuration; a revolute or jointed-arm configuration, or the SCARA (selective compliant assembly robot arm) configuration.

Workspace.   The extent of each robot's reach in each direction, of course, depends on its configuration, articulations, and size of its components (links and other members). The solid geometric space created by subtracting the inner (fully contracted) from the outer (fully extended) possible positions of a defined point (for example, wrist flange, center of gripper, and tip of tool) is called the robot's workspace or work envelope. For a mobile robot this space is greatly expanded--being limited only by physical barriers or programming restrictions--and is called the robot's probability shell.

Payload.   The payload is the weight that the robot is designed to lift, move, and position repeatedly with accuracy, precision, and reliability. . . .

FIGURE 2–5.   Extended description (by characteristics)

1. Gather information about the object or mechanism, if necessary (using the steps in Chapter 9, if you need to find library information).
2. Write a paragraph explaining each part or characteristic (there may be some simple, minor parts or characteristics that can be grouped within one paragraph, however).
3. Write an introductory paragraph that
   a. Defines the object or mechanism or explains its purpose or importance.
   b. Lists the parts or characteristics (that is, provides an overview).
   c. Provides other necessary introductory information.
4. Write a concluding paragraph for your extended description, if necessary.
5. Go on to the section "Developing and Completing Descriptions and Comparisons" for the finish-up work there.

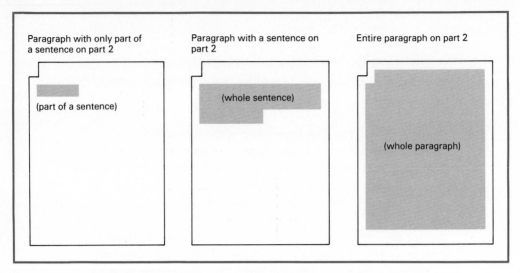

Paragraph with only part of a sentence on part 2

(part of a sentence)

Paragraph with a sentence on part 2

(whole sentence)

Entire paragraph on part 2

(whole paragraph)

FIGURE 2—6. Expanding description of parts from less than a sentence to entire paragraphs

Comparisons

Comparison—which focuses on the similarities and differences between two or more things—is an important tool for technical writers, especially those who are trying to convince associates to take some course of action. In almost any technical discussion, quick sentence-length comparisons help make descriptions and process discussions clearer. The kind of comparisons discussed in this chapter is not, however, the individual sentence that compares, but the whole section of a report that compares—called here an *extended comparison.*

STEP 1B.   On your worksheet briefly describe the objects, mechanisms, or situations you want to compare. For suggestions, see Exercise 6 at the end of this chapter. (If you are thinking about collaborating with someone else on your comparison, see "Collaborating on Technical Reports" in the Introduction for ideas and suggestions.)

Types of Comparisons

You can use comparisons in two distinct ways: to make technical information more readily understandable; and to demonstrate convincingly the advantages of one mechanism, program, or plan over others.

Informative Comparisons.   In an informative comparison you compare an unfamiliar object, mechanism, action, or idea to something else, often something familiar: for example, comparing word processors to typewriters for a nonspecialist audience of secretaries. The point is simply to inform them. An example of an

A Comparison of COBOL and FORTRAN

COBOL and FORTRAN can be compared in terms of their general structure, programming nature, limitations, and amount of effort required to create programs.

General Structure.   COBOL is a more structured language than FORTRAN, in the sense that COBOL has four divisions (identification, environment, data, and procedure) that *must* be included in every program in the sequence specified. FORTRAN, on the other hand, is more flexible; no particular statements must be included.

Ease of Understanding.   A FORTRAN program, because it lends itself more to mathematical applications, may not be as easy to understand as a COBOL program, which looks much more like English. Compare these two chunks of code:

COBOL	FORTRAN
IF SALES – AMT IS GREATER THAN 100.00 MULTIPLY .03 BY SALES – AMT GIVING COMMISSION.	IF (SALES .GT. 100.00) GO TO 20 * * * 20 COMMIS = SALES * .03

Limitations.   In FORTRAN, each field name can consist of a maximum of 6 characters; in COBOL, the maximum is 30 characters. This limitation often causes abbreviated field names in FORTRAN to be less self-explanatory for the user than corresponding names in COBOL. For example, in COBOL a field might be called YEAR-TO-DATE-GROSS-EARNINGS or perhaps Y-T-D-GROSS-EARN. In FORTRAN, the best we can do is something like YTDGRS.

Useful Features.   How much effort the programmer must put forth to code FORTRAN statements that specify precisely what the input or output looks like should be clear from the examples already presented. In COBOL, with the aid of PICTURE clauses, it is usually easier to describe input or output specifications. However, although FORTRAN

(continued)

FIGURE 2–7.   An informative comparison (point-by-point)

is considered to be cumbersome in the area of input/output specifications, it is much easier to code arithmetic operations using FORTRAN. That is, arithmetic instructions are less verbose and easier to write in FORTRAN than in COBOL. In addition, FORTRAN enables the programmer to include complex mathematical functions that cannot be included in a COBOL program. In some business applications, such as sales forecasting or inventory control, there is often the need to use mathematical concepts, such as trigonometric functions. For instance, a formula might require the computer to find the cosine of a particular angle. In FORTRAN, we can easily write an instruction such as:

```
Y = COS(X)
```

and the FORTRAN compiler, or translator, will recognize what is meant by the operation "COS." In COBOL, this cannot be done very easily, since the COBOL compiler is not equipped to recognize the code COS, or most other mathematical functions.

FIGURE 2-7.   (cont.)

extended comparison of programming languages used for informative purposes is shown in Figure 2–7.

Evaluative Comparisons.   Comparisons can also aid in convincing people to take a certain course of action or in helping them to decide on a course of action. In such persuasive efforts audiences are much more convinced when the advantages and disadvantages of several alternatives are discussed rather than the good points of only one.

If you must recommend or propose a course of action, plan to write a comparison of two or more alternatives *even if you are quite sure in your own mind from the very start about which choice is the best*. Investigating other alternatives will make the resulting report or proposal thorough and complete. Readers will be convinced; if they are not, they have the necessary information before them in the same report to make their own choice. Including the comparison of several alternatives shows the logic that led to the choice that you made.

When you gather and compare information on plans, products, or services and then decide which alternative is the best, you are *evaluating*. When you have been requested to do this work, the resulting evaluative comparison is often called a *recommendation*. For example, the boss could walk into your office some day and ask you to do a study of word-processing software on the market and to recommend one for volume purchase by the company. However, if, in the same company, you initiate the idea for purchasing word processors, the resulting report is often called a *proposal*. Recommendations and proposals are discussed in Part IV.

STEP 2B.   On your worksheet briefly explain which type of comparison (informative or evaluative) you plan to write, who the audience is, and why that audience needs the comparison.

Locating Comparative Areas in Report Projects

When you plan a report, think for a moment about what things can be compared within it. Ask yourself questions like these:

* Are there objects or mechanisms discussed in the report that should be compared to more common and familiar things?
* Are there processes or events that should be compared to more common and familiar things?
* Are there concepts in the report that should be compared to more common and familiar things?
* Should any of the objects, mechanisms, processes, events, or concepts in this report be compared to similar ones?
* Are you attempting to recommend or propose a plan of action that can be compared to other plans?

Using questions like these, you may be able to locate areas for comparison in your report project such as the following:

Report Topic	Subtopics for Comparison
Wind-powered electrical generating systems	Costs of different models and designs
	Design features of the different models
	Power output of the different models
	Costs of wind power and conventionally generated electricity
Word-processing software	Word processing on a computer and on a regular typewriter
	Costs of different word-processing programs
	Features of different word-processing programs
	Ease of learning and using
Drip irrigation	Different methods of drip irrigation
	Areas with and without drip irrigation
	Drip irrigation and conventional irrigation methods

STEP 3B.   On your worksheet, list the subtopics in your report that you may need to compare along with what you'd compare them to, and indicate the type of comparison for each.

Identifying Points of Comparison and Criteria

Any time you compare two or more things, you must refer to common features, characteristics, aspects, or points. In what different ways can you compare two or more personal computers, for example? The points of comparison might include some of the following:

size	shape	color
cost	screen size	reliability
technical support	ease of operation	warranties
flexibility	memory capacity	user's manual

When you prepare to write a comparison, you should make a list of points of comparison like this one to make the rest of your work easier and more efficient.

You select from these potential points of comparison and others and then compare the personal computers using these selected points one by one. Select the points of comparison according to the report situation and according to the needs and interests of the audience. The ones above are more likely to interest users of personal computers; different points of comparison are likely to concern computer designers, technicians, and programmers.

Criteria are special kinds of points of comparison. A criterion (the singular of criteria) is a point of comparison whose value is already established. For example, if you could only qualify for a bank loan of $50,000 on a house, you have a cost limitation of $50,000. Think of criteria as requirements, or maximum or minimum values. Criteria are not only related to costs, however. If you plan to do some serious fishing in shallow bay waters, you'd require a boat with a shallow draft, in other words, one that could handle 2- and 3-foot depths.

STEP 4B.   List on your worksheet the main points of comparison you plan to use. Also, list any criteria you plan to use and include their values (for example, minimum or maximum cost).

Selecting a Pattern of Organization

Organizing a comparison is like designing a mold into which you pour the raw materials of the discussion. Organizational patterns for comparisons include the following: the whole-to-whole approach and the point-by-point approach.

Whole-to-Whole Approach.   One of the most natural patterns of organization, but also one of the hardest to handle effectively, is the whole-to-whole approach. This approach does just what it says. It allows you in one or more paragraphs to discuss one item (the UVC Execucomp in Figure 2–8). In the second paragraph or set of paragraphs, it discusses the other item of comparison (the Fujima Docucomp in Figure 2–8).

Whole-to-whole comparisons have two basic problems. If not handled carefully, they can cause readers unnecessary work: the readers have to put together the corresponding information from the two separate paragraphs and make the comparisons themselves. This problem can be solved by writing a third paragraph that

The UVC Execucomp received a rating of 3.3 for ease of operation, on a scale where 4.0 was excellent. As for the reliability of the system and its peripherals, users rated them 3.5 and 3.4, respectively. Both the responsiveness and effectiveness of maintenance service received a high rating of 3.4 as well. In the area of technical support, UVC's troubleshooting assistance was given only a 3.0; its training support, a 2.6; and its vendor manuals, a 2.7. When users were asked how the actual performance of the Execucomp compared with their expectations, they responded with a 3.3 rating. And finally, the users in the survey rated the Execucomp with a 3.3 in overall performance. The survey was conducted among 377 users in the South and Midwest in 1982.

The Fujima Docucomp in a survey . . .

FIGURE 2–8. A whole-to-whole comparison (without transitions or directly stated comparisons)

does the real comparison but that takes up unnecessary space. Still, you may find the whole-to-whole approach useful in certain report-writing situations.

Point-by-Point Approach. Generally, you'll write a more effective comparison if you use the point-by-point approach: it shows more clearly the outcome of the comparison. Writing a point-by-point comparison takes a bit more planning. But once the points of comparison have been selected, the discussion is surprisingly easy to write. Depending on the size and extent of the discussion, you can discuss each point

- in an individual sentence
- in a single paragraph (with the other points)
- in a separate section (one or more paragraphs).

Examples appear in Figure 2–9 and 2–10. In the first example in Figure 2–9 all the points are covered in one sentence. In the second example each point is covered in a sentence all its own.

Now, in Figure 2–10 there is an example of an expanded version of the comparison. Notice in Figure 2–10 that two individual points of comparison receive one or more paragraphs each, compared to the single clause or sentence they each receive in Figure 2–9. How extensive you make your own point-by-point comparison depends on

- your purpose in doing the comparison
- the needs of your audience
- the space limitations of the report or proposal
- the complexity of the subject.

<u>Sentence-Length Point-by-Point Comparison</u>

Although Fujima's Docucomp received higher ratings than UVC's Execucomp in ease of operation, the Execucomp received higher ratings in reliability of the system and its peripherals, responsiveness and effectiveness of maintenance service, technical support, actual as compared to anticipated performance, and overall user satisfaction.

<u>Paragraph-Length Point-by-Point Comparison</u>

In a recent survey, UVC's Execucomp word-processor system rated higher than Fujima's Docucomp in eight out of ten categories. In one of the most important categories, ease of operation, however, Docucomp outrated Execucomp 3.6 to 3.3. However, in the reliability of the system and its peripherals, users rated the Execucomp 3.5 and 3.4, respectively, and the Docucomp 3.2 and 2.9, respectively. In responsiveness and effectiveness of maintenance service . . .

FIGURE 2–9. Sentence- and paragraph-length point-by-point comparisons

A conceptual illustration of comparisons using the whole-to-whole and the point-by-point comparisons appears in Figure 2–11.

STEP 5B.   On your worksheet explain which pattern of organization you are going to use in your comparison and why.

Discussing Differences and Similarities

A discussion that compares, contrasts, or does both is fundamentally different from descriptive or process writing. Processes and descriptions give you a special kind of *content,* either chronological steps or visual details related to a process or object. Comparative discussions, on the other hand, have a special kind of *structure.* Comparisons do their work by sentences that contain information on two or more things being compared, transitions that emphasize the comparisons, and patterns of organization that make comparisons easy to follow.

You can recognize comparative discussions of technical matters by looking for key transitions and certain kinds of organizational patterns. The actual content of those paragraphs may sound like description or process discussion. The framework of comparison, however, tells you that the overall purpose of the passage is to compare. Some of the many transition words and phrases that emphasize similarities and differences are listed here:

Ease of Operation

A number of keyboard features may have led users to give the Docucomp a 3.6 rating compared to Execucomp's 3.3. For example, a user can press the "code" button and the "u" button together, and the system will automatically center the text that the user subsequently puts in by backspacing one character for every two characters typed. The Execucomp has no such comparable feature.

Another feature in which Docucomp excels over Execucomp involves moving large blocks of text. In the Docucomp system the user positions the cursor before the beginning of the text he wants to move and pushes the "move" button. The system responds by asking "move what," after which the user moves the cursor to the end of the text he wants moved and presses the "move" button once again. When the system asks "move where," the user positions the cursor at the place in the text where he wants the text to be moved and presses the "move" button one more time. The text is then entered at the desired location and deleted from the original location.

In the Execucomp, on the other hand, the user must actually count the lines he wants moved and enter this number with his move command. Once he has moved the text, he must go back and delete the text from the original location.

Responsiveness and Effectiveness of Maintenance Service

Linked to the lower rating the Docucomp received on the reliability of its system and the peripherals were its low scores on responsiveness and effectiveness of its maintenance service. Users at a small college on the East Coast reported that . . .

FIGURE 2–10.   A section-length point-by-point comparison

Similarities		Differences	
like	likewise	but	however
as	as well as	whereas	unlike
similarly	same	dissimilar	on the other hand
equally	equivalent	in contrast	although
also	too	while	different (from)

Now, in Figure 2–12 there is a passage in which a number of these transitional words are used to emphasize comparisons.

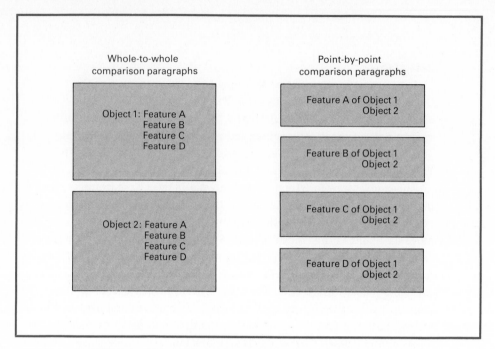

FIGURE 2–11.   Conceptual diagram of whole-to-whole and point-by-point comparisons

An Information-Gathering Strategy for Comparison

When you begin to gather the information for the comparison, consider using a strategy such as the one shown in Figure 2–13. Devise a chart to record the information you gather so as to ensure that you gather the right information and enough of it. An information-gathering chart for an evaluative comparison for automobiles, of course, would need a number of other points of comparison such as roominess, smoothness of ride, and so on, but this excerpt should give you the idea.

Sources of Information for Comparisons

Although it may be easy enough to figure out the points of comparison, finding sufficient and reliable information for each of those points may be difficult. Of course, you can do the necessary research, measurements, or surveys yourself. See Chapter 9 on gathering information from nonlibrary sources.

If direct gathering of comparative information is not convenient or possible, you can locate certain kinds of comparative and evaluative information in the library or in literature available from businesses.

Company Brochures.   You can get brochures from companies that provide products or services. Look them up in the phone book, call, drop by in person, or write these companies. If you simply ask, sales representatives may supply additional

DESCRIPTIONS AND COMPARISONS

Microwave ovens are famous for cooking fast, clean, and cool. They are not, however, famous for browning foods or for cooking evenly. In these two areas, cooking with a conventional oven is still far superior to microwave cooking. While browning may not be important to most people, even cooking certainly is. The source of this problem has to do with the different design and operation of microwave and conventional ovens. In a microwave oven the energy is piped in from the magnetron (the source of the microwave energy) at the top of the oven as opposed to a conventional oven in which heat fills the entire oven cavity. To overcome this problem, most microwave ovens have a rotating reflector near the top of the oven to distribute the microwaves.

In microwave cooking you lack many of the familiar clues that tell you food is cooking, such as browning or crisping that occur in conventional cooking. In many microwave-oven models, this problem has been eased by the development of a temperature probe. Another important related difference has to do with standing time: a roast cooked in a conventional oven continues to "cook" after it has come out of the oven; the same thing happens with a microwave oven, except that the internal temperature may increase by as much as 10 to 15 degrees. For this reason, then, oven temperature in a microwave should be set 10 to 20 degrees lower than in a conventional oven.

"Microwave Ovens," Consumer Reports (May 1983), 222–24.

FIGURE 2–12. Transitions used in discussing differences and similarities

	Fuel Economy	Handling Ease	Reliability	Cost
Automobile 1	27/35	very good	good	$10,000
Automobile 2	24/39	very good	fair	9,887
Automobile 3	21/30	fair	poor	11,016

FIGURE 2–13. An information-gathering chart for comparisons

information—sometimes of a much more detailed and technical nature than is found in ordinary advertising brochures.

Thomas Register.   If there are few or no businesses in your area from which to get brochures related to the subject of your comparison, consider using the *Thomas Register.* This reference source indexes U.S. companies according to products and services, tells you about their size in terms of assets, summarizes their specific business, and gives you their addresses. You can write inquiry letters to the largest ones for product information; chances are you will get a great deal of information, or at least get pointed in the right direction for finding more. If you are not sure how to write an inquiry letter, see Chapter 11, "Corresponding with Business and Professional Associates." (There are other resources like the *Thomas Register,* in some cases more specialized; ask your librarian for help in finding them.)

Consumer-Oriented Studies.   One of the best sources of information for evaluative comparisons is the "consumer report" study. Most people are familiar with *Consumer Reports,* but remember that many other periodicals contain similar kinds of consumer-oriented reports as well. To locate information like this that is relevant to your report topic, consult one of the following:

> *Consumers Index to Product Evaluations and Information Sources*
> *Readers Guide to Periodical Literature*
> *Magazine Index*
> *Business Index*

Consumers Index is an index of consumer-report articles; it's potentially the most helpful, although some libraries may not have all the magazines that it indexes. In *Consumers Index* you look up the name of the product or service in order to locate reports and articles on it.

Specialized Product Evaluation Sources.   More specialized product evaluations, such as those done by publishers like Datapro, are also available. Datapro publishes evaluation reports on telecommunications, copiers, microcomputers, and about twelve other categories of equipment. Each of these reports consists of one or more looseleaf binders of information so that reports on one category are filed together and can be easily updated.

Ratings of other more industrial as opposed to consumer products can also be located through specialized indexes such as *Business Periodicals Index* or *Applied Science and Technology Index.*

STEP 6B.   **On your worksheet design an information-gathering chart similar to the one shown in Figure 2–13, and then list the sources of information that you plan to use. If the sources listed thus far are not enough, go to Chapter 9 and follow the steps there.**

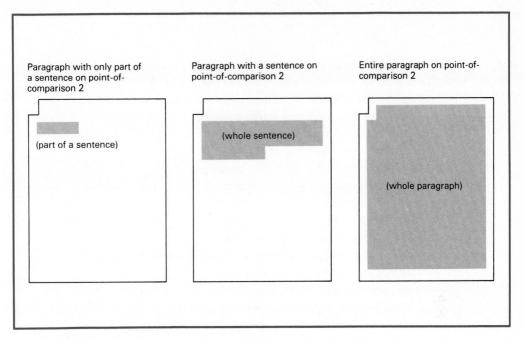

Paragraph with only part of
a sentence on point-of-
comparison 2

(part of a sentence)

Paragraph with a sentence on
point-of-comparison 2

(whole sentence)

Entire paragraph on point-of-
comparison 2

(whole paragraph)

FIGURE 2–14.   Expanding the discussion of points of comparison

Determining Length for Comparisons

At this point in the chapter you're ready to decide on the length your comparison should be—whether it should be a short (only a paragraph or two) or an extended comparison. The audience for the comparison and the purpose and need for the comparison will help you make this decision. The way points of comparison can be expanded is represented in Figure 2–14.

Short Comparisons.   In a single-paragraph comparison you discuss each of the points of comparison in only a sentence or two. In such a small space you can't usually get into much detail or explain why the differences or similarities occur. An example of a short comparison is shown in Figure 2–15.

Extended Comparison.   In an extended comparison, you have all the room you need to discuss each of the points of comparison in whole paragraphs or even whole sections. An example is provided in Figure 2–16.

STEP 7B.   On your worksheet explain whether your comparison is a single-paragraph or an extended discussion and why. Now, go to the appropriate group of steps from the following list.

There are many characteristics that make the Stirling engine an appealing alternative to the internal combustion engine. Foremost are its efficiency and fuel economy: the Stirling engine runs at an efficiency of 37.4 percent, more than double that of the internal combustion engine, and it is projected to give 50% better gas mileage. Also, the Stirling engine produces extremely low emissions: it can meet all 1985 emission standards with none of the special modifications required by internal combustion engines. Unlike the internal combustion engine, the Stirling engine can run on practically any fuel that can produce heat. Also, without the valves and the fuel-air explosions that take place in an internal combustion engine, the Stirling engine operates with very little noise. Finally, the Stirling has a flat torque characteristic, meaning that torque is practically independent of engine speed. Compared to the internal combustion engine, the Stirling engine provides much higher torque, and thus more power, at lower engine speeds. All of these characteristics should lead to the increasing importance of the Stirling engine in the years to come.	overview point of comparison 1 point of comparison 2 point of comparison 3 point of comparison 4 point of comparison 5

FIGURE 2–15.   A short, single-paragraph comparison

Substeps for Short Comparisons

If you write a short comparison (only one or two paragraphs), your job is fairly simple. And, if you've done the steps to this point, you can do the following:

1. Gather information about the topics in the comparison, if necessary (using the steps in Chapter 9, if you need to find library information).
2. Write one or more sentences for each point of comparison.
3. Write several introductory sentences that
   a. Define the things being compared or explain their purpose or importance.
   b. List the points of comparison (that is, provide an overview).

Many characteristics of the Stirling engine make it an appealing alternative to the internal combustion engine found in most cars today. These include (1) high efficiency, (2) low emissions, (3) multi-fuel capability, (4) low noise, and (5) flat torque characteristics.

Efficiency and fuel economy.   The Stirling engine can provide the highest efficiency of any engine cycle. The test run on the Mod I engine (developed by Mechanical Technology Inc., for the Department of Energy) operated with an efficiency of 37.4 percent, more than double the efficiency of present-day spark emission engines. The Stirling engine's efficiency also remains constant over a wide range of speed and load conditions. Neither is this a characteristic of spark emission engines. As you might expect, higher efficiency translated into better gas mileage. When Stirling engines with comparable equipment and accessories are installed, they are projected to give the Toyota Celica 50% better gas mileage and the Chevrolet Impala 52% better gas mileage.

Low emissions.   One of the most notable advantages of the Stirling engine over internal combustion engines is its low emissions. The external combustion of the Stirling engine allows continuous combustion to take place. Continuous combustion with an unlimited air supply results in extremely low levels of NO and CO ...

Multifuel capability.   Theoretically, the Stirling engine can operate on any type of fuel that can produce heat. Mechanical Technology Inc., tested the Mod I engine with five different fuels: unleaded gasoline, commercial diesel fuel, gasohol (90%/10%), marine diesel fuel, and aviation turbine fuel (ERBS). No noticeable difference in engine performance ...

Noise.   Compared to the internal combustion engine, the Stirling engine runs much more quietly ...

FIGURE 2–16.   An extended comparison

4. Write a concluding sentence or two, if necessary, for your comparison paragraph.
5. Go on to the section "Developing and Completing Descriptions and Comparisons" for the finish-up work there.

Substeps for Extended Comparisons

If you write an extended comparison (several paragraphs), your job is rather similar to writing a short comparison:

1. Gather information about the topics in the comparison, if necessary (using the steps in Chapter 9, if you need to find library information).
2. Write a paragraph for each of the points of comparison (there may be some simple, minor points that can grouped within one paragraph, however).
3. Write an introductory paragraph that
   a. Defines the things being compared or explains their purpose or importance.
   b. Lists the points of comparison (that is, provides an overview).
   c. Provides other necessary introductory information.
4. Write a concluding paragraph for your extended comparison, if necessary.
5. Go on to the section "Developing and Completing Process and Causal Discussions" for the finish-up work there.

Developing and Completing Descriptions and Comparisons

Your main goal here in Chapter 2 should be to learn the patterns of organization and other strategies involved in writing descriptions and comparisons. However, you must also adjust the discussion to your readers, include graphic and textual aids to help readers understand, use special sections that complete the discussion, and review the final draft carefully. These skills are covered in the chapters of Parts II and III; however, if you plan to read those chapters later, keep these points in mind.

Adjusting the Discussion to the Audience

With any technical writing you do, one of your most important concerns is to adjust the discussion so that your audience can understand it. Chapter 5 shows you a step-by-step way of doing this, but, for the moment, follow these guidelines in your practice writing:

- Identify *why* your readers need or want your description or comparison. How will they use it?
- Identify your readers' background. What *knowledge* or *capabilities* do they already have, and which do they lack?
- Make a list of the *unfamiliar terms* that your readers are not likely to know, and be sure to define them.

- Provide either *general* or *specific* discussion according to your readers' needs.
- For nonspecialist readers, *translate* technical discussion (using the techniques covered in Chapter 5, for example) so that they can understand.

STEP 8.   On your worksheet write a brief description of your audience, the members' background, and their interest in your discussion. Make two separate lists, one for topics you must cover, and one for topics you can omit. Also, list terms you may have to define for your readers.

Special Sections

If you are writing an *extended* description or comparison, one that is at least several paragraphs long, you'll need an introduction, a conclusion, and possibly other special sections.

Ideas and guidelines for introductions are covered in Chapter 4; however, for descriptions keep these tips in mind:

- Define the mechanism you are describing, if necessary, and explain its purpose and general appearance.
- List the main parts, components, or characteristics that you discuss in the description.

For introductions to comparisons, keep these ideas in mind:

- Define the things that you compare, if necessary.
- Indicate the reason for the comparison and the type of comparison (informative or evaluative).
- If it's an evaluative comparison, explain the reason and background for the evaluation.
- Also with evaluations, list the choices available, and explain the points of comparison (including the criteria).
- With any kind of comparison, be sure to list the points of comparison in the introduction.

Chapter 4 also covers ideas for conclusions, but until you study that chapter in detail, consider these suggestions for ways to conclude descriptions:

- After a part-by-part description, bring all the parts together in an overview; summarize the interrelationship of the parts.
- Provide a brief step-by-step explanation of how the mechanism works.

For conclusions to comparisons, here are some suggestions:

- Summarize the conclusions you've reached during the comparison.
- If it's an evaluative comparison, make recommendations as well as draw conclusions in the final section.

For comparisons, you may need these additional special sections (examples are shown in Chapter 14 on feasibility reports).

- *Background.* In this section explain the situation, the events, or the background that led to the need for the comparison, particularly for the evaluative comparison.

- *Choices.* In this section explain how you selected the items for evaluative comparison; in other words, explain how you narrowed the field.
- *Points of comparison and criteria.* In this section explain the points of comparison and criteria and your reasons for using them.
- *Conclusions.* In this section gather all of the important conclusions you reach during the evaluative comparison and list them.
- *Recommendations.* In this section state your recommendations and elaborate upon them.

STEP 9. If you are writing an *extended* discussion, list on your worksheet the special sections you think are needed, and explain why they are needed. (If you need more information on introductions and conclusions, see Chapter 4.)

Headings and Lists

Headings and subheadings are the titles you see used in this chapter as well as in the examples and models. An example of listing, both the in-sentence and vertical kinds, is shown in Figure 2–4 and in the models at the end of this chapter. Use the examples and models as well as the following suggestions to design headings and lists (discussed in detail in Chapter 6) for your description or comparison:

- If you spend a paragraph or more discussing each part, component, or characteristic, make a heading to introduce the discussion of each part.
- If you spend a paragraph or more discussing each point of comparison, make a heading for each paragraph.
- If you have other sections, such as one for conclusions or recommendations, make headings for them as well.
- Use in-sentence and vertical lists for important points; see an example of lists in Figure 2–4 and in the models.

STEP 10. On your worksheet make a list of the headings for your *extended* description or comparison, and describe areas of your discussion where listing might be useful.

Graphic Aids

Review the graphic aids (drawings, diagrams, schematics, and even photographs) used in the examples and models in this chapter, and decide which kinds your description or comparison needs. Chapter 6 covers graphic aids in detail, but for the moment, keep the following points in mind:

- For each graphic aid, include a number and a title (see examples in this chapter).
- Include source information on all graphic aids you borrow from other books, reports or articles.
- Discuss and interpret the graphic aids you use in nearby text.

- For illustrations of objects and mechanisms, label the parts with names, numbers, or letters for easier reference.
- For comparisons, consider using summary tables to bring important points in the comparison together.
- For evaluative comparisons, consider using scales in which the various points are weighted and totaled in order to make the best selection.

STEP 11.   On your worksheet list the types of graphic aids you think may be needed in your discussion, and briefly describe their contents. (For a detailed discussion of graphic aids, see Chapter 6.)

Revising and Finishing Descriptions and Comparisons

Important in technical writing, as in any writing, is the work you do after you get the first draft down on paper. Revising, proofreading, and final packaging—the fine-tuning phases of a writing project—are covered in Chapters 7 and 10. But if you are not going to study the step-by-step procedures in those chapters now, keep these suggestions in mind:

- Make sure that you've discussed the parts, components, characteristics, or points of comparison *one at a time* in separate sentences, paragraphs, or groups of paragraphs.
- Make sure that your discussion is clear and understandable to the specific audience for whom you are writing.
- Use headings and lists to ensure that things are easy to find in longer descriptions and comparisons.
- Neatly type your practice description or comparison.
- Use scissors and tape to insert your illustrations, and then photocopy the whole description or comparison on a good-quality machine.

STEP 12.   Use the suggestions given thus far to revise your description or comparison. (If you want more detailed information on revising, proofreading, and final packaging, see Chapter 8 and Chapter 10.)

EXERCISES

1. To help you find a topic for the practice description, take a look at the following list.

an insect	a natural area	sphygmomanometer
a mammal	(mountain, coast,	white dwarf (astron.)
a fish	forest, swamp, etc.)	any electric motor
an amphibian	an organ of the body	some component of a
a reptile	a disease	radio, stereo, or TV
an amoeba	aspects of a planet	household electric
a fossil	a tree	circuit
any microorganism	nebula	floorplan of your home
any plant	any medical apparatus	locking mechanism

stapler	greenhouse	lawn mower
blender	any carpenter's,	microwave oven
sextant	plumber's, or auto	coffee maker
telescope	repairperson's tool	water sprinkler
handheld calculator	industrial robot	a house
motorcycle, or some	stereo headphones	any building
part of it	diesel engine	a part of the city
pair of binoculars	photocopying machine	a dam
nuclear reactor	typewriter	a bridge
an electric car	line printer	air conditioner
heat pump	household water heater	ac system
drafting table	backyard fence	window casement
internal combustion	electric drill, sander,	CRT
(or some part of it)	or saw	pencil sharpener
rotary engine	electric fan	solar device
catalytic converter	microscope	drafting table
some part of your car	catcher's mitt	blueprinting machine
or bicycle	pair of sandals	computer chip
a piece of furniture	flashlight	personal computer
plans for a doghouse,	mechanical pencil	acoustic coupler
birdhouse,	cigarette lighter	garbage disposal

2. Think about any three of the following objects or mechanisms that are familiar to you, and then list their parts, components, or characteristics. For each list, identify whether the item entered is a part or a characteristic.

chair	staple remover	can opener	kitchen stove
local lake	dog collar	flashlight	pencil
pencil	local park	stapler	cigarette lighter
telephone	lamp	scissors	hole puncher
pen	desk	hardbound book	pencil sharpener
corkscrew	coffee pot	faucet	tape dispenser

3. Study the following description, and label the descriptive sentences according to the sources of description that they use (see page 000 for a list).

It's one of the greatest advances in radio technology since radio was first developed. The radio itself is $5\frac{1}{2}$ inches by $2\frac{1}{2}$ inches and only about $\frac{3}{4}$ of an inch thick. It's made of a smooth gray plastic and has the following features on the exterior: an AM and FM tuning band, a tuning dial just protruding from the side of the set, a volume dial, a tone dial, and an AM/FM switch. There is also a plug for the headphones. On the back of the set is the battery compartment cover, which snaps in place and is not attached to the set. In the compartment are two AAA-size batteries. Also, on the back of the set is a plastic clip that enables you to fasten the radio to your pocket or belt. As for the headset, it has a gray plastic 18-inch two-stranded cord that attaches permanently to the headphones. The headphones are $1\frac{1}{8}$ inches in diameter and are covered with a black foam rubber that lets the sound come through but that cushions the ear. The two headphones are connected by a semicircle of a thin strip of aluminum that has a wire traveling from one headphone to the other. The whole thing weighs about a pound and costs $13.75.

4. Make a photocopy of a relatively short but complete technical description of something from your field of interest, and then do the following:
   a. Describe the background and knowledge necessary in the audience and its use for the description.

    b. Explain which type of description it is (general, specific, external, or internal) and why.

    c. Identify whether it is arranged by parts or characteristics, and then label or list these elements.

    d. In the margin, label the main sources used in the description.

5. Choose three of the general report topics listed in Exercise 5 in Chapter 1, and do the following: explain (a) where description will be needed; (b) why the description will be needed; and (c) what kinds of description will be needed.

6. If you have difficulty finding a topic for a comparison, use the list here to start you thinking. Compare two or more of any of the following:

refrigerators	books	washers
tires	dryers	radios
stereo systems	televisions	home computers
automobiles	word processors	air conditioners
educational institutions	trucks	farm implements
insurance policies	plans or programs	typewriters
intercom systems	photocopiers	dishwashers
smoke detectors	video recorders	batteries
any construction	microwave ovens	drugs
equipment	any laboratory	any medical equipment
phone-answering	equipment	heating devices
machines	furniture	motorcycles
cameras	insulation	mopeds
lawn mowers	chain saws	any plumber's tools
tape recorders	any carpenter's tools	investments
bicycles	time-recording devices	loans
banks	office spaces	prospective employees
houses	records	

7. Identify the sentences that do the actual comparing of two or more things in the following comparison of several familiar things. Also, make a list of the points of comparison.

      With microwave cooking, many of the familiar clues that tell you food is cooked, such as browning and crisping, are absent. Using a temperature probe can help in determining when food is cooked. A temperature probe is like a meat thermometer, but more versatile. A probe can work with liquids and casseroles as well as with meats. And, because the probe plugs into the oven, it can stop the cooking process when the desired internal temperature of the food is reached. A cord connects the probe to a receptacle in a wall or in the ceiling of the oven's cavity. The probe itself is inserted into the food. Then the oven is set to the appropriate power level and to the desired internal temperature of the food, typically 90° to 200° F. (The range allowed by the Sanyo and the Sears was narrower—115° to 185°—but still adequate.) The oven cooks until the desired internal temperature is reached. ["Microwave Ovens," *Consumer Reports* (May 1983), 223.]

8. Make a list of points of comparison for one of the following topics:

Several cars you'd like to own	Two television shows you occasionally
Two movies you've seen recently	watch
Several different restaurants	Two or more different kinds of soft drinks
you like	Two or more radio stations
Several academic courses you've	Several different jobs or careers you've
taken recently	considered

9. List the points of comparison that you'd use in an evaluation on any of the three topics listed in Exercise 8. With each one, include the purpose of the comparison.

10. Revise the following pair of passages in which no direct comparisons are drawn by (a) using the point-by-point approach, (b) using strong transitional words and phrases, and (c) creating a sentence overviewing the points of comparisons for the beginning of the paragraph.

The Dodge 400's fuel economy is listed as very good; its engine drivability, very good; its shifting, very good; its acceleration, good; its handling precision, very good; its braking ability, excellent; its servicing ease, very good; and its predicted incidence of repair as good. The automobile costs $10,000 and comes equipped with all the standard accessories. Its roominess is rated as good. Raters of the 400 found the gauges easy to read with only a slight bit of glare during the day. The car is fairly quiet on the inside when driving. The 400 has 55 inches of front-seat shoulder room; 41.0 inches, maximum front-seat leg room; 3.5 inches, front seat head room; 55.5 inches, rear seat shoulder room; 2.5 inches, rear seat head room.

Buick Regal's roominess is rated as excellent; it costs $11,016 and comes with all the standard accessories. Its handling precision is listed as fair; its acceleration, good; its servicing ease, very good; its predicted incidence of repair, poor; its fuel economy, fair; its engine drivability, excellent; its braking ability, good; its shifting, excellent. The Regal is luxuriously quiet on the inside when driving. The gauges are difficult to read because of a lack of contrast. In terms of interior space, the Regal has 56.5 inches of front-seat shoulder room; 41.0 inches, maximum front-seat leg room; 4.0 inches front-seat head room; 57.0 inches rear-seat shoulder room; 5.0 inches rear-seat head room.

11. Choose any three topics from the list of general report topics in Exercise 5 of Chapter 1, and explain (a) where comparisons are needed; (b) why the comparisons are needed; and (c) which kinds of comparisons are needed.

Model 2–1:   A Standard Automobile Alternator
(extended description by parts)

A key component of an automobile's charging system, which provides current to recharge the battery and develops electricity to power all other electrical components when the engine is running, is the alternator. The other component of the charging system is the voltage regulator. The basic function of the alternator is to generate the electricity required to start and run the automobile, while the regulator is designed to control the amount of voltage that circulates through the system. This discussion will focus entirely upon the alternator, specifically, the principle of operation by which it works and its main components.

An alternator (see Figure 1) consists of a rotor assembly, a stator assembly, and a rectifier mounted in a housing.

Alternator Housing.   The housing is usually made up of two pieces of die-cast aluminum. Aluminum is used because it is a nonmagnetic, lightweight material that provides good heat dissipation. Bearings supporting the rotor assembly are mounted in the front and rear housing. The front bearing is usually pressed into the front housing or onto the rotor shaft. It is usually a factory-lubricated

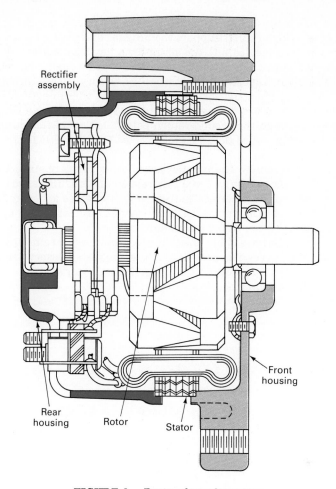

FIGURE 1.   Parts of an alternator

ball bearing. The rear bearing is usually installed with a light press fit in the rear housing.

Stator Assembly.   The stator is clamped between the front and the rear housing. A number of steel stampings are riveted together to form its frame. Three windings around the stator frame are arranged in layers in each of the slots on the frame. At the other end they are connected into the rectification assembly.

Rotor Assembly.   The rotor assembly consists of a rotor shaft, a winding around an iron core, two pole pieces, and slip rings. The rotor is pressed into the core. Six-fingered, malleable, iron pole pieces are pressed onto the shaft against each end of the winding core. They are placed so that the fingers mesh but do not touch. When direct current is passed through the field coil winding, the fingers become alternately north and south poles. A slip-ring assembly is pressed on to the rear end of the rotor shaft and connected to the two ends of the field winding.

Two brushes are held against the slip rings by springs, usually mounted in plastic brush holders that support the brushes and prevent them from sticking. Each brush is connected into the circuit by a flexible copper lead wire. The brushes ride on the slip rings and are connected through a switch to the battery. When the switch is closed, current from the battery passes through one brush, through the slip ring, and then through the field winding. After leaving the field winding, current flows through the other slip ring and brush before returning to the battery through the ground return path. The flow of electrical energy through the field winding, called field current, creates the magnetic field for the rotor.

Rectifier Assembly.   The rectifier assembly consists of six diodes mounted either in the rear housing or in a separate small housing called a rectifier bridge. Three of the diodes are connected to ground, and three are mounted in an insulator. Since the mounting assembly carries off heat caused by the operation of the diode, it is often called a heat sink.

A fan and pulley assembly is either pressed onto the rotor shaft or held with a nut. The pulley drives the rotor through an engine accessory drive belt. The fan behind the alternator pulley pulls air in through vents at the rear of the alternator to cool the diodes.

Model 2–2:   A Comparison of the Pressurized-Water Reactor and the Boiling-Water Reactor*
(extended point-by-point informative comparison)

A nuclear power reactor uses fission reactions to produce thermal energy that is converted to electrical energy. One common class of nuclear reactor is the light-water reactor which uses light water as a moderator and as a coolant. There are two types of light-water reactors: the pressurized-water reactor and the boiling-water reactor.

Basic Operation
  Basically, the operations of the pressurized-water reactor (PWR) and the boiling-water reactor (BWR) are similar, as Figure 1 shows. Water flows through the reactor core, steam is produced, the steam proceeds to turn a turbine-generator, electricity is produced, the steam is converted back to water, and the process is repeated.

Comparison of PWR and BWR
  The differences in the operations of the two light-water reactors involve (a) the method in which the steam is produced, (b) the pressure in the system, and (c) the process through which the steam goes through after being produced.

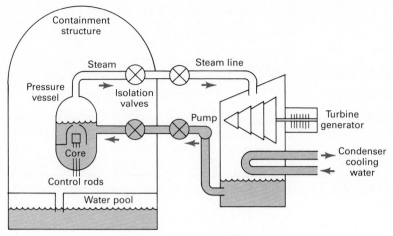

A. Boiling-water reactor (BWR)

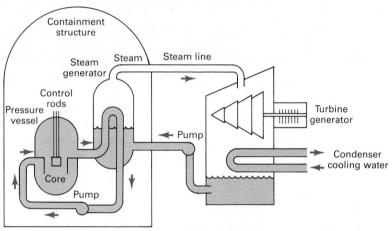

B. Pressurized-water reactor (PWR)

FIGURE 1.   Basic operation of pressurized-water and
boiling-water reactors

Method by Which the Steam Is Produced.   In a pressurized-water reactor, the
primary coolant, after passing through the core and absorbing heat, proceeds to a
secondary system consisting of a steam generator. The primary coolant then
flows through many hundreds of small stainless-steel tubes in the heat exchangers,
which are part of the steam generator. These heat-exchanger tubes are surrounded
by the water of the secondary system which is heated by the primary coolant in
the tubes. Wet steam is then produced (4:72).

Unlike the pressurized-water reactor, the steam in a boiling-water reactor is
introduced directly into the core. Jet pumps circulate the coolant water along the
individual fuel rods in each fuel assembly in the core where it boils and becomes
a two-phase steam-water mixture (1:21).

TABLE 1.   Summary of Differences between the PWR and the BWR

	Pressurized-Water Reactor	Boiling-Water Reactor
Way steam is produced	In secondary reactor core	Directly in the system
Pressure	Varies: 2250 psi, then lowered	Constant, 1040 psi
Produced steam	Goes through steam separators, then to turbine; nonradioactive	Goes through steam separators, then through steam dryers, then to turbine, radioactive

*Source: Jeff DelaCruz, Report on Light Water Reactors (Austin: Univ. of Texas, 1984).

Pressure in the System.   The pressure in a pressurized-water reactor varies from the primary to the secondary system. In the primary system, the pressure is maintained at about 2250 pounds per square inch to prevent steam from forming. The pressure is then lowered for steam, at 600 pounds per square inch, to form. The pressure is controlled by a pressurizer (2:81).

In contrast, the boiling-water reactor operates at constant pressure. The primary system operates at pressure about one-half that of a pressurized-water reactor's primary system while producing steam of equal quality (3:1995).

The Process of Generated Steam.   After the wet steam is formed in a pressurized-water reactor, it passes upward through the risers and enters the steam-separator portion of the steam generator. Here the moisture is removed and returned to the heat-exchanger portion through the downcomers. The dry and saturated steam leaves the top of the steam separator and goes to the turbine (4:72).

The wet steam formed in a boiling-water reactor leaves the core and also goes through a steam separator. However, unlike the pressurized-water reactor, the steam goes through a steam dryer, where additional moisture is removed (1:18). The steam then proceeds to the turbine. This steam, unlike that of the pressurized-water reactor, is radioactive (2:100).

Conclusion

Thus, even though the pressurized-water reactor and the boiling-water reactor are generally similar in operation, there are four main differences between the two systems.

(1) The steam in a pressurized-water reactor is produced in a secondary system while the steam in a boiling-water reactor is produced directly in the reactor core.

(2) The pressure of a pressurized-water reactor varies from the primary system to the output steam while the pressure of a boiling-water reactor remains constant.

(3) The steam in a pressurized-water reactor after coming out of the steam separator proceeds directly to the turbine while the steam in a boiling-water reactor, after coming out of the steam separators, proceeds to a steam dryer and then to the turbine.

(4) The steam produced in a boiling-water reactor is radioactive, whereas the steam produced in a pressurized-water reactor is not.

Literature Cited

1. Bupp, Irwin C., Jr., and Robert Trietel. 1976. The Economics of Nuclear Power. Boston: MIT Press.
2. Burn, Duncan. 1978. Nuclear Power and the Energy Crisis. New York: New York University Press.
3. Cameron, I.R. 1980. Nuclear Fission Reactors. New York: McGraw-Hill.
4. Glasstone, Samuel, and Alexander Sesonske. 1981. Nuclear Reactor Engineering. Princeton: D. Van Nostrand.
5. Myers, Desaix III. 1977. The Nuclear Power Debate. New York: Praeger.
6. Nero, Anthony V. 1979. A Guidebook to Nuclear Reactors. Berkeley: University of California Press.

Model 2–3:   Evaluation of Five Wind-Powered Electrical Systems*
(extended point-by-point evaluative comparison)

Wind-powered electrical systems played an important role in the electrification of many rural homesteads thirty or forty years ago. During the energy crisis of the 1970s, wind systems regained popularity, and new companies specializing in wind systems began trying to develop more powerful and efficient products. One example is the Smith Putnam Company, which built a huge wind system with a propeller diameter of 175 ft and a maximum power output of 1.25 million watts, but it only lasted two years because one of its twin blades snapped at the base. Another company, Dyna Technology, designed a wind system with a maximum power output of 200 watts to power radio stations in remote areas. The following discussion will focus instead on wind systems that can produce 2000 watts of power, which is sufficient for one household.

Points of Comparison

The ideal wind system produces sufficient power in slow wind speeds, lasts for a lifetime, and costs relatively little. Because wind systems come in many different models, this report is limited to five designs, with each design from a different company. The Eagle, the Kedco (Model 1600), and the Dunlite wind systems are a few of the more common wind systems on the market. The Darrieus wind system uses a vertical axis rotor and is not very popular because it does not follow the conventional design of most wind systems. The Zephyr system is one of the newest wind systems and is not yet available on the market except for research purposes.

Although there is quite a variety of designs, three of the primary considerations in selecting a wind system are (a) power output, (b) durability, and (c) cost.

*Adapted from James Matthews, Evaluation of Wind-Powered Electrical Generators (Austin: Univ. of Texas, 1983).

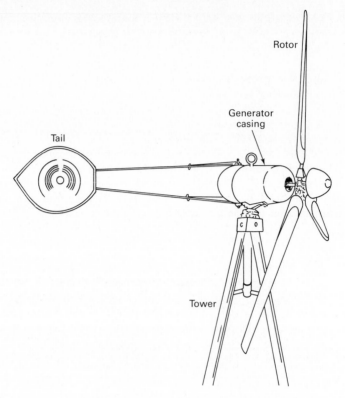

FIGURE 1.   A typical wind-powered electrical generator

Power Output.   The ideal wind system should charge the storage batteries faster than the electricity is consumed. Since a low-power wind system eventually charges the batteries, the rotor should have a low cut-in speed to take advantage of slow winds. To charge the batteries quickly, the generator should produce at least 2000 watts in a moderate wind speed.

The Eagle reaches a maximum of 2000 watts in winds of 20 mph. It accomplishes this output by using a special slow-speed generator and a rotor with a 14-ft diameter. The generator starts producing power in winds of 8 to 10 mph. The Kedco produces 1200 watts in 17-mph winds using a 16-ft rotor. The Dunlite has a rotor diameter of 13 ft and a cut-in speed of 10 mph. In 25-mph winds, the Dunlite attains its maximum power of 2000 watts. The vertical-axis Darrieus requires a motor to start the rotor, but it can produce 4000 watts in a 23-mph wind. The vertical-axis twin-bladed rotor stands 15 ft high, allowing it to absorb more wind energy. The Zephyr, still being tested, can produce 15,000 watts in a 30-mph wind. At cut-in speed it delivers 500 watts of power, an output that is accomplished by using a special low-speed, direct-driven (gearless) rotor with lightweight blades approximately 14 ft in diameter.

Durability.   Obviously, a wind system that lasts a long time can pay for itself in savings from electric bills. Many wind generators have short lifespans because the blades break as a result of the vibrations from high wind speeds. This problem can be solved with some type of governor or braking device to slow the rotor down in high winds. Brush wear is another problem that cuts the lifetime of a wind system, but this problem is easily corrected by using the long-lasting brushes designed by Jacobs Wind Electric Plants.

The Eagle has proven itself to last about 20 years. The rotor uses a flyball governor to turn the blades and to vary the pitch of the wind. The brushes have also been designed for long life. Since the Eagle's generator is directly turned by the rotor, no gears are needed and the system lasts longer. The Kedco uses aluminum blades that feather (or bend) in high winds. It also uses an automatic vibration sensor that shuts off the generator in turbulent winds. The Dunlite has been on the market for 30 years and has proven itself to be reliable. The variable pitch blades are made of galvanized steel and are designed to withstand winds up to 80 mph. The Dunlite generator is designed without any brushes, which gives the system longer life. The Zephyr system uses glide-out spoilers on the blades to protect against overspeed. Because it is still in the testing phase, the lifetime is unknown at this time. The vertical-axis Darrieus system is designed to withstand gusts of 130 mph. The vibration is kept at a minimum because the system's center of gravity is along the rotor shaft.

Cost.   The Eagle system sells for $3500. This price does not include the tower, inverter, or the storage batteries. The total cost is approximately $4700, but the Eagle is maintenance-free for about 15 to 20 years. The Kedco 1600 sells for $2895. This price does not include the tower and other accessories, so the total cost is around $4000. The Dunlite system costs $2000 in Australia where it is manufactured. Adding the costs of delivery and accessories raises the total cost to about $4500. The Zephyr costs $12,000 including the tower and control panel. Should tests and time prove the design to be a good one, public confidence may increase as will production, and thus the price should decrease. For the time being, however, the vertical-axis Darrieus, costing $8000 complete with tower and electrical control gear, is the reasonable choice.

Conclusions

For people who are considering an investment in a wind system, cost is probably the most important factor because these people are already trying to trim their electric bills and save money. The real savings begin when the wind system has paid for itself in electric bill savings. If a household averages a monthly electric bill of $120 and purchases a $4700 Eagle, then the real savings will begin in about three and a half years after the date of the purchase. The cost-efficiency of a wind system can be calculated by dividing the cost of the system by its lifetime.

From the preceding comparison of power, durability, and cost, the following conclusions can be stated:

1. The most powerful system is the Zephyr followed by the Darrieus.
2. The Dunlite has the longest lifetime followed by the Eagle. The Darrieus can withstand the strongest wind.
3. The system with the best cost-efficiency is the Dunlite at $150 per year. If the Eagle reduced its price by $1700, it would equal the Dunlite in cost-efficiency.

Table 1 shows a factual summary of these comparisons. Notice that maximum power and cut-in speed is used to evaluate a wind system's power performance.

TABLE 1.   Factual Summary of Wind Systems

Wind machine	Max. power/ wind speed	Cut-in wind speed	Cost in dollars	Lifespan in years
Eagle	2,000/20 mph	8–10	$4,700	20
Kedco	1,200/17 mph	——	2,895	——
Dunlite	2,000/25 mph	10	4,500	30
Darrieus	4,000/23 mph	motor start	8,000	——
Zephyr	15,000/30 mph	10	12,000	——

CHAPTER 3

Extended Definitions and Classifications

Chapter Objectives
Definitions
    Locating Definition Areas in Report
      Projects
    Choosing the Sources of Definition
    Combining and Organizing the
      Sources of Definition
    Writing Formal Sentence Definitions
    Adding Short Definitions of Other
      Terms
    Sources of Information for
      Definitions
    Determining Length for Extended
      Definitions
Classifications
    Locating Areas in Reports for
      Classification
    Identifying Classes and the Principle
      of Classification
    Discussing the Classes

Sources of Information for
    Classifications
Determining Length for Classifications
Developing and Completing
    Definitions and Classifications
    Adjusting the Discussion to the
      Audience
    Special Sections
    Headings and Lists
    Graphic Aids
    Revising and Finishing Definitions
      and Classifications
Exercises
Models
    3–1. Sickle-cell Anemia
       (multiparagraph extended
       definition)
    3–2. Features of Industrial Robots
       (multiparagraph extended
       classification)

—————————— *Chapter Objectives* ——————————

After you read this chapter, study the examples, work the steps, and do the practice writing, you should be able to:

- Explain the terms *definition* and *classification*.
- Spot areas in report projects requiring definition and classification.
- Recognize extended definitions and classifications in reports.
- Understand how to divide a thing into its classes and how to state the principle of classification you've used.
- Write formal sentence definitions and short definitions and incorporate them into reports.
- Identify the sources needed to write an extended definition or classification.
- Organize the parts of an extended definition or classification by an appropriate pattern.

Among the best ways to supply background information in technical reports and articles are extended definitions and classifications. They provide organizational patterns that allow you to present lots of technical information in an orderly, understandable way. Extended definitions (several paragraphs or more) are particularly important because they give you a preview of writing full-length reports: the planning and outlining are much the same for both. You can also use this chapter to learn strategies for writing *formal sentence definitions* and *short definitions*.

Unlike the two preceding chapters, the sections of this chapter should be read in the order they appear: extended classifications are usually built from two or more extended definitions. If you skip the section on classifications, be sure to finish up with the last section, "Developing and Completing Definitions and Classifications." (Steps specifically for definitions end with *A;* those for classifications end with *B*.)

Definitions

In this section you'll study how to create effective definitions of unfamiliar technical words. *Extended definitions*—a paragraph or more in length—give readers a much more thorough understanding of technical terms. *Short definitions*—a sentence or less in length—can be used practically anywhere in reports to help readers through difficult discussions.

Extended definitions are quite unlike the other kinds of writing and organizational patterns you've seen up to this point in this book. Instead of identifying steps, parts, characteristics, or points of comparison, you identify different kinds of writing that help to explain more fully the word being defined. In other words, you *combine* different kinds of writing to create extended definitions. To define the integrated circuit, for example, you might use the following:

Kind of Writing	To Explain
Description	Physical aspects of the chip
Process narration	Operation of the chip
Comparison	Chips and transistors

Before looking at techniques for writing extended definitions, consider what the word *definition* means. The word definition, as used here, refers to the explanation of the meaning of a word (for example, *blastomere, phytotoxicity,* or *capacitance*) that is unfamiliar or is used in an unfamiliar way. Every field of science and technology is loaded with its own special terminology, often called the jargon of that field.

When you plan or revise a report, remember the reasons people may not understand the meaning of certain words:

- They may have never seen the word at all. (Have you ever heard of the words *albedo, vesicularity,* or *isomerase?*)
- They may have no clear idea of what the word means. (Do you really know what such words as the following mean: *gene, enzyme, chromosome, stress, torque, pulsar, quark, supernova,* or *relativity?*)
- They may think that they understand certain words or phrases, but, either because of misinformation or new discoveries, they really do not. (Are you really sure about such words as *paranoia, natural, interface, cold front, calorie,* or *turbulence?*)
- Finally, a familiar word may be used in an unusual way. (For example, do you know what computer people are talking about when they use such words as *batch, loop, memory, menu, chip, dump, file,* or *bit?*)

STEP 1A.   On your worksheet briefly describe the term on which you want to write an extended definition, and explain who the audience is and why that audience needs the definition. (If you are thinking about collaborating on your extended definition with someone else, see "Collaborating on Technical Reports" in the Introduction for ideas and suggestions.)

Locating Definition Areas in Report Projects

When you write reports, you may often discover that you need to explain certain basics before you can discuss the main subject matter. For example:

- In a report on new treatments for sickle-cell anemia, you'd need a section defining the disease.
- In a report on the benefits of drip irrigation, you'd need to write an extended definition of drip irrigation, explaining how it works and what equipment is used.
- In a report showing small businesses how to weather economic recessions, an extended definition of the term economic recession would be needed first.

As these examples show, any time you must present background information first before the main discussion of a report, you may need to write an extended definition. In most report situations, identifying the term that requires extended definition is easy enough:

Report Project	Term for Extended Definition
New developments in the treatment of sickle-cell anemia	sickle-cell anemia
The economics of drip irrigation	drip irrigation
Strategies for small businesses to weather economic recession	economic recession

Some report topics, however, seem to conceal the key terms requiring extended definition:

Report Project	Term for Extended Definition
Step-by-step function within an integrated circuit	semiconductors
Overhauling an automobile transmission	torque
Best-selling models of wind-powered electrical generators	direct and alternating current

STEP 2A. On your worksheet, list the terms in your report topic for which you may need to write extended definitions.

Choosing the Sources of Definition

When you begin to write an extended definition, consider the various sources of information that can help define the term adequately (for example, description, process narration, causal discussion, and classification). Notice in Figure 3–1 how different kinds of writing are combined in the excerpt from an extended definition. This excerpt combines historical background, description, and discussion of causes as well as a formal sentence definition (the quotation from the act) to define hazardous wastes.

The key to writing a good extended definition is to choose the right kinds of writing to help readers understand the term being defined. Use the checklist in Figure 3–2 to select the kinds of discussion to include in your extended definitions. Remember that only a few of these kinds of discussion can be used in an individual extended definition and that they are not cited in any particular order.

STEP 3A. On your worksheet, list the sources of definition you think you'll use in your extended definition, and briefly describe the information for each source.

II. HAZARDOUS WASTES

Each year 30 to 40 million metric tons of hazardous wastes are generated in the United States. By some estimates, 90 percent of these wastes are disposed of by environmentally unsound methods. Damage from such disposal has thus increased greatly. Hazardous wastes, representing only one hundredth of the total annual solid waste in the United States, are frequently generated and disposed of together with other nonhazardous wastes. Because industries often have difficulty distinguishing hazardous from nonhazardous wastes, or are reluctant to do so, the government has defined the meaning of hazardous wastes through research and has established regulations accordingly.

The Resource Conservation and Recovery Act defines a waste as hazardous if it (a) "causes or significantly contributes to an increase in mortality or an increase in serious, irreversible, or incapacitating illness" or (b) "poses a substantial present or potential hazard to human health or the environment when improperly treated, transported, or disposed of or otherwise managed." In addition, hazardous wastes can be defined by the following characteristics:

1. ignitability
2. corrosivity
3. reactivity
4. leachate toxicity
5. radioactivity
6. infectiousness

7. phytotoxicity (having a toxic effect on vegetation)
8. teratogenicity (causing malformations in animal embryos or fetuses)
9. mutagenicity (causing changes in the genetic structures of subsequent generations)

There are 17 major types of industry responsible for about 85 percent of all hazardous wastes. As shown in Figure 3–1a, the petroleum industry is responsible for roughly half of the generation of hazardous wastes, followed by the chemical industry.

Industry	% of Hazardous Wastes Generated
Petroleum	45.9
Chemical	17.9
Metal	6.0
Food	3.6
Industrial Cleaning	17.4
Misc. & Unknown	9.2
TOTAL	100.0

FIGURE 3–1a. Waste-generating industries

FIGURE 3–1. An extended definition using different kinds of writing

Description	Does anything about the term need to be described? Would the readers be helped by description?
Process narration	Does some process, event, performance, or action related to the term need to be explained?
Further definition	Do additional terms used during the discussion need definition?
Historical background	Should historical background, i.e., events related to the term being defined, be discussed?
Cause or causes	Does the reader need to know about the cause or causes related to the term being defined?
Effects, results, or consequences	Will discussion of some effect, result, or consequence help define the term?
Problems and solutions	Does the term being defined represent a problem or a solution?
Uses and applications	Should the uses or applications related to the term be discussed?
Similarities and differences	Should the term be compared to something similar or more familiar?
Classes, types, categories, kinds	Does the class of the term being defined need to be discussed? Should the term being defined be divided into its own classes?
Examples	Will examples help in the definition of the term?
Word origins	Would an understanding of the roots, or etymology, of the word help to define it?
Future developments or implications	Should the future development related to the term be discussed? Does it have implications—good, bad, or both?
Negative statements	Would negative statements explaining what the term is *not* prevent the reader from confusing the term being defined with others?
Advantages and disadvantages	Should advantages or disadvantages related to the term be discussed?

FIGURE 3–2. Checklist for planning extended definitions

Combining and Organizing the Sources of Definition

When you know which of the kinds of writing to use in your extended definition, consider how they'll combine with each other. An extended definition is a *combination* of different kinds of writing. For example, your report may need some description, but knowing that individual descriptive sentences can be worked into a process section will save you from having to write a separate description section.

• Individual sentences of one kind of writing often work their way into another, resulting in *sentence combinations*. Definition sentences are constantly used throughout technical writing. In the following example, process sentences are used in description.

> The rotor assembly of an alternator consists of a rotor shaft, a winding around an iron core, two pole pieces, and slip rings. The rotor shaft is pressed into the core. Six-fingered, malleable, iron pole pieces are pressed onto the shaft against each end of the winding core. The fingers of the mesh do not touch the pole pieces. *When direct current is passed through the field coil winding, the fingers become alternately north and south poles.* A slip ring is pressed onto the end of the rotor shaft and connected to the two ends of the field winding.
>
> Jay Webster, *Auto Mechanics* (New York: Macmillan, 1980), 285–87.

• Another common combination, the *block combination*, attaches a section of one kind of writing to another, end to end. For example, descriptive sections (the construction section in Figure 3–3) are often followed by process sections (the operation section).
• Sometimes, one kind of writing sets up a frame around another. In the example in Figure 3–4 the first sentence sets up the frame for the rest of the paragraph. Using primarily description, the author discusses one type of heavy oil concentration.

In extended definitions you must *organize* or *arrange* the sources of discussion you choose. For example, you might choose these sources for an extended definition of Alzheimer's disease:

Classification:	Types of Alzheimer's disease
Description:	Population characteristics of Alzheimer's disease
Process:	Steps in the development of Alzheimer's disease
Description:	Anatomical characteristics of the brain of an Alzheimer's disease victim
Causal discussion:	Theories about the causes of Alzheimer's disease

The various strategies for organizing and arranging the parts of technical reports are covered in Chapter 8, but, for the moment, keep these organizational patterns in mind:

• Move from the *simple* to the *complex*. Discuss the simpler, more easily under-

Starter Motor Construction

The starter motor has two major parts, a field winding assembly and an armature assembly.

The Housing.   A three-piece housing holds the starter motor. The tubular center housing contains the pole shoes and field windings. Attached to it at one end is the drive housing. . . .

The Armature Assembly.   The armature assembly is made up of several parts. Each of the loops of wire is held in place by a core made from a number of thin iron plates called laminations. . . .

The Brushes.   Sliding contacts called brushes riding on the commutator direct full battery current into the armature. The brushes are made of a material that provides good electrical contact, usually made from various alloys of copper. . . .

The Field Windings.   The field coil and pole shoe assembly are mounted to the starter housing by large screws. The field windings are protected by an insulation wrapping. . . .

Starter Motor Operation

Principally what happens in the operation of the starter motor is that magnets, mounted to the starter housing or field frame, called pole pieces, create a magnetic field between them. When current is directed through a wire called the field winding which is wrapped around these pole pieces, the strength of this magnetic field increases. . . .

When the engine is cranked, a small pinion gear mounted on the end of the starter armature shaft meshes with the teeth on the engine's flywheel ring gear. . . .

Jay Webster, Auto Mechanics, 308–309.

FIGURE 3–3.   A block combination

<u>Dominant Forms of Floating Hydrocarbons</u>

The most common form of heavy oil concentration was a heavy pool of floating mousse. This was generally brown to reddish-brown in color. Thicknesses were estimated to be typically about 1 mm, although along shorelines thicknesses of as much as 25 cm were observed. A number of near-shore samples were collected and appeared to be very stable in water-in-oil emulsions with 50 to 70 percent water contents. The time required for an oil to form a water-in-oil emulsion or mousse depends on the type of oil and the mixing energy available. For the <u>Amoco Cadiz</u> spill the formation appeared to take place very quickly. During overflights on March 21 and 22 the oil leaking from the ship appeared to change color from black to a brown characteristic of mousse in less than a ship length. A sample was collected on March 26. This sample was obtained at the point where the oil was upwelling to the surface mid-ship at the vessel. It proved to be a well-developed mousse, indicating that the sea-water/oil combination in the ship's tank was forming an emulsion even before it left the ship.

Wilmot N. Hess, ed., <u>The AMOCO CADIZ Oil Spill: A Preliminary Scientific Report</u> (Washington, D.C.: U.S. Department of Commerce and U.S. Environmental Protection Agency, April 1978), 10.

FIGURE 3—4.   Example of frame combinations

stood aspects of the term being defined before going on to the more complex, less easily understood ones:

simple   General behavioral characteristics of the Alzheimer's disease victim

complex   Anatomical characteristics of the brain of an Alzheimer's disease victim

• Move from the *stationary* to the *dynamic*. Discuss an object or mechanism at rest before discussing it in action or use:

stationary   Anatomical characteristics of the brain of an Alzheimer's disease victim

moving   Steps in the development of Alzheimer's disease

• Move from the *close-up* focus to the *broad* focus. Discuss the details of a mechanism, process, or situation before getting into its applications, advantages, or economics:

close-up	Behavioral characteristics of an Alzheimer's disease victim
distant	Population characteristics of Alzheimer's disease

• Move from the *past* to the *present* to the *future*. Arrange the parts of an extended definition chronologically if necessary.

past	Early understanding and treatment of Alzheimer's disease
present	Current theories and treatment of Alzheimer's disease
future	Alzheimer's disease: the potential of current research work

STEP 4A.   On your worksheet arrange the sources you listed in Step 3A in the order you think they should be presented in the extended definition.

Writing Formal Sentence Definitions

In your extended definition you'll need formal sentence definitions for two purposes:

- You'll need a formal sentence definition to define the main term at the beginning of the extended definition.
- You can use a formal sentence definition whenever you need a full sentence to define an important term anywhere within the extended definition.

Formal sentence definitions can be used anywhere in technical reports, not just in extended definitions. You'll see them in both of the following:

- *Glossaries:* Use formal sentence definitions to define terms in glossaries.
- *Report text:* Use formal sentence definitions whenever you need a full sentence to define a term, either because of its complexity or the need to emphasize it.

A formal sentence definition is "formal" only because it uses a certain form, one that tells the reader that a definition is on its way. Several examples appear in Figure 3–5.

Notice that the formal sentence definition is made up of three basic parts:

- A reference to the word or phrase being defined, the *term*
- A reference to the larger category of things, events, or situations to which it belongs, the *class*
- An explanation of its key *characteristics*, what distinguishes it from other members of the same class.

The first part is easy: just make sure that the term to be defined appears in the formal sentence definition. The second part, the reference to the class to which the term belongs, sets up a larger frame of reference or context. It gives readers something familiar with which to associate the term. The term may belong to a class of tools, diseases, geological processes, or electronic components; it may be a term from the field of medicine, computer science, agriculture, reprographics, or finance. The third part, the explanation of the characteristics of the term, sets the term apart

Term	*Class*	*Characteristics*
An algorithm is	a finite description	of a finite number of steps required to accomplish some well-defined task.
Carbohydrate is	a food group	including related substances such as sugars, starches, and cellulose.
Computer memory is	one of three basic components of a computer	that stores information for future use, both data that will be operated on as well as the programs that direct what operations must be performed.
Reservoir rocks are	those rocks	that have sufficient porosity and permeability to allow gas and oil to accumulate and be produced in commercial quantities.
Influenza is	an acute, highly contagious infection of the respiratory tract,	which occurs sporadically or in epidemics and lasts up to a month.

FIGURE 3—5. Elements of formal sentence definitions

from other members of the same class. In the following example, the characteristics section must differentiate two electronic devices, capacitor and resistor:

A capacitor is an electronic device

consisting essentially of two conducting surfaces separated by an insulating material used to store electrical energy, block the flow of direct current, and permit the flow of alternating current.

A resistor is an electronic device

made of a material (like carbon) that has a specified resistance, or opposition to the flow of electrical current, and is used to control or limit the amount of current flowing in a circuit or to provide a voltage drop.

Because the class to which these two terms belong is the same, the characteristics sections must therefore be precise. Vague characteristics sections would not help: for example, to say that either a transistor or a capacitor "manipulates electrical current" would not distinguish the two terms from each other.

When you write formal sentence definitions, keep these guidelines in mind:

- Omit none of the three basic parts of the formal sentence definition. Some writers forget to state the class; other writers, the characteristics.
- Discuss both the class and the characteristics according to your audience and purpose.
- Use the most specific class you can. For example, instead of calling a concussion an "injury" or botulism a "medical problem," call them "a head injury" and "a severe form of food poisoning," respectively.
- Use specific and precise details to write the characteristics section of the formal sentence definition.

Vague class and characteristics

A transistor is an important component that plays a large role in the field of electronics.

Revised class and characteristics

A transistor is an active semiconductor device that has three or more electrodes capable of performing almost all the functions of tubes, including rectification and amplification.

In an extended definition, place the formal sentence definition of the term near or at the beginning of the extended discussion, as in Figure 3–6.

Keep in mind, however, that formal sentence definitions can be used anywhere in a report where additional discussion and emphasis are needed. For example, look at the underlined terms in Figure 3–7.

STEP 5A.   On your worksheet write a formal sentence definition of the term on which you are writing an extended definition.

Stress is a measure of the internal reaction between elementary particles of a material in resisting separation, compacting, or sliding that tend to be induced by external forces. Total internal resisting forces are resultants of continuously distributed normal and tangential forces that are of varying magnitude and direction and are acting on elementary areas throughout the material. These forces may be distributed uniformly or nonuniformly. Stresses can be categorized as tensile, compressive, or shearing, according to the straining action. Strain is a measure of deformation such as (a) linear strain, the change of length per unit of linear dimensions; (b) shear strain, the angular skew in radians of an element undergoing change of shape by tangential forces; or (c) volumetric strain, the change of volume per unit of volume. The strains associated with stress are characteristic of the material.

W. J. Krefeld and W. G. Bowman, "Stress and Strain," *McGraw-Hill Encyclopedia of Science and Technology* (New York: McGraw-Hill, 1977), 202. Reprinted with permission.

FIGURE 3–6. A formal sentence definition used in an extended definition

Adding Short Definitions of Other Terms

Some terms, however, are not going to need formal sentence definitions. Often, only short definitions that are part of longer sentences are necessary. Look at the example passage in Figure 3–8 that uses short definitions (underlined).

Strategy For Writing Short Definitions. Use the following strategy to work short definitions into your rough drafts:

1. Locate words in your text that must be explained.
2. Create or find definitions for those words. (See Chapter 9 on finding specialized dictionaries and encyclopedias.)
3. Combine the essential phrase of each definition with the rest of the sentence where the term occurs.
4. If some of the definitions do not fit, you may need longer, separate definitions.

An example of how this process works begins with Figure 3–9. Assume that you had the passage in that figure.

Such a passage would be difficult for all but specialists in the field of biology; however, it can be translated with short definitions into something most nonspecialist readers can understand. Specialized dictionaries and encyclopedias are a good source for explanations of the unfamiliar terms in this passage.

In a nontechnical translation of the measles passage, some of the jargon can be retained (1) to avoid having to explain each term every time it occurs, and (2) to

Life on Earth is possible because there is liquid water, a blanket of life-supporting gases, and a climate neither too warm nor too cold. Humans may now be altering this equable climate by adding carbon dioxide to the atmosphere. This could make the global climate warmer than at any other time in human history. The change would be effectively irreversible.

The atmosphere contains 75% nitrogen, 23% oxygen, with argon, water vapor, and trace gases--including carbon dioxide (CO_2)--making up the remaining 2%. Carbon dioxide is an odorless, colorless gas which constitutes about 0.035% by volume of the atmosphere but whose significance far exceeds its relative scarcity. It is essential for

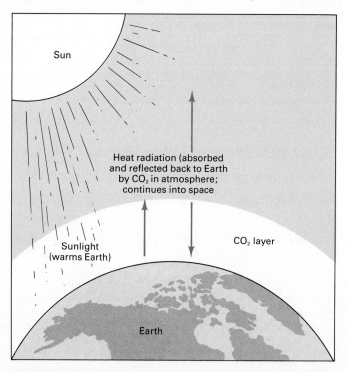

FIGURE 3–7a. How carbon dioxide buildup warms the Earth

David M. Burns, "The Planetary Greenhouse," McGraw-Hill Encyclopedia of Science and Technology: Yearbook (1982–83), 69. Reprinted with permission.

FIGURE 3–7. Formal sentence definitions used in other report areas

photosynthesis, the process by which the Sun's energy is converted into forms usable by plants and animals, and it also helps regulate the critical heat balance of the planet, thus maintaining liquid water.

Carbon dioxide affects the heat balance by acting as a one-way screen. It is transparent to incoming visible sunlight, and allows the Sun's heat to warm the ocean and land. But CO_2 molecules block some of the infrared heat radiated back into space. The reflected heat is absorbed in the lower atmosphere. This is the so-called greenhouse effect (Figure 3–7a), by which a portion of the Sun's heat is trapped, making the Earth's surface warmer than it would otherwise be.

FIGURE 3-7. (cont.)

Program Testing and Debugging. The output produced by a program may contain error messages, indicating the presence of errors in the program. These are messages generated by the computer system to assist the user in locating and correcting these errors, or bugs. Errors can be detected at various stages of program processing and may cause the processing to be terminated (aborted). For example, an incorrect system command or an error in one of the control cards will be detected early in the processing and will prevent compilation and execution of the program. Errors in the syntax of the program, such as incorrect punctuation or misspelling of key words, will usually be detected during compilation of the program and thus are called compile-time errors. Several compile-time errors, sometimes called fatal errors, make it impossible to complete the compilation and execution of the program. Less severe errors may generate warning messages, but the compilation will be continued and execution of the resulting object program attempted.

Other errors, such as an attempt to divide by zero in an arithmetic expression, will not be detected until execution of the program has begun. Such errors are called run-time errors.

Larry Nyhoff and Sanford Leestma, Problem Solving with FORTRAN 77 (New York: Macmillan, 1983), 40.

FIGURE 3–8. Report excerpt using short definitions

[Measles is an] acute, highly infectious viral disease, with cough, fever, and maculopapular rash. It has worldwide endemicity. The infective particle is an RNA virus about 100–150 nm in diameter, measured by ultrafiltration, but the active core is only 65 nm as measured by inactivation after electron irradiation. Negative staining in the electron microscope shows the virus to have the helical structure of a paramyxovirus with the helix being 18 nm in diameter. Measles virus will infect monkeys easily and chick embryos with difficulty. In tissue cultures the virus may produce giant multinucleated cells and nuclear acidophilic inclusion bodies. The virus has not been shown to have the receptor-destroying enzyme associated with other paramyxoviruses. Measles, canine distemper, and bovine rinderpest viruses are antigenetically related.

Joseph L. Melnick, "Measles," McGraw-Hill Encyclopedia of Science and Technology (New York: McGraw-Hill, 1977), 243. Reprinted with permission.

FIGURE 3–9. A paragraph without definitions to aid nonspecialist readers

introduce readers to that jargon. Figure 3–10 has a translation of the measles passage from Figure 3–9, with the original terms retained.

Incorporating Short Definitions in Reports.   In most cases, try to work both short and sentence definitions into the main text of your report. However, if that's a problem, do one of the following:

• Locate the definitions in footnotes on the pages where the terms occur.
• Locate the definitions in a glossary.
• Locate the definitions in a background section that readers can read first (in other words, an extended definition).

STEP 6A.   On your worksheet, list the other terms that you may need to define during the extended definition. After each one, write a brief definition.

Sources of Information for Definitions

Here are some suggestions for finding information with which to write your extended definition. (See Chapter 9 for more on libraries.)

Measles is an acute, highly infectious disease caused by a virus. The illness is characterized by a cough, fever, and a maculopapular (raised red) rash. It has worldwide endemicity; that is, people throughout the world are capable of contracting measles. The infective particle, or organism causing the illness, is a virus about 100–150 nm (a nanometer is 10^{-9} meter) in diameter and contains RNA (ribonucleic acid) as its genetic material rather than DNA (deoxyribonucleic acid). The size of the measles virus was determined by a process known as ultrafiltration, in which filters with extremely small pores are used to gauge the size of microscopic objects. The active core, or actual genetic material (RNA), is only 65 nm. The measurement of the core is made by a technique, called electron irradiation, that bombards the organism with radiation and inactivates the core. Negative staining, a shadowing technique used with an electron microscope, shows the virus to have a helical structure common to a group of viruses known as the paramyxoviruses. The helix, a spiral around a core (similar to a staircase) is 18 nm in diameter.

The measles virus will infect monkeys easily and chicken embryos with difficulty. In tissue cultures (those involving living cells or tissues from other organisms) the measles virus may produce giant cells containing many nuclei and acidophilic inclusion bodies (red stained areas in the nucleus which are a diagnostic laboratory sign for certain viral infections). The virus has not been shown to have the receptor-destroying enzyme, a protein capable of destroying or inactivating a cell-surface molecule, usually associated with other viruses in this classification. Measles, canine distemper (a flu-like disease affecting dogs), and bovine rinderpest (a virus affecting cows) are antigenetically related to the measles virus; that is, they possess similar antigens, or molecules that stimulate the production of an antibody, on their surfaces.

FIGURE 3–10.   A translation of the technical discussion in Figure 3–9

1. Start with general, nonspecialist sources, even if you think you know the term. Use standard dictionaries such as *Webster's* or the *American Heritage* and general encyclopedias such as the *Britannica*, the *Americana*, *Collier's*, or even *The World Book*.

Definition in a Footnote

A small computer is typically a word-addressable machine with a primary-storage capacity of from 64K bytes to 4 megabytes. Its processor has a 16-, 18-, 24-, or 32-bit word size. Its machine cycle time* ranges from about 225 nanoseconds to 100 nanoseconds. [This means that] a processor with a 225-nanosecond cycle time [can] perform about 200,000 instructions per second. A machine with a 100-nanosecond cycle time may perform about 420,000 instructions per second.

*A *machine cycle* is the amount of time used by a computer to complete one operation.

Definitions in a Glossary

semiconductor: a small two-state component having an electrical conductivity that lies between the high conductivity of metals and the low conductivity of insulators; semiconductors include transistors and crystal diodes.

spooling: (simultaneous peripheral operations online): techniques that permit input to be transcribed from a slow-speed device (say, a card reader) to a high-speed data-recording medium (e.g., tape or disk) for subsequent entry into the computer, or that permit output to be written to a high-speed medium from where it can be transcribed into a final form (say, a printed report) at a later time.

spreadsheet program: software developed to aid users in break-even analysis, budget planning and control, cash flow analysis, loan amortization, and other common business applications areas.

Marilyn Bohl, *Information Processing,* 4th ed. (Chicago: Science Research Associates, 1984), 275, 555–56.

FIGURE 3–11. Examples of footnote and glossary definitions

2. Move on to such specialized sources as *The McGraw-Hill Encyclopedia of Science and Technology* or *Van Nostrand's Scientific Encyclopedia.*
3. Locate specialized encyclopedias, handbooks, or dictionaries (see Chapter 9, "Finding Reference Books") to bring your extended definition up to date.
4. If necessary, consult a standard academic textbook in the related field of knowledge for even more in-depth information on your term.

STEP 7A.   On your worksheet, list the names of the sources of information you plan to use to write your extended definition.

Determining Length for Extended Definitions

Once you've found the term to write an extended definition on and identified the sources of definition to use in discussing it, you're ready to decide on the length your extended definition should be—whether it should be a single or multi-paragraph extended definition. Usually, your understanding of the audience for the extended definition and the purpose and need for the extended definition will help you decide.

Single-Paragraph Extended Definitions. Extended definitions can be varying lengths and can be used in various ways. For example, in one section of a report, all you may need is an introductory paragraph providing an extended definition of a term. The example of a single-paragraph extended definition in Figure 3–12 prepares the reader to understand the discussion in the second and following paragraphs.

Multiparagraph Definitions. In some reports a whole section may be needed for the extended definition of a term. In others the whole report may provide an extended definition of a key term. An outline of a report showing how one entire section is devoted to an extended definition appears in Figure 3–13.

A multiparagraph extended definition is shown in Model 3–1 at the end of this chapter. As you can see in Figure 3–14, definitions, like descriptions, process discussions, and other kinds of writing covered here in Part I, can be expanded.

STEP 8A. On your worksheet explain whether your extended definition is going to be a single paragraph or several paragraphs long. Now, go to the appropriate group of steps in the following list.

Substeps for Paragraph-Length Definitions

If you write a paragraph-length extended definition (only one or two paragraphs), your job is fairly simple. And, if you've done the steps to this point, you can do the following:

1. Gather information about the term, if necessary (using the steps in Chapter 9, if you need to find library information).
2. Write one or more sentences with each of the sources of definition you've chosen (for example, description and process).
3. Write several introductory sentences that
   a. Provide a formal sentence definition of the term;
   b. Provide an overview of what is to be discussed.
4. Go on to the section "Developing and Completing Definitions and Classifications" for the finish-up work there.

First described in 1907 by Alos Alzheimer, a German physician, Alzheimer's disease is an adult-onset neurological disorder of unknown etiology manifested by loss of memory, impaired thought processes, and abnormal behavior. When the illness begins before the age of 65, it is termed Alzheimer's disease; when onset is after 65, it is referred to as senile dementia of the Alzheimer's type. Approximately 5% of the U.S. population over 65 have severe dementia; an additional 10% have a mild-to-moderate impairment in memory and cognition. Of these demented individuals, approximately 40 to 50% have Alzheimer's disease, making this disorder the most common cause of dementia in middle and later life.

formal sentence definition

other supplementary definitions

description

Affected individuals are, at first, forgetful. As the memory disorder gradually worsens, the individuals, although able to recall occurrences in the distant past, are unable to remember recent events. Subsequently, speech, the ability to calculate, visuospatial orientation, judgment, and social behavior become progressively abnormal. Eventually, the individuals become profoundly demented, and frequently die of intercurrent infection. . . .

process (of the disease)

Donald L. Price, "Alzheimer's disease," McGraw-Hill Encyclopedia of Science and Technology (New York: McGraw-Hill, 1977), 80. Reprinted with permission.

FIGURE 3–12.   Single-paragraph extended definition

Substeps for Multiparagraph Definitions

If you write a multiparagraph extended definition (several paragraphs), your job is rather similar to writing a paragraph-length definition:

1. Gather information about the term, if necessary (using the steps in Chapter 9, if you need to find library information).

II.   Alzheimer's Disease: Overview of Current Knowledge
  A. Two Main Types of Alzheimer's Disease
    1. Alzheimer's disease (pre–65)
    2. Senile dementia of the Alzheimer's type (post–65)
  B. Demography of Alzheimer's Disease
    1. Age distribution
    2. Sex distribution
    3. Other demographic factors
  C. Process and Characteristics of Alzheimer's Disease
    1. Forgetfulness
    2. Speech disorders
    3. Difficulty in calculating
    4. Visuospatial disorientation
    5. Abnormal judgment and social behavior
  D. Brain Pathology of Alzheimer's Disease Victims
    1. Reduced brain size
    2. Neurofibrillary tangles
    3. Neuritic plaques
    4. Loss of specific populations of nerve cells
  E. Etiology of Alzheimer's Disease
    1. Aging
    2. Inheritance
    3. Infectious agents and toxins

FIGURE 3–13.   Outline of a report with a section of extended definition

2. Write a paragraph using each of the sources of definition you've chosen (there may be some simple, minor sources that can grouped within one paragraph, however).
3. Write an introductory paragraph that
  a. Provides a formal sentence definition of the term;
  b. Provides an overview of what is to be discussed.
4. Write a concluding paragraph for your multiparagraph extended definition, if necessary.
5. Go on to the section "Developing and Completing Definitions and Classifications" for the finish-up work there.

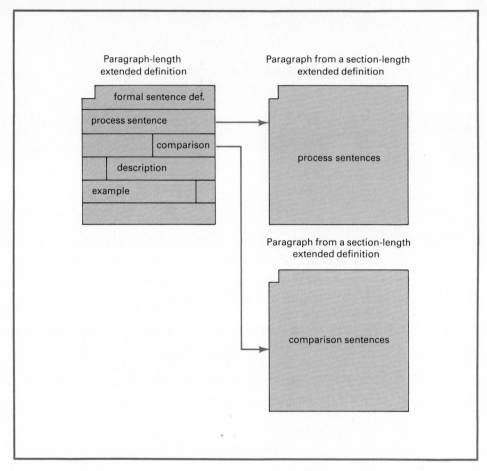

FIGURE 3–14.   Expanding extended definitions

Classifications

In some technical reports, certain paragraphs or sections use a kind of writing and pattern of organization known as *classification*. Classification means either (1) explaining which class a thing belongs to or (2) dividing a group of things into classes. In planning your reports, you may find that classification is an effective way to present background information to your readers.

The term *classification* refers to two ways of handling a subject.

• *True classification.* You are classifying (in the strict dictionary sense of the term) when you place an object, action, or person in one of several classes. For example, a corporation may introduce a new computer that it classifies as a mini-computer rather than a microcomputer. Having discovered a new species of fungus, a botanist must decide how to classify it. Written documents on these questions

Jupiter can be classed as a Jovian planet because of its size and its average density. Indeed Jupiter is the largest planet in our solar system and one of the brightest objects in the sky, having attained a magnitude of -2.5, more than a full magnitude brighter than Sirius, the brightest star in the sky. Jupiter's brightness results from its great size of course but also from its high reflectivity: it reflects about 44 percent of the light it receives. The size and composition of Jupiter's interior are open to much speculation. Some astronomers picture the interior as having a radius of over 30,000 miles and as possibly being composed of liquid hydrogen. The core is small and dense and may contain iron silicates. The other Jovian characteristic of the planet is its density. Even though its diameter is only 11 times that of the Earth, its total volume is $11 \times 11 \times 11$, or over a thousand times that of Earth. More graphically, over 1000 Earths could be packed into the space occupied by Jupiter. The relative size of Jupiter and its distance from the sun are shown in Figure 3-15a.

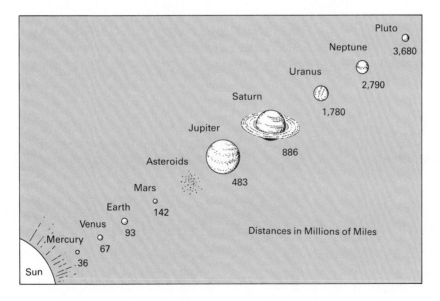

FIGURE 3-15a. Jupiter

Ronald A. Orti and William B. Starbird, <u>Introduction to Astronomy</u> (New York: Macmillan, 1977), 105.

FIGURE 3-15. A true classification (in which an item is located in a class)

would resemble comparison because features of the new item (the computer or the fungus) must be compared to those of the established classes.

An example of a true classification discussion in which the object clearly belongs to one category appears in Figure 3–15.

• *Division*. Classification more commonly refers to breaking a thing down into its types, classes, categories, or kinds and discussing each one. For example, computers for some time now have been divided into several classes: minicomputers, microcomputers, and macrocomputers. And, if you have ever taken biology, you know that terrestrial life is divided into plant and animal kingdoms; the kingdoms, broken down into phyla (the plural of phylum); phyla, into classes; classes, into families; families, into genera (the plural of genus); and genera, into species. Each of these divisions represents a grouping of types. A conceptual illustration of what dividing a group of things into classes means appears in Figure 3–16.

Several key words indicate that classifications are being discussed:

classes	kinds
types	categories
sorts	groups

Classification can be quite useful in technical reports: it breaks the discussion of a subject into smaller chunks and can make the job of evaluation and selection much easier.

STEP 1B.   On your worksheet briefly describe the term on which you want to write an extended classification, and explain who the audience is and why that audience needs the classification. (If you are thinking about collaborating on your classification with someone else, see "Collaborating on Technical Reports," in the Introduction for ideas and suggestions.)

Locating Areas in Reports for Classification

Like extended definitions, classification is often used for presenting background information. To find out whether classification can be used at various places in your report, analyze your topic or outline using questions such as these:

• If you narrate a process, are there other similar or related processes, methods, ways of doing things, or ways that things happen that you should also discuss?
• If you describe an object or mechanism, are there other ones belonging to the same class that you should discuss?
• If you discuss a concept, are there other concepts belonging to the same class that you should also discuss?

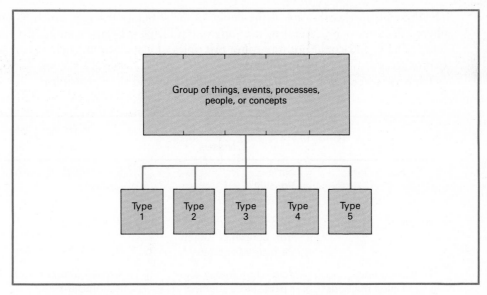

FIGURE 3–16. Classification by dividing a group of objects, people, processes, places, or situations into types

Using questions like these, you can identify possibilities for classification in your report project. Here are some examples:

Report Project	Subtopic for Classification	Classes
Treatment of renal disease	Dialyzing machines	Parallel-flow design Coil design Hollow-fiber capillary type
Nonconventional energy sources	Wind machines	Lift wind machines Drag wind machines

STEP 2B.   On your worksheet, list the terms in your report topic for which you may need to write extended classifications.

Identifying Classes and the Principle of Classification

Once you know which term or terms to divide into classes, your next step is to identify the classes and the principle of classification that you've used. For example, if your topic for classification were dialysis machines used to treat people with kidney disease, you might list these classes:

Parallel-flow-design dialyzers
Coil-design dialyzers
Hollow-fiber capillary dialyzers

The principle of classification is the design of the structure through which blood is filtered. You must be careful to use *only one* principle of classification at a time. For example, you could not mix other principles of classification such as cost and effectiveness.

Here are several other examples of classifications and their principles:

Topic	Classes	Principle of Classification
Electrical circuits	Series Parallel Series-parallel	Pathway of electrical current
Anemias	Blood-loss anemia Iron-deficiency anemia Pernicious anemia	Main cause
Hurricane-track prediction methods	Total climatology and persistence method Particular climatology and persistence method Circulation and climatology method Dynamic model method	Combination of hurricane characteristics
Wind machines	Lift machines Drag machines	Interaction between the wind and propeller blade

STEP 3B.   List the classes that you'll write about in your extended classification along with the principle of classification you used on your worksheet.

Discussing the Classes

When you write the paragraphs that discuss the individual classes, you must

- Write *classification sentences* that introduce the class or classes about to be discussed.
- Choose sources of discussion that enable you to explain each class fully.
- Add comparisons so that readers can see the differences between the classes.

Writing Classification Sentences.   Two kinds of sentences introduce classification: (a) those that list all the classes, and (b) those that name, define, or in some way introduce only one class. Some examples are provided in Figure 3–17.

STEP 4B.   On your worksheet write a classification sentence for each of the classes you plan to discuss as well as one that introduces all of the classes.

Classification Sentences Listing All the Classes

The National Hurricane Center in Miami uses four different track prediction models to pinpoint the location of landfall for hurricanes reaching the United States: the total climatology and persistence method, the particular climatology and persistence method, the circulation and climatology method, and the dynamic model method.

Wind machines that convert the wind's kinetic energy to useful mechanical energy can be classified as either lift machines or drag machines, depending on how they use the wind.

The most important types of wire-line well logging techniques include (1) the sonic amplitude log, (2) the dual induction-laterolog 8, (3) the neutron log, and (4) the fracture identification log.

The five types of vacuum tubes important in electronics are the diode, the triode, the VHF and microwave tubes, and the cathode ray tube.

Classification Sentences Listing Only One Class

One frequently used hurricane prediction model is based on the persistence of a hurricane, the behavior of the storm in the past, and on climatology (information on the speed and direction of previous hurricanes).

The drag-type wind machine is designed in such a way that while one of its S-shaped vanes is pushed by the wind, the other moves against it.

The sonic amplitude log is a wire-line well logging technique used in petroleum exploration which measures the velocity of sound through rock.

The cathode ray tube, or CRT as it is commonly known, is a special type of vacuum tube in which the electrons emitted by the cathode are concentrated into a small narrow beam and strike a specially treated phosphor screen, causing it to glow.

FIGURE 3—17. Classification sentences introducing one or all classes

Choosing Sources of Discussion. Writing the discussion of individual classes is much the same as it is in extended definitions: you select from or combine a variety of sources to explain the classes fully. For that reason then, you can return to the checklist in the section on extended definitions in this chapter, and select the sources you'll use to write your classification. To discuss the three types of dialysis machines for victims of kidney disease, you might use these sources:

Classification of Dialysis Machines

Definition: kidney disease
Description: main components of these different machines
Process: how the different machines operate
Comparison: advantages and disadvantages of these machines

Within each section you can follow the steps within the appropriate chapter here in Part I. Some classifications may be dominated almost entirely by one kind of writing. For example, some classifications can consist almost entirely of descriptive or process sections, as do these two examples:

Classification of Vacuum Tubes	Classification of Hurricane-track Prediction Methods
Description: diodes	Process: total climatology and persistence method
Description: triodes	Process: particular climatology and persistence method
Description: VHF and microwave tubes	Process: circulation and climatology method
Description: cathode ray tube	Process: dynamic model method

STEP 5B.   On your worksheet, list the sources you'll use to discuss the classes (use the checklist in Figure 3–2 on page 120), and briefly describe the information for each source.

Adding Comparisons.   No matter which sources you use in discussing the classes, comparison is an important ingredient. It helps readers distinguish the different classes from each other. To incorporate comparisons into classification, you only need to add short phrases and sentences that refer to the other classes. For example, look at Figure 3–18.

STEP 6A.   On your worksheet write one or more comparison sentences for each of the classes in your extended classification.

Sources of Information for Classifications

The sources of information (books, reports, articles) for classifications are much the same as they are for definitions. General and specialized encyclopedias and dictionaries are excellent starting places.

STEP 7B.   Return to page 130, and on your worksheet, list the sources of information you'll use to write your extended classification.

Pressurized-Water Reactors (PWR).   The first pressurized-water reactor was the submarine thermal reactor built in Idaho in 1953, which had led directly to the first nuclear-powered submarine, the USS Nautilus. As the name implies, a pressurized-water reactor is both cooled and moderated by water under high pressure, thus permitting high temperatures. As indicated in Figure 3—18a, the hot water is pumped from a pressurized vessel containing the nuclear core to a steam generator in which heat is exchanged to produce the steam that drives a turbogenerator. . . .

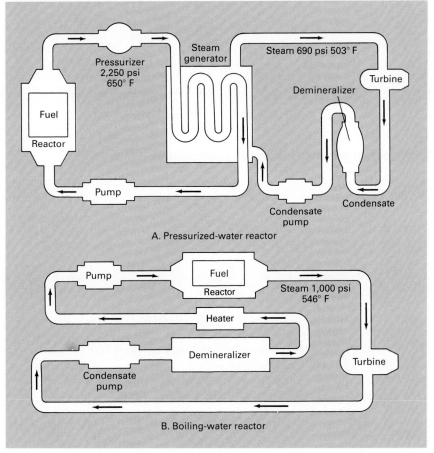

FIGURE 3—18a.   Two main types of thermal reactors
By courtesy of General Electric Company

(continued)

FIGURE 3—18.   Comparison used in discussing classes

<u>Boiling-Water Reactors (BWR)</u>.   Boiling-water reactors have much in common with pressurized-water reactors (see Figure 3–18a.) The main difference is that the intermediate steam generator is omitted, and steam is supplied directly from boiling water in the reactor core. Less pressurization is needed because the water is allowed to boil, and less pumping is needed because of the large amount of heat absorbed by boiling water. An excellent safety feature is the increase in steam production over the pressurized-water reactor that results from an increase in power level, thus reducing the water volume and lessening its moderating ability, a condition that in turn reduces the reactivity.

From "Nuclear Reactor," in <u>Encyclopedia Britannica</u>, 15th edition (1974), 13:319.

FIGURE 3-18.   (cont.)

Determining Length for Classifications

At this stage you're ready to decide on the length your classification should be— whether it should be a single-paragraph or extended classification. Your audience and your purpose in writing the classification should help you make this decision. A conceptual illustration of how the discussion of causes or effects can be expanded appears in Figure 3–19.

Short Classifications.   If you are going to write a paragraph-length discussion of all the classes like the one shown in Figure 3–20, try to follow these guidelines:

- At or near the beginning of the paragraph, write a sentence that lists all of the types under discussion.
- Introduce each class in the order listed, and devote a few sentences on each— enough to familiarize the reader with it.
- Remember to give examples or draw comparisons in order to provide a complete discussion of each class.

In Figure 3–20 you can see a single-paragraph classification with these features labeled.

Extended Classifications.   If you write an extended classification, you'll use a paragraph or more to discuss *each* of the classes, and a separate paragraph must introduce these classes. Try to follow these guidelines in extended classifications:

- Discuss each class separately, in a paragraph or group of paragraphs of its own.

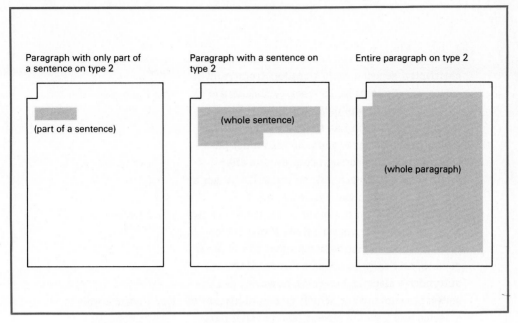

FIGURE 3–19. Expanding the discussion of types from part of a sentence to an entire paragraph

- Begin each paragraph that introduces a new class with a sentence that identifies or defines that type.
- Sometimes, a particular class has subclasses. Discuss these subclasses in the same way as you do the main ones.
- Create a paragraph for miscellaneous or other classes if there are insignificant ones that they do not warrant separate and thorough treatment.

An example is provided in Figure 3–21 in which all of these guidelines except the last can be seen.

STEP 8B. On your worksheet explain whether your classification will be one paragraph or several paragraphs long. Now, go to the appropriate group of steps in the following list.

Substeps for Short Classifications

If you write a short classification (only one or two paragraphs), your job is fairly simple. And, if you've done the steps to this point, you can do the following:

1. Gather information about the classes to be discussed, if necessary (using the steps in Chapter 9, if you need to find library information).
2. Write one or more sentences explaining each class.
3. Write several introductory sentences that
   a. Define the group to which each class belongs or explain its purpose or importance;

Three types of circuits are used in automotive electricity: series circuit, parallel circuit, and series-parallel circuit. In a series circuit, the current flows in one path: from the battery through the switch and through the two light bulbs. In the series circuit, current must pass through all the electrical devices, one after another. If any device fails to work, it will act as a switch and open the whole circuit. In the parallel circuit, on the other hand, there are two or more paths for current flow. If one device fails to work, the current still goes to the other devices, and they continue to work. Most automotive electrical circuits, however, use the series parallel circuit, which is a combination of a series and parallel circuit. The parallel part works like the parallel circuit just described; the series part, like the series circuit.

Jay Webster, Auto Mechanics (New York: Macmillan, 1980), 239–40.

overview: list of the types

type 1 (process)

type 2 (process with comparison)

type 3 (process with comparison)

FIGURE 3–20.   A single-paragraph classification (all classes discussed)

   b. List the classes to be discussed (that is, provide an overview).
4. Write a concluding sentence or two, if necessary, for your classification paragraph.
5. Go on to the section "Developing and Completing Definitions and Classifications" for the finish-up work there.

Substeps for Extended Classifications

If you write an extended classification (several paragraphs), your job is rather similar to writing a short classification:

1. Gather information about the classes to be discussed, if necessary (using the steps in Chapter 9, if you need to find library information).
2. Write a paragraph explaining each class (there may be some simple, minor classes that can be grouped within one paragraph, however).

Disorders of the Red Blood Cells—The Anemias

One of the most important classes of disorders of the hematological system involves the various anemias, or disorders of the red blood cells. The term *anemia* is used to indicate a deficit in the amount of iron, expressed as hemoglobin in the blood. Anemia is further defined and described by the mechanism that causes the inability of the erythrocytes to deliver enough oxygen to the individual cells. Anemia can be the result either of a lack of total numbers of red blood cells or by low amounts of hemoglobin in the individual erythrocytes. Hypoxia is the universal symptom of this condition wherein the patient's blood cannot carry sufficient amounts of oxygen. The most common subclasses of anemia include (1) anemia as a result of blood loss, (2) iron-deficiency anemia, (3) pernicious anemia, (4) aplastic anemia, (5) hemolytic anemia, (6) sickle-cell anemia, and (7) secondary anemia.

Anemia as a Result of Blood Loss. It stands to reason that with any great loss of blood one will become anemic. If you lose some of the red blood cells needed to carry oxygen, the only oxygen that can get to the tissues is that carried by the erythrocytes that are left.

Iron-Deficiency Anemia. The normal nonanemic adult male loses approximately 1 mg of iron per day, principally from his gastrointestinal tract. . . .

Mary Hayward and Connie Clark, *Medical Science for Medical Assistants* (New York: Macmillan, 1982), 157–58.

FIGURE 3–21. An extended classification with subclasses

3. Write an introductory paragraph that
   a. Defines the group to which each class belongs or explains its purpose or importance;
   b. Lists the classes to be discussed (that is, provides an overview).
4. Write a concluding paragraph for your extended classification, if necessary.
5. Go on to the section "Developing and Completing Definitions and Classifications" for the finish-up work there.

Developing and Completing Definitions and Classifications

Because extended definitions and classifications are often the workhorses that explain the fundamentals of a technical subject to nonspecialist readers, you must make sure that they can be understood by such readers; that they make good use of graphic and textual aids; and that you revise, proofread, and do final packaging on the end result of your efforts. These skills are discussed in the chapters of Parts II and III, but if you don't plan to study those chapters right now, keep the points in the following sections in mind.

Adjusting the Discussion to the Audience

Because so much of technical writing is for nonspecialist readers, or at least for people who are not experts or experienced technicians, adapting report discussions to these audiences is a crucial skill. Chapter 5 shows you a step-by-step way of doing this. For the moment, however, you can follow these guidelines for your practice extended definition or classification:

- Identify *who* your readers are and *why* they need your extended definition or classification.
- Identify your readers' background: what *knowledge* about your subject do they already possess; what *capabilities* related to your subject do they possess, and which do they lack? In particular, list the terms they may not know.
- Provide the *right level* of discussion for your specific audience—either general or specific—according to their needs or interests.
- *Translate* difficult technical discussion (using the techniques described in Chapter 5, for example) to help your readers understand the points.

STEP 9.   On your worksheet write a brief description of your audience members, their background, and their interest in your discussion.

Special Sections

If you are writing an *extended* definition or classification, one that is at least several paragraphs long, you'll need an introduction and a conclusion.

- In the introduction to an extended definition, give an overview of the topics you'll be using to discuss the term. (For an example, see the introduction to Model 3–1.)
- In the introduction to a classification, list the types or classes that you'll be discussing.
- Also in the introduction to a classification, indicate the *principle of classification* by which you divided the subject into classes.

For examples of introductions to extended definitions and classifications, see the models at the end of this chapter.

- For the conclusion to an extended definition, shift the focus to some more general topic and discuss it briefly. (See the section on afterwords in Chapter 4.)
- For the conclusion to an extended classification, also consider shifting the focus to a more general topic and discussing it briefly (see the section on afterwords), or briefly discuss miscellaneous and less-important classes.

STEP 10.   If you write an *extended* discussion, list on your worksheet the special sections you think are needed, and explain why they are needed.

Headings and Lists

For extended definitions or classifications, use headings (titles and subtitles in the text) to mark off the main sections. Use numbered or bulleted lists, either within regular paragraphs or in the form of vertical columns, anywhere you want to emphasize important points or itemize things for greater clarity. When you use headings, keep these suggestions in mind:

- In extended definitions use a heading at the start of each new section: for example, a heading at the beginning of a descriptive section, one at the beginning of a process section, and so on. (See Model 3–1.)
- In extended classifications use a heading to introduce each new type or class. (See Model 3–2.)

STEP 11.   On your worksheet make a list of the headings for your *extended* definition or classification, and describe areas of your discussion where listing might be useful. (For more on headings and lists, see Chapter 6.)

Graphic Aids

Graphic aids such as drawings, diagrams, photographs, graphs, charts, and tables play as important a role in definitions and classifications as they do in any other sort of technical writing. You can read the step-by-step method for getting graphic aids into your writing in Chapter 6, or, for this practice definition or classification, you can study the examples and models in this chapter. But keep these ideas in mind:

- If you write about physical things, use some form of illustration (drawings, diagrams, or photos); if you discuss statistical information, use some form of table, graph, or chart; if you discuss important concepts, create some conceptual illustration that will help convey your idea.
- For each graphic aid, include a number and a title (see examples throughout this chapter).
- Include source information on any graphic aid you borrow from other books, reports, or articles.
- Discuss and interpret the graphic aids you use in nearby text.

STEP 12.   On your worksheet, list the types of graphic aids you think may be needed in your discussion, and briefly describe their contents.

Revising and Finishing Definitions and Classifications

A task that is as important as getting something on paper is going back and revising and rewriting it. While step-by-step methods for revising, proofreading, and final packaging are presented in Chapters 7 and 10, you can use these suggestions for your practice definition or classification:

- In your extended definition make sure that you've discussed all the important aspects of the term that you are defining.
- In your classification make sure that you discuss each class or type one at a time, in separate sentences, paragraphs, or groups of paragraphs.
- As with definitions, make sure that you've discussed all the important aspects of the classes or types you are discussing in your classification.
- Make sure that your discussion is clear and understandable to the specific audience you are writing for.
- Make things easy for readers to find in your extended definition or classification: use headings and lists, for example.
- Make a neat typing job of your practice definition or classification.
- Use scissors and tape to insert your illustrations, and photocopy the whole discussion on a good quality machine.

STEP 13.   Use the preceding suggestions to revise your definition or classification. (If you want more detailed information or revising, proofreading, and final packaging, see Chapters 7 and 10.)

EXERCISES

1. Use the following list to help you start thinking of a topic for your practice extended definition:

microwave energy	nuclear fusion	random walk	noise
epidemic	Doppler effect	calculus	stress
word processing	energy	cybernetics	torque
amino acid	diabetes	hydroponics	RNA
bubble memory	probability	black hole	DNA
interface	nuclear fission	computer	loop
heat transfer	antibody	chromosome	gene
Boolean algebra	holography	telemetry	laser
turbulence	BASIC	FORTRAN	COBOL
virus	tension	relativity	light
software	grammar	syntax	data
integrated circuit	jet stream	paranoia	memory
program	language	computer	quasar
hysteria	porosity	permeability	quark
viscosity	well logging	reservoir	pulsar
strain	hypertension	nebula	

2. Locate several highly technical passages in books, textbooks, or articles in a field of interest. Photocopy them, and, using one color, circle the terms that are likely to be unfamiliar to nonspecialist audiences. Using another color, underline or draw boxes

around the actual definitions of these terms, if the writers supply any. If you locate any formal sentence definitions, put an asterisk in the margin by each one.

3. Think of several technical terms from areas you are familiar with, and look them up in the following reference books in this order:

World Book Encyclopedia
Americana Encyclopedia
Britannica
McGraw-Hill Encyclopedia of Science and Technology

Once you have looked up the same terms in these different sources, compare them for the kinds of audiences, information, and purposes that characterize each.

4. For one of the following familiar topics (or for one of the topics listed in exercise 1), list the most important kinds of writing (sources of definition) you'd need to write an extended definition on that topic. Also, briefly indicate what the content of each would be.

rock music	classical music	jazz
science fiction	soap opera	hobby
career	professionalism	suburbia
health	success	happiness
exercise	recreation	vacation

5. Identify the formal sentence definition, the term being defined, and the sources of definition (kinds of writing) being used in the following extended definition.

You hear so much about computers and application programs and software and hardware these days that the terms get very confusing. One of the basic concepts to understand, however, is that of the program. A program is nothing more than a set of instructions in computer language that makes a computer solve problems or accomplish business or recreational activities for you. Imagine that you were suddenly plunked down in Hong Kong and needed to find the American embassy: the instructions would be your program for getting there, and you'd probably want them in English. In computer languages, as with human language, there is wide variability. However, in computer languages, there are three main types or levels: high-level, assembly, and machine language. Machine language uses 1s and 0s in a way that the computer can understand but that is difficult for people to work with. High-level programming languages are rather like human language and therefore are easy to work with; but they must be translated into machine language before they can be used. Some examples are BASIC, Pascal, FORTRAN, and COBOL.

6. Write a formal sentence definition for a nonspecialist audience and then a formal sentence definition for a specialist audience on any three of the terms in exercise 1.

7. Translate one of the following passages by (a) circling the unfamiliar words or phrases; (b) copying on scratch paper definitions for each of the those unfamiliar terms; and (c) rewriting the passage with both the unfamiliar terms and their definitions included.

Nucleic Acids

Nucleic acids are macromolecular polymers that occur in all living things. There are two types, deoxyribonucleic acid (DNA) and ribonucleic acid (RNA). Their chemical composition is best understood in terms of their hydrolysis products. Chemical hydrolysis yields a mixture of heterocyclic amines (purines and pyrimidines), a five-carbon sugar (ribose or 2-deoxyribose), and phosphoric acid. Partial hydrolysis degrades the nucleic acid into somewhat larger subunits, nucleotides and nucleosides.

Branching and Looping with FORTRAN

Widespread use of computers depends on their ability to branch automatically at decision points during the computational process, to loop through calculations repeatedly, and to work through vast quantities of data by modifying addresses of operands as they proceed. The FORTRAN statements needed for branching and looping include the following: logical IF statements, IF-THEN-ELSE (FORTRAN 77); arithmetic IF statements, GO TO statements, and DO statements. The first three are placed at decision points to cause the execution to proceed along alternative paths. The Logical IF and IF-THEN-ELSE allow branching in two directions, and the Arithmetic IF, in three. The GO TO—often called the unconditional GO TO—always directs program execution at the same point. It is used after a branch to transfer execution back to the main stream of program execution or to cause a loop. The DO statement is used for automatic looping.

8. Make a photocopy of an extended definition that uses or combines several different kinds of writing (process narration, description, classification, etc.), and then do the following:
   a. Label each section (paragraph or group of paragraphs) that is dominated by one of the kinds of writing.
   b. For each section that is dominated by one of the kinds of writing, label the parts, characteristics, steps, points of comparison, classes, causes, or effects that make up the organizational pattern of that section.
   c. Explain which kinds of combinations are used (sentence, block, or frame).
   d. For any section in which you cannot identify the kinds of writing or identify the type of combination, explain which kind of writing or combination of them it most resembles, and then give it a name.

9. Study the following report topics for areas in which extended definitions may be necessary in reports on them. Pick any three, and explain which kinds of discussions, or combinations, will be necessary for each:

A report on the development of the integrated circuit

A plan to modify city waste disposal for recycling, cocombusting, or other uses

A report on the effects of caffeine

A report on the problem of acid rain

A report on the different parts of the brain

An evaluation of different software packages

A project to build city bike lanes

A report on medical applications of lasers

A study of the characteristics and potential of jojoba

A report on the greenhouse effect

A feasibility report on different investment plans

A report on a new computer language

A report on drip irrigation

10. Take a look at the following topic suggestions for a practice classification:

primates	cancers	volcanoes
hurricanes	agricultural methods	computer languages
climates	pollution	computers
terrains	architectural styles	industrial robots
telescopes	boats	any computer component
fertilizers	boat-hull designs	radios
trees	furniture styles	any component of radios
enzymes	safety devices	software
any animal(s)	welding methods	printing methods
any plant(s)	nuclear power plant	aircraft
any microorganism(s)	designs	electronic components

forms of matter	earthquakes	cloud forms
solar-energy devices	turbines	fossils
boiler designs	suns	clocks
plastics	nova	knots
motors	supernova	rifles
mental disorders	lightning	money (M1, M2, etc.)
cardiac diseases	seashells	stocks and bonds
ocular problems	rocks	loans
automobiles	soils	missiles
automobile braking	gems	different methods of
systems	land forms	doing something

11. Study the following paragraph that discusses several classes, identify the classification sentences, list the classes discussed, and identify the principle of classification used.

Of all the sorts of applications programs available these days for computers, the favorites are text editors, spreadsheet editors, and graphics tools. With text editors you can create documents such as letters, memos, or reports and then revise them in various ways before ever printing them out. Text editors enable you to change, move, or delete words, sentences, and even whole paragraphs. Spreadsheet editors, on the other hand, are mainly useful with numbers. They enable you to make big columns of numbers, do mathematical operations on them, move them around, and so on. The other kind of applications program many people like are those that enable you to draw pictures. These are called graphics tools: they enable you to draw shapes, use color, add words to your drawings, and of course to edit (change them in various ways).

12. Select one of the following report projects, and list the groups of classes that you might have to discuss if you were writing the report.

Recommendation to develop a nearby area for housing

Proposal to begin citywide recycling

Proposal to purchase word-processing equipment for the secretarial pool

Evaluation of different software

The feasibility of different investment plans

Plans to rezone parts of the city

13. Make a photocopy of a discussion of an extended technical classification, and do the following:
   a. Identify the types being discussed and the principle or basis of the classification.
   b. Label the kinds of discussion used to explain the classes.
   c. Explain what audience level the classification is written for.
   d. Analyze the introductory paragraph, and explain what elements are used within it.

14. Select from the list in exercise 10 any three of the topics suggested for classification. List the individual classes for each, and explain the basis or principle of the classification. (Remember that you can look any of these topics up in general or specialized encyclopedias; see Chapter 9 on finding reference books.)

Model 3–1:   Sickle-cell Anemia
(multiparagraph extended definition)

Sickle-cell disease is a human genetic disorder in which the red blood cells, on giving up their oxygen, assume an elongated shape resembling a scythe or sickle. Normal red blood cells, on giving up their oxygen, change from a bright red to a blue-red color, but retain their usual wheel-like shape. Sickle cells, on deoxygenation, change shape as well as color. If an individual receives the defective gene from both parents, he has sickle-cell disease, often called sickle-cell anemia. In severe forms of this condition, the individual is debilitated, suffers periodically from painful crises, and has a shortened life expectancy.

Inheritance of the Disease

  Sickle-cell disease is not a contagious disease; instead, it is inherited from parents with some combination of the sickle-cell trait or disease. (See Figure 1 for an illustration of the inheritance of sickle-cell disease.)

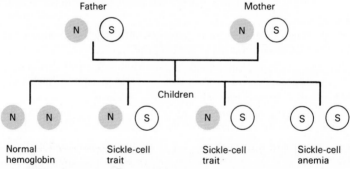

FIGURE 1.   Passage of the sickle cell gene from parents to offspring

  An individual can carry the single defective gene, called the sickle-cell trait, without suffering from it and without knowing it. In more general terms, this is known as heterozygous inheritance. About 1 in 10 Afro-Americans carry the sickle-cell trait (Birney 55). However, two such individuals, each carrying the defective gene, together have a 1-in-4 chance of passing these genes to their offspring. These recipients of the double trait, the homozygous inheritance, will then have sickle-cell disease. It is estimated that 1 in every 400 to 600 black children suffers from this condition.

Mechanism and Process of the Disease

  Recent research in molecular biology has shown specifically what is wrong with these defective red cells (Francis 8). All red blood cells contain hemoglobin, the substance that gives the red color to blood and that carries iron and transports oxygen. In sickle red cells, however, the molecular structure of the hemoglobin is slightly different from that of normal red blood cells. This slight molecular difference, under certain circumstances, produces the distortion in the cell shape known as sickling. (See Figure 2.)

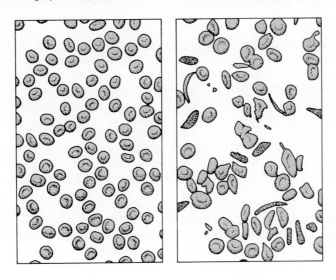

Normal red blood cells   Abnormal red blood cells
(or sickle cells)

FIGURE 2. Normal and sickled red blood cells

In the individual with sickle-cell disease, the majority of the red blood cells circulate in the unusual wheel-like forms. However, under certain circumstances, such as inadequate oxygen levels, the cells begin to sickle while circulating. They become elongated, spiculed, and rigid. As a result, the cells can no longer flow freely, but begin to clog blood vessels, particularly the smaller ones. Wherever the normal blood flow is obstructed, tissue inflammation and destruction begin, and pain and loss of function result. Most commonly, pain occurs in the limbs, the abdomen, the lower back, and the head. The organs most often affected are the lungs, bones, spleen, kidney, heart, and brain.

In addition to their bizarre shape, sickle cells are broken down more readily and more rapidly than normal cells. For this reason, people with sickle-cell anemia are unable to maintain a normal level of hemoglobin, even though they manufacture red cells at a more rapid rate than people with normal red cells. As a result, they have low levels of hemoglobin. They are anemic and often somewhat jaundiced because of the rapid breakdown of red cells. They do not grow normally and are highly susceptible to infections. The effects of malnutrition are more serious for sufferers of sickle-cell anemia, and, because their kidneys are unable to conserve water, the effects of dehydration are more severe. Sickle-cell anemia also makes surgery and childbirth more hazardous.

It must be emphasized, however, that these effects are not present all the time. Even people with the most severe and frequent crises and complications have long periods during which they feel relatively well and can engage in normal activities.

Forms and Severity of Sickle Cell Disease

Sickle-cell condition can occur in mild as well as in severe forms, depending on the combination of the genetic trait for the sickling condition that the parents pass along to their children.

Mild Forms.   Research has shown that individuals with mild forms of sickle-cell disease are usually heterozygous for the sickling condition. In other words, they have received the trait from one of their parents only and will pass it on to 50 percent of their potential offspring. These people have sickle-cell trait, also called heterozygous sickle-cell disease. While they do not usually become ill, they are carriers, and, if untested, they are silent, or unknown, carriers.

Severe Forms.   Individuals with the most severe form of sickle-cell disease are usually homozygous for the sickling condition. In other words, they have received the trait from both their parents and will pass it on to all their offspring. These people have sickle-cell anemia and are called homozygous for sickle-cell disease.

Intermediate Forms.   Individuals with an intermediate form are usually doubly heterozygous for the sickle cell and some other unusual hemoglobins. They are said to have sickle-C disease or a number of other similar conditions.

Occurrence in Populations

While the majority of families affected with sickle-cell disease are black, not all black people have the disease, and some white families are also affected (Francis 9). The disease is very common in certain parts of Africa, such as Ghana, but rare in other areas, such as South Africa. Affected families are also found in southern India, Italy, Greece, and Turkey. In the western hemisphere, sickle-cell disease is found wherever people of African, Indian, or Mediterranean origin have settled.

Origins of the Disease

Two research scientists at the University of California at San Francisco, Yuet Wai Kan and Andre M. Dozy, have traced the form of sickle-cell anemia that affects Afro-Americans to a small area in west Africa (Page 136). According to their theory, the disease is the result of a genetic change that occurred among certain Africans at a time, thousands of years ago, when malaria was ravaging the African continent. Those with the mutated gene survived the malarial epidemic in greater numbers than those without it. Apparently the sickle-cell carriers survived because the malarial parasites infecting their red cells starved from a lack of oxygen.

Diagnostic Tests

The alterations in the physical properties of sickle hemoglobin form the basis of the tests used in diagnosis of sickle-cell disease.

Wet Prep.   The first and oldest of these tests is the so-called "wet prep." In this test, actual sickling can be observed microscopically in a slide preparation as the red blood cells are deoxygenated by mixing the blood with sodium metabisulfite.

Turbidity Test.   The most recently developed test is the turbidity test, which is patented by Orthodiagnostics as Sickledex and is also available in other names. It has become quite popular because results can be obtained in 10 to 15 minutes. In this test, sickle hemoglobin is identified by the precipitate it forms in certain buffered solutions.

Other Tests.   Another test identifies sickle hemoglobin by the liquifaction at freezing temperatures of the gel formed during deoxygenation. Unfortunately, none of these tests differentiates adequately between the heterozygous and homozygous states. Currently this differentiation can be done only by hemoglobin electrophoresis, which involves placing hemoglobin solutions in an electric field. While this test is necessary for accurate diagnosis and proper counselling, it is too expensive and time consuming for initial mass screening.

Treatment of Sickle-Cell Disease

Currently no treatment can eliminate the sickling condition in people who have inherited it. However, knowledge of the condition is important for proper medical treatment of other illnesses potentially acquired by people with sickle-cell disease and for proper surgical and obstetric care. In the chronically ill patient, adequate medical attention may prevent serious crises and may prolong life.

Sometimes in the early stages a crisis can be prevented by prompt use of antibiotics to eliminate infection and by such various techniques as hydration or fluid administration. An acutely ill patient in crisis usually requires oxygen, pain relievers, intravenous fluids, and antibiotics. Sometimes transfusion of red cells is needed, and, in certain crises, the patient may also require anticonvulsants.

Recent experiments have suggested that urea and cyanate can be helpful in the control of crises, but further experimentation in proper use of these drugs is necessary.

WORKS CITED

Birney, Margaret. "Sickle Cell Anemia" In Diseases. Springhouse, PA: Springhouse Corp., 1985.

Francis, Yvette Fay. "Sickle Cell Disease." Collier's Encyclopedia. New York: Macmillan, 1987.

Page, Jake. Blood: The River of Life. Washington, D.C.: U.S. News Books, 1981.

158 DESIGNING AND WRITING THE BASIC REPORT COMPONENTS

Model 3–2:   Features of Industrial Robots*
(multiparagraph extended classification)

An industrial robot is a complex, technical system consisting of several subsystems operating within the robot's physical make-up. Each of these subsystems performs its own carefully defined functions and contributes to the overall function of the industrial robot. Three of the more important of these subsystems include (a) kinematics, (b) the control system, and (c) the drive.

Kinematics
    Kinematics refer to the spatial arrangement, according to the sequence and structure, of the axes of movement in relation to each other. There are four basic types of movement that an industrial robot may have: (1) Cartesian, (2) cylindrical, (3) polar, and (4) jointed-arm. Figure 1 illustrates these four types of movement and their applications.

    Cartesian Co-Ordinate Robot.   The Cartesian co-ordinate robot is one that consists of a column and an arm. It is sometimes called an x-y-z robot, indicating the axes of motion. The x-axis is lateral motion, the y-axis is longitudinal motion, and the z-axis is vertical motion. Thus, the arm can move up and down on the z-axis; the arm can slide along its base on the x-axis; and then it can telescope to move to and from the work area on the y-axis. The Cartesian co-ordinate robot was developed mainly for arc welding, but it is also suited for many other assembly operations (3:15).

    Cylindrical Co-Ordinate Robot.   The cylindrical co-ordinate robot is a variation of the Cartesian robot. This robot consists of a base and column, but the column is able to rotate. It also carries an extending arm that can move up and down on the column to provide more freedom of movement. The cylindrical co-ordinate robot is designed for handling machine tools and assembly (3:16).

    Polar Co-Ordinate Robot.   The polar co-ordinate, or spherical co-ordinate, robot consists of a rotary base, an elevation pivot, and a telescoping extend-and-retract boom axis. These robots operate according to spherical co-ordinates and offer greater flexibility. They are used particularly in spot welding (4:25).

    Jointed-Arm Robot.   The jointed-arm robot resembles a human arm. It usually stands on a base on which it can rotate, while it can articulate at the "shoulder" joint, which is just above the base. The robot can also rotate about its "elbow" and "wrist" joints. With the swiveling and bending at the wrist, six degrees of freedom can be obtained. The jointed-arm robot is the most popular form for a robot and is capable in welding and painting work (3:17).

*Source: From Alicia Leonard, *Report on Industrial Robots* (Austin: Univ. of Texas, 1984), 3.

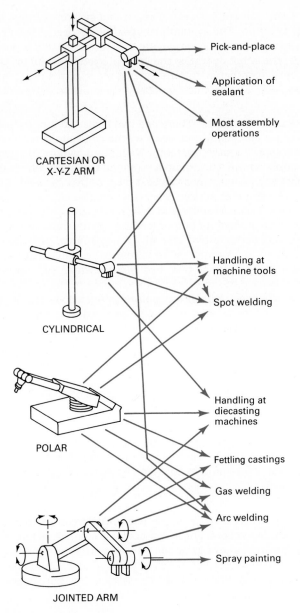

CARTESIAN OR
X-Y-Z ARM

CYLINDRICAL

POLAR

JOINTED ARM

Pick-and-place

Application of
sealant

Most assembly
operations

Handling at
machine tools

Spot welding

Handling at
diecasting
machines

Fettling castings

Gas welding

Arc welding

Spray painting

FIGURE 1. Four basic types of robot configurations and their
factory applications
Source: John Hartley, Robots at Work (London: IFS Publications,
1983), 21.

Control Systems

The control systems of an industrial robot determine its flexibility and
efficiency, within the limits set beforehand by the design of the mechanical
structure.

Purpose of the Control System.   The control system provides a logical sequence for the robot to follow. The system provides the theoretical position values required for each step and continuously measures the actual position during movement. As the robot operates, the control system evaluates the theoretical/actual difference, together with other measured values and stored data (e.g., theoretical speeds), and produce actuating variables to drive the robot.

Types of Control Systems.   There are two basic types of control systems: (1) the point-to-point control system and (2) the continuous path control system.

The point-to-point control system.   With point-to-point control, the robot records the point where it picks up a part and the point where it releases that part. The robot then determines the best path to take between the two points (5:49). The point-to-point system is used when greater repeatability is required, or when the path between endpoints does not matter. Point-to-point control systems work well in loading and unloading applications (2:88).

The continuous path control system.   A continuous path control system is one in which the robot is programmed to follow an irregular path exactly. Inside the control system, the path to be travelled is represented by a large number of points in close proximity; these points are stored in the robot's memory. In the working cycle, the robot follows the points to reproduce the desired path. The system is used for jobs when the robot is required to follow a specific path, such as in welding or painting (6:18).

Drive Systems

The drive of the robot converts the power supplied to the grippers into kinetic energy used for moving the robot. The basic types of drive systems include (1) electrical, (2) pneumatic, and (3) hydraulic (6:31).

Electrical Drive Systems.   Electromechanical drive systems are used in about 20 percent of today's robots. These systems are servo motors, stepping motors, and pulse motors. These motors convert electrical energy into mechanical energy to power the robot (1:72).

Pneumatic Drive Systems.   Pneumatic drive systems are found in approximately 30 percent of today's robots. These systems use compressed air to power the robots. Since machine shops typically have compressed air lines in their working areas, the pneumatically driven robot is very popular. Unfortunately, this system does not make for easy control of either speed or position—essential ingredients for any successful robot.

Hydraulic Drive Systems.   The most popular form of the drive system is the hydraulic system because hydraulic cylinders and motors are compact and allow high levels of force and power, together with accurate control. A hydraulic actuator converts forces from high-pressure hydraulic fluid into mechanical shaft rotation or linear motion. Hydraulic fluid power is more cost effective for short-stroke, straight-line positioning requiring high forces, controlled acceleration, and repetitive motion. No other drive system packs as much power into such a small package; no other drive is as safe or as resistant to harsh environments.

LITERATURE CITED

1. Dorf, Richard C. Robots and Automated Manufacturing. Reston, VA: Reston Publishing Co., 1983.
2. Froehling, Leopold. "Robots to the Rescue?" Datamation, January 1981, pp. 85–96.
3. Hartley, John. Robots at Work. London: IFS Publications, 1983.
4. Hunt, V. Daniel. Industrial Robotics Handbook. New York: Industrial Press, 1983.
5. "Industrial Robots." Modern Materials Handling, 7 March 1983, pp. 46–54.
6. Warnecke, H. J., and R. A. Schraft. Industrial Robots: Application Experience. London: IFS Publications, 1982.

CHAPTER 4

Introductions, Conclusions, and Summaries

Chapter Objectives
Introductions
  Elements of Report Introductions
  Elements of Section Introductions
    Similar Elements
    Special Elements
    Transitional Elements
Conclusions
  Summaries
  Conclusions

Recommendations
Afterwords
Summaries (Abstracts)
  Two Types of Summaries
    Descriptive Summaries
    Informative Summaries
  Selecting Important Information
  Condensing Important
    Information
Exercises

─────────────── *Chapter Objectives* ───────────────

After you read this chapter, study the examples, and work the steps, you should be able to:

- Recognize the elements of report and section introductions and use the right ones.
- Identify the different types of conclusions for reports and use the right ones.
- Construct effective summaries.
- Write complete recommendations.
- Identify the common types of afterwords and use the right ones.
- Recognize the difference in content and phrasing between descriptive and informative summaries.
- Use one or more of the common techniques to summarize reports.

The preceding chapters of Part I focus on organizing and writing some of the most important basic components found in technical reports. These basic building blocks help you plan the content of reports and determine the patterns of organization to use. However, you also need special-function sections that introduce, conclude, and summarize. These sections also have common contents and organizational patterns. As for summaries, several useful strategies are presented here that will help you summarize information in reports more effectively.

Use these ideas for introductions and conclusions to full-length reports (Part IV) as well as practice process discussions, descriptions, causal discussions, comparisons, or extended definitions and classifications (Part I). Look to the section on summaries any time you want to construct a summary, often called an abstract, of your report and to learn some useful strategies in summarizing information, for whatever purpose. (Steps for introductions end with *A*; those for conclusions end with *B*; and those for summaries end with *C*.)

Introductions

Just as a process discussion or a description can make up a whole report or only a section or paragraph within a report, introductions can also vary in length and function:

- *Report introductions* introduce whole reports.
- *Section introductions* introduce sections within reports.

Elements of Report Introductions

The elements of introductions discussed in this section are all suggestions for you to consider when you plan your own introductions or when you revise them: you won't need all of these elements in any one introduction, nor will you use them in the same order as described here.

• *Subject.* Place some reference to the precise subject of your report early in the introduction. However, avoid this approach: "The subject of this report is a new computer design for synthesized speech." Just be able to circle the words relating to the main subject of the report in one of the first sentences. Look at the two examples in Figure 4–1 of ways to introduce the subject.

Report on

TREATMENT OF SICKLE-CELL ANEMIA WITH
5-AZACYTIDINE

I. INTRODUCTION

The drug 5-azacytidine has successfully been used to manipulate genes to initiate fetal hemoglobin production in sickle-cell anemia patients. . . .

AN OVERVIEW OF ULTRASOUND: THEORY, MEASUREMENT,
MEDICAL APPLICATIONS, AND BIOLOGICAL EFFECTS

I. INTRODUCTION

Ultrasound, pressure waves propagated in a medium at frequencies which are above the normal ranges of human audibility, can be propagated in liquid, solid or gaseous media. The highest audible frequencies for humans are about 16–18 kHz, and for some animals even higher. Ultrasound has found increasing application in recent years. . . .

Harold F. Stewart et al., An Overview of Ultrasound: Theory, Measurement, Medical Applications, and Biological Effects, (Washington, D.C.: U.S. Department of Health and Human Services, July 1982), 7.

FIGURE 4–1. Early references to the subject in report introductions

• *Purpose and main point.* Somewhere in the introduction, indicate the purpose and main point of the report. Generally, reports serve one or a combination of three purposes: to inform, instruct, or recommend (that is, to convince or propose). Be careful about the informative purpose: few reports merely inform or acquaint readers about something. In Figure 4–2 are four examples; notice particularly how informative purpose statements are handled.

A main-point statement indicates what the main assertion or argument of the report will be: for example, that building city bike lanes would be advantageous to the city in a variety of ways or that they would disrupt traffic, endanger bicyclists, and cost the city too much. The main point is sometimes not directly stated in the introduction to keep the audience from becoming hostile or to build some suspense; in these situations, a "placeholder" for the main point is used:

Main-Point Statement	*Placeholder Statement*
This report will show that recycling and cocombusting municipal solid waste are not economically feasible at this time.	This report reviews the basic technical and economic aspects of recycling and cocombusting municipal solid waste and arrives at a number of conclusions concerning the feasibility of such a project.

The purpose of this report is to analyze the information that is currently available on municipal recycling programs in order to determine their feasibility and to recommend a plan for Luckenbach, Texas. This report proposes to the city council the construction of five fully-equipped softball parks for municipal use on city-owned vacant land.

In accordance with the committee's instructions, this report analyzes the market for word-processing software and recommends the corporationwide purchase of a particular model for use in all of its offices.

The purpose of this report is to present to members of the board and to local citizens a review of the land disposal methods currently employed in the United States and of the safety aspects associated with each method. We hope that this information will contribute to the process of developing a new disposal plan.

The purpose of this report is to present results and conclusions of the first-year environmental emissions investigation of the two stoker-fired generator units using coal and refuse-derived fuel.

FIGURE 4–2. Purpose statements for informative reports

STEP 1A.   On your worksheet write one or more sentences that explain the purpose of your report. Also, if your report makes a main point, write a sentence explaining that main point and then a placeholder version of it.

• *Overview and scope.* In your introduction, list the contents of the report. This gives readers a clear idea of what is to come and in what order it will appear and gives them an even clearer idea of what the report will be about—a more specific subject statement, or miniature table of contents. Figure 4–3 contains two examples (notice the use of lists, covered in Chapter 6).

The scope statement is quite similar to the overview, except that it indicates

• How generally or specifically the topics will be discussed
• Which topics will *not* be covered
• Why these topics will be handled this way in the report.

You must incorporate a scope statement in your introduction because it outlines what you will and will not do in the report to follow and explains why. It is like a contract with the reader. Three examples of scope statements are presented in Figure 4–4. Notice the negative phrasing of some, indicating what will not be covered.

STEP 2A.   Write an overview sentence that covers the main areas of discussion in your report and one or more scope statements that indicate (1) how technical the discussion of the report subject is going to be and (2) what aspects or subtopics of the discussion are not covered in your report and why.

The major aspects of the mechanically induced hydraulic fracture method of well treatment to be discussed in this report are (1) the basic theory of hydraulic fracturing, (2) the uses of hydraulic fracturing, (3) propping agents, and (4) fracturing fluids.

In this report on a continuously operating system processing municipal solid waste for use as supplemental fuel in existing steam generators, the following sections present

• A statement of the objectives of the study
• A description of the boilers
• A description of the experimental design and sampling methods used
• The results of the study

The results of the environmental investigations have been analyzed statistically; the full text of this statistical study is presented in Appendix B.

FIGURE 4–3.   Overview statements from report introductions

This report will only discuss research that has been done with 5-azacytidine as a gene manipulator; the other aspects or uses of this drug will not be covered here.

The actual costs of the hydraulic fracturing procedure are not presented here in that they are highly dependent on individual formation characteristics.

The analysis will be confined to the light-water-cooled reactor (LWR) fuel cycle incorporating the recycle of both uranium and plutonium. All components of the conventional LWR fuel cycle will be discussed with the exception of waste management, which is omitted because of uncertainties in process definition. Although accidents in the fuel cycle may involve the release of toxic chemicals to the environment, only effects of radiation on human health (somatic effects) will be considered. Similarly, occupational risks and the risks to the public from deliberate acts of sabotage or diversion of nuclear materials are considered outside the scope of the current study.

FIGURE 4—4. Scope statements from report introductions

• *Audience*. In your introduction indicate the intended or appropriate audience for the report. Readers need to know whether the report is too advanced or too elementary for them. The audience is often implied rather than directly stated. Notice in the four examples in Figure 4–5 how special knowledge expected of the reader is identified.

STEP 3A. On your worksheet describe the audience of your report, and include any details about the knowledge and capabilities your audience must have to read your report. (For more on audiences, see Chapter 5.)

• *Background elements*. Background elements such as the following help ease readers into the main parts of the report:

definitions   theory
historical background   importance of the subject

Background elements either help enable readers to understand more readily or stimulate their interest, concern, or curiosity. Figure 4–6 has two examples of the use of background elements.

> Although the field of medicine is full of technical terms, a general introductory-level understanding of biological science should enable the reader to comprehend this report.
>
> The purpose of this report is to provide an introduction to the development of today's commodity markets, different types of people trading in those markets, and the determination of futures contract prices. In addition, the beginning trader will learn the right approach to begin investing and gain some valuable advice on avoiding the kind of mistakes beginners so often make.
>
> Because this manual is to be used in the teaching of the first four courses in the nuclear medicine technology program, college-level courses in anatomy and physiology, chemistry, physics, and basic mathematics are all prerequisites. The fundamentals of these sciences are not included here except for the mathematics review in the appendix.
>
> This [report] is aimed at the informed scientific reader. A working knowledge of physics and chemistry and a familiarity with scientific units are assumed. Also assumed is a basic vocabulary of geology, although the use of specialized terms is avoided where possible. Those that might be unfamiliar to most scientists are explained.

FIGURE 4–5.   Indications of the audience level in report introductions

Remember, however, that if any of the background elements takes up too much space, either condense it or move it into the body of the report and make it a separate section. (An introduction for a 20-page report, for example, normally has an introduction of no more than 3 pages.)

STEP 4A.   On your worksheet, explain which of the background elements above you think might be right for your introduction, and briefly describe the content for each.

• *Report situation.* For every technical report there exists a real life business or professional situation in which it is written—the why, when, what, and for whom of a report. Report situations have to do with questions such as these:

On what date was the contract to do the project or write the report agreed upon? When did the work begin? When did it end?

Report on

MECHANICALLY INDUCED HYDRAULIC FRACTURE SYSTEMS

I. INTRODUCTION

Hydraulic fracturing has become the most widely used and most successful well stimulation process yet devised. The procedure was first devised in the Hugoton gas field in 1947. In 1968 a study was done to determine the results of hydraulic fracturing. A review of 1250 fractured wells producing from 240 different formations and spread over 10 different states shows that only 126, or only 10 percent, of those wells failed to show an increase in production....

_____

Report on

THE EFFECTS OF INCREASED ATMOSPHERIC CARBON DIOXIDE

I. INTRODUCTION

By the year 2020 the climate of earth may be much warmer than any time in the past thousand years. This change, which is incredibly fast by geological time scales, will be brought about by increased levels of carbon dioxide and water vapor in the atmosphere which trap solar radiation in the earth's atmosphere--a process known as the greenhouse effect.

The most ominous effects of this change will be the shifting of local weather patterns and resulting problems in agricultural production in a world already unable to feed its citizens adequately. Other scary consequences of the greenhouse effect include severe droughts, record high temperatures, flooding brought about by melting at the polar caps, and increased storm activity. Since the most we can do is to lessen the severity of this situation, it is of utmost importance that human society throughout the world begin to understand the significance of the greenhouse effect and begin to plan for adapting to it well in advance.

The purpose of this report is to examine these climatic changes....

FIGURE 4–6. Background elements in report introductions

For whom was the work performed?

Who performed the work?

What conditions within the organization or community brought about the need for the project?

What was the precise nature of the assignment?

In the excerpt in Figure 4–7 look for references to the report situation.

EVALUATION OF THE AMES SOLID WASTE
RECOVERY SYSTEM: PART TWO

Section 1: Introduction

The Ames Solid Waste Recovery System is a continuously operating system that is processing municipal solid waste (MSW) for use as a supplemental fuel in the existing steam generators of the Ames Municipal Power Plant. This system consists of a nominal 136-Mg/day (1509-ton/day) processing plant, a 454-Mg (500-ton) Atlas storage bin, pneumatic transport systems, and the existing municipal power plant. The processing plant incorporates two stages of shredding, ferrous and nonferrous metal recovery, and an air-density separator. The three steam generators consist of one pulverized coal tangentially fired unit (No. 7), two spreaders, a return traveling grate, and stoker-fired units (Nos. 5 and 6).

The EPA Grant No. R803903–01–0 for the first year of research study of the Ames Solid Waste Recovery System was officially awarded 4 February 1976. A detailed work plan was submitted in March 1976, and included: (a) environmental evaluations of steam generator units Nos. 5, 6, and 7, including the particulate collector; (b) a boiler-performance study; (c) boiler-corrosion studies; (d) an economic evaluation of the solid waste process plant and of the city power plant; and (e) an interim characterization of the RDF.

This report concerns itself with the determination of the following objectives:

- Evaluation of boiler efficiency
- RDF fuel utilization
- Particulate collector efficiency

FIGURE 4–7. Report introduction with situation elements

- Other boiler-performance behavior including excess air flow; characterization of coal, RDF, grate, and collector ash, including major chemical analysis; ash softening temperatures and calculation of slagging and fouling indices
- Corrosion experience.

The actual studies commenced 1 June 1976. Because of boiler unit availability at the power plant, major research emphasis was on the environmental evaluation and boiler performance of the stoker-fired units Nos. 5 and 6 while firing coal and coal-RDF.

U.S. Environmental Protection Agency, Evaluation of the Ames Solid Waste Recovery System Part II: Performance of the Stoker-Fired Steam Generators (Cincinnati: EPA, 1979), 1.

FIGURE 4-7.   (cont.)

STEP 5A.   On your worksheet describe the situation for which you are writing your report. (For ideas on inventing realistic report situations, see Chapter 5.)

- *Problem or question.* Not all technical reports explain a problem or discuss a solution to that problem. The ones that do, however, should contain a clear statement of the problem or question in the introduction. An example is provided in Figure 4–8.

STEP 6A.   If applicable to your report project, write a brief explanation of the problem or question that is the focus of your report.

- *Criteria.* In introductions to recommendations, proposals, or evaluations, explain the standards or requirements you've used to recommend or propose certain courses of action. These standards or reasons are called *criteria:* for example, in a proposal to purchase company airplanes, passenger capacity and cost would be two important criteria (see Chapter 3 for more on criteria). The introduction must list and explain such criteria clearly, as shown in Figure 4–9.

STEP 7A.   If applicable to your report project, list and write a brief explanation of the criteria you are using.

Elements of Section Introductions

A *section introduction* is the paragraph or two that introduce an individual section within a report. Section introductions generally use the same elements that report

Report on

INVESTIGATIONS OF BEACH PROCESSES

According to our best estimates, 64,000 tons of Amoco Cadiz oil came ashore along 72 km of the shoreline of Britanny during the first few weeks of the 16 March 1978 spill. A prevailing westerly wind pushed the oil against the west-facing headlands and into shoreline embayments as it moved east. The wind reversal in early April moved the oil in the opposite direction, contaminating previously untouched areas and transporting the oil as far southwest as Pointe du Raz (southwest of Brest). At the end of April, the total volume of oil onshore was reduced to 10,000 tons, but, by that time, 320 km of shoreline had been contaminated.

The objectives of the work discussed here are to describe the influence of beach processes and sedimentation on the dispersal, grounding, burial, and long-term fate of the Amoco Cadiz oil. These observations should provide valuable insights for coastal-zone managers in the United States concerned with contingency planning for oil spills. This is true especially with regard to understanding the vulnerability of different coastal environments to oil spills, as well as to planning for the availability of equipment and manpower needed for shore protection and clean-up in the event of a major spill.

Hess, The Amoco Cadiz Oil Spill, 10.

Figure 4–8. **A problem statement in a report**

introductions do but differ in that (1) they are ordinarily much shorter than report introductions; (2) they need not repeat information that is the same in the report introduction; and (3) they contain transitions that guide readers and link sections of reports to each other.

Similar Elements. Although section introductions are much shorter and have elements similar to those in report introductions, you should write them as carefully as you do those for whole reports.

In addition to its investigation of the feasibility of converting the U.S. Forest Service's facilities to wood-fired systems, the committee determined these three standards to be essential:

- Whatever system is used, there should be minimal combustion exhaust pollutants. While some equipment may be exempt from air-quality standards by its size, all equipment or systems must meet current threshold air-quality standards applicable to the equipment and fuel in the state where the project is located.
- There should be optimum use of the energy available in the wood fuel. This criterion necessitates an investigation of efficient heat exchangers, thermal storage to the level of demand-supply-combustion efficiency variations, and unique approaches in designing solid fuel systems with interruptible use.
- Any system that is used must have a low life-cycle cost. Investigators were asked to balance investment in equipment, operating costs, and maintenance costs.

FIGURE 4–9. Criteria statements from a report introduction

- In a section introduction indicate the *topic* of the section just as you do for the main subject matter of a whole report in the report introduction. For example, the topic of the report might be increased atmospheric carbon dioxide; the topic for a section within that report might be sources of the increased carbon dioxide.

- If the *scope* of an individual section varies from that of other sections, explain this as well. You may need to explain what you are excluding from a section and why, just as you would in report introductions.

- Use the same kind of listing statement, or *overview,* in section introductions to indicate the contents of each section. You can use the same listing techniques as you do in report introductions.

- If the *audience* varies and, for example, a section is much more technical than the preceding one, explain this in the section introduction. In reports designed for combined audiences with varied backgrounds or interests, different sections can be intended for distinctly different readers. One section can be for the design expert; another, for the operator or technician; and another, for financial and marketing people.

- Include brief *definitions,* historical *background,* or *theory* in section introductions as necessary.

II. PHYSICAL PROPERTIES OF SOUND

Before you can adequately comprehend even the most elementary rules that govern the acoustics within a building, you must first know something about the properties of sound. The word <u>sound</u> has two definitions: (1) physically speaking, it is a fluctuation in pressure, a particle displacement in a medium, called <u>objective</u> sound; (2) physiologically, sound is an auditory sensation evoked by the physical fluctuation just described, called <u>subjective</u> sound. This section concerns itself only with aspects of objective sound: its origin and propagation; its frequency, wavelength, and velocity; sound pressure, intensity, and loudness associated with it; and the directionality of this form of sound.

Origin and Propagation of Sound

Sound has its origins in ...

II. APPLICATIONS OF A WAG-CO_2 PROCESS TO THE CAPROCK FIELD

A WAG-CO_2 miscible flood is one method that can be used to recover the remaining oil beneath Caprock Field. In the Water-Alternating Gas CO_2 miscible process, alternate volumes of water and carbon dioxide are injected into a reservoir. For a WAG-CO_2 miscible to be feasible, the Caprock's producing horizon, the Tubb formation, must be compatible. The oil in the Tubb formation must have the correct properties for CO_2 flooding. Also, existing surface facilities must be reviewed.

Reservoir Characteristics

An analysis performed on the reservoir properties of the Tubb formation produced the following data ...

FIGURE 4–10.   Section introductions

Two section introductions in which some of the preceding elements occur appear in Figure 4–10.

Special Elements.   Introductions to each of the different kinds of writing generally have one or two special elements. When you write section introductions to the kinds of writing in the following list, you may need to include the elements listed to the right:

Type of Section	Element in the Section Introduction
Description	A general description of what the object or mechanism looks like A list of the parts or components
Process discussion	Why and how the process is performed Some theory or basic principles of operation related to it A list of the steps
Extended definition	A formal sentence definition
Comparison	A list of the points of comparison A list of the things being compared
Causal discussion	An explanation of the situation or problem whose causes and effects are explored A list of the causes and effects
Classification	An explanation of the principle of classification A list of the types

Transitional Elements.   One of the most important elements in section introductions is the transition. Transitional elements, as explained in Chapter 7, are writing techniques used to guide the reader from idea to idea, from sentence to sentence, from paragraph to paragraph, and from section to section. As readers begin each new report section, they need to know how one section links with the preceding one and why they should want to read the section.

Transitions that help readers bridge the gap from one section of a report to another usually contain three components, not necessarily in this order: (1) a reference to the topic in the preceding section, the *review* component; (2) a transitional word or phrase; and (3) a reference to the topic in the next section, the *preview*. Notice in these section introductions, the topic of the preceding section is echoed and builds a verbal bridge between the topics of the two sections.

STEP 8A.   On your worksheet write an overview sentence that lists the subtopics to be covered in the section for each of your section introductions. Also, write a trial transition sentence for each of those section introductions, and circle the review and preview elements.

Conclusions

The term *conclusion* refers loosely to the final section of a report. Actually, however, at least four kinds of final sections exist, of which conclusions are only one type. Each has a different function and can be combined with the others.

Summaries

Summaries do not introduce new and important information but review what has already been presented. By emphasizing the right aspects of the report, good sum-

3. MEASUREMENT OF ULTRASOUND FIELDS

As is evident in the preceding discussion of   review
the characteristics and interactions of ultrasound
fields, the acoustic pressure within an ultrasound
field may vary considerably spatially and temporally. The spatial distribution of the field can be
quite complicated depending on such factors
as focusing, transducer radius, ultrasound wavelength, distance from the source, and even on
how the transducer's element is mounted or
clamped. It may also be expected that any
biological effect and potential risk produced by
ultrasound will depend quantitatively on the
temporal and spatial characteristics of the
ultrasonic field. It is therefore necessary to   transition
consider the methods available for making the   preview
physical measurements that will allow determination of the interrelation between equipment
output levels used in human exposure and
the results of biological experimentation.

In practice, these measurements are divided
mainly into two parts: measurements on   more preview
liquidborne and airborne ultrasound; however,
this report will only address liquidborne
ultrasound which is used in all current medical
applications.

Liquidborne ultrasound fields can be
measured ...

Harold F. Stewart et al., An Overview of Ultrasound: Theory, Measurement, Medical Applications, and Biological Effects (Washington, D.C.:
U.S. Department of Health and Human Services, 1982), 31.

Fracture Detection Using Wire-Line Logging Devices

A much faster and less expensive method of   review
detecting fractures in exploratory wells than
coring and core-analysis techniques is wire-line   preview
log analysis. Logging can be defined as the
storing of information that has been learned

FIGURE 4–11. Section introductions

about a well. Anything that may be of importance in producing an accurate subsurface geological map is logged. Logs are kept of cores, drilling muds (the fluids used to reduce friction during drilling), drilling rates, and other important factors. This information is gained by lowering a probe (sonde) into a well at the end of multiconductor cable (the wire line). The probe then records physical properties as a function of depth, and the record is reproduced as a well log on some type of graph paper.

Several wire-line well logs exist that can be used to determine, or at least partially determine,   more preview whether a formation is fractured. The logs to be discussed here include (1) the sonic amplitude log, (2) the dual induction—laterolog 8, (3) the neutron log, and (4) the fracture identification log (FIL).

The Sonic Amplitude Log.   The sonic amplitude log ...

II. TWO METHODS OF DETECTING FRACTURES

With an understanding of the forces under-   review ground that cause or can cause fractures, such as folding or faulting of the earth's surface, deep erosion of the overburden, or volume shrinkage, and an understanding of the migration and accumulation of oil within these fractures, oil explorers and drillers can use a variety of   preview techniques to produce the oil found there. Fractures can be detected by direct or indirect examination. The direct method, coring, is an important tool for examining fractures directly, whereas the indirect method, wire-line log analysis, is faster and less expensive.

Detecting Fractures Using Core Analysis

In an exploratory well 50-foot-long cores are taken relatively frequently because ...

FIGURE 4-11.   (cont.)

maries make sure readers don't feel confused after reading the report. This final-section kind of summary is quite different from the abstract summary, which is discussed later in this chapter. An example of a final-section summary appears in Figure 4–12.

STEP 1B.   For the final section of your report, list on your worksheet the major points or areas of discussion.

Conclusions

Conclusions bring together, restate, and emphasize the logical implications of the report. In most reports, individual conclusions are usually mixed in with facts and concepts presented as proof or support. In the main body of the report they are often unstated and are buried in the surrounding discussion. In the final section, conclusions can be presented (1) in paragraph form or (2) in separate, numbered sentences, as shown in Figure 4–13.

VIII. SUMMARY

This report has shown that as the supply of fresh water decreases, desalting water will become a necessity. Although a number of different methods are in competition with each other, freezing methods of desalination appear to have the greatest potential for the future.

The three main freezing techniques are the direct method, the indirect method, and the hydrate method. Each has some advantage over the others, but all three freezing methods have distinct advantages over other methods of desalination. Because freezing methods operate at such low temperatures, scaling and corrosion of the pipe and other equipment are greatly reduced. In nonfreezing methods, corrosion is a great problem that is difficult and expensive to prevent. Freezing processes also allow the use of plastic and other protective coatings on steel equipment to prevent their corrosion, a measure that cannot be taken in the other methods that operate at high temperatures.

Desalination, as it has been shown, requires much energy, regardless of the method. Therefore, pairing desalination plants with nuclear or solar power resources may be a necessity. Some of the expense of desalination can be offset, however, by recovering and selling the magnesium, calcium, and other precipitates from the process.

FIGURE 4–12.   Example of a report summary section

V. SUMMARY

Solar heating can be an aid in fighting high fuel bills if planned carefully, as has been shown in preceding sections. Every home represents a different set of conditions; the best system for one home may not be the best one for next door. A salesman can make any system appear to be profitable on paper, and therefore prospective buyers must have some general knowledge about solar products.

A solar heating system should have as many of the best design features as possible and still be affordable. As explained in this report, the collector should have high transmissivity and yet be durable enough to handle hail storms. Collector insulation should be at least one inch of fiberglass mat. Liquid circulating coils should be at least one inch in diameter if an open loop system is used. The control module should perform all the required functions with no added circuits. Any hot-water circulating pumps should be isolated from the electric drive motor by a nontransmitting coupler of some kind.

Homeowners should follow the recommendations in the guidelines section carefully. In particular, they should decide how much money they are willing to spend and then arrange their components in their order of importance. The control module designs vary the most in quality and therefore should have first priority. The collector is the second in importance, and care should be taken to ensure compatibility. Careful attention to the details of the design and selection of solar heating devices discussed in this report will enable homeowners to install efficient, productive solar heating systems.

VII. CONCLUSIONS

1. Both the ASEA IRb-60 and the Unimate 2000 robots are adequate for this company's welding. (See p. 10.)
2. The ASEA is more accurate than the Unimate by ± 0.6 mm.
3. The ASEA has a greater repeatability than the Unimate (± 0.2 mm compared to the latter's ± 1.27 mm). (p. 12)
4. The ASEA has greater reach both horizontally and vertically than does the Unimate (262 mm and 27 mm greater, respectively).
5. The Unimate has a load capacity of 76 kg more than does the ASEA.

(continued)

FIGURE 4–13.   Examples of report conclusion sections

6. The Unimate has a greater memory size than the ASEA and can store 1548 more steps. (p. 15)
7. The Unimate costs $30,000 to $44,000 less than the ASEA.
8. The ASEA requires less space within which to operate (80 cm × 80 cm compared to 3 m × 3 m). (p. 17)
9. The added cost of the ASEA is justified by its greater ability in precision welding.
10. The ASEA is a better investment for the precision welding needs of this company and is the better choice. (p. 19)

FIGURE 4-13. (cont.)

STEP 2B. If your report reaches conclusions, list them on your worksheet, along with summaries of the facts that support them.

Recommendations

Recommendations actually advise readers to take certain courses of action: for example, to build the city bike lanes, to purchase UVC's Execucomp office computer for corporation offices, or to relocate the firm. A recommendation is quite different from a conclusion: it's one thing to *conclude* that personal computer A is more useful to your business than personal computer B, but quite another to *recommend* the purchase of personal computer A. Recommendations are based on conclusions concerning cost, maintenance, and availability of software and consultants. An example of the use of recommendations is provided in Figure 4–14.

STEP 3B. If your report makes recommendations, list the recommendations along with the steps needed to implement them.

Afterwords

The *afterword,* as the term is used here, neither summarizes nor concludes but provides a few final general thoughts. An afterword actually takes up a new aspect of the subject, but in a way that requires no more than a page or two. Afterwords are often combined with the other kinds of conclusions. Final sections containing all three elements—summary, conclusion, and afterword—are common.

Here is a list of suggestions for the content of afterword-type final sections:

• Some afterwords look to the future in general terms and speculate on future developments.

VIII. RECOMMENDATIONS

I recommend that XYZ company do the following:

- Contact representatives of the ABC Robotics Corp. to begin discussions of the purchase of 10 ASEA IRb-60 robots for precision welding uses.
- Appoint a supervisor to facilitate the changeover to robots.
- Hire a technical writer/editor to prepare a report reviewing the details of robotic operation, costs, and advantages for upper management.
- Begin planning appropriate changes in floorspace to accommodate the robots.
- Design and institute a training program for employees who will be operating the robots.
- Instruct the Personnel Office to assist in the equitable relocation of those employees whose jobs are eliminated by the new robots.

If you find these recommendations sound and are ready to begin this project, please inform me. My office will begin the search for a supervisor and will contact ABC Robotics Corp. representatives as soon as you give the word.

FIGURE 4–14. Report recommendation section

- If the main part of the report was concerned with a problem, the afterword can explore solutions, which of course are not discussed with any great detail.
- After the description of a mechanism, the final section can take readers through one cycle in the operation of that mechanism.
- In instructions it may be a good idea to conclude with some cautionary or guideline statements.
- Afterwords also discuss the economics, social implications, problems, legal aspects, advantages, disadvantages, benefits, or applications of the report subject—although only generally and briefly.

Figure 4–15 contains an example of an afterword that looks to the future. Compare this approach with the focus on suggested solutions in the example in Figure 4–16. As shown in Figure 4–17, another approach involves the incorporation of guidelines and cautionary statements. A final example of an afterword on applications appears in Figure 4–18.

VII. CONCLUSION: FUTURE TRENDS

Everyone seems to agree that the car of the future must weigh even less than today's down-sized models. According to a recent forecast by the Arthur Anderson Company, the typical car will have lost about 1000 pounds between 1978 and 1990. The National Highway Traffic Safety Administration estimates the loss of another 350 pounds by 1995. To obtain these reductions, automobile manufacturers will have to find or develop composites such as fiber-reinforced plastics for the major load-bearing components, particularly the frame and drive-train components.

Ford Motor Company believes that if it is to achieve further growth in the late 1980s, it must achieve breakthroughs in structural and semistructural load-bearing applications. Some of the breakthroughs Ford sees as needed include improvements in the use of continuous fibers, especially hybridized reinforced materials containing glass and graphite fibers. In addition, Ford hopes to develop a high-speed production system for continuous fiber preforms.

In the related area of composite technology, researchers at Owens Corning and Hercules are seeking the best combination of hybrid fibers for structural automotive components such as engine and transmission supports, drive shafts, and leaf springs. Tests thus far have led the vice-president of Owen Corning's Composites and Equipment Marketing Division, John B. Jenks, to predict that hybrid composites can compete with metal by the mid-1980s for both automotive leaf springs and transmission supports.

With development in these areas of plastics and automobiles, we can look forward to lighter, less expensive, and more economical cars in the next decade. Such developments might well provide the needed spark to rejuvenate America's auto industry and to further decrease our rate of petroleum consumption.

FIGURE 4–15. Afterword focusing on the future

STEP 4B. On your worksheet, explain which of the ideas for afterwords just discussed might be effective in the final section of your report, and then briefly describe the content you'd use in them.

VIII. <u>CONCLUSIONS: COUNTERING THE GREENHOUSE EFFECT</u>

The severity of the consequences of a major climatic change described in this report requires that we take action to lessen our input of carbon dioxide into the atmosphere. The greenhouse threat is a global problem calling for global action. Unfortunately, however, the political structure of the world tends to impede this kind of large-scale cooperation that is needed. The United States, as the world's leading consumer of energy, should in the current absence of world cooperation take steps to influence world opinion. It can stimulate global action and concern by taking decisive measures such as the following:

1. A concerted effort must be made to conserve fuel with a goal of reducing global consumption 20 percent worldwide by the year 2000. The public must be made aware of the effects of CO_2 on our climate. A tax on fossil-fuel use might provide the extra incentive to conserve. The revenue from such a tax could be used to finance further development of alternative energy resources.

2. The use of a combination of fossil fuels that will minimize the input of CO_2 into the atmosphere must be emphasized. Natural gas is the cleanest of the fossil fuels, and large reserves of it have been found. Coal, which will be used in increasing amounts in the near future, should be deemphasized because it releases 75 percent more CO_2 into the atmosphere per unit of energy than does natural gas.

3. Alternate sources of energy such as solar and nuclear should be developed rapidly. The public should weigh its emotional opposition to nuclear power against the consequences of relying even more heavily on fossil fuels such as coal. If nuclear power proves to be unacceptable to the public, a massive push for development in such alternate energy sources as solar, wind, wave, and geothermal must be started.

4. Reforestation on a massive global scale is needed in order to provide a large biotic sink in the next decades. The total respiration of CO_2 and the total photosynthesis of CO_2 must be

(continued)

FIGURE 4—16.   Afterword with suggested solutions

> brought into equilibrium as nearly as possible. Fast-growing
> trees, such as the American sycamore, can absorb as much as
> 750 tons of carbon per square kilometer per year; water
> hyacinths, 6000 tons.
>
> 5. Research into the carbon cycle is needed to reduce the
> uncertainties surrounding predictions of climatic changes.
> Although the amount of carbon dioxide that is released and the
> amount that remains airborne are well known, the methods
> by which CO_2 is assimilated into sinks such as the ocean and
> biosphere are only poorly understood.
>
> Even with these measures, some of the effects of increased carbon
> dioxide in the atmosphere will still be felt in the next several decades.

FIGURE 4-16.   (cont.)

Summaries (Abstracts)

In most reports, particularly long ones, you must summarize the contents and emphasize the most important findings, concepts, or facts of the report. Readers use these summaries, often called abstracts, in two ways:

- To help them to decide whether to read an entire report at all
- To make decisions on courses of action

Often, they may make their decisions solely on the basis of informative summaries, without reading much or any of the body of the report.

Two Types of Summaries

Most reports make use of one or both of the two types of summaries: the descriptive summary and the informative summary.

Descriptive Summaries.   The descriptive summary has the following characteristics:

- It tells the reader what the report is about but does not give any of the actual details of the report.
- It is short, usually not more than two or three sentences.

VIII. <u>ADVICE FOR BEGINNING TRADERS</u>

Beginning traders in commodities can expect to make many mistakes. However, by following the advice given by experts, they can minimize their mistakes and begin profiting from their speculations earlier.

1. The most important advice to follow is that of investing no more than a modest portion of one's net worth. A beginner can expect to make mistakes: the smaller the early investments, the less costly the mistakes.
2. Once the trader has chosen his commodity and determined the amount of capital he can invest, he should be careful not to invest all of that capital in one trade. Profits made in a small trade may not be as large, but neither will the losses. A common rule is to invest no more than a tenth of one's available capital in a single trade. If only one out of every four trades is profitable, the trader will likely show a profit.
3. Another important guideline is that the trader should never add capital to a losing trade, nor should he lower the price at which he has chosen to sell his position at a small loss.
4. Finally, commodities traders must be disciplined, patient, and consistent. Commodity trading can be profitable only for those who manage not to let their emotions rule their minds.

FIGURE 4–17. Afterword with guidelines and cautionary statements

- One or more of its sentences briefly list the contents of the report. In fact, a descriptive summary is much like a short-paragraph version of the table of contents.
- It is usually located on the title page or in some other separate, easily noticeable page early in the report.

Figure 4–19 contains several examples of descriptive summaries.

STEP 1C.   On your worksheet write one or two sentences on the contents of each of the main sections of your report as well as on any other aspect of your report that readers should know about; then rewrite and condense these sentences into a descriptive summary.

VII. APPLICATIONS OF LASER TECHNOLOGY

Considering the process by which laser and maser beams are produced and the enormous power that characterizes it, the applications it has in a variety of fields should be evident.

Among the most noticeable applications are those that utilize the high-speed controllability of the tiny focal spot of a laser beam. For example, high-speed automatic scanners identify library cards, parking-lot passes, and supermarket purchases and perform a variety of functions known as optical processing.

Other uses for the laser's programmable control include information storage and retrieval (including three-dimensional holography and videodisk reading), laser printing, micromachining, and automated cutting. Further applications involving its high power include weaponry, laser welding, laser surgery (self-cauterizing), laser fusion, and materials processing. Optical communications utilize the laser's high frequency, which makes possible high information capacity. Some of the more specialized applications include laser gyros, laser velocity sensing, optical testing, meteorology, and laser spectroscopy (including pollution monitoring).

FIGURE 4–18. Afterword on applications

Informative Summaries.   The informative summary has the following characteristics:

- It gives readers the details of the most important facts, findings, ideas, or concepts contained in the report.
- It is usually about 10 to 20 percent of the length of the whole report, but never more than two double-spaced typed pages.
- It proportionately reflects all the major sections of the report; in other words, if one section takes up one-fifth of the report, one-fifth of the summary should contain summarized information from that section.

Look at the example of the paralleling of a table of contents with its companion summary provided in Figure 4–20.

When using informative summaries, keep the following points in mind:

- Informative summaries can either be a single paragraph or have paragraph breaks in the same location where they occur in the body of the report. (Style varies here.)

This report presents the theory of underground stress fields and its relation to hydraulic fracture orientation. The various uses of hydraulic fracturing are discussed along with a review of the types of proppants and fluids used in fracturing and guidelines for their selection.

This report surveys the major applications of microwave energy, reviews some of the features of microwave processing, describes the types of industrial microwave equipment, and discusses the uses to which microwave energy is being applied. Considerable emphasis is placed upon the safety features built into the equipment, and recommendations are made for ensuring that radiation leakage levels do not exceed the design limits.

This report is a study of two common land disposal methods for hazardous wastes: landfills and deep-well injection. Background information on hazardous wastes, including a definition of hazardous wastes, sources and locations of their generation, their threat potential, and their regulation, is also presented. These background sections are followed by detailed descriptions of the two methods and their safety features.

FIGURE 4–19. Descriptive summaries

- The informative summary is ordinarily located on a separate page of its own just before the first page of the introduction to the report itself.
- Despite the importance of brevity, no articles (*the, a,* or *an*) that would normally be used should be omitted. Although the sentences may be a bit longer and more densely packed with information, sentences should read as good, clear, understandable English.
- No footnotes are necessary, because the same information is documented in the body of the report where it occurs.
- General, common-knowledge, introductory information in the report should be left out of the informative summary. (Examples of this kind of information are shown in the excerpts in the following section, "Condensing the Important Information.")
- Important statistical information must be included. The informative summary should not be vague or overly general about the report; the crucial facts and figures must be incorporated. Figure 4–21 has two versions of the same summary excerpt, the first of which does not have the most important statistical information in it.

TABLE OF CONTENTS

LIST OF FIGURES..iv

ABSTRACT v

I.   INTRODUCTION...1

II.   HUMAN VOICE PRODUCTION..................................2
      Generating Sound 2
          Voiced Sounds...3
          Unvoiced Sounds 4
      Factors Affecting the Human Voice 4

III. THE ISOLATED-WORD-RECOGNITION SYSTEM 7
      The Preprocessor..8
          The Spectrum Shaper 8
          The Speech Analyzer...................................8
      The Feature Extractor......................................9
      The Classification Phase 10
          The Time Normalizer 10
          The Training Mode and Reference Pattern Memory 10
          The Classifier...11
      Decision Algorithms 11
          Dynamic Programming 11
          Zero Crossing Rate....................................13
          Linear Predictive Coding...............................14
          State Diagrams..15

IV.   APPLICATIONS OF VOICE-RECOGNITION SYSTEMS 17

V.   PROBLEMS WITH SPEECH RECOGNITION 20
      Recognition Accuracy......................................20
          Background Noise......................................20
          Conversing with Others................................20
      Limited Vocabulary Size...................................21
      Privacy...21

VI.   GOALS IN THE SPEECH-RECOGNITION INDUSTRY............22
      Continuous Speech 22
      Speaker Independence 23

FIGURE 4—20.   **A report outline and informative summary (abstract)**

ABSTRACT

Computerized speech recognition takes advantage of the most natural form of communication, the human voice. During speech, sound is generated by the vocal cords and by air rushing from the lungs. If the vocal cords vibrate, a voiced sound is produced; otherwise, the sound is unvoiced. The main problem in speech recognition is that no two voices produce their sounds alike and that an individual voice varies in different conditions. Because voices do vary and because words blend together in a continuous stream in natural speech, most recognition systems require that each speaker train the machine to his or her voice and that words have at least one-tenth of a second pause between them. Such a system is called an isolated-word-recognition system and consists of three major components that process human speech: (1) the preprocessor, which removes irregularities from the speech signal and then breaks it up into parts; (2) the feature extractor, which extracts 32 key features from the signal; and (3) the classification phase, which identifies the spoken word and includes the training mode and reference pattern memory. Spoken words are identified on the basis of a certain decision algorithm, some of which involve dynamic programming, zero crossing rate, linear predictive coding, and the use of state diagrams.

Voice-recognition systems offer many applications including data entry, freedom for mobility, security uses, telephone access, and helpful devices for the handicapped. However, these same systems also face problems such as poor recognition accuracy, loss of privacy among those who use them, and limited vocabulary sizes. The goal of the industry is the development of speaker-independent systems that can recognize continuous human speech regardless of the speaker and that can continually improve their vocabulary size and recognition accuracy.

FIGURE 4-20. (cont.)

• Generally you should avoid the kind of phrasing used in descriptive summaries; it is inadequate for informative summaries and cannot substitute for the important information itself. In the example in Figure 4–22 inappropriate descriptive summary phrasing is revised.

Problem Informative Summary

Costs for the implementation of the WAG-CO_2 flood in the Caprock Field, including those for the carbon dioxide, the CO_2 pipeline, the implementation of the water facilities, the injector conversion for CO_2, and the separation of the CO_2 from the produced fluid, are all explained in the report. Generally, the costs are in keeping with those for other projects like this one. At current per-barrel oil prices, a WAG-CO_2 flood could produce large profits with conservatively estimated amounts of oil recovered and much larger profits with highly successful recovery.

Revision

Implementation costs for the WAG-CO_2 flood in the Caprock Field are as follows:

1. Carbon dioxide to supply the entire flood of the field: $1,060,000.
2. CO_2 pipeline costs: $2,475,000.
3. Minimal costs to set up water facilities.
4. Injector conversion for CO_2: $1,647,000.
5. Separation of CO_2 from the fluid produced from the field: $326,000.

The total cost of this CO_2 flood amounts to $5,508,000, which is in keeping with current costs for such operations. At $25 per barrel of recovered oil and with a 50 percent recovery, the operation would produce $14,804,000 (before taxes) in profit for the operator; a 90 percent recovery, $31,054,000.

FIGURE 4–21. An informative summary revised for statistical detail

• Many summaries are accompanied by so-called keywords to help bibliographers, librarians, and indexers to catalog reports appropriately so that users can find them. If, for example, you had written a report on the design of a new solar collector, keywords might be *solar collector*, *solar components*, or *solar energy*, depending on what the commonly used keyword is. Your report would be catalogued, indexed, or listed in a computerized database under that keyword along with other reports on the same subject. The example in Figure 4–23 is from a dissertation on the dance language that bees use.

Check your keywords against those in standard professional indexes in your field: for example, *Engineering Abstracts*, *Biological Abstracts*, *Psychological Abstracts*, *Biological and Agricultural Index*, *Business Periodicals Index*, or *Applied Science and Technology Index*. (See Chapter 9 for information on finding specialized indexes.) Check also the indexes of *Government Reports and Announcements* and the *Library of Congress Subject Headings* to make sure that your keywords are standard.

Problem Informative Summary

This report reviews the basic considerations involved in the design of earth-sheltered buildings. Site-design considerations include the various orientations of the building. Soil and groundwater must also be analyzed carefully before attempting to build a terractecural structure. Covered also are the advantages of using earth cover in buildings. Specifications for effective use of insulation are explained as well. Passive solar designs can be efficiently employed in terratecture because of the reduced heating load and smaller volume of the thermal storage. Also discussed in this report are the kinds of waterproofing materials necessary for terractectural buildings. In the structural design of underground buildings the designer must consider advantages and disadvantages of the various materials and the loads acting on the structure. . . .

Revision

Considerations involved in design of earth-sheltered buildings are site, energy, waterproofing, structure, economics, and psychological effects. The site design includes the orientation of the building for the sun, wind, and views. Soil and groundwater conditions should be analyzed carefully before attempting to build on the site. Using the advantage of earth cover in buildings results in energy savings because of less infiltration and lower heat transmission. Insulation can be effectively used if it is placed on the exterior of the building. It should have resistance to earth pressure, chemicals, and moisture penetration. Passive solar designs can be efficiently employed in terratecture because of the reduced heating load and smaller volume of the thermal storage tank. Waterproofing materials include asphalt, polyurethane, butyl, ethylene prophylene diene monomer, and bentonite. They should have good crack-bridging ability and be resealable underground. In structural design of underground buildings, the designer must consider the advantages and disadvantages of the various materials such as concrete and steel and the loads acting on the structure such as include earth pressure, wind, dead load, and live load. . . .

FIGURE 4–22.   An informative summary revised to exclude descriptive-summary phrasing

COMPARATIVE STUDIES OF THE DANCE LANGUAGE AND
ORIENTATION OF FOUR SPECIES OF HONEY BEES

Order No. DA8504412

Dyer, Fred Colin, Ph.D. Princeton University, 1984. 259pp.

The sun is the primary reference by which forager honey bees
(genus *Apis*) navigate in the field and by which they indicate to hive
mates--in the dance language--the direction of the food, and yet bees
can fly and dance on completely overcast days. Von Frisch and
colleagues had suggested that bees see the sun through the clouds in
the ultraviolet, but experiments reported in this thesis suggest
otherwise. Instead, bees learn the sun's course with respect to local
landmarks and then rely upon this memory, compensated for solar
movement, to dance when the sky is cloudy. Working in the U.S. with
A. mellifera and in India with *A. cerana,* I trained bees to seek food
along prominent landmarks and observed dances after displacing the
hive to a site having similar landmarks oriented in a different
direction. On cloudy days bees always searched in the new direction,
but oriented their dances according to a memory of the sun's position
relative to the original landmarks. On sunny days the bees were not
tricked in this way; the difference between sunny and cloudy days
suggests that bees cannot see the sun in an overcast sky. Similar
experiments have yielded additional insights into the solar compass
of bees.

It was impossible to test whether *A. dorsata* or *A. florea* locate the
sun in the same way while flying on a cloudy day, but the former may
do so when flying on moonlit nights: I observed nocturnal dances that
referred not to the moon, but instead probably to the extrapolated
position of the sun, which the bees must have determined by reference
to landmarks in a different context. The other species normally dance
on a vertical with gravity as a reference for the sun, but *A. florea*
dances on a horizontal surface and orients to the sky directly. I found
that they can also orient according to a memory of their previous
dance orientation relative to nearby landmarks.

FIGURE 4—23. An informative summary with keywords

In other experiments with *A. florea* my data showed, in contrast to previous studies, that dancers may process gravity information in order to orient to celestial clues when on different slopes. This and the other new insights provided by this thesis help to refine our assumptions concerning the evolution of the dance language.

Keywords: Language, bees, biology

Dissertation Abstracts International, Vol. 45, No. 12 (June 1985), 3920–B. Published with permission of University Microfilms International.

FIGURE 4–23.   (cont.)

• Different fields of knowledge and different professions have their own special requirements for summaries: for example, some require separate paragraphs with headings; others require keywords. Consult summaries written for reports in your field or a style manual or guide to the literature of that field. (See Chapter 9.)

Despite the variations in summarizing, the main point in informative summaries remains the same: to condense and summarize the most important facts and concepts into the briefest piece of prose reasonably possible.

Selecting Important Information

There are several methods you can use to glean the most important facts, findings, concepts, or ideas from a report for your informative summary.

• Using the outline or table of contents to remind you of the report's main ideas and content, write an informative summary of your report. Go into the main body of the report only for the most important points or facts that you cannot remember.

STEP 2C.   With an outline of your report in front of you, write a rough-draft summary of the most important details of each of the main-body sections, without referring to the rough draft. (Leave blank spaces for details you cannot remember.)

• Use different colored markers to highlight the most important sentences in a photocopy of your report. Then, copy these sentences onto a separate sheet of paper, combining them as you can and filling in the gaps with transitions. Remember, however, not to highlight too much information. Figure 4–24 contains an example of a section of a report highlighted for summarizing purposes.

II. <u>THE SILICON SOLAR CELL</u>

This section describes the silicon solar cell, examines how it works, and discusses its present applications.

<u>Description of the Typical Silicon Solar Cell</u>

The solar cell is the basic building block of all photovoltaic power systems. Even though each cell produces little electricity, approximately 0.5 volts or 0.6 watts of power, hundreds of cells strategically arranged on panels resembling huge windows and exposed to sunlight can generate a sizable amount of energy. The individual cells themselves are slightly larger than a poker chip with an area of a few square centimeters. The main component of each cell is a thin wafer, typically silicon, containing two regions. The cell also includes thin wires, a special coating, and an outer "skin."

The basic part of the photovoltaic cell is a nearly pure crystalline silicon wafer approximately 1 millimeter thick and 25 millimeters long. Silicon is a semiconductor that conducts electricity better than an insulator such as glass but not as well as a conductor such as copper. The addition of impurity atoms (usually phosphorus) makes one section of the wafer contain an abundance of electrons. This ultra-thin top layer is approximately 2.5 millimeters thick. This side of the wafer is called the "n-side." The addition of another type of impurity, often boron, causes the other region to contain an abundance of holes (like electrons but positively charged). This area is referred to as the "p-side." The interface between these two parts is an electrical connection known as the "p-n junction." Thin wires serve as electrical contacts and are attached to the front and back of the cell.

The cell is coated with an anti-reflective material, for example, silicon dioxide, to minimize the amount of light reflected from the surface of the cell (and therefore to maximize the amount of light absorbed). Such a coating reduced the reflection from 32 to 22 percent. The entire cell is encapsulated in a protective "skin."

FIGURE 4–24.   **Highlighting report drafts for summarizing purposes**

IV. THE ECONOMICS OF PHOTOVOLTAIC POWER GENERATION

Cost projections and market forecasts along with consumer demand, benefits, costs, and need as discussed in this section all confirm the potential for investment in photovoltaics.

Cost Projections

Solar cells have low efficiencies, low energy densities (that is, many cells are needed to produce a sufficient amount of power), and high manufacturing costs. The price of solar cells will have to decrease dramatically (by a factor of 20 or 30) in the near future if they are to become competitive with present traditional energy sources. Still, the current cost of a solar array is decreasing by more than 30 percent each year, or about 25 percent as the production volume doubles. For instance, a typical photovoltaic system with moderate storage facilities has dropped in price from $200 per peak watt in the 1960s to $10–20 per peak watt, or $1.50 per kilowatthour (KWH) today and is expected to decrease further to $0.15 per KWH by 1990. Cost is independent of the size of the system.

Prices will decrease over the long run as the following occur: (1) an expanded market continues to allow for more efficient production and (2) research and development produce less expensive photovoltaic devices.

Market Forecasts

The photovoltaic industry, currently a $50 million industry, has been growing about 65 percent per year. Photovoltaics are expected to be a billion-dollar industry by 1990 and to continue growing rapidly into the next century. As the prices of solar cells and modules continue to drop, the number of applications for which solar cells are the best choice for energy generation will greatly increase, and the market will grow exponentially.

Carol Robinson, Residential Rooftop Silicon Solar Cell Power Systems Austin: Univ. of Texas, 1983), 15–18.

FIGURE 4-24.   (cont.)

STEP 3C.   Make a photocopy of a draft of your report, highlight the most important facts, and then write a rough-draft summary using those highlighted sentences.

• Make a list of questions readers might ask about your report before they begin. Such questions usually include the following: What does it cost? How does it work? What does it look like? What advantages, benefits, or improvements does it offer? What is the basic problem here? What is the cause of the problem? How can we solve the problem? Without looking at the body of the report itself, write answers to questions like these based on your memory of the report, and then arrange your answers according to the table of contents. Here is an example of this process:

Outline

   I. SOLAR PANELS
      A. Solar Collector
         1. Types of Absorbers
         2. Collector Efficiency
         3. Angle of Inclination
         4. Size of Collector Array
      B. Thermal Storage Tank
      C. Auxiliary Heater and Heating-Coil Fan
      D. System Operation
      E. Control System
  II. ECONOMICS OF SOLAR ENERGY

Summary Questions

What is the basic function of the solar collector? What are its parts? How does it operate?

What are the different types of absorbers? How do they differ?

How energy efficient are collectors? What factors increase their efficiency?

At what angle should collectors be inclined toward the sun? How do geographical location and seasonal change affect the angle of inclination?

How much area of collector is necessary for heating and cooling the average-size home? What is the ratio of collector area to housing area?

What is the function of the thermal storage tank? How is it constructed? How and where does it fit into the overall system? What is its typical size?

What is the function of the auxiliary heater? Where is it located? What is its typical size?

What are the steps in the operating cycle of a solar system?

What control systems regulate temperature, flow, etc.?

STEP 4C. Make a list of questions that would be most likely asked about your report, and then write answers to those questions, referring to your report whenever necessary.

• Use the kinds of writing that make up your report to plan your summary. If your report contains description and process discussion, summarize the basic parts of the mechanism and the main steps as in the following example:

II. PRESSURIZED-WATER REACTORS
 The Major Components   DESCRIPTION
  The Core   Part 1
   The Fuel   Subpart 1
   The Fuel Rod   Subpart 2
   Fuel Assembly   Subpart 3
  Control Rods   Part 2
  The Reactor Vessel   Part 3
  The Steam Generators   Part 4
   Heat Exchangers   Subpart 1
   Steam Drum   Subpart 2
  The Pressurizer   Part 5
 The Production of Electricity PROCESS DISCUSSION
  Circulating Water to Primary System Step 1
  Producing Steam in Secondary System Step 2
  Separating the Steam   Step 3
  Producing Electricity   Step 4

If your report recommends something, summarize the problem, the alternatives, the conclusions, and, finally, the recommendations. If you report on research, summarize the method of the research, the problem, the hypotheses, the most important findings, the implications of those findings, and so on.

STEP 5C. Make a list of the kinds of writing that you use in the various sections of your report. Write summaries of each of those kinds (summarizing by parts, steps, characteristics, classes, etc.).

Condensing Important Information

After extracting the most important information from the report, you must combine that information into a smoothly reading piece of writing. Combine the ideas or sentences, and insert transitions to do this. An example of this process is provided in Figure 4–25.

 In the final step you do whatever you can, within reason, to condense the draft of your summary down to its leanest, most economical length. In this step you look for (1) redundant phrasing that can be cut without losing any meaning, (2) information that does not seem so important after all, and (3) ways to combine sentences to reduce length. Remember that the result must still read as good English prose,

Extracted Information

causes of subsidence—groundwater withdrawal, exploit. of
    resources, active growth faults, hous. area growth—1300 new
residents/week, led to increased
    water pumping (746 mill. gal/day to 837) growth faults—formed
in response to gravity, sediments
    become overloaded, compaction occurs; resulting unstable
    coastal sediments lead to surface displacement faulting
episodes, measured at 0.09 mm to 3.33 mm vertical
    displacement from one hour to 4 days, total of 1.6 in/yr
    in some areas; mainly induced by human activity, ex.,
    withdr. of groundwater, prod. of oil and gas exploitation of
resources—formation of salt domes (large depsts. of sulfur, good stratigraphic
    trap for hydrocarbs.), mining for sulf., and drilling for oil leads to subsid.;
    Spindletop: 5 ft of sub. attrib to oil drilling, another 10 ft to sulf. mining.

Summary

The causes of subsidence in the Houston area are the withdrawal of groundwater, the exploitation of other underground resources, and active growth faults. The average growth in population of the Houston area in the late 1970s by 1300 new residents per week led to an increase in groundwater pumping from 746 to 837 million gallons per day. The mining of sulfur and the drilling of oil have also contributed to the subsidence: salt domes, which contain large deposits of sulfur and are good stratigraphic traps for hydrocarbons, are dramatic instances of such subsidence. At Spindletop, five feet of subsidence is attributed to oil drilling and another ten feet to sulfur mining.

FIGURE 4–25. Condensing information into an informative summary (abstract)

with no omitted articles and with no overly long and convoluted sentences. Figure 4–26 contains an excerpt from a summary before and after this condensing stage.

STEP 6C.   Using the materials you have written in the preceding steps, write a complete first-draft informative summary of your report. When you've done this, condense your draft summary as much as possible using the three techniques just presented.

In the final step, compare your informative summary to the report itself to make sure no important information has been left out.

Wordy Summary

Everyone knows that utility costs have gone up dramatically in the past fifteen years and are destined to continue going up for the foreseeable future. For this reason, many people have been looking to alternative sources of energy. One such source is the wind-powered electrical system. Producing electricity from a wind-powered electrical system is a pollution-free process that does not require any combustion of fuels such as coal or gasoline. The wind is a clean and free source of energy. Most of the wind systems available on the commercial market today are based on the engineering work of Joseph and Marcellus Jacobs of Jacob Wind Electric Plants. They built a special rotor that is aerodynamically balanced and that has three blades. It is equipped with a governor that feathers the blades in high winds. They also designed a special slow-speed generator. The output of this slow-speed generator varies directly with wind speed.

Revised Summary

Producing electricity from wind-powered electrical systems is a pollution-free process not requiring any combustion of fuels. Most modern wind systems are based on the engineering work of Joseph and Marcellus Jacobs of Jacobs Wind Electric Plants. They built an aerodynamically balanced three-bladed rotor with a governor to feather the blades in high winds and a special slow-speed generator whose output varies directly with wind speed.

FIGURE 4–26.   Reducing the length of a summary by economizing on words

EXERCISES

1. Locate three technical reports or articles, preferably in a field of knowledge you know something about, copy the introductions of these articles, and label the elements of each. Make a list of the elements discussed in this chapter that are left out, and try to decide if these omissions make the introductions less effective.

2. Locate three technical reports or articles in a field of interest, photocopy their final sections, and label which kind of final section each has, or label each part of any final section that uses a combination of the different kinds of conclusions.

3. Locate a technical report or article that lacks a descriptive summary, make a photocopy of it, list the major parts of that article or report on a sheet of paper, and then write a descriptive summary for it.

4. Locate three informative summaries of technical reports or articles, and reconstruct the tables of contents of the original documents.

5. Condense the following wordy informative summary:

   Computers have become part of our everyday lives in just a few short decades. It is common now for middle-income families to have a home computer, and it goes without saying that most businesses, even the smaller ones, rely on computers. Essential to computers is their use of semiconducting devices. Semiconductor theory consists of several important concepts. Each of these concepts builds on another to enable people to make semiconductors and thereby computers to function. Since semiconduction is based on the behavior of atomic particles and atomic structure, they must be studied in this report. From this study, it is shown that subatomic particles exhibit the wavelike characteristics of radiant energy. Also discussed in the report is the fact that each particle has its own unique energy level. It is at this level that it is in a state known as equilibrium. If any energy is added, the particle will leave its equilibrium state. The particle will then move to a different location of higher energy. When it returns to its equilibrium level, energy is released in the form of radiant energy.

6. Locate the guidelines for writing summaries in your specific field or profession by consulting a guide to the literature of your field, a style manual, or a guide for students and scholars in your field. See Chapter 9 for information on finding these reference books.

PART II

Writing Readable Technical Discussions

Chapter **5.** **Translating Technical Discussions**

Chapter **6.** **Constructing Graphic and Textual Aids**

Chapter **7.** **Strategies for Revising Paragraphs and Sentences**

Introduction

You can use the chapters of Part II to "fine-tune" your technical writing, to make your technical discussions more understandable, readable, and usable. More specifically, you can use these chapters in two basic ways:

- *Before* you begin writing, to analyze your audience, plan "translating" strategies, decide on the graphic aids to use, and anticipate paragraph and sentence problems.
- *After* you write a rough draft, to make sure your audience can understand the discussion, look for difficult areas of the discussion that need further "translation," find areas that need graphic aids, and revise paragraphs and sentences.

If, for example, you had written a rough-draft technical description of a mechanism, following the steps in Chapter 2, you can use the skills and strategies presented here in the chapters of Part II.

Part II Skills and Strategies	*Chapter*
• Adjust the reading level of your discussion so that your specific audience can read and understand it.	5
• Find "translating" strategies to help your audience understand the discussion more easily.	5
• Design graphic aids (such as illustrations, graphs, and tables) that will help readers understand your discussion.	6
• Design textual aids (such as headings, tables of contents, lists of figures, and appendices) that will help readers follow your points and locate things on later reference.	6
• Revise paragraphs so that they are more organized and coherent.	7
• Revise sentences so that they are as clear and concise as they can be.	7

The chapters in this part of the book present detailed discussions, plenty of examples, and step-by-step methods for applying these skills.

To get the best use out of the chapters in Part II, you should have a rough draft of a report or practice writing; the steps in these chapters show you how to find ways to improve your writing and then how to make those improvements. For example, in the graphic-aids chapter, you reread your rough draft for areas where numbers—statistical information—are or could be presented. If the statistics are already in the draft, you then see how to re-present them in the form of a table, graph, or chart. If they are not there, you then consider finding statistical information that supports or illustrates your point, create a graphic of it, and insert it at that point in the draft.

Of course, Chapter 5, "Translating Technical Discussions," and Chapter 6, "Constructing Graphic and Textual Aids," can also be used *before* writing the first draft: you can use Chapter 5 to analyze your audience, to plan the kinds of information to include or exclude from your report, as well as to decide on how much detail and how much technicality to include in that information. Similarly, you can save plenty of time if you know *before* you begin your information search which kinds of graphic aids your report will need and what their specific content should be.

CHAPTER 5

Translating Technical Discussions

Chapter Objectives
Analyzing the Report Audience
  Steps for Analyzing Audiences
  Using an Audience Analysis
Translating Technical Discussions
  Definitions of Unfamiliar Terms
  Comparisons to Familiar Things
  Elaborating the Process
  Providing Descriptive Detail
  Providing Examples and
    Applications

Shorter Sentences
The "In-Other-Words" Technique
Posing Rhetorical Questions
Explaining the Importance
  of a Topic
Providing Historical Background
Reviewing Theoretical Background
Providing the Human Perspective
Combining the Translating
  Techniques
Exercises

─────────────── *Chapter Objectives* ───────────────

After you read this chapter, study the examples, and work the steps, you should be able to:

- Describe the specific audience for whom the report is written.
- List the reasons the audience needs or wants the report.
- Identify and list the knowledge, background, or capabilities that the audience must have to understand the report.
- Describe the report-writing situation in which the report is written.
- Use an audience analysis to identify which topics to cover in a report and how to discuss them.
- Identify and use the common translating techniques to make technical discussions understandable.

The ability to explain complex, technical matters with ease, grace, and simplicity so that nonspecialist readers understand almost effortlessly is one of the most important skills you can develop as a technical writer. This ability to translate difficult-to-read technical discussions is important because so much of technical writing is aimed at nonspecialist audiences. These audiences include important people such as supervisors, executives, investors, financial officers, government officials, and, of course, customers.

This chapter shows you a step-by-step method for

- Analyzing report-writing situations and report audiences so that you can write reports that meet the demands of both much more closely
- Inventing a realistic report-writing situation if you are writing a report for a technical-writing course
- Translating technical discussions, that is, specific techniques you can use to make difficult technical discussions easier for nonspecialist readers to understand.

Return to this chapter whenever you need some reminders on how to do a thorough audience analysis and some good ideas for translating technical material for beginners and nonspecialists.

The business of translating begins with a careful analysis of the report-writing situation:

- The audience of the report and its background (its knowledge and capabilities) concerning the report subject
- The needs or uses the audience has for the report
- The event, circumstance, or situation that requires the report to be written.

You use these considerations to decide

- What information to include in the report
- What information to exclude from the report
- How to discuss the information you do include in the report.

Analyzing the Report Audience

To adapt or translate reports for specific situations, you must understand the different types of audiences, the different reasons why audiences read reports, and the situations out of which reports arise. When you analyze the readers of your report, you are essentially asking yourself

- Who are they?
- What is your relationship to them?
- Why do they need the information?
- What are their current capabilities and knowledge?
- What kind of information do they need?
- What is the situation that requires the report?
- How will they acquire the information they need?
- How will they feel about acquiring that information?

Steps for Analyzing Audiences

When you analyze your audience, decide which of the preceding questions will matter in your report.

STEP 1.   On your worksheet write the information about the audience, need, and situation of your report as requested in the following steps.

- *Identify who the audience is.* You can identify your audience in dozens of ways, for example, by their

occupation	position or rank
education	socioeconomic characteristics
political views	religion
ethnic characteristics	age
area of residence	tastes in music, food, etc.

But only a few of these factors ordinarily matter for a specific report project. If you are writing an operator's manual for customers overseas, then you may have to adjust the examples you use to make them understandable culturally.

Audience Characteristic	Problem	Solution
Different country	Likely not to understand examples relating specifically to American culture.	Make sure that examples are culturally neutral; avoid American slang.
Little education	Likely not to understand written material well or easily.	Keep sentences short; vocabulary, simple. Repeat important concepts; use graphics often.

• *Identify the type of audience.* Based on their need for the report and their background, audiences can be divided into several types: experts, technicians, executives, and nonspecialists (traditionally known as laymen).

The *expert* knows practically everything about a technical subject matter—its theory, applications, uses, problems, and recent developments. Here are a few examples of experts:

integrated-circuit designer	software engineer
cancer researcher	metallurgist
mechanical engineer	petroleum geologist
geneticist	hospital dietician

The *technician* knows plenty that is technical about a subject also, but that knowledge usually has more to do with building, operating, maintaining, and repairing things. Whereas the expert's knowledge may tend toward the theoretical, the technician's knowledge tends to be more practical. Here are a few examples of technicians:

computer-system operator	photocopier repairperson
X-ray technician	automobile repairperson
electrical subcontractor	PBX operator

The *executive* usually knows less about a technical subject than the expert or the technician, but he or she may know plenty about costs, profits, and organizational impact related to the technical subject. The executive's knowledge is thus practical, too, but in a different way from that of the technician. Most importantly, executives make decisions about technologies: whether to purchase, build, implement, regulate, and so on. Here are some examples of executives:

owner of a software-development company	investor in an oil-well drilling venture
member of a hospital board	chief executive officer of a real estate firm
city-council member	
voter in a bond election	

The *nonspecialist* reader has the least amount of knowledge about a technical subject and reads out of general interest and curiosity; he or she has no direct, practical reason for doing so:

average reader who is curious about astronomy	beginning computer hobbyist
landowner looking into forestry practices	computer-systems designer interested in brain research
midwest farmer curious about the greenhouse effect	high school student wanting to learn about the physics of sailing

Although the term *nonspecialist* refers to that kind of reader with little knowledge or capability in a technical subject, it's a relative concept: a specialist in computer programming is most likely a nonspecialist in medicine.

• *Analyze your relationship to the audience.* In many cases, reports are written for people who are total strangers to the writer. But when that's not the case, the relationship between the writer and the audience must influence the writing of the report. The following are influences in writer-audience relationships:

• *Familiarity*—are the audience members relatively close acquaintances of or total strangers to the writer?
• *Organizational relationship*—are the audience members higher than, lower than, or at the same level in the organization as the writer?
• *Business relationship*—are the audience members customers or clients of the writer?

Relationship to Audience	Problem	Solution
Audience above you in position	May find your recommenda-tions too aggressive, pushy, presumptuous.	Always defer the decision to the reader; state recommen-dations with less emphasis.

• *Describe the audience's need for the information.* Audiences vary in their *needs* or *uses* for technical reports: they read technical discussions for one or a combination of reasons:

• To satisfy an interest or curiosity (no direct, practical motive) in a technical subject
• To learn how to build, operate, maintain, or repair something
• To make a decision on whether to do something with a technology (for example, whether to invest or build)
• To assess the validity of the ideas, results, or assertions related to a technology.

Audience	Report Project	Audience's Need or Use for the Report
Owner of a software-development company	Current computer-assisted instruction in collegiate technical-writing courses	Analysis of the market for this sort of educational software
City-council member	Proposal to equip city-owned housing with solar water-heating devices	Evaluation of the proposal: decision to approve or reject
Architectual engineer	Aspects of hemodialysis: the medical problem, the technology, the personnel, the procedures	Understanding of the aspects in order to design a hemodialysis clinic

Audience	Report Project	Audience's Need or Use for the Report
Coastal residents	Potential environmental impact of a proposed offshore oil-loading dock for supertankers	Decision whether to take legal action to prevent construction of the dock
Owners of a drafting company	Currently available CADAM hardware and software	Decision whether to use CADAM in its operations and which vendors to use
Local voters in a bond election concerning nuclear plants	Nuclear power plants: basic operations, safety mechanisms, regulations, past history, energy production	Information for making informed decisions on whether to vote for or against nuclear power

As you define your audience's needs for the information, think about the *scope* of those needs: for example, consider an audience that needs to know how to write a COBOL program that calculates interest rates; its information needs are of a rather *narrow* scope. Consider, however, an audience that needs to know COBOL for general business purposes; its information needs are of a *broad* scope. If its information needs are of a broad scope, you as a writer have a problem: how to provide all that information.

Audience Need	Problem	Solution
To program in BASIC	Too much information to cover	Cover half a dozen BASIC commands in depth with examples; recommend BASIC books for continued study.
To understand the current widespread concern over nuclear power	Technicality of the subject matter; large amount of information	Avoid going into much technical detail; simplify the discussion. Cover three or four main points only.

• *Identify the audience's knowledge and capabilities.* Audiences vary according to their *background*, that is, their *knowledge* and their *capabilities*, in a technical area. Think of an audience's knowledge as its reading knowledge, or passive knowledge; its capabilities, as its working or active knowledge. Knowledge and experience can be ranked: for example, from *much*, to *some*, to *little*, to *no* knowledge or experience.

Audience's Current Knowledge and Capability	Problem	Solution
Audience already knows simple BASIC commands	May or may not need review but would be irritated by laborious explanation	Place review of simple commands in appendix

• *Identify what kind of information the audience needs.* Information can be loosely divided into *instructional* information and *reference* information. Instructional information helps people do, build, or repair things. Reference information increases people's understanding about things; their reasons for seeking reference information have to do with their *need* for the information.

Kind of Information Needed	Problem	Solution
Reference	Potential investors need to understand a new oil-recovery technique	Prepare an informational report on the steps in the technique and its advantages
Reference	Business group needs to understand computer graphics capabilities in order to decide whether to purchase hardware and software for graphics	Prepare an informational report describing the features and capabilities of computer graphics and review the major packages and costs
Instruction	City council wants to assist citizens in reducing energy consumption	Prepare a report that shows citizens how to add insulation, save on heating and air conditioning costs, and to take other energy-saving steps
Instruction	Patient with kidney disease equipped with a home dialysis unit needs full understanding of how to operate it	Prepare instructions on how to operate the unit in a variety of situations as well as how to do maintenance on the unit.

• *Describe the situation in which the report is needed.* An important element of the report-writing situation is the situation itself: that event or circumstance that requires a report. The situation is the event or action that causes the audience to need or demand the report, the writer to write the report, and the audience to read the report.

Report Situation	Problem	Solution
Small 10-person engineering firm considering purchase of ten-workstation minicomputer with advanced CADAM capabilities	Needs a study to determine if the additional productivity is justifiable economically	Write an evaluative report comparing different CADAM systems by capabilities, costs, and ease of use and projecting labor and time savings

If as a technical-writing student you lack an authentic business or professional situation within which to write your report, you may have problems with the length of the report: the audience, purpose, and scope cannot be defined. Without a well-defined report situation, it's hard to know when to stop writing, how much detail to go into, and which topics to exclude from the report.

If you have an authentic situation within which to write your report, you are fortunate. For example, people at your work may need information on fire-prevention systems. In this case, you know the situation—the audience and the purpose of the report—and can plan your report accordingly. If you do not have a report situation, try to invent a realistic business or professional context. (More ideas on this are discussed in the following sections.)

Reports arise out of specific situations—a demand, need, or reason for writing the report. Individuals or groups of individuals have different needs for reports and make different uses of them:

- An engineer may need a technical report on some new technology in order to determine the constraints that will govern the design of a structure that will house it.
- A lawyer may need a technical report on a new technology to prepare for a legal case involving that technology.
- An investor or financial officer may need a technical report on a new technology in order to decide whether to invest in a project involving it.
- A government official may need a technical report on some new technology in order to decide whether to implement it or whether it meets certain standards.

These individuals do not have the time to do lengthy library searches and scan stacks of books and articles to find the right information. They want the information in a neat, tidy, well-organized package—in other words, in a report.

• *Invent a realistic report situation, if necessary.* If you lack a real report situation, use your imagination and invent a realistic one, or work with your instructor to develop one. This will guide your writing and enable you to produce a much better report. Without an audience and situation requiring a report, you could write practically forever and never finish. Here are some suggestions you can use to invent realistic report situations:

• Try to imagine a specific individual or group that might realistically need information on your topic. For example:

residents near a lake	citizens voting in a bond election
city planners	city-council members
neighborhood association	owner of a 500-acre tract suitable for
owner of a music store	development
real estate developer	

• Try to imagine their specific uses for the information in your report. For example:

To use a text-editing program
To write business programs in FORTRAN
To do maintenance work on an automobile
To select a certain model of photocopying machine
To make a decision on the upcoming bond election
To understand how a hemodialysis machine works
To be able to care for a patient with Alzheimer's disease
To understand the widespread concern over nuclear power

• Try to imagine what the audience is likely not to know about your report topic. For example:

Architectural engineer developing plans for a nuclear medicine facility	No medical background
Computer programmer customizing software for a law firm	No legal background
Investment officer looking into a biomass energy company	No background in alternate energy technology

• Try to imagine the actual event, action, or situation that brings about the demand for the report.

For example, if you want to report on hemodialysis, imagine that you are writing for an engineer who is bidding for a contract to design a hemodialysis clinic or unit in a hospital. He needs information to help him develop plans for the clinic, to prepare estimates for his bid, and in general to speak with knowledge and confidence to hospital administrators with whom he negotiates. He is not likely to know much about medicine or hemodialysis in particular. If you want to report on the technology used to create fuel from grain and other biomass, imagine that you are writing for a financial officer to explain to her its potential.

When you invent a report situation, you imagine when, where, why, and for whom the report might be written in an actual business or professional situation. Here are more examples of report topics and the realistic situations for them:

Topic	*Report Situation*
Laser surgery	You are a member of a hospital staff and want to interest the board in laser surgery.
Cocombustion	You are writing a report for the city council to initiate a project to cocombust municipal solid waste.
Space-shuttle rockets	You are explaining the technical background for a nonspecialist writer who is doing a popular magazine article on this subject.
Artificial heart	You are trying to interest potential investors in the work your firm is doing or plans to do in this area.
A health problem	You are trying to get funding to start a research project to attack this problem and must present background on it.
Electric vehicles	You want to propose that the city or university use electric vehicles and must review the current knowledge on them.
Offshore oil wells	Your audience is a group of coastal residents opposing any construction of offshore oil wells.
Robots	You want to interest management in introducing robots in part of the manufacturing process.
Greenhouse effect	An investment firm wants information on the potential short-term effects of increased CO_2 in the atomsphere in order to plan its own strategies for the future.

• *Describe how the audience will acquire the information.* Readers usually sit down in a quiet place and read written information; but not always! Just imagine the variety of ways some people must acquire information: on their backs underneath a car; in front of a totally disassembled machine; perched high on a ladder; or in the middle of a cluttered, busy kitchen. Reports and instructions for them must be designed so that they can do their work and still refer to the information easily.

Some audiences need reports for reference only; others need reports to read straight through once and then for frequent quick reference thereafter. Reports for them must be designed so that they are not forced to reread the whole report each time. Some audiences are busy people: reports have to be designed and written for them so that they can somehow get the message, whether it's on the bus, plane, or train or during a quick lunch break.

How the Audience Will Acquire the Information	Problem	Solution
One straight reading but frequent return for quick reference	Reader won't want to reread whole report just for quick reference; but needs thorough explanation.	Number steps for easy reference; use labeled tabs for ease in finding sections. Separate in-depth discussion from quick reference areas.
Quick reference reading in emergency situations	Readers must locate the right information immediately	Use a problem-solution format; use large letters and contrastive colors. Keep words to a minimum.
Selective leisure reading by general-interest audience	Readers need to find interesting sections easily and be able to skip uninteresting ones	Use fully explanatory headings at the beginning of each major section.
Difficult, multistep process to acquire instructions	Readers will have difficulty following the steps and finding the right parts	Supply illustrations for each major step; label the parts clearly; use two columns: one for the illustrations, the other for the text

• *Explain how the audience feels about acquiring the information.* In report-writing situations, you can't always expect undivided attention, patience, or even interest. Understanding an audience's attitude toward acquiring the information you seek to deliver can also be important in how you design and write a report.

For example, most computer hobbyists are enthusiastic about acquiring information about systems and programs; clerical workers who have used typewriters and filing cabinets for years and who have been ordered to switch to computerized writing and filing systems may be much less enthusiastic. Some audiences may be downright apprehensive about acquiring certain information. Others may even stubbornly resist acquiring it. Some audiences view written material, particularly instructions, as obstacles: they are in such a hurry to use the computer or the food processor or the video recorder, they have no patience with the accompanying reading matter that goes with it. Still other audiences, particularly those about to read reference information, are almost determined to be bored.

When you analyze an audience with questions like these, you are looking for potential problems—potential barriers to the effective transmission of information. The insights you gain from your audience analysis should then help you plan ways to eliminate, avoid, or reduce such problems.

To pull all these considerations together, you can use the chart in Figure 5–1 to analyze the audience for your report.

Audience's Feelings	Problem	Solution
Apprehension, uneasiness about a new technology	Unable to follow instructions; problems concentrating	Explain everything fully in nonthreatening language; use simple, nontechnical vocabulary; provide plenty of reassurance.
Resistance	May read instructions carelessly	Stress importance of the actions; make steps as foolproof as possible.

Audience Analysis Chart

Use this chart to identify *problems* your audience may have with your report:

	Problem	Solution
1. Audience identity (occupation, position, age, education, region, etc.)		
2. Relationship to audience (close, stranger, superior, subordinate, client, customer, etc.)		
3. Audience's need for the information (to understand, decide, act)		
4. Type of information needed (reference or instruction)		
5. Audience's current knowledge and capability		
6. Acquiring the information		
7. Audience's feelings		

FIGURE 5–1.   Audience analysis chart

Using an Audience Analysis

With a thorough analysis of your audience, you can make many key decisions about the content and design of your report. Review every section and subsection of your report outline or rough draft and consider the following points:

Decisions about:	Questions to ask:
Report content	Is this information needed by the audience? Does the audience need this section or that subsection considering its use for the report? Will this report give its audience everything it needs to make its decisions or to act effectively?
Level of detail	Is there too much detail for the audience here? Is there too little detail for the audience? How will the audience use the detail?
Level of technical expertise required to read the report	Do I need to explain some of these technical concepts more thoroughly for nonspecialists? Can I assume that my audience is knowledgeable in this area and discuss these concepts more rapidly?
Design of the graphic and textual aids	Will readers go through the report just once from beginning to end, or will they refer to sections back and forth? Will the audience be a mixture of specialists and nonspecialists who'll need headings to show them which parts of your report to read? If the audience is nonspecialist, are the illustrations and tables simple enough? Are readers overloaded with unnecessary technical detail?
Paragraph and sentence length	Are sentences relatively short for nonspecialist readers who may have trouble understanding the report? Are important points noticeable? Have I placed them in shorter paragraphs or at the beginning of paragraphs?

STEP 2. On your worksheet explain how you will adjust content, level of detail, graphic and textual aids, and paragraph and sentence length according to your audience.

Translating Technical Discussions

One of the most important things that you can learn from an audience analysis is how much to translate the technical discussion in your report for your audience.

Thorough audience analysis can also tell you how to design the graphic and textual aids (see Chapter 6), how to shape the individual paragraphs and sentences of your report (see Chapter 7), and what information to include and what information to exclude (see Chapter 8).

Translating is particularly important because it means supplying the right kinds of information to make up for the reader's lack of knowledge or capability. Translating thus enables readers to understand and use your report. Some combination of the techniques discussed in this section should help you create a readable, understandable translation:

Defining unfamiliar terms	Using the "in-other-words" technique
Comparing to familiar things	Posing rhetorical questions
Elaborating the process	Explaining the importance or
Providing description	significance of a topic
Providing examples and	Providing historical background
applications	Reviewing theoretical background
Using shorter sentences	Providing the human perspective

This list by no means exhausts the possibilities. Other chapters in this book cover techniques that also aid in translating:

- *Using lists and headings*—see Chapter 6 on how to construct lists that break up text and emphasize points and on how to construct headings that guide readers from section to section.
- *Including graphic aids*—see Chapter 6 on creating illustrations and tables that reinforce or supplement readers' understanding.
- *Strengthening transitions*—see Chapter 7 on techniques for guiding readers carefully through difficult technical discussions.

Definitions of Unfamiliar Terms

Defining potentially unfamiliar terms in a report is one of the most important ways to make up for readers' lack of knowledge in the report subject. Ideally, definitions of a sentence or less in length can be inserted practically anywhere in reports. Notice the use of definitions in the passage in Figure 5–2.

Comparisons to Familiar Things

Comparing technical concepts to ordinary and familiar things in our daily lives makes them easier to understand. For example, things in the world of electronics and computers—downright intimidating areas for many people—can be compared to channels of water, the five senses of the human body, gates and pathways, or other common things. Notice how comparison is used in the passages in Figure 5–3.

STEP 3.   On your worksheet explain how definitions and comparisons might help translate the technical discussion in your report. List the terms you'll need to define and the things you'll compare.

Facial Characteristics of FAS Victims

Taken as a whole, the face of patients with FAS, or fetal alcohol syndrome, is very distinctive. Structural deficiencies are thought to be the result of reduced cellular proliferation in the developing stages of the embryo because of the direct action of the alcohol. As shown in Figure 5–2a, the face has a drawn-out appearance with characteristics that include short palpebral fissures, epicanthic folds, a low nasal bridge, a short upturned nose, an indistinct piltrum, a small midface, and a thinned upper vermilion.

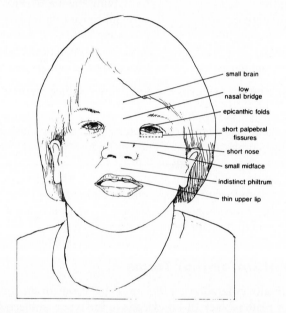

FIGURE 5–2a. Facial features characteristic of FAS
Photo courtesy of Dr. Ann Pytkowcz Streissguth, Department of Psychiatry and Behavioral Sciences, University of Washington, Seattle, Washington 98195.

Palpebral features are the longitudinal openings between the eyelids. In FAS victims they tend to be short, possibly because the eye size is so small. Most deficiency of the eye is reflected in these shortened palpebral fissures. Epicanthic folds are the vertical folds of skin on either side of the nose, sometimes covering the inner corner of the eye. They are present as a normal characteristic in persons of

FIGURE 5–2. Using definitions to translate technical discussion

certain races and also occur as a congenital malformation in patients
with FAS. The piltrim is the vertical groove in the middle of the
upper lip and below the nose region. It tends to be smooth in patients
with fetal alcohol syndrome, and as a consequence, the upper lip
may lack its usual indentation bow. The upper, red portion of the
upper lip is the vermilion; it is often very thin in patients with FAS.
The thinned vermilion is a major feature in contributing to the overall
drawn-out appearance of the face....

FIGURE 5–2. (cont.)

Elaborating the Process

Explaining in detail the processes involved in the report subject can also help readers. Consider a paragraph like this one, containing only a sketchy reference to the process:

> The Video Alert and Control dashboard system, a newly developed system to help drivers avoid accidents, graphically projects an image of hazards in the road.

This brief reference can be converted into a more complete explanation, as illustrated in Figure 5–4.

Providing Descriptive Detail

Descriptions also help nonspecialist readers by making the report discussion more concrete and down-to-earth. An example of a description used in this way appears in Figure 5–5.

STEP 4. On your worksheet explain which processes in your report you could discuss in more detail and which things you could describe to help translate your technical discussion.

Providing Examples and Applications

Equally useful in translating complex or abstract technical discussions are examples or explanations of how a thing can be used. For example, if you are trying to explain a Pascal command, showing how it is used in an example program helps readers greatly. If you are explaining a new design for a solar heating and cooling system, showing its application in a specific home can help also. Look, for example, at the approach in Figure 5–6. Figure 5–7 contains a passage with a longer, extended example.

The helical configuration of the DNA strands is not haphazard. The nitrogen bases on each strand align themselves to form nitrogen base pairs. The pairs are T-A and C-G. Each pair is held together by hydrogen bonds. The pairing of the bases serves to fasten the two helical nucleotide strands together <u>in much the same way as the teeth of a zipper hold the zipper together</u>. The existence of the complementary base pairs explains the constant ratios of T/A and C/G. For every T there must be a complementary A and for every G there must be a complementary C.

Reprinted from <u>Invitation to Chemistry</u> by David S. Newman by permission of W. W. Norton & Company, Inc. Copyright © 1978 by W. W. Norton & Company, Inc., 380–81.

All the death and all the misery from a virus so small that 2½ million of them in a line would take up one inch. Flu viruses fall into three types: A, B, and C. Type A, the most variable, causes pandemics as well as regular seasonal outbreaks; type B causes smaller outbreaks and is just now receiving greater attention; type C rarely causes serious health problems.

<u>In appearance, a flu virus somewhat resembles the medieval mace--a ball of iron studded with spikes. These spikes are two surface proteins called hemagglutinin (HA) and neuraminidase (NA).</u> Inside the virus is a thick tangle of genes. In many other viruses, a number of different genes fit onto one strand of nucleic acid; but each flu gene is a separate segment of ribonucleic acid (RNA)--eight threads in all. <u>The mace metaphor provides a crude but vivid picture of the influenza virus at work. Hemagglutinin is the substance that in effect bashes into a cell during infection and allows the virus access to the cell interior where it can replicate.</u> Neuraminidase permits all the viral offspring to break free of the host cell once replication is complete.

Stephen S. Hall, "The Flu," <u>Science '83</u> (November 1983), 56–57. Reprinted with permission.

FIGURE 5–3.   Comparison used for translation

STEP 5.   On your worksheet describe the examples you could use and applications you could discuss as ways of making your report more understandable.

Shorter Sentences

As simple a technique as it may seem, reducing the length of sentences can make a technical discussion easier to understand. Consider the pair of example passages in

The Video Alert and Control dashboard system uses a number of components to help drivers avoid accidents. The infrared detector is the key detecting device in that it searches for warm objects in or near the path ahead of the car. The infrared detector senses the upcoming trouble well before the driver by sensing its warm-bloodedness and then alerts the driver. The infrared detector also senses the heat of oncoming traffic. All of these objects are shown graphically on the video screen; to differentiate wildlife from other cars, the X-ray unit is used to check for metal in the object ahead. Thus, if a warm object is detected with metal in it, the computer reads it as a car and shows it on the screen as a yellow dot. On the other hand, if no metal is detected in the warm object, it is read as an animal and plotted as a red dot. . . .

FIGURE 5—4. **Elaborating the process as a way of translating**

Jarvik and his colleagues have been working on other designs, such as a portable artificial heart, which they think will be ready for a patient within the next two years.

Jarvik has been developing electric-energy converters and blood pumps during the past year. The electrohydraulic energy converter has only one moving part. The impeller of an axial-flow pump is attached to the rotor of a brushless direct-current motor, with the impeller and the rotor supported by a single hydrodynamic bearing. Reversing the rotation of the pump reverses the direction of the hydraulic flow. The hydraulic fluid (silicone oil of low viscosity) actuates the diaphragm of a blood pump just as compressed air does in the Jarvik-7 heart design. This hydraulic fluid is pumped back and forth between the right and left ventricles.

The energy converter is small and simple and therefore can be implanted without damaging vital structures. It weighs nearly 85 grams and occupies nearly 30 cubic centimeters. The converter

(continued)

FIGURE 5—5. **Description used to translate a technical discussion**

requires an external battery and an electronics package, which is connected to the heart by a small cable through the patient's chest. The batteries weigh 2 to 5 pounds and can be worn on a vest or belt. The battery unit requires new or recharged batteries once or twice a day. The cable through which the power is transmitted from the battery to the heart also carries control signals from the microcomputer controller. (See Figure 5–5a.)

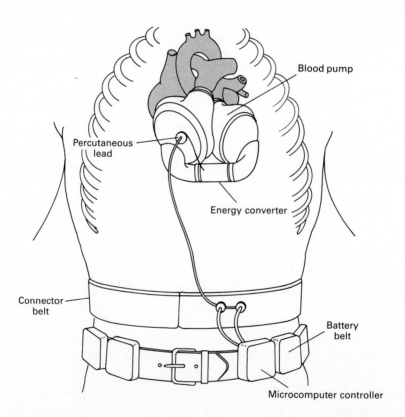

FIGURE 5–5a.   Electrically driven artificial heart system

Source: From "The Total Artificial Heart," Robert K. Jarvik. Copyright © January 1981 by Scientific American, Inc. All rights reserved.

FIGURE 5–5.   (cont.)

Continuous Speech

Continuous speech causes many problems in computerized speech recognition. In fluent speech, many words overlap. For example, when the "t" in "cat" combines the "y" in "your," the phrase, "You gave the cat your dinner," sounds like, "You gave the catcher dinner". Some words have built-in pauses that are often longer than word boundaries. For example, the word "vector" has a natural pause between the "c" and the "t." In an actual experiment, a machine listened to the phrase, "recognize speech," and printed, "wreck a nice beech". As vocabularies increase, words are more likely to become confused. Some words are subparts of others, such as "plea" and "please," while some words have similar acoustics, such as "what" and "watt".

FIGURE 5—6. Examples used in translation

The user "scrolls" the worksheet right and left or up and down to bring different parts of it into view. Each position (that is, each intersection of a column and a row) on a screen corresponds to a record in memory. The user sets up his own matrix by assigning to each record either a label, an item of data or a formula; the corresponding position on the screen displays the assigned label, the entered datum or the result of applying the formula.

Consider a simple example. A company comptroller might enter the label Cash in the record corresponding to Column B, Row 1 (position B1), Reserves at C1 and Total at D1. He might then enter $300,000 at B2, $500,000 at C2 and the formula $+B2+C2$ at position D2. The screen will show $800,000 at D2. If the comptroller changes the B2 entry to $200,000, the program will reduce the total displayed at D2 to $700,000. Moreover, what is entered in records B2 and C2 need not be primary data; it can be a function of data held in other records.

From "Personal Computers," Hoo-Mi D. Toong and Amar Gupta. Copyright © (December 1982) by Scientific American, Inc. All rights reserved.

FIGURE 5—7. Discussion of applications used to translate a technical discussion

Figure 5–8, the second version of which contains shorter sentences. (The passage still needs other translating techniques, particularly definitions, but the shorter sentences do make it more readable.)

The "In-Other-Words" Technique

Another way of translating technically difficult content is to give the reader two views of the same idea by restating it in different or simpler terms. The second, simpler explanation is often preceded by a phrase such as "in other words." Figure 5–9 contains two examples of this technique.

Original Version: Longer Sentences

UV-fluorescence was determined on aliquots of the hexane extracts of subsurface water using the Perkin-Elmer MPF-44A dual-scanning fluorescence spectrophotometer upon mousse sample NOAA-16, considered the best representative of cargo oil. Every day that samples were processed, a new calibration curve was developed from serial dilutions of the reference mousse (NOAA-16) at an emission wavelength of ca. 360 nm, and other samples were compared to it as the standard. Emission was scanned from 275–500 nm, offset 25 nm from the excitation wavelength, with the major peak occurring at 360 nm for the reference mousse solutions. In each sample, the concentration of fluorescent material, a total oil estimate, was calculated from its respective fluorescence, using the linear relationship of fluorescence versus concentration of the reference mousse "standard," with a correction factor applied to account for the reference mousse containing only about 30 percent.

Revised Version: Shorter Sentences

UV-fluorescence was determined on aliquots of the hexane extracts of the subsurface water. These measurements were performed using a Perkin-Elmer MPF-44A dual-scanning fluorescence spectrophotometer. Mousse sample NOAA-16 was used as the best representative of cargo oil. Other samples were compared to it as the standard. Every day that samples were processed, a new calibration curve was developed from serial dilutions of the reference mousse (NOAA-16). Tests were run at an emission wavelength of ca. 360 nm. Emission was scanned from 275–500 nm, offset 25 nm from the excitation wavelength. The major peak occurred at 360 nm for the reference mousse solutions. In each sample the concentration of fluorescent material, a total estimate, was calculated from its respective fluorescence. The linear relationship of fluorescence versus concentration of the reference mousse "standard" was used. A correction factor was applied to account for the reference mousse containing only about 30 percent oil.

FIGURE 5–8.   Shorter sentences for translation purposes

With no electric field present, semiconductor electrons are quite happy to remain bonded in their valence bands. Only when an electric field is applied or the temperature is raised (heat can also increase electron energy) do the valence electrons begin to break their bonds, jump the energy band gap, and become conduction electrons.

When a bond is broken, a vacancy or hole is left. The region in which this vacancy exists has a net positive charge. The area where the freed electron exists has a net negative charge. In a semiconductor, both electrons and holes contribute to electrical conduction. If a valence electron from another bond fills the hole without ever gaining energy sufficient to become free, the vacancy appears in a new place. It is as if a positive charge (equal to that on a electron) has moved to a new location. In other words, conduction in semiconductors is the result of two separate and independent particles carrying opposite charges and moving opposite directions under the influence of an applied electric field.

Fatigue is a phenomenon that has plagued engineers for years. It is especially bothersome when metals are involved. Simply stated, fatigue is the slow growth of a crack that ultimately leads to failure after a number of load reversals. A paperclip breaking after repeated bending is an example of fatigue. The process by which fatigue leads to failure can be divided into three stages: initiation, propagation, and failure. The nature of the second stage, propagation, is what enables composites to be immune to failure.

W. J. Krefeld and W. G. Bowman, "Stress and strain," *McGraw-Hill Encyclopedia of Science and Technology* (1977), 202. Reprinted with permission.

FIGURE 5—9. The "in-other-words" technique

Posing Rhetorical Questions

In technical writing you occasionally see questions posed to the readers. Such questions are not really for readers to answer; they are meant to stimulate readers' curiosity, renew their interest, introduce a new section of the discussion, or allow for a pause. For example, read the passage in Figure 5–10.

When an animal runs, its legs swing back and forth through large
angles to provide balance and forward drive. We have found that such
swinging motions of the leg do not have to be explicitly programmed
for a machine but are a natural outcome of the interactions between the
controllers for balance and attitude. Suppose the vehicle is traveling
at a constant horizontal rate and is landing with its body upright.
What must the attitude controller do during the stance to maintain the
upright attitude? It must make sure that no torques are generated at
the hip. Since the foot is fixed on the ground during stance, the leg

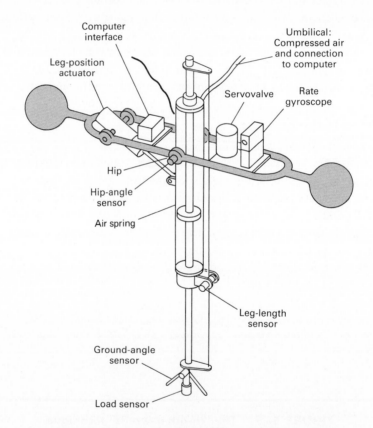

FIGURE 5–10a. Two-dimensional hopping machine

From "Machines that Walk," Marc H. Raibert and Ivan E. Sutherland.
Copyright © (January 1983) by Scientific American, Inc. All rights
reserved.

FIGURE 5–10. Asking rhetorical questions as a
translating technique

must sweep back through an angle in order to guarantee that the
torque on the hip will be zero while the body moves forward.

On the other hand, what must the balance servo do during flight to
maintain balance? Since the foot must spend about as much time in
front of the vehicle's center of gravity as behind it, the rate of travel
and the duration of stance dictate a forward foot position for landing
that will place the foot in a suitable spot for the next stance period. Thus
during each flight the leg must swing forward under the direction of
the balance servo, and during each stance it must sweep backward
under the control of the attitude servo; the forward and back sweeping
motions required for running are obtained automatically from the
interplay of the servo-control loops for balance and attitude. (See
Figure 5–10a.)

FIGURE 5–10.   (cont.)

Explaining the Importance of a Topic

Some translating techniques work because they motivate readers. Sometimes readers
need to be talked into concentrating on a difficult technical discussion: one way is
to explain to them or to remind them of the importance of what is being discussed.
In the example in Figure 5–11, the last paragraph emphasizes the importance of
the discussion.

It was Linus Pauling and his coworkers who discovered that sickle cell
anemia was a molecular disease. This disease affects a very high
percentage of black Africans, as high as 40 percent in some regions.
About 9 percent of black Americans are heterozygous for the gene that
causes the disease. People who are heterozygous for sickle cell anemia
contain one normal gene and one sickle cell gene. Since neither gene
in this case is dominant, half the hemoglobin molecules will be normal
and half sickled. The characteristic feature of this disease is a sickling
of the normally round, or platelike, red blood cells under conditions
of slight oxygen deprivation. The sickled red blood cells clog small
blood vessels and capillaries. The body's response is to send out white
blood cells to destroy the sickled red blood cells, thus causing a
shortage of red blood cells, or anemia.

FIGURE 5–11.   Explaining the importance of a topic as
a way of translating technical discussions

The sickle cell gene originated from a mistake in information. A DNA molecule somehow misplaced a base, which in turn caused an RNA molecule to direct the cell to make hemoglobin with just one different amino acid unit among the nearly 600 normally constituting a hemogolobin molecule. So finely tuned is the human organism that this tiny difference is enough to cause death.

Since the disease is nearly always fatal before puberty, how can a gene for a fatal childhood disease get so widespread in a population? The answer to this question gives some fascinating insight into the mechanism and purposes of evolution, or natural selection. The distribution of sickle cell anemia very closely parallels the distribution of a particularly deadly malaria-causing protozoan by the name of Plasmodium falciparum, and it turns out that there is a close connection between sickle cell anemia and malaria. Those people who are heterozygous for the sickle cell gene are relatively immune to malaria and, except under reasonably severe oxygen deprivation such as that found at high altitudes, they experience no noticeable effects due to the sickle cell gene they carry. Half the hemoglobin molecules in the red cells of heterozygous people are normal and half are sickled, thus under ordinary circumstances the normal hemoglobin carries on the usual respiratory functions of blood cells and there is little discomfort. On the other hand, the sickled hemoglobin molecules precipitate, in effect, when the malaria-causing protozoan enters the blood. The precipitated hemoglobin seems to crush the malaria protozoan, thus keeping the malaria from being fatal.

The significance of all this should be pondered. Nature is willing to sacrifice approximately half the children in the malaria-infested regions of Africa so that the species can survive. The reason half the children die is that, on the average, approximately one-quarter of the children will be homozygous for abnormal hemoglobin and will die of sickle cell anemia, while one-quarter will be homozygous for normal hemoglobin and will likely die of malaria. The half of the population that is heterozygous will survive to reproduce. This means that the species, not the individual, is the ultimate unit of Darwinian evolution.

Reprinted from Invitation to Chemistry by David S. Newman by permission of W. W. Norton & Company, Inc. Copyright © 1978 by W. W. Norton & Company, Inc.

FIGURE 5—11.   (cont.)

STEP 6.   On your worksheet explain the importance of your report subject matter or the importance of the report you are writing.

Providing Historical Background

Discussion of the historical background of a technical subject helps readers because it gives them less technical, more general, and sometimes more familiar information. It gives them a base of understanding from which to launch into the more difficult sections of the discussion. Two examples of this approach appear in Figure 5–12.

Now that alcohol is being consumed in more and more social settings, recognizing its teratogenic effects is extremely important. Teratogenic, or malforming, agents produce an abnormal presence or absence of a substance that is required in physical development. Although Sullivan first reported on the effects of maternal drinking during pregnancy in 1899, the serious implications of his findings were virtually ignored for the next 50 years. It was not until the dramatic identification of a pattern of malformations, termed the fetal alcohol syndrome (FAS) by Jones et al. in 1973, that the scientific community acknowledged the potential dangers of heavy maternal alcohol use. Since then, there has been increasing recognition that alcohol may be the most common drug in causing problems of malformations in humans.

Each morning in the soft, coral flush of daybreak, a laser dawns on Mars. Forty miles above frigid deserts of red stone and dust, it flares in an atmosphere of carbon dioxide. Infrared sunlight kindles in this gas a self-intensifying radiance that continuously generates as much energy as a thousand nuclear reactors. Our eyes are blind to it, but from sunrise to sunset Mars bathes in dazzling lasershine.

The red planet may have lased in the sun for eons before astronomers identified its sky-high natural laser in 1980. The wonder is that its existence was unknown for so long. In 1898, in The War of the Worlds, H. G. Wells scourged earth with Martian invaders and a laserlike death ray. Pitiless, this "ghost of a beam of light" blasted brick, fired trees, and pierced iron as if it were paper.

(continued)

FIGURE 5–12.   Providing historical background as a translating technique

In 1917 Albert Einstein speculated that under certain conditions atoms or molecules could absorb light or other radiation and then be stimulated to shed their borrowed energy. In the 1950s Soviet and American physicists independently theorized how this borrowed energy could be multiplied and repaid with prodigious interest. In 1960 Theodore H. Maiman invested the glare of a flash lamp in a rod of synthetic ruby; from that first laser on earth he extorted a burst of crimson light so brilliant it outshone the sun.

Allen A. Boraiko, "Lasers: 'A Splendid Light,' " <u>National Geographic</u> (March 1984), 335. Reprinted with permission.

FIGURE 5–12. (cont.)

Reviewing Theoretical Background

To understand some phenomena, technologies, or their applications, readers must first understand the principle or theory behind them. Theoretical discussions need not be over the heads of nonspecialist readers. Discussion of theory is often little more than explanation of the root causes and effects at work in a phenomenon or mechanism. In the example in Figure 5–13, the writer establishes the theory before discussing the findings that have come about through the use of NMR on living tissue.

To the extent that objections persist about the validity of modern biochemistry, they continue to be about reducing the processes of life to sequences of chemical reactions. "The reactions may take place in the test tube," one hears, "but do they really happen that way inside the living cell? And what happens in multicellular organisms?" Here I shall describe how one technique is beginning to answer these questions by detecting chemical reactions as they occur inside cells,

Figure 5–13. Reviewing theoretical background as a translating technique

tissues and organisms including man. The technique is nuclear-magnetic-resonance (NMR) spectroscopy. It relies on the fact that atomic nuclei with an odd number of nucleons (protons and neutrons) have an intrinsic magnetism that makes each such nucleus a magnetic dipole: in essence a bar magnet. Such nuclei include the proton (H-1), which is the nucleus of 99.98 percent of all hydrogen atoms occurring in nature, the carbon-13 nucleus (C-13), which is the nucleus of 1.1 percent of all carbon atoms, and the phosphorus-31 nucleus (P-31), which is the nucleus of all phosphorus atoms.

In NMR spectroscopy two fields are applied to cells, to tissue or to parts of a living organism. The first field is a strong magnetic field. It causes the nuclear dipoles (that is, the hydrogen-1, carbon-13 and phosphorus-31 nuclei in the sample) to orient themselves so that the dipole of each nucleus is aligned either with the field or against it. Alignment with the field is a state in which the nucleus stores less energy than it does when it is aligned against the field.

From "NMR Spectroscopy of Living Cells," R. G. Shulman. Copyright © (January 1983) by Scientific American, Inc. All rights reserved.

FIGURE 5–13. (cont.)

STEP 7. On your worksheet explain the historical and theoretical background that you could discuss to make your report more understandable to nonspecialist readers.

Providing the Human Perspective

Nonspecialist readers often appreciate details about the people who developed, need, use, or are affected by the technology being explained. This human perspective helps to place technical subject matter in a more familiar, practical world—one that is less abstract and strange than the world of equations and formulas. For example, look at Figure 5–14.

STEP 8. Describe the human perspective you could include in your technical discussion to make it more understandable.

The Discovery of Lasers

Many lasers were made before anybody succeeded in making a similar device that worked in the visible part of the spectrum. In 1957, Gordon Gould, a graduate student at Columbia, was working on the problem and hit upon an idea that he thought could provide the solution. He went down to his neighborhood candy store in the Bronx and had the page of his notebook on which he wrote his idea notarized to establish his legal priority. Townes was also working on the problem and came up with a similar idea at about the same time. (Just who discovered what, and when, has been the subject of lengthy court battles over patent rights. ...) These new ideas led to the construction of what was at first called an "optical laser" but was soon called a laser, for "light amplification by stimulated emission of radiation." Less than two years after the theoretical principles were first put forth, Theodore Maiman at Hughes Aircraft built the first working model.

Reprinted from Invitation to Physics by Jay M. Pasachoff and Marc L. Kutner by permission of W. W. Norton & Company, Inc. Copyright © 1981 by Jay M. Pasachoff and Marc L. Kutner.

FIGURE 5–14. Providing the human perspective as a translating technique

Combining the Translating Techniques

This last section concludes the discussion of techniques for translating difficult technical prose to be presented here. However, take a look at writing in fields you know about, and look for other kinds of translating techniques used there. Figure 5–15 contains an extended passage of technical writing that combines several of the strategies discussed thus far.

STEP 9.   Review the notes that you've taken in the preceding steps, and make a list of the translating techniques you think will be the most useful in your report. Also, describe any other ideas for translating strategies you have.

Fine-Tuning the Spectrum

To know lasers, one must first know the electromagnetic spectrum, which ranges from long radio waves to short, powerful gamma rays.

The narrow band of the spectrum we know as visible, or white, light is made up of red, orange, yellow, green, blue, and violet light. These frequencies, as well as all radiation waves, are jumbled or diffused, much as noise is a collection of overlapping, interfering sounds. Laser light is organized and concentrated, like a single, clear musical note.

In lasers, nature's disorder is given coherence, and photons--the basic units of all radiation--are sent out in regular ranks of one frequency. Because the waves coincide, the photons enhance one another, increasing their power to pass on energy and information.

The first devices to emit concentrated radiation operated in the low-energy microwave frequencies. Today laser technology is extending beyond ultraviolet toward the high-energy realms of x-rays. Each wavelength boasts its own capacities as a tool for man.

A laser's beam can be modulated into an infinite number of wavelengths using fluorescent dyes like those produced at Exciton Chemical Company in Ohio. At Hughes Research Laboratories in California, a blue-green laser reflected at an acute angle aneals silicon microchips, while a low-energy red laser monitors the process.

Harnessing Light

As a bow stores energy and releases it to drive an arrow, so lasers store energy in atoms and molecules, concentrate it, and release it in powerful waves.

When an atom expands the orbits of its electrons, they instantly snap back, shedding energy in the form of a photon. When a molecule vibrates or changes its geometry, it also snaps back to emit a photon.

In most lasers a medium of crystal, gas, or liquid is energized by high-intensity light, an electric discharge, or even nuclear radiation. When a photon reaches an atom, the energy exchange stimulates the emission of another photon in the same wavelength and direction, and so on, until a cascade of growing energy sweeps through the medium.

(continued)

FIGURE 5—15. Translating techniques used in combination

The photons travel the length of the laser and bounce off mirrors--one a full mirror, one partially silvered--at either end. Photons, reflected back and forth, finally gain so much energy that they exit the partially silvered end, emerging as a powerful beam.

Out of the Darkness: Laser Eye Surgery

Sight-saving shafts of light able to enter the eye without injuring it, lasers are revolutionizing eye surgery.

Using techniques of New York opthalmologist Frances L'Esperance, eye surgeons employ four levels of laser energy. Exposure time ranges from 30 minutes for low-energy photoradiation to several billionths of a second for photodisruption.

With microscopic focus, beams weld breaks in the retina or seal leaking blood vessels by photocoagulation. A painless 20-minute operation called an irridectomy relieves the excess fluid buildup of glaucoma.

When an artificial lens is placed behind the iris, the supportive membrane often grows milky. A laser beam is pinpointed on the taut tissue in a series of minute explosions. This photodisruption causes the tissue to unzip and part like a curtain. Bloodless scalpels, lasers can make extremely delicate incisions, cauterize blood vessels, and leave tissue unaffected only a few cell widths away.

Beams that Heal

Surgical trauma, the jarring aftermath of the surgeon's knife, may one day be consigned to the annals of primitive medicine--thanks to a procedure called "least invasive surgery" by its growing number of practitioners. Using an endoscope, surgeons can view the interior of the body and operate with the least amount of damage.

Twisting and probing with the end of the scope, he can identify and coagulate a bleeding ulcer in the stomach or blast tumors in the esophagus. The beam is fed through the scope by an optical fiber from a laser machine ... that might cost the hospital from $20,000 to $150,000.

Allen A. Boraiko, "Lasers: A Splendid Light," National Geographic (March 1984), pp. 338—46. Reprinted with permission.

FIGURE 5—15.   (cont.)

EXERCISES

1. Locate two versions of a discussion of the same technical subject, one simple and one advanced (for example, in a grade school textbook and in a graduate-level textbook). Photocopy passages of similar discussions, and then analyze the simpler version for the translating techniques it uses. Mark them on the copy, and label them in the margin.

2. Copy a highly technical discussion of a subject (in an advanced textbook or scholarly journal, for example) with which you are familiar, and decide which of the translating techniques you would have to use to make it understandable to nonspecialist audiences. Mark and label the copy at the spots where you'd insert the translations.

3. Write a revised, translated version of the passage of writing that you analyzed in exercise 2.

4. Find a classmate, friend, or work associate who has no knowledge of the subject matter of the passage that you chose in exercise 2, and try to explain the passage orally to that person. If that person is a classmate and has a technical passage that you do not know much about, have him or her explain that passage to you. As you explain to each other, make notes on the kinds of translating techniques you use. When you have satisfactorily explained the technical passages to each other, do exercise 3 and trade translations.

5. Locate a technical report (using the steps for finding government documents in Chapter 9, if necessary) or a technical article on a subject familiar to you, and make a list of the background topics that must be discussed before a nonspecialist reader could understand the report.

6. Locate a technical report (using the steps for finding government documents in Chapter 9, if necessary), and describe the audience for whom it was written or for whom it is appropriate: describe the audience in terms of its background (education, training, experience) and its need or use for the report.

7. Select a technical topic (using the list in Chapter 8 if necessary) with which you are familiar, design a situation (audience and purpose) in which a report on that topic might be written for a nonspecialist audience, and then make a list of the background topics you'd need to discuss to make that report understandable to the audience.

CHAPTER 6

Constructing Graphic and Textual Aids

Chapter Objectives
Graphic Aids
  Graphic Aids for Physical Things
    Photographs
    Line Drawings
  Graphic Aids for Numbers
    Tables
    Graphs
  Graphic Aids for Key Concepts
    Flowcharts
    Organizational Charts
    Other Conceptual Line Drawings
  Graphic Aids for Words
  Planning and Developing Graphic
    Aids
    Finding Materials for Graphic Aids

    Scanning Report Drafts for
        Graphic Aids
      Guidelines for Graphic Aids
Textual Aids
  Headings
  Titles
  Table of Contents
  List of Figures or Illustrations
  Lists
  Pagination
  Title Page
  Cover Label
  Glossary and List of Symbols and
    Abbreviations
Exercises

CHAPTER OBJECTIVES

After you read this chapter, study the examples, and work the steps, you should be able to:

- Recognize the need for graphic aids in reports.
- Identify the type of graphic aid needed.
- Properly entitle, number, label, document, and discuss graphic aids.
- Use headings to mark different sections of reports.
- Identify the need for lists in report drafts and create them.
- Create fully descriptive titles for reports.
- Design effective tables of contents, lists of figures, and title pages.
- Design useful glossaries and lists of symbols or abbreviations, when necessary.

Essential to most technical reports and articles are graphic and textual aids. *Graphic aids* are the familiar charts, tables, diagrams, flowcharts, and even photographs found throughout most reports. *Textual aids* are the chapter titles, headings, lists, page numbers, table of contents, list of figures, and other such devices that guide readers through reports.

Graphic Aids

Graphic aids are crucial in conveying information to readers of technical reports. Often, certain concepts or relationships cannot be expressed adequately or at all unless graphic aids are used. Before getting into the planning of graphic aids for reports, however, consider the reasons they are used and their different types:

- Graphic aids such as photographs and drawings help readers *visualize* mechanisms or actions.
- Graphic aids such as conceptual line drawings help readers *conceptualize* important ideas discussed in reports.
- Graphic aids such as tables *emphasize* points in a report by repeating the important statistical information in the preceding text, but in a different format.
- Graphic aids, both tables and figures, *substitute* for regular discussion when the idea cannot be conveyed quickly or easily in words or when it is impractical to do so (for example, a large table of numerical values).
- Graphics aids of any sort can also serve readers as a *reference* tool; for example, solar-energy reports often contain tables that show how to set the angle of inclination of the collector according to latitude.

Now consider what kinds of things graphic aids illustrate, represent, or symbolize. Although graphic aids are usually divided into a half dozen or so categories such as photographs, drawings, diagrams, flowcharts, bar graphs, and circle graphs, it may help you to plan the graphic aids for your report by thinking about what they depict:

physical things
numbers
key concepts
words

This classification is a powerful tool in planning for graphic aids in a report and in scanning rough drafts for the need of additional graphic aids.

Although you should plan ahead for the kinds of graphic aids your report will need, you should also review your rough drafts for areas in which additional graphic aids are needed as well, as indicated in Figure 6–1.

Graphic Aids for Physical Things

Graphic aids that illustrate physical objects, mechanisms, organisms, and places include photographs and line drawings.

Photographs.   Because they provide the greatest amount of detail possible, photographs can be both good and bad in reports. If all you want is to give readers an idea of the appearance of a thing, a photograph works fine. But if you want to discuss the parts and operation of that thing in detail, a photograph does not work as well as a simplified drawing. If you want photographs in your report, you may have a problem: photocopies of photographs usually turn out quite poorly. (See Chapter 10 for some solutions.)

Line Drawings.   Line drawings are any simplified illustration of an object. Line drawings include freehand drawings, diagrams, schematics, blueprints, and any other kind of illustration showing the appearance of a thing and the relationship of its parts. With line drawings, you can vary the amount and kind of detail: think of the differences between a freehand sketch of the components of a radio and a schematic of them. Line drawings are simplified illustrations of objects; but they are simplified according to a specific purpose and audience. Obviously, simplification for a nonspecialist reader who simply wants to visualize a mechanism is quite different from a simplification for a specialist who wants to design or repair that mechanism. Notice the amount of detail included in the example in Figure 6–2.

STEP 1.   On your worksheet, list the things in your report that you may need to illustrate, and indicate the type of illustration you think you'll use for each.

Graphic Aids for Numbers

Numbers are, of course, usually shown in tables, graphs, and charts. Included in this group are all the ingenious variations on line graphs, bar graphs, and pie charts.

Tables.   A table is any array of statistical information set up in rows and columns. One example appears in Figure 6–3.

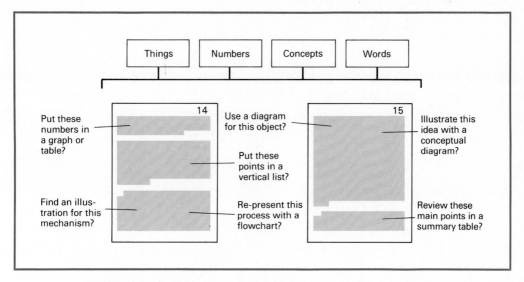

FIGURE 6–1. Analyzing pages of a rough draft for areas in which graphic aids are needed

Trombe Walls

Basic System Configuration.   The Trombe wall is a south-facing concrete or masonry wall covered on the exerior by light-transmitting glazing. Its uninsulated interior face is exposed to the heated face. The recommended design has vents at the top and bottom to permit air flow by natural convection from the outer surface of the wall into the building. A variety of system designs have been built, and optimization of the design for specific climates is possible. The design illustrated in Figure 6–2a is considered cost effective for heating applications in the majority of U.S. climates. The modular dimensions and particular construction details used here should help to simplify the contractor's tasks of estimation and installation.

Materials.   The design consists of an outer glazing system, an inner thermal energy storage wall, backdraft dampers for air flow control, and various optimal trim and structural integration details. The outer curtain wall/window system is aluminum framing in ...

(continued)

FIGURE 6–2. Using line drawings in technical reports

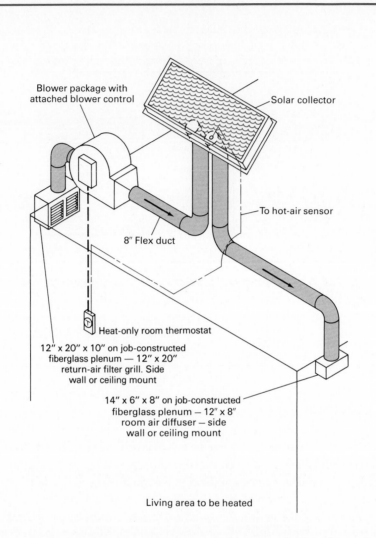

Blower package with attached blower control

Solar collector

To hot-air sensor

8″ Flex duct

Heat-only room thermostat

12″ x 20″ x 10″ on job-constructed fiberglass plenum — 12″ x 20″ return-air filter grill. Side wall or ceiling mount

14″ x 6″ x 8″ on job-constructed fiberglass plenum — 12″ x 8″ room air diffuser — side wall or ceiling mount

Living area to be heated

FIGURE 6–2a.   Trombe wall design

U.S. Department of Energy, Introduction to Solar Heating and Cooling Design Sizing (Washington, D.C.: U.S. Government Printing Office, August 1978), 3–37.

FIGURE 6–2.   (cont.)

By the end of 1979, U.S. firms had cumulatively invested almost $193 billion to develop subsidiaries, conduct joint ventures, build facilities, or acquire properties in foreign countries. The greatest proportion of these investments had been in Western Europe, Canada, and Latin America. (See Table 6–3a.)

TABLE 6–3a.   U.S. Investment Abroad, Cumulative through 1979

| | Investment | |
Region/Country	U.S. Billions ($)	Percent of Total
Developed countries		
Western Europe	81.5	42.3
Canada	41.0	21.3
Other	15.4	8.0
Developed subtotal	137.9	71.6
Developing countries		
Latin America	36.8	19.1
Other	11.0	5.7
Developing subtotal	47.8	24.8
International and unallocated	6.9	3.6
TOTAL	192.6	100.0

Source: Survey of Current Business, August 1980.

The United States is also the world's greatest importer ....

Joel R. Evans and Barry Berman, Marketing (New York: Macmillan, 1982), 584–86.

FIGURE 6–3.   Using tables in technical reports

Notice several important things about the design of this table:

- Items like "Region/Country" and "Investment" are called *column headings*; they tell what you are looking at in the column below only.
- Items like "Developed countries" and "Latin America" are called *line headings*; they tell you what you are looking at in the row of figures extending to the right.
- *Subheadings*, such as "U.S. Billions ($)" and "Percent of Total" in the line headings can also be used in tables.
- The item "Region/Country," usually called the *stub heading*, tells you about only those headings below it and cannot refer to anything to the right.

Keep in mind that you can also create *informal tables*, which do not require figure numbers and titles or elaborate headings and subheadings. Informal tables are often used to re-present statistical information that has just been discussed; they give readers two looks at the same information. For example, examine Figure 6–4.

Smoking is another factor directly affecting the oxygen-carrying capability of red blood cells. The smoke of a typical American cigarette contains about 4 percent carbon monoxide (20,000 ppm). The average concentration inhaled is 400–500 ppm, which produces anywhere from 3.8 to 7.0 percent carboxyhemoglobin (HbCO) in the blood. This compares with 0.5 percent HbCO in the nonsmoker.

Continuous Exposure Level of CO, ppm	HbCO in Blood, %
50	8.4
40	6.7
30	5.0
20	3.3
10	1.7
—	0.5 (nonsmoker)

The blood of divers who smoke has a HbCO level higher than it would have been if the divers were exposed to 20 ppm carbon monoxide for 12 hours. This is the maximum level for carbon monoxide allowed in USN divers' breathing air. Considering that it takes a heavy smoker approximately 8 hours to eliminate 75 percent of the carbon monoxide he has inhaled, it is clear that even a light smoker diving 8 hours after the last puff has an HbCO level almost twice that of a nonsmoker $(0.95)(3.8 \times 25\%)$.

Smoking Habits	Median HbCO Level, %	Expired CO, ppm
Light smoker (less than ½ pack per day)	3.8	17.1
Moderate smoker (more than ½ pack but less than 2 packs per day)	5.9	27.5
Heavy smoker (2 packs or more per day)	6.9	32.4

FIGURE 6–4. **Informal tables and related text**

A type of table particularly useful in comparisons involves *scales*. When you are comparing things with too many points of comparison to keep in mind, scales are a good way to help you make up your mind. In a simple scale you evaluate with a numerical scale, with choices numbered from 1 to 5, for example, and then add up the score to see which choice wins. However, when some of the points of comparison are more important than others, you have to *weight* the scale. In the example in Figure 6–5, ease of operation, actual versus anticipated performance, and overall satisfaction are weighted by a factor of 3 because they are more important. By weighting the scales, the Smith & Smith does not get the highest score simply because it scored well in the less-important areas of maintenance and technical support. (If you use weighted scales, remember to explain them and justify the weights you've assigned.)

Graphs.   The category of graphs includes the whole range of interesting and sometimes ingenious illustrations such as line graphs, bar graphs, and circle graphs, as well as the multiple and combined forms of these. Just as line drawings present

	Raw Scores			Weighted Scores		
	UVC Execu-comp	Fujima Docu-comp	Smith & Smith	UVC Execu-comp	Fujima Docu-comp	Smith & Smith
Ease of operation (3)*	4	5	3	12	15	9
Reliability of the system (2)	4	4	4	8	8	8
Reliability of the peripherals (2)	4	5	4	8	10	8
Responsiveness of maintenance (2)	4	3	5	8	6	10
Effectiveness of maintenance (1)	4	3	5	4	3	5
Technical support:						
Troubleshooting (1)	4	4	5	4	4	5
Training (1)	4	4	5	4	4	5
User's manuals (1)	2	2	5	2	2	5
Actual vs. anticipated performance (3)	5	4	3	15	12	9
Overall satisfaction (3)	5	4	3	15	12	9
TOTALS	39	38	42	80	76	73

*Weighted value

FIGURE 6–5.   An example of a weighted scale

less detail than photographs, graphs present less statistical information than tables. Instead, graphs present selected information in order to emphasize certain points about it. Think how much more vividly a graph would present the increasing costs of energy in the United States since the 1960s than would, for example, a table with 20 columns and 25 rows. Figure 6–6 contains examples of the main types of graphs.

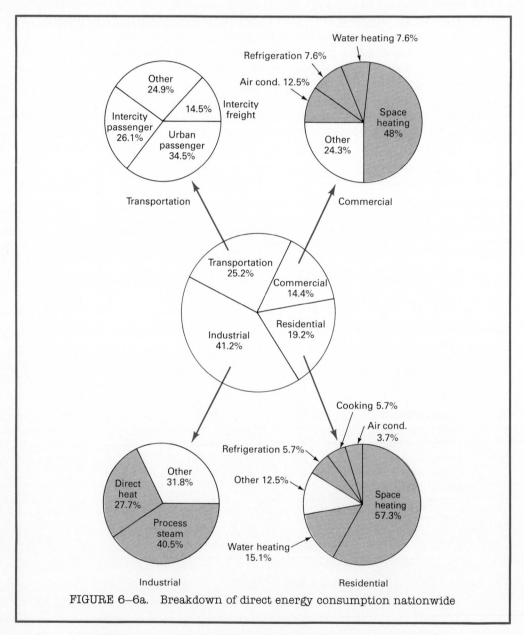

FIGURE 6–6a.   Breakdown of direct energy consumption nationwide

FIGURE 6–6.   **Using different kinds of graphs in technical reports**

Some estimates indicate that solar energy may contribute as much as 25 percent of the nation's total energy requirements by the year 2020. Cost, legislation, fossil fuel depletion, and tax incentives are important factors as to whether or not these expectations will be met. Figure 6–6a shows a breakdown of direct energy consumption nationwide.

Notice that in every breakdown of a specific section, except for transportation, the possibilities of solar are immense.

U.S. Department of Energy, Introduction to Solar Heating and Cooling Design and Sizing, DOE: CS-0011 (Washington, D.C.: U.S. Government Printing Office, 1978), 1–8.

For a specific business the revenue function is the product of price and volume sold and thus is essentially a straight line over a considerable range of volume change. For this condition the relationship between volume and fixed costs, variable costs, and revenue is shown in Figure 6–6b. These are commonly called breakeven charts.

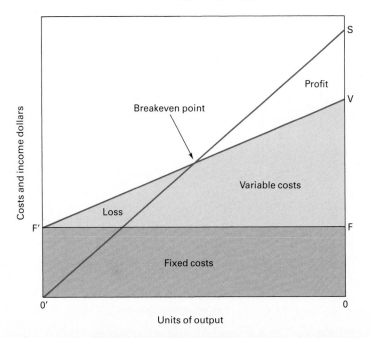

Figure 6–6b.   Typical breakeven chart for a business enterprise
(continued)

FIGURE 6–6.   **(cont.)**

In breakeven charts the fixed costs, variable costs, and revenue are plotted against output, either in units, dollar volume, or percent of capacity. Thus in Figure 6–6b the line F'F represents the fixed costs of production. The line F'V shows the variation in total variable cost with production.... Inasmuch as F'V represents the total costs of production and O'S the total revenue from sales, the intersection of these two lines is the point at which revenue is exactly equal to costs and is often called the breakeven point.

E. Paul DeGarmo et al., Engineering Economy (New York: Macmillan, 1979), 34–35.

The preliminary study focused on finding a low-cost filter that could be used on small and intermediate size farms in conjunction with anaerobic digesters. The moisture content should be decreased to a level where the manure can be used as a feed-ingredient or to a level where further dehydrating with other methods, such as heat treatment, would become economically feasible. Figure 6–6c shows the cost of drying chicken manure at different moisture contents down to 10 percent moisture.

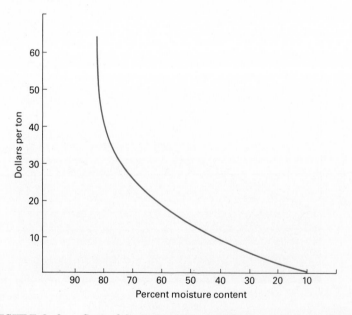

FIGURE 6–6c. Cost of drying waste at various moisture contents (heating oil at $0.50/gal)

FIGURE 6–6. (cont.)

The graph indicates that removing moisture by heat treatment is extremely expensive for mixtures of high moisture content. The moisture content of anaerobically digested manure is approximately 95 percent water. Zero–20 percent moisture removal is necessary before refeeding.

U.S. Environmental Protection Agency, Energy and Economic Assessment of Anaerobic Digesters and Biofuels for Rural Waste Management (Cincinnati: EPA, 1978), 116–17.

Figure 6–6d shows the changing age distribution in the population of the U.S. from 1960–2000. The under-five and five-through-thirteen age groups are becoming a much smaller percentage of the overall population. In 1960 these groups accounted for 29.5 percent of the population. In 2000 they will represent 20.4 percent. On the other end of the scale, the thirty-five to forty-four, forty-five to fifty-four, and sixty-five-and-over groups are projected to have large growth during the last part of this century.

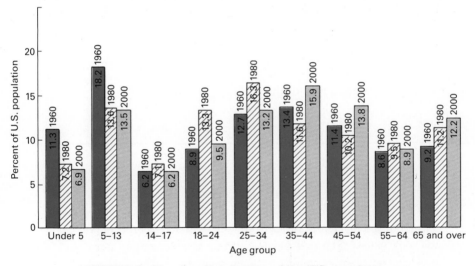

FIGURE 6–6d. Age distribution of the U.S. population

Source: U.S. Bureau of the Census, *Current Population Reports*, Series P-25, Nos. 310, 311, 519, 704, 721. (Projections based on Series II assumptions.)

Joel R. Evans and Barry Berman, Marketing (New York: Macmillan, 1982), 88–90.

FIGURE 6–6. (cont.)

STEP 2.   On your worksheet, list the different areas of your report in which you'll discuss numbers, and describe the type and content of the illustrations that you think will be best for each.

Graphic Aids for Key Concepts

Nonphysical and nonnumerical concepts can also be illustrated using symbolic, or *conceptual*, line drawings. The typical organization chart is an example: the various officers and divisions of a corporation are not *physically* arranged as shown in such charts, but *conceptually* (in terms of hierarchy and channels).

Flowcharts.   One often-overlooked opportunity for effective illustration is the flowchart. It indicates the pathway of things or people through a structure or organization. Flowcharts often repeat in nonprose form what is discussed in paragraph form, but they can also save laborious explanation. Imagine having to explain all of the events pictured in the example flowchart in Figure 6–7.

Organizational Charts.   Organizational charts depict the components of organizations and their interrelationships. The connecting lines represent the channels of responsibility and information flow, and vertical location represents level of authority. Figure 6–8 contains one example.

Other Conceptual Line Drawings.   Various geometrical shapes are commonly used to represent concepts in reports. As you plan, write, or review the rough draft of a report, try to identify the key concepts and imagine drawings that could symbolize those concepts. Of all the different graphic aids discussed here, this type is the most often overlooked. In the example conceptual illustrations in Figure 6–9, the explanations are a part of the legend.

The fermentation reaction gives off energy as it proceeds (about 500 Btu per pound of ethanol produced). There will be a normal heat loss from the fermentation tank as long as the temperature outside the tank is less than that inside. ... Thus, the fermenters must be equipped with active cooling systems, such as cooling coils and external jackets, to circulate air or water for convective cooling.

Solar Energy Research Institute, Department of Energy, Fuel from Farms: A Guide to Small-Scale Ethanol Production, SERI/SP-451-519 (Washington, D.C.: U.S. Government Printing Office, 1980), 33–35.

(continued)

FIGURE 6–7.   Example of a flowchart

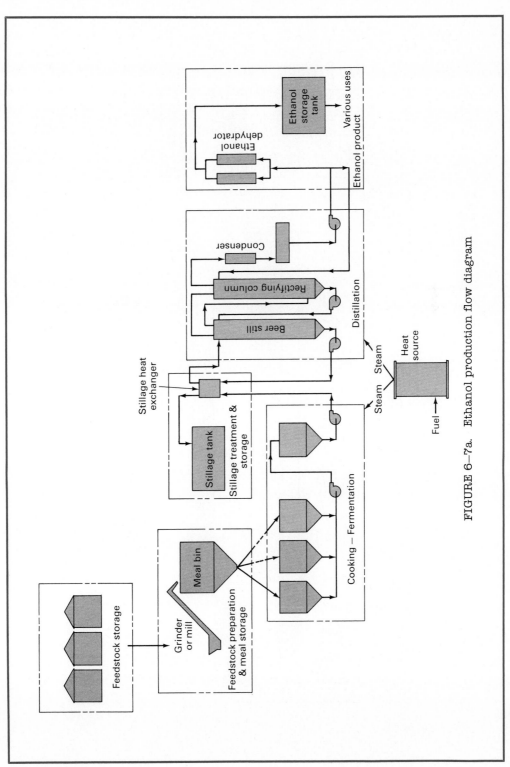

FIGURE 6–7a.   Ethanol production flow diagram

FIGURE 6–7 (cont.)

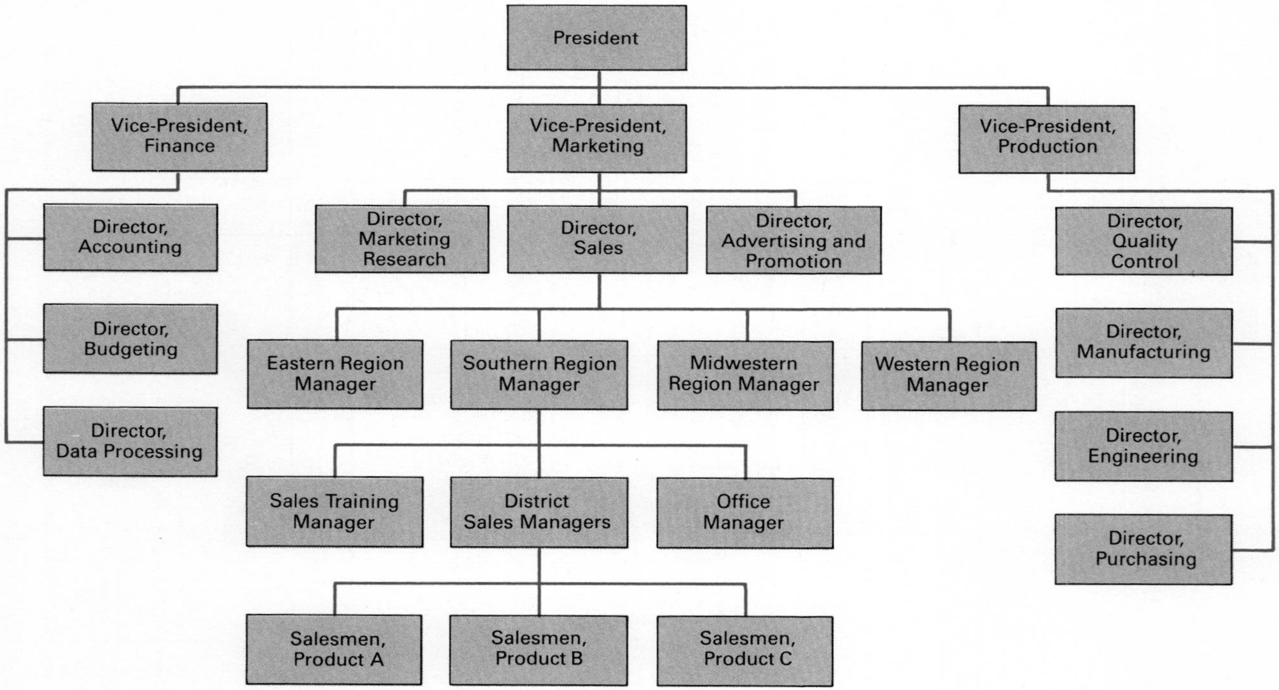

FIGURE 6–8. **Example of an organizational chart**

FIGURE 6–8a. Organizational structure

(continued)

Organizational Structure

Figure 6–8a shows the organizational chart of a hypothetical manufacturing firm. In this example, work units are grouped by type of work (finance, marketing, and production), geographic area (regional and district sales offices), and product line. Of course, an organizing scheme which is logical and efficient for one company may not be desirable for another.

An organizational structure must be flexible because of constantly changing technological, social, and economic factors....

Donald H. Sanders, Computers in Business: An Introduction (New York: McGraw-Hill, 1975), 475–76. Reprinted with permission.

FIGURE 6–8. (cont.)

Graphic Aids for Words

Quite often discussion is summarized in tables that contain words in the rows and columns as well as numbers. They summarize the key points in a report discussion. Figure 6–10 contains two examples of *summary tables*.

STEP 3. On your worksheet, list the key concepts that you think could be illustrated using some form of conceptual line drawings (flowchart, organizational chart, or other conceptual line drawing). Describe or sketch the illustrations you think you'd use for these key concepts in your report.

Planning and Developing Graphic Aids

When you plan a report, make a list of the tables and illustrations you think will be needed. This kind of planning can save you time and duplication of effort; also, writing with copies of your graphic aids in front of you is much more efficient because you can refer to them directly as you write. Here are some steps you might follow to make this process work for you:

1. Identify the type and content of graphic aids your report will need. For this purpose, set up a chart like the one in Figure 6–11.

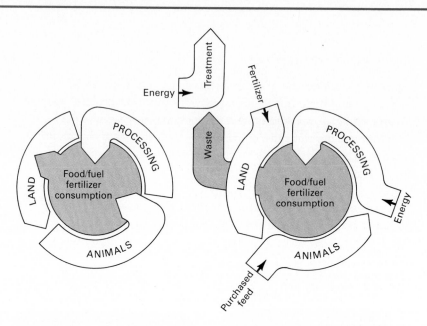

FIGURE 6–9a. A diagrammatic representation of the operations of the traditional agriculture. Although yields were small by modern standards, all waste products were fed back into and absorbed by the land, which was also the sole energy source.

FIGURE 6–9b. Modern intensive agriculture has permitted enormously increased food yields, but at the price of external energy and nutrient inputs and the production of waste in greater quantities than the land can absorb. Disposal or neutralization of this waste requires a further energy input.

Martin Pawley, Building for Tomorrow: Putting Waste to Work (San Francisco: Sierra Club Books, 1982), 29.

FIGURE 6–9. A conceptual line drawing used in a technical report

2. Think about the contents of your report, its purpose, and audience; refer to the outline; and ask yourself these questions about each area of your report:

Will I discuss objects, mechanisms, or situations here that should be illustrated?

Will I need to present statistical information at this point in the report?

Are there important concepts or ideas in this section that could be shown conceptually with line drawings?

Telescopes: A Comparative Survey

	Binoculars	Refractors	Newtonian reflectors	Rich-Field reflectors
Common sizes	7 × 35, 7 × 50	2.4 in.–4 in.	3 in.–6 in.	4 in.
Manufacturers	Jason, Selsi, and some telescope companies	Edmund, Mayflower, Pentax, Tasco, Unitrax	Cave, Coulter, Mead, Criterion, Edmund, Tasco	Edmund
Price range	$45–80	$200–600	$150–450	$150–250
Performance (on Sun, Moon, and planets)	poor–adequate	excellent	good	adequate–good
Performance on stars and star clusters	good	adequate–good	good–excellent	good
Performance on nebulae and galaxies	good	poor–adequate	excellent	excellent
Advantages	• wide angle • portable • rugged • inexpensive • sealed optics • other uses	• sharp images • portable • rugged • sealed optics • steady images	• inexpensive • color-correct • compact • portable • stable mounts	• wide angle • bright images • compact • portable • color-correct • sealed optics
Disadvantages	• chromatic ab. • low magnif. • small apertures	• expensive • chromatic ab. • small field	• open tube • delicate • awkward viewing	• low magnif. • focus at edge of field

Scott Woodward, "Purchasing a Telescope," Austin Community College, March 31, 1984.

FIGURE 6–10.   Example of a summary table

Report Topic	Type of Graphic	Contents of the Graphic
Heart transplant	Line graph	Heart-transplant survival rate
	Pictorial diagram	Jarvik-7 mechanical heart
	Flowchart	Blood flow in the heart
	Photograph	Associated heart-transplant equipment
Mechanically induced fracturing in oil drilling	Conceptual diagram	Stresses on rock element
	Pictorial diagram	Formation damage from fluid infiltration
	Photograph	Hydraulic fracturing equipment
	Table	Oil recovery with hydraulic fracturing and without
Residential solar heating and cooling	Pictorial diagram	Flat-plate solar collector Types of absorber plates
	Schematic diagram	Solar heating and cooling piping system
	Table	Economic comparisons: solar heating and other methods Visible absorptance and infrared emissivity of selected coatings

FIGURE 6–11. Graphic-aids planning chart

3. Decide which kinds of graphic aids these areas of your report will require. For example, should you present statistical information in a table or in a graph? Should you illustrate a mechanism in a drawing, diagram, or photograph?

Kind of Information	Choice of Graphic Aids
physical things	line drawings diagrams flowcharts photographs
numerical data	line graphs bar charts pie charts tables

Kind of Information	Choice of Graphic Aids
key concepts	conceptual drawings flowcharts summary tables organizational charts
words	summary tables

4. Find or create as many of the illustrations that you think are needed *before* you begin writing the first draft. As you write, you can refer to them more readily and discuss specific details about them.

STEP 4.   Review your notes on the preceding steps, and fill out a chart like the one in Figure 6–11. Be sure to indicate the purpose of each graphic aid you intend to use.

Finding Materials for Graphic Aids.   When you have located areas in your text that will require statistical information, consider the following routes for locating appropriate accompanying statistics. Resources such as the following contain statistical information:

> *Statistical Abstract of the United States*
> *Statistical Yearbook of the United Nations*
> *The World Almanac and Book of Facts*

More specialized sources of statistical information for specific fields such as nursing, medicine, the health sciences, energy, or petroleum engineering include these examples:

> *Facts about Nurisng*
> *Facts at Your Fingertips: A Guide to Sources of Statistical Information on Major Health Topics*
> *Hospital Statistics: Data from the American Hospital Association Annual Survey*
> *The Complete Energy Factbook*
> *Basic Petroleum Data Book*
> *World Energy Book*

If your cannot find the statistics you need, use one of these two resources:

> Paul Wasserman, *Statistical Sources*
> American Statistics Index, *Statistical Reference Index*

Subject guides and guides to the literature of a specific field are also useful in finding specific statistical reference books. See Chapter 9 for steps on finding them.

Step 5.   On your worksheet, list or describe the sources from which you plan to get statistical information for your graphic aids.

Scanning Report Drafts for Graphic Aids.   After you have written a rough draft of your report, always review it for the need of graphic aids you might not have noticed in the planning or writing of the draft. Look particularly for chances to create illustrations of key concepts, the one type of graphic aid often overlooked. Review your report draft for additional graphic aids by doing the following:

- Look for discussion of objects or mechanisms that are not illustrated, and ask yourself whether a line drawing would help readers follow your discussion.
- Look for discussion of statistics in your report draft that are not presented graphically, and ask yourself whether a table or graph of that information would be effective.
- Look for discussion of key concepts and ideas, and ask yourself whether line drawings that presented those concepts symbolically would be effective.

When you review your report draft for graphic aids, look for any discussion whose information can be *re-presented* in graphic form. All the information you need for a table or line drawing may be sitting in your rough draft; create the illustration and supplement the discussion with it. That way, readers will get two views of the same information.

Guidelines for Graphic Aids

Keep the following suggestions in mind when you design graphic aids for reports:

- Locate graphic aids *as close as possible* to the text where they are discussed.
- Use illustrations that are *less than a full page long* to help break up large blocks of text.
- Refer to and discuss *all* graphic aids you use in your report. Interpret illustrations for readers, and explain the important points in tables and graphs. Don't assume that readers automatically understand the significance of a table.
- Give each of your illustrations a *title* and a *number*. Different systems of numbering are common: for example, arabic numerals for the illustrations and roman numerals for the tables.
- As for guidelines on photocopying, trimming, taping, and documenting illustrations from other sources as well as advice on drawing your own illustrations, see Chapter 10.
- Keep your tables and illustrations simple; don't overwhelm your readers with needless detail. Instead of presenting monstrous tables no one will use, present selections of important detail from them. Include the big tables in the appendix of your report.
- Locate illustrations and tables in the appendix of your report if you do not refer to them directly in the report or if you refer to one so much that it would be easier for readers to use them in the appendix.

STEP 6.   When you have written a complete first draft of your report, scan it for additional graphic aids that may be needed, and review all of your graphic aids using the preceding guidelines.

Textual Aids

Textual aids are those devices that help readers find their way around in the report and locate the information they need quickly. Such devices include page numbers, chapter numbers, indexes, and tables of contents. You may be used to writing essays that require no other textual aids than titles and page numbers. Technical reports, however, usually require a full range of textual aids, with headings being one of the most important.

Headings

Headings are the titles and subtitles used in the actual text of an article, report, or book. They break up a piece of writing into manageable units and give readers a sense of what comes next. Headings are used throughout this book. For example,

- "Textual Aids," the heading that introduces this section and starts at the left margin, is a first-level heading.
- "Headings," which heads the current paragraph, is a second-level heading.

Headings are like titles for individual sections or paragraphs that give readers an overview of the contents and organization of that section.

A Common System of Headings.

If you are planning your report, consider using the system that is about to be presented. First, here is an outline version of the headings to be used:

II. THE LANDFILL
    The Sanitary Landfill
    The Secure Landfill
      Barrier Walls
      Cover
      Individual Cells

III. DEEP-WELL INJECTION
    Historical Background
    Area Geology Requirements
    Waste Requirements
    Well Requirements
    State Safety Requirements

In Figure 6–12 are excerpts of the report itself in which these headings occur.

Technical reports use a variety of styles in the design of headings, but they all depend on one essential principle: the use of visual tricks to indicate the organization, relationship, and level of the different sections. In this chapter notice that "Textual Aids" and "Graphic Aids" are first-level headings and the most noticeable when you glance through this chapter. Less noticeable is the third-level heading,

---

II. THE LANDFILL

The landfill is currently the most common method of hazardous-waste disposal. Although there are many problems associated with a landfill, namely, lack of available sites and contamination of ground and surface water ...

The Sanitary Landfill

Sanitary landfilling has been used for a number of years as a method of disposing of various types of waste materials. Hazardous wastes are often disposed of at these sites. ...

The Secure Landfill

The secure landfill is similar to the sanitary landfill except that it is specifically designed to ...

Barrier Walls.   Impermeable barrier walls surround the wastes on all sides. The barriers are usually made of clay. ...

Cover. After completion of the landfill, a 2-foot clay cover, followed by 6 inches of soil for vegetation, is placed on top of the landfill ...

FIGURE 6–12.   A common system of headings

"Guidelines for Using Heads." The visual tricks that cause headings to be more or less noticeable are such things as the following:

position on the page	indention	large dots
capital letters	colors	asterisks
underlining	different types faces	dashes
boldfacing	numbering	

When you type your report on an ordinary typewriter, you are probably limited to positioning, using capital letters, indenting, underlining, and numbering, which are usually quite adequate.

Guidelines for Using Headings.   The following advice should help you design effective headings for your reports:

• Have an idea of the headings you'll use *before* you start writing. Inserting headings *as* you write the rough draft rather than *after* should help you write in a more organized way and eliminate the problems involved in inserting them afterwards.

• Use your outline to plan the headings for your report. When you reach a new section, it's time for another heading.

• After you've written a rough draft, review it to assess the need for second-, third-, and even fourth-level headings, especially when more than two pages of text occur with no headings.

• If you go back and insert headings after writing a rough draft, reread the sentences before and after each inserted heading, and rephrase them if they are at odds with the surrounding text or with the headings.

• Avoid referring to the heading with "this," "it," "these," or other such pronouns. Write the text following the heading as if the heading were not there at all. Usually, you can rephrase the sentence so that the repeated element is at the end of the sentence, as the revision of the second example in Figure 6–13 illustrates.

• Have some text, even if only a sentence or two, between any two headings. If you are at a loss about what to insert in such gaps between headings, consider these possibilities:

Definition of any term about to be discussed
Historical background related to the subtopic about to be discussed
Some transitional element to ease the reader from the preceding section into the
   new one
Most importantly, an overview of the subtopics about to be discussed.

One example you might follow appears in Figure 6–14.

• If you design your own headings, or modify the system used here, remember this main principle: the lower the level of the heading, the less readily the eye should notice it as it scans the page. For example,

1. A centered, capitalized, underlined heading is the most noticeable of all the headings in this text's examples.
2. A left-margin, initial-capital, underlined heading is not quite as immediately noticeable.
3. A run-in, initial-capital, underlined heading is still less noticeable.
4. A run-in, initial-capital, nonunderlined heading is the least noticeable of these examples.

• Make the phrasing of your headings indicate as fully as possible the subject matter of the sections they introduce. Here are some examples:

Vague Headings	Revised, Descriptive Headings
Background	Early Development of Intravenous Therapy
Operation	Basic Operation of the Dialysis Unit
Discussion	Implications of the Findings in Dialysis Research
Advantages	Benefits of Increased Writing Requirements in Nursing Programs

Problem Headings and Text

Radiant Energy

This is produced in a variety of ways such as the warmth from a glowing fireplace, the light reflecting off snow in the mountains, and the X-rays used by a dentist. All of these forms of radiant energy share certain fundamental characteristics. . . .

Quantum Theory

This important theory in physics is concerned with the rules that govern the gain or loss of energy from an object. Planck's contribution was to see that the gain or loss of energy from objects of atomic or subatomic size was quite different from that of objects of ordinary dimensions. . . .

Revision

Radiant Energy

Radiant energy is produced in a variety of ways such as in the warmth from a glowing fireplace, the light reflecting off snow in the mountains, and X-rays used by a dentist. All of these forms of radiant energy share certain fundamental characteristics. . . .

Quantum Theory

Planck's observation that the gain or loss of energy from objects of atomic or subatomic size is quite different from that of objects of ordinary size led to development of the quantum theory. The essence of his theory is that. . . .

FIGURE 6–13. Phrasing problems using headings

• Make headings more or less the same length. Avoid overly long headings, for example, "The Total Climatology and Persistence Method of Predicting the Paths of Hurricanes." Shorten it to "The Total Climatology and Persistence Method."

• Make the phrasing of your headings as parallel as you can. (For more on parallelism, see Appendix D.) Look at the versions of a set of headings in Figure 6–15.

Rough-Draft Version

Clampers

   Positive Diode Clamper. The output from each circuit is clamped to a dc voltage reference. The output of the positive diode clampers is always above the reference, whatever it may be. . . .

   Negative Diode Clamper. The cathode of the negative diode clamper in each circuit is connected to the reference rather than the anode as in the positive clamper. . . .

Revised Version

Clampers

   A clamper is a circuit that permits the voltage of a wave form to rise or fall only as far as a specific reference voltage. Clampers may have a negative or positive reference voltage and thus are called positive diode clampers and negative diode clampers.

   Positive Diode Clamper. The output. . . .

   Negative Diode Clamper. The cathode . . .

William P. Hand and Gerald Williams, Basic Electronics: Components, Devices, and Circuits (New York: Glencoe, 1980), 204–6.

FIGURE 6–14. Revising for text between headings

• Avoid having only one heading on a level. It's the same problem as having one-item outline entries. In such cases, you can (1) delete the single heading altogether, or (2) create another heading to go on the same level with it. Figure 6–16 has an example of this problem and a revision.

• Make sure that your headings correctly show the relationships between the sections and subsections of your report. Look carefully at the incorrect and correct captions in Figure 6–17.

The problem version runs together the first six headings on the *components* of the space shuttle's engines and the next set of headings on the *stages* in the process of producing the thrust. But a component is not the same as a stage. In the revision

Nonparallel Version	Revised, Parallel Version
II. Description and Function of the Components	II. Description and Function of the Components
A. The Infrared Detector	A. The Infrared Detector
B. How the Radar Sender/Receiver Works	B. The Radar Sender/Receiver
C. The X-Ray Sender/Receiver	C. The X-Ray Sender/Receiver
D. The Computer	D. The Computer
1. Using the Map Disks	1. The Map Disks Detector
2. Receptions from the Detector	2. Receptions from the Detectors
E. The Video Screen	E. The Video Screen
F. The Keyboard	F. The Keyboard
1. Positioning the Car	1. Positioning the Car
2. Intersection Statements	2. Intersection Statements
III. Using the VAC System	III. Operating Cycle of the VAC System
IV. Economic Feasibility of the VAC System	IV. Economic Feasibility of the VAC System
V. What Are the Advantages of the VAC System?	V. Advantages of the VAC System

FIGURE 6–15. Parallelism in headings

the headings for the individual components and stages are downshifted to a third level, and second-level headings introduce the components section and the stages section.

Decimal Numbering Systems for Headings.   Technical reports often use decimal numbering with headings. Here is a common variation:

Title Heading

1 FIRST-LEVEL HEADING
  1.1 Second-Level Heading

1.1.1 Third-level heading.
1.1.2 Third-level heading.
1.1.3 Third-level heading.
1.2 Second-Level Heading
2 FIRST-LEVEL HEADING
2.1 Second-Level Heading
2.2 Second-Level Heading
2.2.1 Third-level heading.
2.2.2 Third-level heading.
2.3 Second-Level Heading

If this chapter had used this system, the headings would have looked like this:

6.1 Graphic Aids
6.1.1 Graphic Aids for Physical Things
6.1.1.1 Photographs
6.1.1.2 Line Drawings

Problem Headings

VII. USE OF COMPOSITES IN TODAY'S AIRCRAFT

Within the past few years this country's major aircraft-manufacturing firms have started to use composites more than ever before. In aircraft such as the Douglas DC-9 Super 80 and Lockheed's L-1011, there is extensive use of Kevlar and graphite epoxy in the secondary structure. The two new aircraft from Boeing, the 757 and the 767, use composites in both primary and secondary structures. In the private sector an aircraft made entirely from composites has recently been certified by the federal aviation administration; this aircraft is the Lear Fan 2100.

The Lear Fan 2100

The Lear Fan 2100 is the largest production aircraft to be designed specifically for composites. The aircraft would be impractical to build with conventional aluminum. Its basic design consists of twin turboshaft engines turning a single propeller. The eight-person aircraft is capable of speeds of 400 mph and altitudes of up to 41,000 feet.

(continued)

FIGURE 6—16. Revision of problem headings

VIII. CURRENT RESEARCH IN NEW APPLICATIONS OF COMPOSITES

Scientists and engineers continue to ...

Revision

VII. USE OF COMPOSITES IN TODAY'S AIRCRAFT

Within the past few years this country's major aircraft-manufacturing firms have started to use composites more than ever before.

Douglas and Lockheed

In aircraft such as the Douglas DC-9 Super 80 and Lockheed's L-1011, there is extensive use of Kevlar and graphite epoxy in the secondary structures. The two new aircraft from Boeing, the 757 and the 767, use composites in both primary and secondary structures.

The Lear Fan 2100

In the private sector an aircraft made entirely from composites has ...

VIII. CURRENT RESEARCH IN NEW APPLICATIONS OF COMPOSITES

Scientists and engineers continue to ...

FIGURE 6—16. (cont.)

Problem Headings

V. THE SPACE SHUTTLE'S MAIN ENGINES

The space shuttle's main engines (SSME) consist of six major components and a regenerative cooling system. There are also six processes that go along with these components. The major parts of the SSME are (1) the external tank, (2) the low-pressure turbopumps, (3) the high-pressure turbopumps, (4) the preburners, (5) the combustion chamber, and (6) the nozzle.

FIGURE 6—17. Revising the level of headings

The External Tank

The external tank is a large fuel tank that holds the liquid hydrogen and oxygen for ...

Low-Pressure Turbopumps

The low-pressure turbopumps (LPT) raise the pressure of the oxygen and hydrogen several hundred psi. ...

High-Pressure Turbopump

The high-presure turbopump (HPT) is similar to the LPT in that it is a pump turned by ...

Preburners

The preburners are a baffled injector that mixes gaseous hydrogen and liquid oxygen. ...

Main Combustion Chamber

The main combustion chamber (MCC) is the component in which the hot hydrogen and super-heated steam from the preburners mixes with the oxygen under very high pressures. ...

The Nozzle

The nozzle accelerates the flow of combusted propellants out of the engine; this action produces the thrust. ...

The process of the operation of the SSME involves the following stages: (1) storage of the propellants; (2) low pressurization of the propellants; (3) high pressurization of the propellants; (4) preignition; (5) ignition of the propellants; and (6) expansion.

Storage of the Propellants

The external tank stores the liquid hydrogen at temperatures below $-450°$ F and ...

Low Pressurization of the Propellants

The low-pressure turbopumps raise the pressure of the propellants several hundred psi. ...

(continued)

FIGURE 6–17 (cont.)

Revised Headings

V. THE SPACE SHUTTLE'S MAIN ENGINES

The Space Shuttle's main engines (SSME) consist of six major components and a regenerative cooling system. There are also six processes that go along with these components.

Main Components of the SSME

The major parts of the SSME are (1) the external tank, (2) the low-pressure turbopumps, (3) the high-pressure turbopumps, (4) the preburners, (5) the combustion chamber, and (6) the nozzle.

The External Tank.   The external tank is a large fuel tank that holds the liquid hydrogen and oxygen. . . .

Low-Pressure Turbopumps.   The low-pressure turbopumps (LPT) raise the pressure of the oxygen and hydrogen. . . .

High-Pressure Turbopump.   The high-pressure turbopump (HPT) is similar . . .

Preburners.   The preburners are a baffled injector that mixes gaseous hydrogen and liquid oxygen. . . .

Main Combustion Chamber.   The main combustion chamber (MCC) is the component in which . . .

The Nozzle.   The nozzle accelerates the flow of combusted propellants out of the engine; this action produces the thrust. . . .

Operation of the Main Engines

The process of the operation of the SSME involves the following stages: (1) storage of the propellants; (2) low pressurization of the propellants; (3) high pressurization of the propellants; (4) preignition; (5) ignition of the propellants; and (6) expansion.

Storage of the Propellants.   The external tank stores the liquid hydrogen. . . .

Low Pressurization of the Propellants.   The low-pressure turbo-pumps raise the pressure . . .

FIGURE 6–17.   (cont.)

266

STEP 7. If you have not written the rough draft yet, use or develop an outline for headings to insert as you write. If you already have a rough draft, use the guidelines just cited to insert headings or to make sure that the hedings you've used are well designed.

Titles

As opposed to headings, titles here refer to an overall title of a book, a chapter within a book, a report, or an article.

• Make titles of reports as fully self-explanatory as possible. Watch out for overly general titles like the ones in the following list; attempt to make your report title reflect the specific focus of the report itself. Here are some examples:

Overly General Titles	*Specific Titles*
A Technical Report on Aircraft Design	A Technical Report on the Use of Composites in Aircraft Design
Report on Hazardous-Waste Methods	Report on Land Disposal of Hazardous Wastes
Report on Alcohol	Report on Maternal Consumption of Alcohol during Pregnancy
Report on Oil-Well Drilling	Report on Mechanically Induced Hydraulic Fracture Systems
Report on Acid Rain	Report on the Chemical Processes in Acid Rain
Technical Report on the Space Shuttle	Technical Report on the Development of the Space-Shuttle Engines

• Make titles cover important subtopics within reports. The title "Financial Aid to Nursing Students" is less comprehensive than "Scholarships and Loans Available to Nursing Students." The colon is useful for indicating the subtopics covered in a report. (Watch out for overly long titles, however.) Here are some examples of well-designed report titles that indicate subtopics:

The Space Shuttle's Main Engines: Development, Operation, and Testing
Computerized Speech Recognition: Design, Applications, and Problems
The Greenhouse Effect: The Mechanisms, the Effects, and Possible Solutions
Solar Heating and Cooling: Design, Sizing, and Economics

• Beware of obsolete trends in titles. "Beyond" and "toward" are buzzwords often used in titles now, but use them sparingly. Also, beware cute, clever, catchy, or poetic-sounding titles: "Beyond the Heart Transplant," "The Miraculous World of the Salmon," "Life in Limbo", and "The Challenge of 3 East."

• Include in your report title some phrase indicating the kind of report you are writing. Is it a "report," a "feasibility study," a "proposal," or a "review"? Does it focus on research-oriented concerns, theory, or administrative, practical, or educational issues? Here are some examples that indicate the type of report (that key word or phrase indicating the type of report is italicized):

Bereavement and the Elderly: A *Critical Review* with Implications for Nursing Practice and Research
Report on the *Feasibility* of Using Cocombustion in Lawrence, Kansas
Hemodialysis *Manual*: A *Guide* to Health-Care Personnel
Progress Report on the Construction of Bike Lanes for Austin, Texas
Health Care for Refugees: Some *Recommendations*
Primary Health-Care Delivery and Public Health Departments: A *Model* and *Simulation*
Investigative Report on the Kansas City Hyatt Regency Walkways Collapse
Survey Report on Citizens' Support of the Proposed Recycling Program
Proposal to Revitalize the Downtown Area
Women in Leadership Positions: A *Survey* of Allied Health Chairpersons
Doctoral Education and Nursing: A *Historical Analysis*

STEP 8.   On your worksheet write several titles for your report, modeling them after any of the preceding examples.

Table of Contents

For reports of ten pages or more in which there are sections and subsections with headings, include a table of contents. The following guidelines should help you create attractive, useful, and professional-looking tables of contents:

• List not only the main section titles (first-level headings) but also lower-level titles (second- and even third-level headings). A good table shows which aspects of the report topic you cover and how the report is organized. It enables readers to choose sections that they want to read.
• Also list in the table of contents those important report elements such as introductions, abstracts, conclusions, recommendations, glossaries, and special appendices.
• Design the graphics of the table of contents carefully. In the example in Figure 6–18 notice the following:
The major section titles are in all capital letters and thus stand out more.
The subsection titles are initial capitals only.
At least one line is skipped between major sections in the table to make reading easier.
The use of leader dots makes finding page numbers easier.

• The phrasing of items in the table of contents should be the same word for word as the items appear in the text.

Table of Contents

List of Figures iv

Abstract. v

   I. INTRODUCTION. 1

  II. HUMAN VOICE PRODUCTION. 2

     Generating Sound. 2

        Voiced Sounds 3

        Unvoiced Sounds. 5

     Factors Affecting the Human Voice. 7

 III. THE ISOLATED WORD RECOGNITION SYSTEM 9

     The Preprocessor 9

        The Spectrum Shaper. 9

        The Speech Analyzer 12

     The Feature Extractor. 14

     The Classification Phase. 15

        The Time Normalizer. 15

        The Training Mode and Reference Pattern Memory. 18

        The Classifier 19

     Decision Algorithms. 20

        Dynamic Programming. 20

        Zero Crossing Rate 22

        Linear Predictive Coding 23

        State Diagrams 25

  IV. APPLICATIONS OF VOICE RECOGNITION SYSTEMS 26

   V. PROBLEMS WITH SPEECH RECOGNITION 29

     Recognition Accuracy 29

     Limited Vocabulary Size. 31

     Privacy. 32

  VI. GOALS OF THE SPEECH-RECOGNITION INDUSTRY. 34

 VII. CONCLUSION. 36

     APPENDICES. 37

        List of References. 38

        Glossary. 39

        List of Companies Involved in Speech-Recognition

        Design and Production 40

FIGURE 6—18.   A table of contents

List of Figures or Illustrations

If you have charts, tables, diagrams, flowcharts, or other illustrations in your report, list them just after the table of contents. Here are some guidelines to remember:

- Although a list of figures for less than three or four tables or illustrations is not necessary, prepare a list anyway if readers need a way to find certain important figures quickly. If it's a short list, include it at the bottom of the table of contents page.
- A *table* is an array of statistical information in columns and rows, while a *figure* is anything else such as a diagram or photograph.
- If you have both illustrations and figures, do one of the following:
  If there are more than four or five tables and illustrations both, as happens in long reports, create two separate lists, one for the tables, another for the illustrations.
  If there are only a few tables and illustrations, combine them, and call it a list of figures.
  If both lists are short, you can also include them on the same page. (See examples in the following sections.)
- If you have two separate lists, one for tables and one for figures, number them differently. For instance, give tables roman numerals; figures, arabic numerals.
- The phrasing of the title of the illustration in the list and in the text of the report itself must be the same. You can, however, shorten titles for the list by deleting some of the final words in the text version. Look at the list of illustrations, list of figures, and list of tables in Figure 6–19.

Lists

Another important textual aid is the list. There are two kinds of lists: the in-sentence list and the vertical list. Their main purposes are to emphasize or highlight certain points and to make reading easier at key places in a report.

You've seen the in-sentence list often in this book: when there is an important list of items to be presented, each item is preceded by a number (or letter) in parentheses. The items in parentheses can be (1) single words, (2) phrases, (3) clauses, or (4) whole sentences. You've also seen plenty of vertical lists in this book: they provide even greater emphasis because of the way they appear on the page. An example appears in Figure 6–20.

When you use lists, remember these guidelines:

- Punctuate in-sentence lists just as you would if they did not have the numbers in parentheses.
- Use a colon to introduce an in-sentence list *only* if it would be used in the sentence anyway.
- Use either numbers or lowercase letters in in-sentence lists, but use one or the other consistently.
- Do not punctuate after each item in a vertical list (with a comma or semicolon, for example) unless each item is a complete sentence or unless each item completes the sentence introducing the items.

LIST OF ILLUSTRATIONS

Illustration	Page
1. Ice-crystal photomicrographs	6
2. Equilibrium freezing curve for seawater	10
3. Wash-separation column	11
4. Vacuum freeze-vapor compression method	13
5. Vapor-absorption method	16
6. Butane method	17
7. Seawater desalting costs	23
8. Capital equipment	24
9. Installation items	24
10. Power requirements	25

LIST OF FIGURES

Figures	Page
1. Cross Member	7
2. Classes of Fiber Reinforcement	12
3. Failure of Fibers	14
4a. Plunger-Type Injection Molder	16
4b. Reciprocating Injection Molder	17
5. Compression Molding	27

LIST OF TABLES

Tables	Page
1. Plastic Substitutions to Save Weight	3
2. Average Material Costs for Auto Materials	4
3. Breakdown of Automotive Scrap by Type	5
4. Production Energy for Automobile Materials	10
5. Weight-Savings Ratios for Substitutes	10
6. RIM Fascia Usage	18

FIGURE 6–19. Lists of figures, tables, and illustrations

- In vertical lists, number the items if they are a sequence of steps; use asterisks for items having no particular order.
- Make the items in both types of lists parallel; in particular, avoid mixing complete sentences with incomplete ones. (For more on parallelism, see Appendix D.)

<u>The Memory Unit</u>

The memory unit of a computer consists of an array of cells in which information can be stored. The physical realization of a memory cell in a particular computer depends on the state of technology at the time the computer is designed and on its projected selling price. When computers first appeared, their memory was made from arrays of relays and vacuum tubes. Today, semiconductor chips and magnetic cores are used to construct memory units.

Each cell of the computer memory has a distinct address and a content. The address specifies the location of the cell, and the content is the data stored in the cell.

<u>The Store Operation.</u>   The function of the store operation in a computer is to store or to write data into a particular memory cell. The CPU has to do the following:

1. Place the address of the memory cell or word that will be used to store the given data in the address register.
2. Place the data in the data register.
3. Check the memory word specified by the given address to see if it is empty.
4. If the cell is empty, transfer the data from the data register to the selected memory word; otherwise, select another address, place it in the address register, and go back to step 3.

Adapted from Mo Kim Cheng, <u>Report on Computer Structures and Logic Design</u> (Austin: Univ. of Texas, 1983), 16.

FIGURE 6–20.   Using vertical lists

STEP 9.   If you've not written a rough draft yet, make a list of the areas of your report in which you think listing will be effective. If you do have a rough draft, scan it for areas where lists can improve your report.

Pagination

When you put in the page numbers of a report, remember the following general guidelines:

• *Every* page, every piece of paper within the two covers of a report gets a number.

- All pages preceding the first page of the introduction of the report are usually given lowercase roman numerals and are usually located at the bottom of the pages.
- All pages beginning with the first page of the introduction are given arabic numerals, which, with the following exception, are placed in the upper right or upper middle of the page.
- Usually, the numeral "1" does not appear on the first page of the introduction.
- On the first page of a major section or chapter, the page number usually appears at the bottom of the page.
- On divider pages, such as the page that has only the title "Appendix" on it, no page number appears.

Keep in mind that these guidelines are only one common system. For pagination rules in your field, find a style guide for report writing in that field (see Chapter 9).

Title Page

The design of title pages varies widely, but here is a common approach:

- Include the full title of the report plus any subtitles.
- Include the name and title of any specific individual to whom the report is addressed, plus the name of the organization.
- Include the date when the report was finished.
- Include your name (and title, and the organization of which you are a part, if applicable).
- Include a descriptive abstract, and locate it just below the writer's name.
- Try to keep the title page neat, balanced, and uncluttered.

For an example of this approach, look at Figure 6–21.

Cover Label

Always remember that seemingly minor but crucial finishing touch—the cover label. A big report without a label on a busy executive's cluttered desk may never get read. When you prepare the label, make sure it is neat and symmetrical. Include the title of the report, your name (and title, if possible), and a date. Make sure that the adhesive on the back of the label is strong; beware of cheap labels that dry and fall off in a week or so. An example of a typical cover label appears in Figure 6–22.

Glossary and List of Symbols and Abbreviations

The glossary is the place for technical terms readers may not know. The list of symbols or abbreviations (or both) spells out the full meaning of symbols and abbreviations used in a report. Sometimes, the glossary and the lists are combined into one and called a glossary. If you include a glossary or list of symbols in your report, call attention to it in the early pages of the report in this manner:

Reaction injection molding can be used to produce both unreinforced and reinforced plastic automobile parts. Unreinforced parts include front and rear fascias (for this and

Report on

SATELLITE TELEVISION ANTENNA SYSTEMS

Submitted to

Dr. David A. McMurrey

for

English 1633:
Technical Writing
Austin Community College
Austin, Texas

December 9, 1987

by

Jane Allen Hughes

The report examines satellite television antenna systems, describing their basic components, operation, legal considerations, and costs. Also discussed in this report is program availability in the central Texas area.

FIGURE 6–21.   **A title page**

```
                              Report

                                on


              EFFICIENT RESIDENTIAL SOLAR HEATING DEVICES

                        for the Austin Area

                                by


                          Michael J. Waters
                       Austin Community College
                          October 15, 1987
```

FIGURE 6–22.   A cover label

any other unfamiliar terms, see the glossary at the end of this report). Unreinforced reaction injection molded urethane is used on more than 30 percent of all General Motors cars.

The preceding statement occurs just after the first unfamiliar term in the report. No further reference to the glossary is necessary. Glossaries can be located just after the list of illustrations or, more commonly, in the appendix. An example of a glossary is provided in Figure 6–23. Then, look at the example from a list of symbols and abbreviations in Figure 6–24.

STEP 10.   If your report requires a glossary or list of symbols or abbreviations, list the terms, symbols, or abbreviations on your worksheet along with their definitions or meanings.

Exercises

1. Find a report or section of a report or book that uses no headings (or get a copy of one from your instructor), and create headings for 10 to 15 pages for it, using the guidelines in this chapter. Be sure to revise the introductory sentences after the headings, if necessary, and to create text in between any two headings that occur together.
2. Create a line graph from the following information, making sure to include a figure number, title, and labels within the graph.

   From an article in the January 1981 issue of *Television Bureau of Advertising*, pages 2–3, entitled "Trends in Television, 1950 to Date," you are taking information for a line graph

GLOSSARY

British Thermal Unit----the quantity of heat needed to raise one
pound of water one degree Fahrenheit

Die----a tool for shaping

Elastomer----a polymer that is highly elastic and rubbery

Elastomeric----having the ability to recover its original size and
shape after deformation

Ester----an organic compound formed by the reaction of an acid and
an alcohol

Fascia----the front part of an automobile that consists of the area
surrounding the headlights and the grille

Fatigue----the tendency of a material to break under repeated stress

Flash----excess plastic that is compressed outside the mold

Flexural strength----the ability of a material to bend without
breaking

Gas chromatography----a process of separating a solution of closely
related compounds

Homogenizing----a process in which different types of plastic
granules are made more uniform throughout

Hybridized----composed of two or more different elements

Mass spectrometry----a method of determining the index of refraction

Matrix----something within which something else originates

Modules----the degree to which a material possesses a certain
property

Monomer----a chemical compound that can undergo polymerization

Polymer----a chemical compound or mixture of compounds formed
by polymerization

Tensile----capable of tension

FIGURE 6–23. Example of a glossary

showing the growth of television ownership in the United States from 1950 to 1980. Total households with color sets: 1950, 2.0 (million); 1955, 2.0; 1960, 2.0; 1965, 4.5; 1970, 22.2; 1975, 50.0; 1980, 61.0. Total households with televisions for the same years: 5.0, 31.0, 46.0, 53.0, 58.0. 67.0, 73.5. Total households in the United States over these same years: 42.5, 46.5, 54.5, 57.5, 61.0, 70.5, 76.0. (Numbers are approximate.)

3. Using the following information, create a bar chart and give it an appropriate number and title.

LIST OF SYMBOLS AND ABBREVIATIONS

E.T.	external tank
ft/sec	feet per second
q	force due to gravity
HPHT	high-pressure hydrogen turbopump
HPOT	high-pressure oxygen turbopump
HPT	high-pressure turbopump
lbs	pounds
lbs/sec	pounds per second
LPHT	low-pressure hydrogen turbopump
LPOT	low-pressure oxygen turbopump
LPT	low-pressure turbopump
MPTS	main propulsion testing series
NSTL	National Space Technical Laboratory
psi	pounds per square inch
sec	seconds

FIGURE 6–24.   **A list of abbreviations and symbols**

From the *U.S. Census of Populations: 1940, 1950, and 1960*, Vol. 1, and the Current Population Reports Series P-20, Nos. 207, 295, 314, both published by the U.S. Bureau of the Census, you have taken this information to show the distribution of the U.S. population by educational level from 1960 to 1979 (for people 25 years old and over). In 1960, 58.8 percent of the population had no high school education; 41.2 percent were high school graduates; 16.5 percent had some college education; and 7.7 percent were college graduates. In 1970, these percentages were 44.9, 55.1, 21.2, and 11.0, respectively. In 1979, these percentages were 32.3, 67.7, 31.1, and 16.4, respectively.

4. Create a table from the following information; include a table number and title and appropriate titles for the columns and rows within the table.

   You are adapting information from a March 1980 *Merchandising* article entitled "Saturation Levels: 1979 Percentages and Totals of Wired Homes with These Products," pages 60–61. You want to show the change in ownership of various products between 1960 and 1979 and 1979 saturation levels (the percent of wired homes with the products based on 79,398,569 total wired homes). Homes owning air conditioners—in 1960, 7.8 (million); 1979, 44.0; saturation level in 1979, 55.5 (percent). Homes owning blenders: 4.2, 41.6, 52.4, respectively. Homes owning coffee makers: 30.2, 79.3, 99.9. Homes owning dishwashers: 3.7, 34.1, 43.0, respectively. Homes owning freezers: 12.1, 35.5, 44.7. Homes owning irons: 45.7, 79.3, 99.9. Homes owning microwave ovens: none, 6.1, 7.6. Homes owning food mixers: 29.0, 73.7, 92.8. Homes owning color televisions: negligible, 71.3, 89.8. Homes owning toasters: 37.2, 79.3, 99.9. Homes owning vacuum cleaners: 38.4, 79.3, 99.9. Homes owning washers: 28.6, 61.4, 77.3.

5. Locate statistical information that will make the following passage more factual and specific, and create a table from it to incorporate within the text.

In the 1970s the price of petroleum products began to rise dramatically in all areas. Reasons were the increased costs of producing oil domestically but, more importantly, the rising price of imported oil. By the 1970s oil imports to the United States had risen to well over half of the oil used in the United States. Partially as a result of these price increases, the United States went through an economic recession during the 1970s. Production and employment dropped. Interest rates and prices in general rose. Naturally, demand for goods and services fell as well.

6. Read the following discussion and design a conceptual line drawing for it.

The three parts of an argument, considered in terms of the functions or operations they perform in producing proof, may be likened to the parts of a bridge over a river. The *evidence*, as the foundation upon which the argument rests, is comparable to the pilings planted on the riverbed. The *warrant*, as the part of the argument which applies or carries the *evidence* to the *claim*, is comparable to the steel superstructure that rises from the pilings and supports the roadway over which the traffic passes. And, finally, the *claim*, as the contention the argument is intended to establish and support, is comparable to the roadway itself as it rests jointly upon the pilings and the superstructure.

Arranged in the customary order of *evidence* (pilings), *warrant* (superstructure), and *claim* (roadway), a complete argument would appear as follows:

(E)	Evidence	John is an honors student at Webster High School.
(W)	Warrant	Since honors graduates of Webster High School invariably do well in college,
(C)	Claim	John may be expected to do well in his college work.

From Douglas Ehninger, *Influence, Belief, and Argument* (Glenview, Ill.: Scott, Foresman, 1974), 11.

7. Read the following passages and revise each by transforming some of the discussion into an in-sentence list and into a vertical list:

From a functional standpoint, membrane systems are involved in a number of biological functions. These activities include the active transport of substances across the membrane, an involvement in protein synthesis, phagocytosis (a process of engulfing foreign matter), pinocytosis, wound healing, and increasing the movement of small molecules across the membrane.

When diving in cold water, you must take a number of precautions. Wear thermal protection appropriate for the water temperature. Also, note the first signs of cold hands and feet, and any loss of dexterity or grip strength. Note any difficulty in performing routine tasks, confusion, or a tendency to repeat tasks or procedures. Note any feelings of being chilled followed by intermittent shivering, even though you can still perform routine tasks. Terminate your dive if *any* of these symptoms is present. Be aware that even when you are properly dressed, hypothermia may develop without shivering. Watch your buddy diver and take heed of any behavioral changes that may indicate existing or approaching hypothermia.

CHAPTER 7

Strategies for Revising Paragraphs and Sentences

Chapter Objectives
Revising Paragraphs
  Topic Sentences
  Paragraph Organization
  Paragraph Coherence
  Paragraph Development
  Paragraph Length
Revising Sentences
  Overnominalization
  Redundant Words and Phrases

Weak Pronouns
Weak Use of the *Be* Verb
Problems with the Passive Voice
Expletive Problems
Predication Problems
Awkwardly Phrased Sentences
Sentence Length
Problems with Grammar, Usage,
  and Punctuation
Exercises

———————————— *Chapter Objectives* ————————————

After you read this chapter, study the examples, and work the steps, you should be able to:

- Spot the need for topic sentences.
- Construct different kinds of topic sentences.
- Identify problems with organization, coherence, and development in paragraphs and revise.
- Identify and revise paragraphs that are either too long or too short.
- Identify and revise the following sentence problems:

  Overnominalization
  Redundant words and phrases
  Weak use of pronouns
  Weak use of the *be* verb
  Weak use of the passive voice
  Awkwardly phrased sentences
  Sentence length

The purpose of this chapter is to show you some ways to look for paragraph and sentence problems and to fix those problems. To get the best use out of this chapter, you should have at hand a rough draft of a report or some practice writing from one of the chapters of Part I. You can then immediately apply the techniques you read about here to that rough draft.

The section entitled "Revising" in Chapter 10, "Developing Reports: Note Taking, Rough Drafts, and Final Packaging," gives a broad overview of the revision and editing phase of writing reports. This chapter is designed to focus in detail on the heart of the revision process: locating and fixing paragraph and sentence problems that cause reports to be unclear and ineffective.

Before looking at the specific revision techniques presented in this chapter, consider what your goals are during the revision stage. They are not simply to get the spelling and punctuation right, but rather to consider

- The *content* of the report: Is there omitted or unnecessary information?

- The *audience* of the report: Is the information right for the intended audience?

- The *organization* of the report: Are the subtopics within the report presented in the right order?

- The *coherence* of the report: Does the report make it clear how the subtopics fit together?

- The *purpose* of the report: Does the report fulfill its purpose (for example, to inform, instruct, or evaluate)?

- The *clarity* and *conciseness* of the report:

  Are the sentences in the report clear and concise? Are they the right length?

- The *consistency* of the report:

  Does the report handle things (for example, format and numbers) consistently?

- The *layout* of the report:

  Is it easy to find your way around in the report, to go to specific parts of the discussion, to review the key points, or to locate important statistics? Does the layout suit the way that the report is to be used?

- The *graphic aids* of the report:

  Does the report contain the right illustrations, tables, charts, graphs, flowcharts, and other such aids to help readers understand the discussion?

- The *textual aids* of the report:

  Does the report use a good binder with a cover label, good pagination, a list of figures, a table of contents, lists, headings, bibliography, and other such readers' tools?

Revision means thinking about all these aspects of your report, looking for potential problems in each. Many of these considerations are discussed elsewhere: specifically,

- Chapters 1, 2, 3, and 8 can help you decide on the *content* for your report.
- Chapter 5 can help you identify, analyze, and write for the specific *audience* of your report.
- Chapters 12, 13, and 14 can help you identify and think clearly about the *purpose* of your report.
- Chapter 6 gives you general guidelines on report *layout*; and Chapters 12, 13, and 14 provide specific models of report layout.
- Chapter 6 helps you plan, design, and construct both the *graphic* and *textual* aids of your report.

The focus of this chapter, on the other hand, is the nuts and bolts of revision work: the structure, flow, and clarity of paragraphs and sentences.

Revising Paragraphs

There are a number of ways that you can improve the clarity of the paragraphs in your technical writing. Start your editing and revising process at the paragraph level of your report in order to get the larger, organizational matters right—then plunge into the revision of the individual sentences. (That's why the section on revising sentences comes second.)

Topic Sentences

One of the first things to do when you begin analyzing your report draft is to think about the topic and purpose of each paragraph and each section. Your next job is to check the first sentence or two of each to see if it clearly indicates that topic and purpose.

Usually located at the beginning of a paragraph, a *topic sentence* indicates the topic, main point, or contents of the paragraph. Topic sentences give readers a firm sense of purpose, organization, direction, or structure of the paragraphs they introduce—a view of the forest before the plunge into the details of the individual trees. The more difficult and technical the discussion, the more topic sentences are likely to make reading easier. In Figure 7–1 are two versions of a paragraph, one with and one without a topic sentence:

Paragraph without Topic Sentence	Possible Topics
Causes of Atherosclerosis	
Diet is generally a key factor in atherosclerosis. Diets rich in calories, saturated fats, cholesterol, sugar, and salt have been found to play an important role in producing several of the traits and abnormalities that intensify the disease process.	Diet? Atherosclerosis?
Among these abnormalities are obesity, high blood pressure, diabetes mellitus, and high levels of cholesterol and other fatty substances in the blood.	Abnormalities?
Cigarette smoking is another major risk factor, and a lack of exercise also increases a person's tendency to develop the disease. High levels of uric acid in the blood plasma and certain personality traits and behavior patterns have also been implicated.	Cigarette smoking?
Finally, it has been found that a susceptibility to atherosclerosis may be inherited in some instances.	Genetics?

FIGURE 7–1. Revising paragraphs by adding topic sentences

Revised Paragraph with Topic Sentence	Topics and Subtopics
Causes of Atherosclerosis	
There is no single cause of atherosclerosis; <u>instead, a number of factors play varied roles in different people to produce the disease.</u> Diet is generally one of the most important factors in atherosclerosis. Diets rich in calories, saturated fats, cholesterol, sugar, and salt have been found to play an important role in producing several of the traits and abnormalities that intensify the disease process. Among these abnormalities are obesity, high blood pressure, diabetes mellitus, and high levels of cholesterol and other fatty substances in the blood. Cigarette smoking is another major risk factor, and a lack of exercise also increases a person's tendency to develop the disease. High levels of uric acid in the blood plasma and certain personality traits and behavior patterns have also been implicated. Finally, it has been found that a susceptibility to atherosclerosis may be inherited in some instances.	Topic: causes of atherosclerosis Subtopics: diet abnormalities cigarette smoking lack of exercise uric acid other

FIGURE 7–1. (cont.)

In the problem version in Figure 7–1, you might at first think that only dietary problems will be covered. But as you read, you realize the topic of the paragraph is apparently something else. The topic sentence in the revision tells you that several potential causes of the disease will be covered. Another example appears in Figure 7–2 (disregard the paragraph break in this one).

This dense technical discussion would probably be tough going for nonspecialists; a strong topic sentence would help. A more serious problem in the paragraph in Figure 7–2 is how it shifts the topic midway through: from the earth's long-term temperature cycle to the greenhouse effect. The beginning sentence on temperature cycles is therefore misleading: a more accurate and comprehensive topic sentence would refer to *both* the natural temperature cycles *and* the greenhouse effect. A

Paragraph without a Topic Sentence	Possible Topics

II. <u>NATURAL WEATHER PATTERNS AND THE GREENHOUSE EFFECT</u>

The earth's climate naturally changes over extended periods of time. Temperatures have been much warmer for 80 to 90 percent of the last 500 million years than they are today. The polar ice caps are a relatively new phenomenon, having been formed 15 to 20 million years ago in the Antarctic and perhaps as recently as 3 to 5 million years ago in the Arctic.

Earth's climate

Natural climate changes

Polar ice caps

The climate is still dominated by natural cycles of warming and cooling. The most influential of these natural weather patterns is the 180-year cycle. The 180-year cycle predicts that temperatures in the Northern Hemisphere reach a minimum every 180 years. Climate records for the Southern Hemisphere are incomplete. The bottom of the last cycle was in the early 1800s, which suggests that we may be in a peak of coldness. The winters of 1976 through 1979, which were unusually bitter, seem to reinforce the theory behind the 180-year cycle. This current cooling trend would mask any warming caused by an increased greenhouse effect. However, the 180-year cycle predicts that a natural warming trend will occur shortly before the end of this century. At the same time the effects of elevated CO_2 levels on atmospheric temperatures will become strong. Therefore, temperatures could reach their highest level in several hundred years shortly after the year 2000 and their highest level in 125,000 years by the midcentury.

180-year cycle

Current cooling trend

Effects of the greenhouse effect

Greenhouse effect after cooling trend

FIGURE 7–2. A paragraph needing a topic sentence

variety of topic sentences, as Appendix C shows, can be used for the paragraph in Figure 7–2. Consider, for example, the possibilities in Figure 7–3.

The *main point* topic sentence states precisely the main idea; the *placeholder* indicates the topic but not the main idea; the *list* topic sentence is like a miniature version of a table of contents, telling you about the subtopics to be covered.

To determine the need for topic sentences, try these steps:

1. Read the paragraph (or paragraphs) carefully, and identify the topic or topics, particularly where the paragraphs are long and the discussion is highly technical.
2. Reread the first few sentences: Is the topic of the paragraph announced in some way?
3. If not, compose several possibilities for topic sentences either in your mind or on scratch paper.
4. If a topic sentence adds clarity, use it.
5. Adjust the phrasing of the rest of the paragraph to accommodate the new sentence.

STEP 1.   Apply the preceding questions to any five paragraphs in your report for topic sentences, and, on your worksheet write one or more potentially usable topic sentences.

Paragraph Organization

The *organization* of a paragraph is the way ideas, points, or subtopics are arranged within it. Call these elements the individual "units of discussion"; they can be a

Type	Possible Topic Sentences
Main point	The earth's natural weather pattern may obscure long-term changes in the weather resulting from the greenhouse effect.
Placeholder	Understanding the precise nature of the greenhouse effect is made a bit more difficult by the long-term natural changes in weather patterns.
List	Two sorts of long-term changes are at work on earth's weather patterns: one having to do with natural cycles and the other with the greenhouse effect.

FIGURE 7–3. Examples of different types of topic sentences

sentence or more in length. While the topic of a paragraph stays the same in the paragraph, the individual units of discussion state different things about that topic. If a paragraph is poorly organized, the sentences are not in an appropriate order—they don't seem to fit together or flow. To test organization, make a list of the units of discussion—an inventory. Then study it to determine whether the sequence of the units makes sense. Figure 7–4 has an example of a *well-organized* paragraph with an inventory list to its right (note that the second unit of discussion is made up of two sentences).

When you have set up an inventory like this one (either on scratch paper or in your mind), it's much easier to think about the sequence of the ideas—the organization of the units of discussion within the paragraph.

- Do units 1 and 2 fit together? Yes, it makes sense to follow unit 1, applications of glass-fiber technology, with unit 2, the properties of glass fiber that make those applications possible.
- Do units 2 and 3 fit together? Again, yes. We now move from unit 2 on properties to unit 3, a more specific example of how those properties are used in medicine.

In *disorganized paragraphs*, the sequencing of the units is somehow wrong. Some disorganized paragraphs seem to waffle back and forth, as the example in Figure 7–5 does (each of the units of discussion here consists of several sentences).

One of the more important results of the application of materials research to glass technology has been the development of glass fibers for use in medicine and communications. Certain kinds of fibers transmit light only along the axis of the fiber. The fiber is nearly opaque perpendicular to this axis. If fiber is bent, light passing through it will also bend. Physicians wishing to directly examine inaccessible regions of the body, such as the lungs, bronchial tubes, bladder, and so on, can now do so by using thin glass fibers to transmit light and to see through.

1. An important application of glass technology

2. Properties used in this application

3. How this application is used in medicine

Reprinted from Invitation to Chemistry by David S. Newman by permission of W. W. Norton & Company, Inc. Copyright © 1978 by W. W. Norton & Company, Inc.

FIGURE 7–4. Taking inventory of paragraph organization

The two coronary arteries that nourish the coronary-heart muscle branch off from the aorta, the big system artery leading from the heart. The arteries cross along the surface of the heart, leading to a network of smaller and smaller branches. Every part of the heart is supplied with nourishment from this treelike coronary-artery system. A healthy main coronary artery has a diameter of 2 to 3 mm. In coronary atherosclerosis, the internal bore of these coronary arteries decreases. This disease may develop early in life, and all of us have it in some degree by the time we reach middle age. Each coronary artery is made up of an outer core, a middle portion, and inner lining. The inner lining, called the intima, consists of several layers. Blood carries many substances, including lipids, or fatty materials. The atherosclerosis process starts when the cells in the first layer of the intima become more permeable to cholesterol and other lipids and allow them to pass through and be deposited on the lining.

1. The artery (structure and function)

2. Medical problems in coronary arteries

3. Structure and function

4. Medical problem

FIGURE 7–5.   **Inventorying a disorganized paragraph**

Now, here is an inventory of the paragraph in Figure 7–5:

- Do units 1 and 2 fit together? The shift from the structure and function of the coronary-artery system (unit 1) to medical problems of that system (unit 2) seems to work, so far.
- Do units 2 and 3 work together? No, suddenly we shift back to the structure and function of a healthy heart (unit 3) from coronary atherosclerosis (unit 2). The organizational sequence is this: healthy heart, diseased heart, healthy heart (but for no apparent reason).
- Do units 3 and 4 fit? Locally, they do, but in terms of the whole paragraph, no. Unit 4 moves back to a discussion of diseased hearts.

The cure for this paragraph is to put together units 1 and 3 and to follow them with units 2 and 4. This revision, first, establishes the structure and function of a healthy heart, and, second, discusses coronary atherosclerosis. Now, read the revision in Figure 7–6.

The two coronary arteries that nourish the heart muscle branch off from the aorta, the big artery leading from the heart. The coronary arteries cross along the surface of the heart, leading to a network of smaller and smaller branches. Every part of the heart is supplied with nourishment from this treelike coronary-artery system. Each coronary artery is made up of an outer core, a middle portion, and inner lining. The inner lining, called the intima, consists of several layers. Blood carries many substances including lipids, or fatty materials. The atherosclerosis process starts when the cells in the first layer of the intima become more permeable to cholesterol and other lipids and allow them to pass through and be deposited on the lining. A healthy main coronary artery has a diameter of 2 to 3 mm. In coronary athero-sclerosis, the internal bore of these coronary arteries decreases. This disease may develop early in life, and all of us have it in some degree by the time we reach middle age.

1. The coronary-artery system (structure and function)

2. Structure and function

3. Medical problems

4. Medical problems

FIGURE 7–6.   Revising the disorganized paragraph in Figure 7–5

Paragraphs can also seem disorganized because the units of discussion have their own required sequence the writer ignores. For example, look at Figure 7–7.

In the disorganized version in Figure 7–7, types of solar collectors are discussed before the function of all collectors. One of the parts of the collector is discussed before the preview of all the parts. Instead, a well-organized version of Figure 7–7 would read as in Figure 7–8.

Paragraph Coherence

Sometimes, however, a paragraph may seem disorganized, but an inventory proves otherwise, as in Figure 7–9.

Solar Collector

There are various types of solar collectors; however, the flat-plate solar collector is currently the most common and shall be the focus of discussion here. The most important part of a solar heating system is its solar collector, whose function is to heat circulating water necessary for space heating. A typical solar collector has layers of glass with intervening air spaces to produce a heat-trapping effect. Also, most solar collectors consist of a black plate absorber covered by one or more of these transparent cover plates made of either glass or plastic, with the sides and bottom of the box insulated.

Temperatures produced in the collector are below the boiling point of water; however, temperatures of 150 degrees above ambient temperature can be reached. The hot water generated in the solar collector is used directly for space heating. The water in the collector circulates through or below the absorber component, which heats up and in turn heats the circulating water.

1. Types of solar collectors

2. Function of solar collectors

3. Parts of a solar collector

4. Operation of a solar collector

FIGURE 7–7. Another kind of disorganized paragraph

An inventory of the paragraph in Figure 7–9 and a little knowledge of electronics show that the units of discussion are not so disorganized as they may first seem. The problem, instead, involves *coherence*.

Closely related to organization, coherence refers to the way in which certain words and phrases show the relationship between the ideas and sentences within a paragraph, or a group of paragraphs. An incoherent paragraph lacks adequate wording to lead the reader from one idea to the next. Transitional devices are a primary means of guiding readers through a discussion. An incoherent paragraph may be perfectly well organized except that the writing within it obscures that organization. A coherent paragraph, on the other hand, is both well organized and makes good use of transitional devices. Transitional devices are those signals to

<u>Solar Collector</u>

The most important part of a solar heating system is the solar collector, whose main function is to heat water to be used in space heating. There are various types of collectors; however, the flat-plate collector is the most common and shall be the focus of discussion here. A flat-plate collector consists of a black plate absorber covered by one or more transparent cover plates of glass or plastic, with the sides and bottom of the box insulated.

The layers of glass or plastic have an intervening air space that produces a heat-trapping effect. Water circulates through or below this absorber component, which heats up and in turn heats up the water. Temperatures produced are below the boiling point of water; however, temperatures of 150 degrees above ambient temperature can be reached. The hot water produced in the collector is used directly for space heating.

1. Function of a solar collector

2. Types of solar collectors

3. Parts of a solar collector

4. Operation of a solar collector

FIGURE 7–8.   Revising the disorganized paragraph in Figure 7–7

The simplest semiconductor is called a diode. A diode serves as a rectifier to convert alternating current (ac) to direct current (dc). The usual current in the United States is ac with a frequency of 60 Hz. Many electronic devices require dc for at least part of their function. Diodes are p- and n-type semiconductors that have been joined together.

1. Definition of diode
2. Function of diodes: convert current

3. Different currents typically used

4. Two components of diodes

FIGURE 7–9.   A paragraph with coherence problems

readers concerning the flow or direction of the thought in a paragraph or group of paragraphs (for more detail, see Appendix C). They include

- Repeated key words and phrases
- Transitional words and phrases
- Parallel phrasing
- Other kinds of sentence rephrasing.

The lack of transitional devices is precisely the problem in Figure 7–9. It contains few transitions to guide the reader from one unit of discussion to the next, depending instead on repetition of a key word. It leaves most of the mental work of connecting the ideas to the reader. A revision is provided in Figure 7–10.

Checking for coherence (or the transitions) is like checking for organization except that you also look specifically for transitional devices. First, you inventory the paragraph or section and test it for organization. If you find that the paragraph or section is well organized, you ask yourself questions about the transitions like the following:

What is the overt transitional device I used here to guide my reader from the preceding sentence to this one?
Is the transitional device I used strong enough?
Is any overt transitional device needed here at all?

Here's how this technique for checking the coherence of a paragraph works (the junctions between the sentences and the sentences themselves have been labeled for easier reference):

a. The simplest semiconductor is called a diode. [1] *b.* A diode serves as a rectifier to convert alternating current (ac) to direct current (dc). [2] *c.* The usual current in the

The simplest semiconductor is called a diode.	1. Definition of a diode
A diode serves as a rectifier to convert alternating current (ac) to direct current (dc). While the	2. Function of a diode: convert current
usual current in the United States is ac with a frequency of 60 Hz, many electronic devices	
require dc for at least part of their function. The	3. Different current requirements in U.S. households
diode solves this mismatch of currents by its	
basic design in which a p- and n-type semicon-	4. How the diode solves the problem
ductor are joined together.	

FIGURE 7–10.   Revising the incoherent paragraph in Figure 7–9

United States is ac with a frequency of 60 Hz. [3] *d*. Many electronic devices require dc for at least part of their function. [4] *e*. Diodes are p- and n-type semiconductors that have been joined together.

Junction 1

Organization: How do we get from sentence *a* to sentence *b*? How do we get across the gap? What's the connection? Sentence *a* and sentence *b* do logically relate to each other: sentence *a* introduces the term *diode* and explains that it is a semiconductor; sentence *b* defines it by explaining its basic function.

Coherence: What is the transitional device that gets us from sentence *a* to sentence *b*? Is it strong enough? The transitional device is a repeated word: the word *diode* appears at the end of sentence *a* and at the beginning of sentence *b*, making an adequate transition across junction 1.

Junction 2

Organization: How do we get from sentence *b* to sentence *c*? What's the connection? There is an appropriate, logical connection (although it takes a bit of extra thought to see it): the diode is useful in houses equipped with ac that must use devices with dc; the diode solves this problem.

Coherence: What is the transitional device that indicates the connection between these two sentences? The only conceivable transitions here are the words *current* and the abbreviation *ac*, but these repeated key words do not make the connection clear. We have to wait to get the idea.

Junction 3

Organization: What's the logical connection between sentences *c* and *d*? Sentence *d* states the rest of the problem, the discussion of which was begun in sentence *c*: what to do about dc devices in houses with only ac? The organization makes sense here once again.

Coherence: What transitional device indicates the connection between sentences *c* and *d*? Only the repeated "dc" acts as a transition here, referring back to sentence *b*, again a very weak transition that leaves all the mental work to the reader.

Junction 4

Organization: How does the reader get across junction 4? What's the relationship between sentences *d* and *e*? Diodes solve the problem of situations where the devices with ac and dc conflict by combining p- and n-type semiconductors.

Coherence: What transition connects sentence *e* to the preceding sentence or sentences? Again, only repeated key words are the transitional device used here: *diodes* and *semiconductors*.

STEP 2.   Use the organization and coherence tests just described to test the organization and coherence of any five paragraphs in your report. Describe on your worksheet any problems you find.

These same techniques for locating potential problems of organization and coherence work for whole groups of paragraphs. The principles and the techniques are the same; only the units of discussion are larger. In Figure 7–11 are several paragraphs upon which the tests for organization and coherence are used.

III. ORIGINS OF NUCLEAR WASTE

The primary sources of nuclear waste are commercial nuclear electric power plants. Since 1942 nuclear power plants have generated about 8,000 tons of nuclear waste. The fuel used in fission reactions consists of small pellets of uranium oxide sealed in long tubes of stainless steel or zircaloy. The fuel rods are bound together in components called fuel assemblies.

    1. Main source of nuclear waste

During the fission reaction, two important processes occur. First, the uranium-235 decays, creating over 180 different radioactive products as well as some free neutrons which cause a chain reaction. Second, uranium-238 absorbs some neutrons and decays into plutonium-239 in a three-step process. The plutonium can also serve as a fuel to continue the process.

    2. Process in fission reactions

The two most abundant by-products of the fission reaction are strontium-90 and cesium-137 which compose about 5 percent of the total mass of the fuel rods. These two products both

    3. By-products of the reaction

(continued)

FIGURE 7–11. Analyzing the organization and coherence of sections of a report

have a half-life of about 30 years. This means
that they are very active and will be active for a
long time. There are also fission products such
as cesium-135 and iodine-129 with very long
half-lives of over a million years. The general
rule of thumb is that the waste has to be
contained for 10 to 20 half-lives.

Eventually these by-products in the fuel rods
build up, and the fuel rods have to be replaced.
This need to replace fuel rods occurs every three
years or so. These fuel rods are not only
radioactively hot, but thermally hot also. They
must be stored for about 6 months in large
water-filled basins while the short-lived fission
products decay. These spent fuel rods must next
either be reprocessed or disposed in a permanent
repository.

4. Buildup of the by-products requiring disposal

Despite the over 8,000 tons of these spent fuel
rods that have been generated by the nuclear
industry since 1942 and despite the great danger
of contamination that this spent nuclear fuel
represents, the federal government still has not
been able to develop a comprehensive policy
for permanent and safe nuclear waste disposal.

5. Volume of nuclear waste and lack of federal policy

FIGURE 7–11. (cont.)

Now, here is an analysis of the organization and coherence in the preceding
paragraphs:

Unit 1 to Unit 2: Unit 1 introduces the topic of discussion, nuclear waste
sources, and describes the fuel pellet, the chief source; unit 2
explains the process by which these pellets produce nuclear
power. The transition from unit 1 to unit 2 is the repeated
key phrase *fission reaction*.

Unit 2 to Unit 3: We move from the energy-generating process (discussed in 2)
to the waste by-products (3). Again, the transition is the term
fission reaction.

Unit 3 to Unit 4:   From the description of the waste by-products (3), we move to a discussion of how they build up and must be removed (4). This time, the transitions are the word *Eventually*, which indicates a movement in time, and the key phrase *these by-products*.

Unit 4 to Unit 5:   We move from the necessity of removing spent fuel rods (4) to a discussion of how much of this spent fuel has accumulated and how much a good federal policy is needed to govern its disposal (5). The transition here is the phrase *these spent fuel rods*.

STEP 3.   Use the organization and coherence tests on any sequence of five paragraphs in your report. Describe on your worksheet any problems you find.

Paragraph Development

Paragraph development refers to the resources for explaining a topic that have been used. If a paragraph lacks development, more details and further elaboration are needed. A paragraph lacking in development may seem either too general or vague and to lack enough information.

To test for development, you can ask yourself certain questions at various points in the paragraph:

1. Do I need to *define* some word or phrase used in the preceding sentence?
2. Do I need to elaborate on the *cause* or *effect* (benefits, advantage, problems, solutions) related to the information in the preceding sentence?
3. Do I need to *describe* something mentioned in the preceding sentence in greater detail?
4. Do I need to *compare* something in the preceding sentence to something else in the report or something common and familiar to all readers?
5. Do I need to divide something in the preceding sentence into *classes* or locate it within a class?
6. Do I need to provide a short or extended *example* to illustrate something in the preceding sentence?
7. Do I need to explain a *process*, how something in the preceding sentence works, operates, or is used? Should I explain how something works or happens?
8. Do I need to give a bit of *history* on something in the preceding sentences?
9. Do I need to restate in different or *simpler terms* what I said in the preceding sentence?

In the paragraphs in Figure 7–12, question 1 is used right away to define injection molding.

In Figure 7–13 are two example paragraphs whose development is weak.

When you test a poorly developed paragraph like the ones in Figure 7–13, you ask yourself: Should I use an example here? Should I describe the equipment used there? Should I define this term here? It's better not to pester yourself with questions like these during the rough-drafting phase and just go with your intuitions; leave

Injection Molding

Injection molding is a process that involves
the heating and homogenizing of plastic granules
until they are sufficiently fluid to allow for
pressure injection into a relatively cold mold. In
this mold the plastic solidifies and takes the
shape of the mold cavity. Injection molding has
been one of the fundamental methods for
processing thermoplastics for decades now.

Use question 2 here:
What are some of the
advantages of this
process?

The advantage of using injection molding for
thermoplastics lies in its versatility. In addition,
good dimensional control and part-to-part
uniformity can be maintained in this process.
When injection molding is used for thermoplastics, no chemical changes occur within the
plastic, and consequently the process is
repeatable.

Question 4 works here:
How does this process
compare to others?

Injection molding of thermoplastics differs
from other molding processes in that the
cylinder heating is designed to homogenize and
preheat the reactive materials and in that the
mold is heated to complete the chemical cross-
linking reaction that forms the interactable
solid. Solid particles in the form of pellets or
granules constitute the main feed for injection-
moldable plastics. Among the advantages of
injection-moldable plastics are the speed of production, the minimal requirements for postmold-
ing operations, and its ability to perform
simultaneous multipart molding.

Now, questions 3 and 7
are appropriate: What
does it look like and
how does it operate?
And, these questions
suggest another
one, question 5:
different types?

Injection molding is done with the use of an
injection machine. There are two types of
injection machines. This plunger is hydraulically
driven and is capable of developing pressures of
10,000 and 25,000 psi.

FIGURE 7–12.   Using development questions

The second and more common type of injection-molding machine is the rotating-screw type. In this machine the screw acts as a material plasticizer as well as an injection ram. This injection ram forces the plastic into the mold. As the screw rotates, it is forced backward by the buildup of viscous plastic at the nozzle end of the cylinder.

Question 7 again: How does this type work?

When an appropriate amount is accumulated, rotation stops and the screw acts as an injection ram forcing the plastic into the mold. It remains forward until the material in the mold solidifies. Following this, the injection returns to the beginning position and is ready to repeat the cycle.

Reaction Injection Molding (RIM).   One type of injection molding used frequently in the automotive industry is reaction injection molding (RIM). This process mixes two or more reactive liquids (plastics) at high pressure at the moment of injection into the mold. Thus, molds are less massive and require only low locking forces; little heat input is required for the molding process. The development of RIM allowed the rapid molding of liquid materials. The major advantage of RIM over conventional injection-molding techniques is the reduction in the steps necessary to achieve a molded part. In addition, the process involves fewer preprocessing steps and has the capability for almost complete automation. These advantages mean that capital outlay and energy use are small compared to other high-volume molding processes.

Question 7: How does it work?

Question 2: What are some of the advantages?

(continued)

FIGURE 7–12.   (cont.)

RIM has proven particularly effective for high-speed molding of polyurethane automobile parts from steering wheels to bumpers. The excellent mechanical properties of polyurethane, coupled with the relatively simple production technique, allows large numbers of components to be produced. The only area in which RIM does not excel is dimensional stability. For example, if a body panel is produced by the RIM process, one area of the panel may be 0.1 inches thick while another area of the same panel may be only 0.09 inches thick.

Here, question 6 works: How about an example?

FIGURE 7–12. (cont.)

Thoughtful location and orientation of buildings on a site can contribute to noise reduction. Distance is one of the primary means of reducing noise. The greater the distance, the greater the reduction of noise. Buildings can also be located in such a way and rooms can be arranged in such a way that noise is reduced.

Question 6: How about an example?

Question 6: How about examples of this too?

Question 2: What's the result? How much noise reduction?

In the Ames test for mutagens, highly purified saccharin was administered to rats. No mutagenic effect on tissues was observed, but the urine was affected. Although the results of the Ames test are not proof that saccharin is carcinogenic, they do provide more evidence leading to that conclusion.

Question 1: What's a mutagen?

Question 7: How's that again?

Question 9: How about more on the test process?

FIGURE 7–13. Testing poorly developed paragraphs

Thoughtful location and orientation of buildings on a site can contribute to the reduction of noise. Distance is one of the primary means of reducing noise. By doubling the distance between the source of the noise and its receiver, a reduction of 4 to 6 dB can be accomplished. Orientation is another way of reducing noise. Buildings can be located in such a way that the side with windows faces the quiet side, while the heavy windowless wall faces the source of noise. In general, this kind of arrangement will cause a decrease in sound level of 3 dB.

The Ames test for mutagens has also been used to test for the carcinogenicity of saccharin. Mutagens act by changing the genetic material in cells which is then passed on to daughter cells during cell division. In other words, mutagens cause birth defects. Almost all chemicals known to be carcinogenic have been found to be mutagenic by the Ames test. In the Ames test the chemical being observed is administered orally to mice, and the mice are observed for any mutations in their urine and body tissues. When highly purified saccharin was tested on the mice, no mutagenic effect on tissues appeared, but the urine was affected. These results are not proof that saccharin is carcinogenic, but they do constitute more evidence in the direction of that conclusion.

FIGURE 7–14. Revising the poorly developed paragraphs in Figure 7–13

questions like these for the revising phase. Revisions of the two paragraphs in Figure 7–13 are provided in Figure 7–14.

In the revisions in Figure 7–14 notice that, for example, description might be *possible* in the two paragraphs, but it is not *necessary*, considering the purpose and audience. Supply the additional development sentences only when you think readers need them to understand the discussion, not just because the development questions indicate a possibility.

STEP 4.   Use the preceding test for development on any five paragraphs in your report, and describe on your worksheet any problems you find.

Paragraph Length

An easy paragraph problem to spot is the paragraph that is too long or the series of paragraphs that are too short. Paragraphs mark changes of thought or topic within a discussion; also, they group related ideas. Paragraphs either give readers a break from concentrating or show readers the parts of a discussion by their grouping. Readers grow weary of paragraphs that never seem to end, but they also lose their train of thought in short, choppy paragraphs.

Think about the writing situation when you must decide on the length of paragraphs. For example, use short paragraphs for instructions for greater clarity, but longer paragraphs for historical and theoretical discussions for greater continuity.

An example of an overly long paragraph and a revision of it appear in Figure 7–15.

Problem Paragraph

Blood circulation is the major function of the heart. In one cycle of that circulatory function, the right atrium receives oxygen-poor blood from two major veins: the superior and inferior vena cava, which enter the atrium through separate openings. From the right atrium the blood flows through the tricuspid valve, which consists of three flaps, or cusps, of tissue. This valve directs blood flow from the right atrium to the right ventricle. The tricuspid valve remains open during diastole, or the filling of the ventricle. However, when the ventricle contracts, the valve closes, seals the opening, and prevents backflow into the right atrium. Five cords attached to small muscles, called the papillary muscles, on the ventricle's inner surface prevent the valve's flaps from being pushed backward. From the right ventricle, blood is pumped through the pulmonary or semilunar valve, which has three half-moon-shaped flaps, into the pulmonary artery. Through the pulmonary artery, blood is pumped to the lungs, where it gives up its carbon dioxide and receives oxygen, and then is returned to the heart's left side through four pulmonary veins (two from each lung) to the left atrium. From the left atrium it then passes through the mitral valve, a two-flapped valve also called a bicuspid valve, to the left ventricle. As the ventricle contracts, the mitral valve prevents backflow of blood, and the blood is driven through the aortic valve into the aorta, the major artery that supplies blood to the entire body. The pulmonary valve, like the aortic valve, has a semilunar shape and a unidirectional function.

FIGURE 7–15.   Revision by paragraph breaks

Revision

Blood circulation is the major function of the heart. In one stage of that circulatory function, the right atrium receives oxygen-poor blood from two major veins: the superior and inferior vena cava, which enter the atrium through separate openings. From the right atrium the blood flows through the tricuspid valve, which consists of three flaps, or cusps, of tissue. This valve directs blood flow from the right atrium to the right ventricle.

The tricuspid valve remains open during diastole, or the filling of the ventricle. However, when the ventricle contracts, the valve closes, seals the opening, and prevents backflow into the right atrium. Five cords attached to small muscles, called the papillary muscles, on the ventricle's inner surface prevent the valve's flaps from being pushed backward.

From the right ventricle, the blood moves into the second stage of the cycle. It is pumped from the right ventricle through the pulmonary or semilunar valve, which has three half-moon-shaped flaps. Through the pulmonary artery, blood is pumped to the lungs where it gives up its carbon dioxide and receives oxygen, and then is returned to the heart's left side through four pulmonary veins (two from each lung) to the left atrium. From the left atrium it then passes through the mitral valve, a two-flapped valve also called a bicuspid valve, to the left ventricle.

The third stage of the cycle begins when the left ventricle contracts and drives the blood through the aortic valve into the aorta, the major artery that supplies blood to the entire body. The mitral valve, a two-flapped valve also called a bicuspid valve, prevents backflow of the blood into the left atrium. The pulmonary valve, like the aortic valve, has a semilunar shape and a unidirectional function.

FIGURE 7–15. (cont.)

Notice a few things about this revision by paragraph break:

- The new paragraphs begin at the natural turning points (here, the "stages" of the cycle).
- The first sentences of the new paragraphs are strengthened with topic sentences and transition words (the repetition of the word *stages* at the beginning of each paragraph and the words *first*, *second*, and *third*).

Remember that you can't always just slap in a paragraph break without adjusting the phrasing around it.

Figure 7–16 contains an example of the opposite problem—too many short paragraphs—and a revision of it. Notice this about the revision: the paragraphs have been grouped to provide an introductory discussion (paragraph 1), a discussion of normal blood pressure (paragraph 2), a discussion of normal variation (paragraph 3), and a discussion of abnormal variation (paragraph 4).

Problem Paragraphs

One of the most common forms of heart disease is hypertension. <u>Hypertension</u> is the medical term for persistent and sustained high blood pressure. An understanding of blood pressure in normal, healthy individuals is necessary in order to understand hypertension.

Blood pressure is simply the force exerted against the walls of the body's arteries as blood flows through. The force, produced primarily by the pumping action of the heart, is essential for the circulation of the blood and its life-supporting nutrients to all parts of the body.

Every time the heart contracts, or beats (called a systole), blood pressure increases. When the heart relaxes between beats (diastole), the pressure decreases.

The normal systolic pressure of a person at rest is between 100 to 140, and the normal diastole is 60 to 90. Blood-pressure readings are expressed by both figures, with the systolic over the diastolic: for example, 140/90.

As these ranges suggest, there is a wide span of blood pressures for healthy people. Also, blood pressure varies for healthy people during different times of the day and under different circumstances. It is lower when an individual is asleep than when he is excited or exerting himself physically.

Therefore, a single blood-pressure reading above 140/90 does not indicate abnormality. When the pressure is continuously elevated, a person is considered to be suffering from hypertension.

FIGURE 7–16.   Revision by paragraph consolidation

Hypertension is a stealthy problem: a physician can discover it easily enough, but not a patient. Mild elevations, for example, may produce headaches, dizziness, fatigue, and weakness. But the patient is not likely to recognize these symptoms as having any other source than the increased elevation.

Revision

One of the most common forms of heart disease is hypertension. Hypertension is the medical term for persistent and sustained high blood pressure. An understanding of blood pressure in normal, healthy individuals is necessary in order to understand hypertension.

Blood pressure is simply the force exerted against the walls of the body's arteries as blood flows through. The force, produced primarily by the pumping action of the heart, is essential for the circulation of the blood and its life-supporting nutrients to all parts of the body. Every time the heart contracts, or beats (called a systole), blood pressure increases. When the heart relaxes between beats (diastole), the pressure decreases. The normal systolic pressure of a person at rest is between 100 to 140, and the normal diastole is 60 to 90. Blood-pressure readings are expressed by both figures, with the systolic over the diastolic: for example, 140/90.

As these ranges suggest, there is a wide span of blood pressures for healthy people. Also, blood pressure varies for healthy people during different times of the day and under different circumstances. It is lower when an individual is asleep than when he is excited or exerting himself physically. Therefore, a single blood-pressure reading above 140/90 does not indicate abnormality. When the pressure is continuously elevated, a person is considered to be suffering from hypertension.

Hypertension is a stealthy problem: a physician can discover it easily enough, but not a patient. Mild elevations, for example, may produce headaches, dizziness, fatigue, and weakness. But the patient is not likely to recognize these symptoms as having any other source than the increased elevation.

FIGURE 7–16.   (cont.)

STEP 5.   In the rough draft of your report, identify all paragraphs under 5 lines long or over 12 lines long, decide whether any of them should be combined with other paragraphs or divided into shorter paragraphs, and explain your decisions on your worksheet.

Revising Sentences

Begin looking for problems in the individual sentences of a report rough draft only *after* you've worked on the larger paragraph-level concerns discussed in the preceding section: after all, why waste time revising individual sentences if they must be discarded?

This section focuses on the kinds of writing problems that cause sentences to be unclear and difficult to read. Discussion of grammar, usage, and punctuation is left to Appendix D. Usually, errors in usage (for example, fragments, subject-verb agreement, and so on), punctuation, and spelling cause minor distractions to readers and make them wonder about the writer's education and competence; they do not regularly cause readers to struggle for meaning.

Sentence problems like the ones covered in this section of the chapter really do cause headaches. The problems covered here are often classed as "stylistic" problems in that they do not involve grammatical correctness. *Sentence style* in technical writing refers to the *clarity*, *conciseness*, and *effectiveness* of writing at the sentence level. Problems with sentence style inflate writing; they cast a fog around the meaning and frustrate readers. Certainly, grammar and usage problems are important, but sentence style is critical if a report is to accomplish its purpose of conveying a message.

Overnominalization

One of the major problems in business and technical prose is overnominalization, which refers to the confusing, mind-numbing practice of jamming nouns and noun phrases together in strings:

Overnominalized Sentences

There is a growing awareness of *organizational employee creative capacity*.

Position acquisition requirements are any combination of high school graduation and years of increasingly responsible secretarial experience.

The Quality Circle participation roles and tasks and time/cost requirements of *Quality Circle organizational implementation* will be described.

Proper integrated circuit packaging type identification and applications are crucial to electrical system design and repair.

Cerebral-anoxia-associated neonatal-period birth injuries can lead to epileptic convulsions.

Reading sentences like these is tough going. Notice in the revisions how these long noun strings are simplified:

Revisions

There is a growing awareness of the creative capacity of employees in all organizations.

To qualify for the position, you'll need to be a high school graduate and have had increasingly responsible secretarial experience.

The tasks of the participants in Quality Circles and the time and cost requirements involved in the implementation of Quality Circles will be discussed.

Identifying the proper type of packaging for integrated circuits is crucial to the design and repair of these electrical systems.

Birth injuries associated with cerebral anoxia in the neonatal period can lead to epileptic convulsions.

STEP 6.   Select any five paragraphs in your report rough draft, and search for overly long noun phrases (overnominalization problems). If you find any such problem sentences, copy them onto your worksheet and write revisions of them.

Redundant Words and Phrases

Another sentence problem is the scatter-gun approach. Some sentences seem designed to shower readers with generous helpings of vaguely appropriate words and phrases, as if bulk wordage can get the job done. The real effect, however, is needless repetition and loss of clarity. One common category of this problem is the needless piling up of synonyms joined by *and*:

Redundant-Phrasing Problems

With increasing numbers of part-time employees in the work force, the need for *special attention and consideration* for these employees has become apparent.

Manufacturers should be aware of the *disadvantages and limitations* of the different integrated-circuit packages.

This report will focus on the different *uses and applications* of the laser in medicine.

This report *discusses and explains* the historical development of the laser.

Nothing is lost by eliminating one of the pair in each of these examples:

Revisions

With increasing numbers of part-time employees in the work force, special consideration for these employees is needed.

Manufacturers should be aware of the disadvantages of the different integrated-circuit packages.

This report will focus on the different uses of the laser in medicine.

This report discusses the historical development of the laser.

Redundant phrasing also arises from certain set phrases that use three or four times as many words as necessary. Here is a list of some of the most common set phrases that cause wordiness, followed by a passage containing redundant phrases:

as already stated	in view of the fact that
at this point in time	it is recommended that
as per your request	in light of the fact that
being of the opinion that	in the near future
during the time that	it would be advisable to
due to the fact that	in this day and age
for the reason that	in my own personal opinion
to the fullest extent possible	in accordance with your request
four in number	predicated upon the fact that
inasmuch as	pursuant to your request
in connection with	take cognizance of the fact that
it has come to my attention that	with reference to the fact that
	with regard to
in close proximity to	to the extent that
in the neighborhood of	until such time as
has the ability to	that being the case

Redundant-Phrasing Problems

Coherence. *It is evident that* the most dominant feature of laser light is that the laser *has the ability to* produce coherent light. Coherence is the primary property that differentiates the laser *with respect to* ordinary light. The theory of coherence *has reference to aspects* of electromagnetic waves used in laser-beam production *with the inclusion of* wave frequency and wave phase. Coherence *by way of definition* is composed of wave trains vibrating in phase with each other, or expressed simply, parallel rays of light. Coherence is *in reference to* different light beams *in the state of being* totally in step with each other, as a *result of the fact* of the stimulated emission.

Each of these italicized phrases can be slashed to one or two words, producing leaner, more economical prose:

Revision

Coherence. The dominant feature of laser light is the laser's ability to produce coherent light. Coherence is the primary property differentiating laser light from ordinary light. The theory of coherence involves electromagnetic waves used in laser-beam production and includes wave frequency and wave phase. Coherence by definition is composed of wave trains vibrating in phase with each other, or simply expressed, parallel rays of light. Coherent light is light in which the different beams are totally in step with each other because of the stimulated emission process.

STEP 7.   Select any five paragraphs from your rough draft, and search for sentences with redundant phrasing. If you find any such problems, copy the sentences onto your worksheet, and write revisions of them.

Weak Pronouns

A common frustration for readers is the use of weak pronouns such as *this, it, that*, or *which* in situations where the reference (antecedent) is unclear. Consider these examples:

Weak Pronoun Sentences

The firm is not a mechanical unit but an organic whole in which the parts are related not just functionally but socially to one another. *This* means mutual interdependence between the parts in such a way that each group within the firm influences and is influenced by others.

Because of the cost of using the telephone system for regular business, most factories request *this* to be used only when necessary.

For all employees with high goals and leadership ability, the social work group provides a means of exercising these talents. For part-time employees, *this* can prove frustrating if they cannot even become true members of the group.

Telex machines offer companies the capacity to transmit communications to all offices immediately. *This* is extremely efficient for transmitting requests for price information.

Most readers must stop and figure out what the word *this* in these examples refers to. (*This* is the weak pronoun; the word *this* refers to the pronoun's reference, or antecedent.) The solution is to find a noun or noun phrase to substitute for the weak pronoun or to use with it. Here are revised versions of the preceding weak-pronoun sentences:

Revisions

The firm is not a mechanical unit but an organic whole in which the parts are related not just functionally but socially to one another. *This organic relationship* means mutual interdependence between the parts in such a way that each group within the firm influences and is influenced by others.

Because of the cost of using the telephone system for regular business, most factories request *nonbusiness use of the phone* to be kept to a minimum.

For all employees with high goals and leadership ability, the social work group provides a means of exercising these talents. For part-time employees, *this potential* can prove frustrating if they cannot even become true members of the group.

Telex machines offer companies the capacity to transmit communications to all offices immediately. *This system* is extremely efficient for transmitting requests for price information.

The summary of the topic of discussion in these revisions (1) reminds readers of the topic of discussion and keeps their attention focused, (2) enables writers to supply more detail and to emphasize important points, and (3) strengthens the coherence, the flow, of a piece of writing.

STEP 8.   Select any five paragraphs from the rough draft of your report, and search for weak pronouns such as those just discussed above. If you find any, copy the sentences onto your worksheet, and write revisions of them.

Weak Use of the Be Verb

Another common sentence problem involves using the verb *to be* when an action verb is preferable. Such weak use obscures the action and puts a fog around the meaning of a sentence:

Problems with the Be Verb

The contribution of Quality Circles is mostly to areas of training and motivating people to produce higher-quality work.

Measurement of temperature is done in degrees of Fahrenheit or Celsius, and its indications are by colored marks on the outside of the thermometer.

The beginning of the clonic phase is when the sustained tonic spasm of the muscles gives way to sharp, short, interrupted jerks.

During speech, the generation of sound is by vocal chords and the rushing of air from the lungs.

The response of the normal ear to sounds is in the audio frequency between about 20–20,000 Hz.

To fix problems like these, study the sentence for a noun that can be turned into an action verb, and rewrite the whole sentence around it:

Revisions

Quality Circles contribute to the training and motivating of people to produce high-quality work.

Temperature is measured in degrees of Fahrenheit or Celsius and is indicated by colored marks on the outside of the thermometer.

The clonic phase begins when the sustained tonic spasm of the muscle gives way to sharp, short, interrupted jerks.

During speech, sound is generated by the vocal cords and by rushing air from the lungs.

The normal ear responds to sounds within the audio-frequency range of about 20–20,000 Hz.

STEP 9.   Search for weak *be* verbs in any five paragraphs in your report, copy any problems of this sort that you find onto your worksheet, and then write revisions of them.

Problems with the Passive Voice

Although the passive voice may be preferable in certain sentences, its misuse can lead to problems, specifically, a vague, confusing, highly impersonal, or overly formal writing style. Here is an example:

At present, all library research involving laser theory, laser types, and laser applications *has been completed*. In this work, books, reports, and journals *have been consulted*. Information from Phillips Petroleum Company that supplements this research *is expected*. Currently, research *is being done* on the economics of laser use.

Now here is a revision:

I have just completed all library research on laser theory, laser types, and laser applications. In this work I've been using books, reports, and journals. Also, I'm expecting information from Phillips Petroleum Company that will supplement my research. My current work involves the economics of laser use.

Notice how much more personable, honest, and direct this revision is and how the use of *I* does not create an inappropriately informal tone. For more on passive voice, see Appendix D.

STEP 10.   Search for weak use of the passive voice in any five paragraphs of your report rough draft, copy any such sentences that you find onto your worksheet, and write revisions of them.

Expletive Problems

A problem similar to the weak use of the verb *to be* involves the weak use of expletives. An expletive is any form of *it is* or *there are*. Although the expletive can be a useful tool in certain sentences, it is easy to overuse and can quickly lead to wordy, awkward, inflated writing:

Sentences with Unnecessary Expletives

When *there is* a very strong buildup at the front of the plane, *it is* what is known as a shock wave.

When *there is* decay of a radioactive substance, *there is* the emission of some form of a high-energy particle—an alpha particle, a beta particle, or a gamma ray.

It is the results of studies of the central region of the M87 galaxy that have shown that *there are* stars near the center that move around as though *there were* some huge mass at the center that was attracting them.

Revising sentences with this kind of problem is usually rather easy: delete the expletive and rephrase the remainder of the sentence if necessary.

Revisions

When a very strong buildup occurs at the front end of the plane, a shock wave occurs.

When a radioactive substance decays, some form of a high-energy particle—an alpha particle, a beta particle, or a gamma ray—is emitted.

Recent studies of the central region of the M87 galaxy have shown stars near the center moving around as though some huge mass at the center were attracting them.

Predication Problems

Sentences with predication problems sound like wordy, awkward writing but also like diction problems. The term *predication* refers to the process of putting words together to make phrases, clauses, and whole sentences. A problem with predication, therefore, means that a subject, verb, direct object, and complement do not make sense together. Typically, predication problems involve a subject and a verb that do not go together logically (as is the case with the italicized subjects and verbs in the following examples):

Sentences with Predication Problems

The *causes* of the disappearance of early electric automobiles *were devastating* to the future of energy conservation in the United States.

Currently, *electric vehicles are experimenting* with two types of energy sources.

Consequently, *the body* is more coordinated and is less likely to *commit mental mistakes.*

In the first example, "causes" are not devastating; the disappearance of early electric vehicles is. In the second example, "electric vehicles" cannot "experiment" with anything; researchers or designers can. In the third example, the body cannot commit "mental mistakes." Here are some revisions:

Revisions

The disappearance of early electric automobiles destroyed the future of energy conservation in the United States.

Currently, research on electric vehicles involves two types of energy sources.

Consequently, workers will be more coordinated and commit fewer mental errors.

Awkwardly Phrased Sentences

For many reasons, sentences can read awkwardly. Somehow the phrasing is not quite right, and sentences can read in a rough, choppy, awkward manner. Usually, the problem is not a grammar and usage error nor any of the other problems discussed thus far; the sentence is just hard to read. Sometimes the problem is a combination of the sentence problems discussed in this section of the chapter. Here are some examples:

Awkward-Phrasing Problems

Most of the research has been formulated into paragraphs that organize and explain the material so that it may be placed directly into the report. In consideration of the amount of research that remains to be completed and the other procedures involved in the production of this document, approximately 60 percent of the report has been completed.

The major difficulties involved in explaining the technical aspects of laser usage in surgery will be incurred in describing the technology of the laser and the technology of various surgical procedures.

Technical knowledge relations can be enhanced through the use of graphic aids such as pictorial drawings.

Because of this link to cancer and other medical treatments, a large degree of literature has been published regarding lasers in biochemistry.

Using laser technology in medicine is a beneficial practice which has been effective in treating cancer.

The reader will be predominantly informed from a biochemical standpoint with an emphasis being placed on the benefits of the usage of lasers in medicine.

Because of these factors it is essential that management understand the aspects which affect the employee as to whether or not his fullest potential is reached.

This point really links up with the first principle in so far as it is the lack of satisfaction or the sense of frustration experienced in their jobs by these would-be leaders in the part-time work force that is the bottom cause of such trouble in the work environment.

How can you spot such problems?

- Have friends read your writing out loud and mark places in sentences where they hesitate or stumble while reading.
- Watch for odd groupings of words within sentences such as *be* verbs followed by prepositions or several prepositions occurring together.

How can you correct such problems?

1. Visualize the different pieces of the awkwardly phrased sentence as pieces of a jigsaw puzzle.
2. Juggle them around in your mind, trying out different arrangements.
3. In particular, try taking the last part of the sentence, placing it at the beginning of the sentence, and rewriting the whole sentence accordingly.
4. Eventually you will find an order that seems smoother, more natural, and easier to read.

Here are revisions of the preceding awkward sentences; notice how in some the main parts have been switched:

Revisions

The research has been written up so that it can be used directly in the report. About 60 percent of the research and other work on the report has been completed.

Discussion of laser technology and the various surgical procedures related to it will be difficult.

Graphic aids, particularly drawings, will make the technical discussion clearer.

Because of the laser's importance in the treatment of cancer and other health problems, much literature has been published.

Laser treatment of cancer can be effective.

The main focus will be on the benefits of lasers in medicine.

For these reasons, management should try to understand how employees can reach their fullest potential.

This point illustrates the first principle: part-time workers with leadership ability who experience dissatisfaction and frustration in their jobs are the main cause of such trouble in the work environment.

STEP 11.   Search for awkward sentences in any five paragraphs in the rough draft of your report, copy any such sentences that you find onto your worksheet, and then write revisions of them.

Sentence Length

Problems also arise when sentences are too short and choppy and when they are too long. With short, choppy sentences, readers lose the flow of the discussion and have to figure out the transitions for themselves. On the other hand, overly long sentences cause readers to lose their way. Look, for example, at the problems with the paragraphs in Figure 7–17.

For the short, choppy sentences in the first two paragraphs, the solution is to do some combining. The overly long sentences in the last two paragraphs, on the other hand, must be split into shorter and more readable ones. Revisions of the paragraphs in Figure 7–17 appear in Figure 7–18.

Remember, however, that the idea is not to make all the sentences in a report approximately the same length. Although the average length is between 17 and 25 words, sentences over and under this average are common and can be effective. Some must be longer to convey a thought; others are shorter to create greater clarity and emphasis by contrast to the longer ones. Figure 7–19 has effective sentences of varying lengths.

STEP 12.   Circle any sentence over 25 words long or under 8 words long in your report draft, and decide whether revising these longer and shorter sentences would result in easier, clearer reading. Revise these sentences on your worksheet.

Problems with Grammar, Usage, and Punctuation

Problems or errors in grammar, usage, and punctuation can lead to problems in communication and can be distracting to readers and embarrassing to the writer. To increase your ability to recognize and correct such problems, consider following these steps:

1. Take the diagnostic test available in the Instructor's Manual.

II. <u>The History of Lasers</u>

The history of lasers arises from the basic theory of light production. Max Planck proposed light theory in the 1800s. This theory was expanded on through the years. Most of the modern expansion of the theory came with Albert Einstein's modification in 1905. Einstein's modification established light theory as the basis for lasers. After Einstein's work, an actual laser was built. The building of the laser led to research and development on laser applications. Safety studies during this research resulted in the development of laser use in medicine.

<u>Bohr's Theory</u>

In the 1800s Max Planck submitted his theory of light formation. He theorized about the production of light. He argued that light results when the atoms of a compound move from an upper energy level to a lower energy level. Energy is emitted when an atom moves from a higher level to a lower level. This happens because excess energy of the higher level will not fit in the lower level. The excess energy is emitted in a package known as a quanta of light. Many of these quanta of energy result in light. This is the kind of light as the human eye knows it.

<u>Basic Theory of Laser Light</u>

In order to understand how a solid, liquid, or gas can be made to give off radiation in the form of a laser beam, one must understand some of the basic theory behind laser light. Laser beams, which have many properties that distinguish them from ordinary light, result from the emission of energy from atoms in the form of electromagnetic waves whose range in most laser beams is 10^{-3} to 10^{-7} meters.

Like ordinary light, laser light results because atoms in a medium absorb energy, move to a higher energy level, become unstable, then drop to a lower energy level, resulting in the emission of energy known as photons which travel in electromagnetic waves to yield visible light.

FIGURE 7–17. Problems with sentence length

The history of lasers arises from the basic theory of light production, first proposed by Max Planck in the 1800s. The theory was expanded upon through the years, with most of the modern expansion coming with Einstein's contributions in 1905. After Einstein's modification of the theory, which applied light theory directly to lasers, an actual laser was built. The building of the laser led to research and development in the applications of laser, and safety studies done during this work led to the development of laser use in medicine.

In order to understand how a solid, liquid, or gas can be made to give off radiation in the form of a laser beam, one must understand some of the basic theory behind laser light. Laser beams result from the emission of energy from atoms in the form of electromagnetic waves. The range of electromagnetic waves found in most laser beams is 10^{-3} to 10^{-7} meters. Most laser beams are just beams of light but with properties that distinguish them from ordinary light.

Like ordinary light, laser light results because atoms in a medium absorb energy, move to a higher energy level, become unstable, then drop to a lower energy level. The drop to a lower energy level results in the emission of energy known as photons which travel in electromagnetic waves to yield visible light.

FIGURE 7–18.   **Revision by combining or shortening sentences**

2. Study the sections in Appendix D that correspond to the categories of the diagnostic test in which you missed a substantial number.
3. Study your rough drafts for these same kinds of problems.
4. As you discover other grammar, usage, and punctuation problems in your writing, study the corresponding sections in Appendix D.

STEP 13.   For grammar, usage, and punctuation problems, follow the steps outlined in the preceding section.

Exercises

1. Do the test for organization on the following paragraph, decide how to rearrange the sentences within it, and then write a new version of it, making sure you create a smoothly reading paragraph.

Townes and other physicists began work on the "optical maser" (laser), but it is Theodore Maiman, in 1960, who is credited with the discovery of the first operable laser. During his study of the "optical maser," Townes published his hypotheses concerning the operation and construction of the laser. These hypotheses revealed that when atoms in an excited state are placed between two flat parallel mirrors, the atoms would (1) energize each other, (2) be reflected back and forth through the two mirrors in the amplification process, and (3) transport the atomic energy obtained to waves that are emitted as coherent light. Maiman, a research scientist with Hughes Aircraft Research Laboratory in California, used a synthetic ruby of approximately 0.5 cm diameter and 1.5 cm in length, a flash tube that pumped light to stimulate (excite) the ruby crystal, and general concepts outlined in Townes's hypotheses to produce the first operable laser. This device became known as the ruby laser. It is the pioneer in devices. . . .

Reprinted from Invitation to Physics by Jay M. Pasachoff and Marc L. Kutner by permission of W. W. Norton & Company, Inc. Copyright © 1981 by Jay M. Pasachoff and Marc L. Kutner.

FIGURE 7–19. Paragraph with varied-length sentences

Paragraph with Organization Problems

Acid Rain

Acid rain is defined as precipitation with a pH below 5.6–5.7. The first accurate report of acid rain appeared in 1911 in Leeds, England, where pH values approached 4.0. Acid rains were common during the eighteenth and nineteenth centuries, when coal was the primary industrial source of heat and power and when the smelting and refining industries used coal. Hydrogen ion concentrations that constitute acid rain are obtained when pure water is in solution equilibrium with aerial carbon dioxide at 25° C. In North America, acid rains were noted at several locations in the Northeast by 1939, and recalculations of data on earlier storms suggest that some of these precipitations may have been acidic. Reports of acid rain are now common in the mid-1980s throughout the Western world and in Japan, with pH values of 3.8–4.5 becoming almost the norm. Most researchers consider acid rain to be of significance when pH values are at least tenfold more acid than 5.7, that is, 4.7 and below.

2. Study the following paragraph that has coherence problems, and using the suggestions that follow it, insert transitional devices that will make it read more smoothly. The suggestions are keyed into the paragraph by the numbers in brackets.

Paragraph with Coherence Problems

Earthquakes

In recent years there have been many advances in earthquake-prediction research. [1] The goal of being able to predict with a high degree of certainty the magnitude, location, and time of occurrence of impending major seismic events is far from realization. Theoretical developments, including the dilatancy-diffusion model, have provided a qualitative understanding of some of the changes in geodetic, geophysical, and geochemical phenomena that have been reported prior to large earthquakes. [2] In the past few years, much has [3] been learned from the examination of a rapidly growing empirical database. This [4] has largely been the result of improvements in instrumentation which have allowed the continuous or near-continuous monitoring of many different natural phenomena that may show significant changes before a large earthquake. [5] A system that has recently been developed is the automated radon-thoron monitor. A network [6] now routinely records radon and thoron concentrations in several boreholes in southern California.

Suggestions for Improving Coherence

a. Combine these two sentences, or add a transitional word or phrase to the next sentence.

b. Combine these two sentences, or add a transitional word or phrase to the next sentence.

c. Add a transitional word or phrase here.

d. Repeat key words or phrases here.

e. Add a transitional word or phrase here.

f. Use repeated key words or phrases here.

3. Use both the tests for organization and coherence to analyze and rewrite the following passage.

Passage with Organizational and Coherence Problems

Heart Transplants

The first heart transplant was conducted in 1961 by South Africa's Dr. Christiaan Barnard. The first heart-transplant survived only 18 days. Enthusiasm was high for cardiac transplant operations at first. It was realized that rejection and complications were likely, and the number of recipients declined.

During the 1970s there were improved patient selection, earlier and more specific diagnosis of rejection, and better immunosuppression management. There have been better results and wider application since then. Since 1967, about 500 people in the United States have received heart transplants. The current five-year survival rate is 42 percent. In Figure 1, the black diamonds represent patients accepted for cardiac transplantation who never received a donor heart and died within the year. The white squares show the patients who underwent transplantation in 1968 through 1981. Early operations (1968–1981) are indicated by the black squares. Early transplants had a much lower survival rate than current recipients. •

4. Study the following paragraphs, and write one or more topic sentences for them.

Paragraph Needing a Topic Sentence

Coronary bypasses are the most frequently performed heart operations in the United States. The first coronary bypass operation involved the grafting of a vein from a patient's leg into the heart to serve as a detour around clogged arteries. Drugs are also used in the treatment of heart

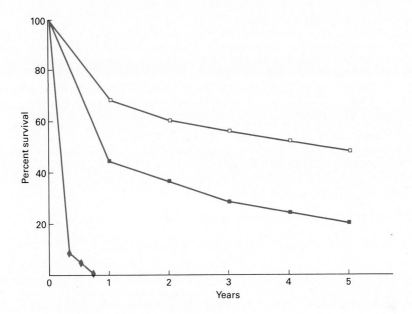

FIGURE 1. Cardiac transplantation activity worldwide

Source: Bruce A. Reitz, and Edward A. Stinson, "Cardiac Transplantation—1982." *Journal of the American Medical Association* (10 September 1982), 1226. Copyright 1982, American Medical Association.

disease. Propranolol is used for the treatment of heart irregularities. More recently, it has been used to treat angina, hypertension, and even second heart attacks. Another drug, cyclosporine, is used to help prevent the body's immune system from rejecting the transplant without impairing the body's ability to fight off infectious diseases. The discovery of how this drug selectively shuts down the immune system has dramatically advanced the successes of heart transplants. Finally, calcium blockers, only recently introduced into the United States, aid in combating heart disease by suppressing irregular heart rhythms and preventing coronary spasms. Also, they alleviate the pain that calcium ions cause when they cause blood vessels to contract.

Patients with the Jarvik-7 artificial heart are permanently tethered to 375 pounds of equipment: two compressors, a backup compressor, a three-hour supply of pressurized air (to operate the heart in case of a power failure), a drier to dehumidify the air, and mechanisms that control the air pressure and heart rate. All of this equipment can be placed on a rolling unit, thus making it portable, although the entire complex of devices and equipment must always be within 6 feet of the patient (the length of the power lines that emerge from just below the recipient's rib cage). One bioengineer, William Kolff, believes that the true future role of the artificial heart is "merely as a stopgap while the patient awaits a transplant" and as a lifesaver for those who may never receive a donor heart.

5. Study the following underdeveloped paragraph and the accompanying development sentences, and decide where to insert each of the development sentences (the development sentences are not in any order). When you've decided where the development sentences should be inserted, rewrite the whole paragraph with the inserted sentences into a smoothly reading, well-developed paragraph.

Paragraph Lacking Development

Biomagnetics is a new science that offers new information about living things. The body produces its own magnetic fields in two main ways: by electromagnetic currents and by ferromagnetic particles. The electric currents that produce such magnetic fields are the ion currents generated by muscles, nerves, and other organs. The ferromagnetic particles are insoluble contaminants of the body. Because these fields, due either to currents or particles, can give information about the internal organs not otherwise available, they have potential application in research and clinical diagnosis.

These biomagnetic fields are very weak, usually in the range of 10^{-10} to 10^{-5} gauss. The fields at the upper end of this range (stronger than 10^{-6} gauss) can be measured with a simple but sensitive magnetometer called a fluxgate.

Development Sentences for the Paragraph

- The most important ferromagnetic particles are dust particles in the lungs, which are primarily Fe_3O_4 (magnetite) oxide.
- By comparison, the Earth's magnetic field is about 1 gauss.
- For example, the same ion current generated by heart muscle, which produces the electrocardiogram, also produces a magnetic field over the chest.
- A gauss is a basic unit of measurement of magnetic induction.
- Thus, there is increasing interest in the use of biomagnetic fields, and research is under way throughout the world to measure them more and more accurately.
- Biomagnetics can be defined as the study and measurement of magnetic fields produced by organisms, particularly the human body.
- Weaker magnetic fields are measured with the extremely sensitive cryogenic magnetometer called the SQUID (superconducting quantum interference device).
- The same ion current generated by the brain, which produces the electroencephalogram, also produces a magnetic field over the head.

6. The following sentences, most would agree, are overnominalized. Rewrite them so that they are easier to read.
   a. Particulate matter removal air pollution control devices do not, however, reduce gases and odors.
   b. Increasing municipal fly-ash collection is partly the result of profitable uses discoveries.
   c. Small-scale, internal-use incinerator-plant waste heat recovery is fairly common in the United States.
   d. Combustion-chamber exit gas temperatures are approximately 2400° F.
   e. A voltage regulator can be defined as a constant output voltage value maintenance device.
   f. Microcomputer engine ignition control systems are just one application of modern integrated-circuit technology.
   g. Printed circuit board integrated-circuit packages use copper traces rather than traditional wires.
   h. High-temperature automated chemical circuitry molecule-formation techniques are required to produce one-quarter-inch chips.
   i. Noncritical application-special crystal-controlled clock-generator integrated circuits are used to ensure that each operation occurs at exactly the right time.

7. The following sentences are loaded with redundant phrasing; try your hand at revising them.
   a. As per your request for twenty copies of the reference book, you will be advised that the shipment will be remitted to you with the greatest possible expediency.

b. In regards to your request to have access to your vacation time on the dates of August 4 through August 21, it would be advisable for you to delay that scheduling until such time as the company experiences a slowdown with respect to its work orders.

c. Due to the fact of varying operation requirements and local customs, other company holidays not inclusive of those listed above may vary in connection with a given company's area of locality.

d. Employees should take cognizance of the fact that they have the ability to take full vacation time at any point in time during the calendar year, notwithstanding the fact that all the aforesaid time may or may not have been earned to its maximum.

8. The next sentences are plagued by a weak use of the *be* verb; rewrite them with *active* verbs to replace the *be* verbs.

a. The strengthening of the cardiorespiratory system coming from aerobic exercise *is* what will cut down on workers' illness and absenteeism.

b. The major areas in which caffeine has received attention *are* in pregnancy and cancer.

c. Transportation of oil from offshore oil rigs to refineries on shore *is* where spillage is most likely to occur.

d. The source of the vast majority of our fuel *is* through petroleum, natural gas, and coal.

e. The reason these resources are called fossil fuels *is* because they are the result of the decomposition of living matter.

f. The death of living vegetable matter—usually trees—over 200 million years ago *is* when the formation of fossil fuels began.

9. Transform the following weak, passive-voice sentences into active-voice sentences.

a. Excessive amounts of caffeine should try to be avoided to ensure a proper frame of mind and a healthy lifestyle.

b. Recent involvement has stirred a strong interest in owning ultralight aircraft.

c. In order to estimate company sales, industry expectations should first be looked at by the firm, because the sales of an individual company are reflected by them.

d. If the sky is gazed at long enough, the fact that the entire dome of stars rotates about a star in the North will be noticed.

e. The idea that stars are suns was come up with by Giordano Bruno, an Italian monk of the sixteenth century.

PART III

Gathering, Organizing, and Reporting Technical Information

Chapter **8.** **Planning Reports: Invention, Narrowing, and Outlining**

Chapter **9.** **Finding Information for Reports: Library and Nonlibrary Sources**

Chapter **10.** **Developing Reports: Notes, Drafts, and Final Packaging**

Introduction

You can use the chapters in this part of the book in two basic ways:

- As a guide through the most important phases of writing a full-length report
- For help on specific problems that arise when you are doing the practice writing in Part I chapters.

Each of the three chapters here in Part III provides you with step-by-step methods for working through the most important phases of planning, writing, and finishing a report. These phases include:

Phases in Technical-Report Writing	*Chapter*
1. Selecting a subject for a report and narrowing that subject to a manageable report topic	8
2. Generating content for the report topic, narrowing, and developing a tentative outline	8
3. Finding books, articles, reference works, government documents, trade and association literature, and computerized information-retrieval resources in libraries	9
4. Investigating sources of information for the report outside the library	9
5. Gathering information for the report through various means such as direct quotations, paraphrases, and summaries	9
6. Writing the rough draft of the report	10
7. Revising, editing, typing, and proofreading the report	10
8. Putting a finished report into a final, neat, professional-looking package	10

Of course, you may not need to use the steps in these chapters for all of the phases of report writing just listed: for example, you may already know how to take notes the traditional way and only need a quick review of it. Return to the chapters in Part III, however, if you run into problems like these:

Using Part III Chapters: Examples	*Chapter*
• You can't think of a topic for your report or for one of the practice writing assignments in Part I.	8
• You have a topic for a report but can't think of what to say about it, in other words, what topics to cover.	8
• You're not sure how to make an outline of your report project.	8
• You have a large topic and are not sure how to narrow it to something manageable, something you can do within a reasonable amount of time (and paper).	8
• You need to find information on your report topic in the library but are not sure how to look up books, articles, reference books, and government documents.	9
• You think there may be useful information on your report topic outside the library but are not sure how to locate it.	9
• You have lots of information to gather and save but need a good note-taking system to do it.	10
• You need a good, thorough system for editing and revising your rough drafts.	10
• You're not sure what sort of binders to use for your finished report, what sort of typing paper, how to insert the illustrations, how to do the final typing job, or what should be on the cover label.	10

CHAPTER 8

Planning Reports: Invention, Narrowing, and Outlining

Chapter Objectives
Overview of Technical Reports
   Informational Reports
   Feasibility Reports
   Instructions
Finding a Subject for the
   Technical Report
   Major, Future Courses, and Textbooks
   Instructors' Ideas and Topic Lists
   Magazines, Journals, and Periodical
     Indexes
   Career Plans, Interviews, and Current
     Work
   Ideas for Local Improvements
   Problems
Analyzing Your Report's Audience
   and Purpose

The Invention or Brainstorming Stage
Narrowing Report Subjects
The Outlining Stage
   Exploratory Reading
   Arranging the Parts of the Outline
   Elaborating the Rough Outline
Finishing the Outline
   Comparing the Outline to the Rough
     Draft
   Adjusting Items in the Outline
   Eliminating One-Item Outline Entries
   Checking for Parallel Phrasing
   Making Outlines Self-Explanatory
   Adjusting the Graphics
Exercises
Model: Example Report-Topic
   Proposal (memo)

───────── *Chapter Objectives* ─────────

After you read this chapter, study the examples, and work the steps, you should be able to:

- Explain the difference between the three main types of reports.
- List ways to find report topics.
- Make a list of topics related to a report subject using the invention checklist.
- Elaborate a rough outline.
- Arrange parts of an outline according to some appropriate pattern.
- Identify and revise common problems in outlines.

This chapter shows you some techniques for the early stages of your report-writing project. Specifically, you can use this chapter

- To find a subject to write a report on
- To "brainstorm" on that subject
- To narrow a report subject to a more manageable topic
- To develop a detailed outline for a report project

Overview of Technical Reports

Although Chapters 12, 13, and 14 describe the different kinds of reports in detail, all you need right now to choose a topic for your report is a quick overview. Terminology for the different kinds of reports varies, but reports can be divided into those that inform, recommend, and instruct.

Informational Reports

A great variety of informational reports simply present information in an objective, organized way. People often need informative reports that gather and present information on a subject in one neat package. These people don't have time to do an exhaustive library search nor time to read stacks of books and articles looking for their information. Instead, they find individuals or groups to do the information gathering and report writing for them. Here are some examples of the kinds of information these people might need:

New methods in helping diabetics
The laser in eye surgery
Survey of recycling programs in major U.S. cities
Technologies used in wind-powered electrical generators
Chemical and nonchemical methods of insect control

Feasibility Reports

Recommendations, or feasibility reports as they are called here, go one step further than informational reports. They not only provide information but also argue for certain courses of action (to build or not to build, to purchase or not to purchase).

Feasibility reports present information to prove whether a project can be done and whether it is worth doing. For example, a company may benefit from a new technology, but no one is sure whether the expense, the downtime, and the payoff will be worth it. A community may be considering a plan to build some new facility or to start some new program; but people disagree about its value or potential benefit to the community. Again, a feasibility report tries to answer these questions. Here are some more specific examples:

The acceptability of bike lanes in the city
The profitability of recycling municipal waste
Whether a saltwater-conversion facility would solve the county's fresh-water problems
Whether solar-energy devices will save money if installed in city-owned housing

Instructions

Another common use of technical writing is instructions: explanations of how to operate or repair machinery, how to perform certain actions, or what to do in certain situations. Informational-report-type information is also supplied in instructional writing: descriptions of the devices being used or explanations of principles and theory related to the activity being explained. Here are some examples of instructional topics:

How to write a metric-conversion program in Pascal
How to read architectural drawings
How to develop your own photographs
How to graft a fruit tree
How to take blood pressure
How to overhaul a carburetor

STEP 1.   On your worksheet briefly explain which type of report you are going to write. If it's not quite like any of the types just described, explain.

Finding a Subject for the Technical Report

To find a good report topic, let your mind wander; do some casual, relaxed browsing around. Scribble down the ideas that come to you. If you have several ideas, keep them all in mind through the early stages of your report work until one proves to be more interesting or manageable.

STEP 2. On your worksheet write the information requested in the following sections.

Major, Future Courses, and Textbooks

An obvious place to start your search is with your academic major. On your work-sheet jot down a description of your major; include any information on special areas of interest or curiosity and on reasons you are majoring in the field. Also, list descriptions of majors or fields that you almost went into or have some interest in. When you've done this, think about what you've written down for a moment: what report topics does the list suggest? On your worksheet write any topic that comes to mind during this process. Consider the topics these majors suggest:

Nursing	Criminology	Computer science
Data processing	Business	Accounting
Biology	Technical communications	Physical education
Real estate	Financial planning	Elementary education

Take a look at your degree plan or your course catalog: what specialized courses will you be taking? Write brief descriptions of these on your worksheet, particularly ones you are looking forward to. Think about these descriptions, and scribble down any topics that come to mind. Courses or fields like these suggest a variety of technical-report topics:

Management of small business	Computer graphics
Technological innovation: bioethical issues	Economics of health care
Pascal programming	Issues in nutrition and health
Business law	Urban transportation problems
Development of the young child	Introduction to word processing
Criminology	Interior design
Introduction to artificial intelligence	COBOL for business applications
The money market	Nonverbal communication

Investigate textbooks in your major, in particular, textbooks in advanced or specialized courses such as those you listed in the section on future courses. Glance at the tables of contents of these books and at the headings (titles and subtitles within the chapters). As this process begins to suggest ideas for report topics, scribble them on your worksheet.

Instructors' Ideas and Topic Lists

Instructors in your major or related fields are also good prospects for helping you find report topics. Drop by their offices for a chat; see what ideas they have. If they make interesting suggestions, jot them down (and remember that these instructors can also serve as helpful guides in your future work on the report). Librarians are also good prospects. Ask your librarian (or your technical-writing instructor) for a list of report subjects. Scan lists like the one in Figure 8–1 for interesting subjects. As you glance at this list, jot down the topics that interest you.

Pain relief without drugs
Offshore oil ports
Flat-rate taxation
Artificial heart
Nuclear fusion
Computer crime
Growing strawberries, grapes, etc.
Taking blood pressure
Soil analysis
Hypoglycemia
The *Viking* spacecraft
The Moon landing
Drafting techniques
Effects of caffeine
Fetal alcohol syndrome
Automotive uses of plastics
Computer sound synthesis
Reconstructive surgery
Missile guidance systems
Computer graphics
Genetic engineering
Hydraulic fracturing
Artificial intelligence
Pyramid power
Beekeeping
Restaurant management
Hyperkinetic behavior
Psychosomatic disorders
Chemotherapy

Photographic techniques
Types of investments
Handling your own divorce
Microprocessors
Continental drift
B-vitamin complex
Treating sickle-cell anemia
Adopting a child
Electric cars
Secondary oil recovery
Solar panels
The planet Venus
Mount St. Helens
Desalination plants
Synthetic fuels
Industrial waste disposal
Computer chips
Obstructive lung disease
Implants
Archeological technology
Ultrasound
Scuba-diving equipment
Wood-burning stoves
Geriatric nursing
Thermal power
Drill-bit design
Turbomachines
Cancer

Burglar alarms
Microwave oven
Rotary drilling
Hurricanes
Multiphase telemetry
Windpower
Well-logging
Waferboard
CPR procedure
Dream analysis
CAT scanners
Greenhouses
IQ
Drip irrigation
IV machines
Hemodialysis
Bridge design
Space shuttle
Oil shale
Holograms
Dietary fiber
Cryogenics
Euthanasia
Diodes
Lasers
UFOs
Aphasia
The brain
Hormones
Pesticides
Biorhythms
COBOL

FIGURE 8—1.   Sample list of report-subject possibilities

Animal migration	Food additives	Cable TV
Pascal	Interferon	Cocombustion
Integrated circuits	Pheromones	Rain forests
Jogging	ENIAC	Nuclear war
Sahara Desert	Recycling	Earthquakes
Three Mile Island	Word processors	Ozone
Tornadoes	Atomic bomb	Cameras
Motorcycle	Plate tectonics	Video
maintenance	Fire alarms	equipment

FIGURE 8–1.   (cont.)

Magazines, Journals, and Periodical Indexes

Another good strategy (and an enjoyable pastime as well) for finding report topics is to do some selective browsing through magazines and journals. Check the tables of contents, and skim the titles for interesting articles in both recent and back issues. Look into magazines and journals of fields that you are curious about but may have shied away from because of their technicality. As you browse, jot down brief descriptions of possible report topics.

A good way to look at a lot of magazine article titles at once is to do some selective browsing through periodical indexes. (See Chapter 9 on finding periodical indexes.)

Career Plans, Interviews, and Current Work

An interesting strategy is to sit back and imagine what you'll be doing in five to ten years. Visualize the work you'll be doing or would like to be doing, and in particular, the situations that might require you to write reports. As you muse upon your future, jot down the technical subject areas you think you'll be involved in. For example:

drafting	agriculture	forestry
electronics	city planning	college administration
wildlife preservation	medical technology	
nursing	programming	

Similarly, talk to business and professional people whom you know: ask them about the reports that they write or that they know about. Who knows? You may end up writing a technical report for someone! And, if you currently have a job, take a look around you and see what kinds of things are going on that might require written reports. Ask:

- What reports are written or, in fact, need to be written?
- What changes or innovations are needed?
- What new equipment can be acquired to streamline the office?
- Can you propose that the business open up a new store somewhere else in town or in a nearby city?

Projects like these often require written reports. As these ideas occur to you, jot them down on your worksheet.

Ideas for Local Improvements

Another way to find topics is to jump in the car with a friend and go driving around looking for civic projects that would make your community a better place in which to live:

- Are there esplanades or vacant areas that could be planted with trees or turned into community gardens?
- Is parking a problem in certain areas of the city?
- How is municipal garbage handled?
- Is there a recycling program in town?
- Are there bike lanes?
- Are more recreational facilities, for example, softball parks, needed?
- Are there old, unused, run-down buildings that could be renovated and used for worthwhile causes or projects?
- Would city residents be attracted to an outdoor theater for concerts, plays, and musicals?

You can also visit business people, government officials, or directors of nonprofit organizations and ask them about their needs. For example, the local senior-citizens center may need barriers removed and other facilities built so that its members can get to the nearby park. For such needs you can do the design work, calculate costs, and find out about administrative approvals that are needed. If you do your work well, the senior citizens will receive a useful report that will save them much time and effort.

Problems

Good report topics can also be found by free associating around the word *problems*. Think about the problems that exist in your community, your city, your county, or your state. (Just take a look at today's newspaper or watch the evening news if you need some stimulation!) Think about problems geographically (as just discussed) or socially (in terms of age, sex, race, handicaps) or in other ways (medicine, environment, politics, energy, or military). Does your field or major offer solutions, or are you interested in some of the new solutions under research? As ideas come to you, jot them down on your worksheet.

Analyzing Your Report's Audience and Purpose

Early in your planning for a technical report you must identify the specific audience that will read your report and the purpose your report will serve. To analyze the report audience, you must consider these questions carefully:

- Why does the audience need or want this report?
- What is the audience's technical background (knowledge, training, first-hand experience)?
- What is the report's purpose?
- What kinds of information will have to be included and excluded from the report, considering the audience?
- How should the information in the report be presented?

If you are not familiar with analyzing report audiences and purposes, return to the discussion and steps in Chapter 5. Understanding the audience and purpose of your report becomes very important when you *narrow* your report subject.

STEP 3.   Briefly describe your audience, its background, capabilities, and interest in your report. (For a step-by-step method of analyzing your audience, see Chapter 5.)

The Invention or Brainstorming Stage

Once you've picked a *subject* for your report, the next step is to list the *topics* related to it. During this stage, the invention or brainstorming stage, use the following suggestions to explore your report idea:

- Let your report subject itself suggest topics: for example,

Subject	Possible Topics
The sun	its temperature its composition its unusual phenomena its relative size
Ultrasound in medicine	its physical properties equipment used medical uses advantages

- Free associate on your report subject; sit back, relax, and let your mind wander freely around the report subject. Keep scratch paper handy, however. Don't expect the ideas to come all at once in a ten-minute session. Ideas for reports come at the oddest moments—in the shower, on the bus, in your backyard, in your car, or on your bicycle.

• Use an invention checklist like the following. If you ask yourself the questions listed in Figure 8–2 you'll be less apt to overlook important topics; and, with use, these questions eventually become almost automatic.

Generating Topics for Report Outlines:
A Checklist of Invention Questions

Set up a report worksheet to scribble answers to any of the following questions that apply to your report project.

Problems or needs	Does your report concern itself with a problem or a need?
Solutions and answers	Should your report discuss potential solutions or answers to the problems or questions presented in the report?
Historical events and natural phenomena	Does your report concern itself with some historical event or natural (or mechanical) phenomenon?
Causes and effects	Should your report discuss the causes, effects, or both related to the phenomenon, historical event, or problem you are discussing?
Descriptions	Which aspects of your report subject require description?
Processes	Does your report subject involve processes, procedures, routines, or repetitive events that must be discussed in steps?
Classes	Can any topic within your report be divided into classes or types?
Comparisons to similar or familiar things	Can similar things in your report be compared to each other? Can you compare something complex in your report to something familiar or common?

FIGURE 8–2. Invention checklist for reports

Illustrative examples	Will a discussion of examples related to your report subject be effective?
Theoretical background (definitions)	Are there unfamiliar terms in your report? Can they be presented in a theoretical or background section? If so, list the terms.
Applications	Can you discuss the applications related to your report subject?
Advantages and benefits	Should you discuss the advantages or benefits related to your technical-report subject?
Disadvantages and limitations	Are certain disadvantages, problems, limitations, or drawbacks associated with your report subject?
Warnings, cautions, and guidelines	Does your report need cautionary or guideline statements?
Economics or financial considerations	Should you discuss cost factors, purchase expenses, maintenance and operation costs, production or output costs, or savings?
Importance of the report subject	Should you discuss the importance of your subject, or why people should be concerned about it or interested in it?
Historical background and important names	Is there some important historical background—events and names—that should be discussed in your report?
Future developments	Should your report speculate about future developments or possibilities related to the report subject?
Social, political, legal, or ethical implications	Does your report subject raise certain social or ethical questions, as for example, certain medical technologies do?

(continued)

FIGURE 8—2.   (cont.)

Reasons for or against	In your report should you try to convince readers to take certain actions or think a certain way concerning your report subject?
Conclusions	Should your report draw certain conclusions about what it discusses?
Recommendations	Should your report make certain recommendations to its readers?
Alternatives or choices	Should your report discuss several alternatives or choices related to your report subject matter?
Criteria	Will your report use certain criteria to draw its conclusions or to make its recommendations?
Tests and methods used	Should you have a section on the tests you perform, the methods or theories you use, or the procedures and equipment you use?
Statistical presentations and analyses	Should you include sections that summarize and analyze the data you collect in your project?
Legal and administrative demands	Should your report discuss which agencies to apply to, which forms to fill out, or which steps to take in order to accomplish the purpose of your report?
Business or professional contexts	Should you describe the specific business or professional situation, for example, a supervisor's orders, that generates the need for your report? (This applies if you invent a report-writing situation, also.)

FIGURE 8–2.   (cont.)

Figure 8–3 contains an excerpt of a brainstorming session in which these questions were used.

Comprehensive Topic List for a Report on
Wind-Powered Electrical Systems

How does a wind-powered electrical system (WPES) work? What are the steps in its operation?

Savings: discuss the amount of money that can be saved using WPES.

Relationship between average windspeeds and electrical output: What happens when there's no wind? Only very light breezes? Too much wind?

Basic parts: rotor, generator, tail assembly, tower

Different manufacturers of WPES: How can you get a good system and avoid being ripped off?

Dimensions, materials, construction of common models of WPES; sensitivity to low wind speeds

Historical background on WPES: the time when more WPES were being used, just before rural electrification in the 1930s; who were the first developers? when did interest in WPES reappear? why?

Two general classes of wind machines: lift and drag machines

Lightning protection of WPES

Aerodynamic principles as they apply to WPES

Understanding weather patterns and seasonal and geographical factors affecting wind

Principles of electricity: circuits, generators, types of current, meanings of terminology

Federal tax credits and research support in wind-systems research and WPES purchase by consumers

---

FIGURE 8–3.   Example of a topic list developed with the invention checklist

STEP 4.   Use any of the invention questions in Figure 8–2 that apply to your report project, and make a topic list like the one in Figure 8–3. (If you are not quite ready for this step, go directly to step 6, and return to this step.)

Narrowing Report Subjects

No matter how fascinating your report subject is, you still must spend some time narrowing it. Narrowing a report subject means reducing it to a manageable size—something you can accomplish within a certain amount of time and within a certain number of pages. Narrowing is like zooming in on a subject and selecting only a few topics to report on, according to your report-writing situation, specific audience, and specific purpose. Narrowing also means deciding whether to cover those topics in a general, specific, technical, or nonspecialist way. To narrow a report subject, follow these steps:

1. Make as complete a list of topics related to your report subject as you can by following the steps in the section "The Invention or Brainstorming Stage."
2. Look up entries on that subject in both general and specialized encyclopedias to help develop this topic list, also. (See Chapter 9 on finding reference books.) Encyclopedia entries are usually written in a comprehensive way; use them to build your topic list.
3. When you have a sizable list of topics related to your report subject, you are ready to do the real work of narrowing, which means asking questions like these:

   Is this section necessary to address my audience's needs?
   Will my audience be lost and confused without this subsection?
   Is the information included in this section crucial to my audience members' understanding and to the uses to which they'll put my report?
   Could I delete this section without harming the overall effect or purpose of my report?
   Is the level of discussion in this section too general for my audience? Too technical? Not technical enough?

The audience and purpose of your report act like filters, screening out the unnecessary topics. An audience of homeowners interested in wind-powered electrical systems would want to read general information on how such systems work, what are the financial savings, and how to select a system (topics 2, 4, 5, and so on in the narrowed topic list in the diagram in Figure 8–4). If you are not familiar with the different audiences that reports commonly have, see Chapter 5. The steps there show you how to analyze your audience systematically and what to do if you're not sure who your audience is.

4. One last step in the narrowing process is to decide how to discuss the topics you've selected. You can discuss topics within a report in several ways:

   • *General* discussion gives a rapid overview of a topic and can take up less space in a report. General discussion can be for either specialist or nonspecialist readers. In a general discussion for specialists, you save space by assuming those readers have a certain level of knowledge.

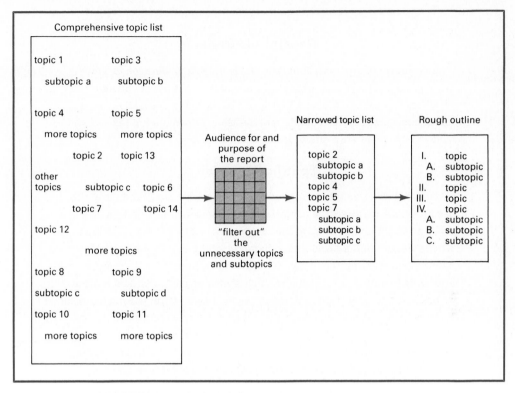

FIGURE 8–4. Audience and purpose used to narrow a report topic

- *Specific* discussion gives much detail about a topic and thus usually takes up more space within a report. Specific discussion can also be for either specialist or nonspecialist readers. In a specific discussion for nonspecialist readers, you make sure every detail is explained thoroughly so that those readers can understand.

In Figure 8–5 are two excerpts, one of which is discussed generally; the other, specifically and technically.

Based on the audience and purpose just described, here's how the individual topics for the wind-power report might be handled:

Report section	Level of detail
Engineering background on WPES	general
Basic components of WPES	general
Basic operation of WPES	general
Selection of a WPES system	specific
Economics of WPES	specific
Other considerations	specific
WPES designs and manufacturers	general

General Discussion

A common component found on modern launch vehicles is the fairing. Its purpose is to protect the payload of the space mission, satellites, space capsule, or other types of payloads. Basically, it is a metal covering that surrounds most of the payload during takeoff and that is jettisoned with the second or third stage.

Specific Discussion

Fairing. The metal fairing, which protects the payload during the ascent phase through the atmosphere, is jettisoned in flight during the second-stage burn at an altitude of approximately 120 km. The fairing, which weighs 826 kg and has a diameter of 3.2 m and a height of 8.65 m (external dimensions), is bulb-shaped to provide a diameter and useful volume compatible with satellites or payloads. The bottom, or boat-tail, section of the fairing is made of radio-transparent material to allow communications with the payload. If two satellites are to be carried, the bottom satellite is placed in an egg-shaped structure called the DOSLAS (double satellite launch system). The DOSLAS is a 180-kg aluminum-honeycomb, carbon-filament-covered structure that ...

Ralph W. Jaeger, "Launch Vehicle," McGraw-Hill Encyclopedia of Science and Technology (New York: McGraw-Hill, 1977), 247. Reprinted by permission.

FIGURE 8–5.   General and specific discussion of a technical subject

The three sections labeled "specific" are vital to an audience that wants to decide on wind systems and to be able to select a particular design.

STEP 5.   On your worksheet, copy from your topic list the topics you think should be discussed in your report, and then indicate which ones you'll discuss in detail and which you'll discuss generally.

The Outlining Stage

When you write a technical report, you must not only think of the right information to include (or exclude) but also find a good way to arrange it. The first task involves invention, or brainstorming, and narrowing; the second, outlining.

Outlines for technical reports are usually hard to handle solely in your mind; it's a little like trying to add a list of large numbers in your mind. You must get report outlines on paper in order to think about the arrangement of the topics within them. A good working outline serves you in at least four important ways:

- It shows you which areas of information to investigate and gather information on.
- It shows you which areas you can safely ignore (thus saving you plenty of time).
- It enables you to schedule your work into manageable units of time.
- It gives you a global view of your report project, an overall sense of the contents, parts, and organization of the report.

Exploratory Reading

If you have trouble getting started on the rough outline, do some exploratory reading in nonspecialist encyclopedias, introductory chapters of general-audience books, or articles in science magazines for nonspecialists. If necessary, move on from these resources to more specialized ones like the *McGraw-Hill Encyclopedia of Science and Technology* or Van Nostrand's *Scientific Encyclopedia*. As you do this exploratory work, read briskly without taking detailed notes; try to get a general sense of the subject.

STEP 6.   If you need a general introduction to your report subject, refer to the nonspecialist encyclopedias just listed, or see Chapter 9.

Arranging the Parts of the Outline

If you went through the brainstorming and narrowing steps, you have a list of topics that you can rearrange into a rough outline. It will be a rough outline because it may still need further rearrangement and addition of other topics or subtopics. The topic list that follows concerns cocombustion, which is the incineration of municipal solid waste (MSW) with conventional fuels to reduce conventional fuel-consumption costs and related MSW disposal problems. Imagine that you had developed a topic list on this subject and then had narrowed the list to these topics:

Advantages of cocombustion	Historical background on
Disadvantages of cocombustion	cocombustion
Economics of cocombustion	Steps in cocombusting MSW
Composition of MSW	Special components for cocombustion

The next step in outlining is to arrange the items in an appropriate order. There are so many different patterns of arrangement that only the most common ones can be reviewed here.

• One of the most common patterns in outlining is the *chronological* one. In a historical background section of an outline, the chronological approach is just about the only one you can use. Here is an outline excerpt concerning the historical background of nuclear research.

II. Historical Background of Nuclear Research
    A. Becquerel's Theory of Radiation in
       Uranium (1896)
    B. The Work of the Curies (1900s)   (far past)

   C. The Work of Rutherford (1910s)
      1. Demonstration of the internal
         structure of the atom (1911)
      2. Transmutation of atoms (1919)
   D. Development of Technology to Study
      Atomic Structure
      1. Cascade transformer (1928)
      2. Linear accelerator (1931)
      3. Cyclotron (1932)
      4. Betatron (1940)
   E. Hahn-Strassmann Discovery of
      Uranium Fission (1938)
   F. Oppenheimer Work on Nuclear Chain   **(near past)**
      Reactions (1940s)
   G. Explosion of the First Atomic Bomb
      (1945)

• In some outlines, however, you almost don't notice the chronological pattern. For example, effects come after causes; solutions, after problems; or findings, after research method. The chronological pattern is most important in a research-proposal outline:

   I. Introduction
     A. Historical Background on Caffeine   **(past)**
       Studies
     B. Objectives of the Study
     C. Limitations of the Study
     D. Plan of Development
   II. Review of the Literature on Caffeine
   III. Experimental Method to Be Used
   IV. Results of the Tests
   V. Discussion of the Results
   VI. Summary and Conclusions
   VII. Implications for Further Research   **(future)**

Chronologically, the researcher first defines the problem, reviews the literature on the problem, plans a research method, conducts the research, gathers data, analyzes the data, and draws conclusions from it. Afterward, she may consider areas for further research on the problem.

• Another common outlining pattern is to start with an *object at rest*, motionless as if in a photograph, and then to move to a discussion of it *in operation*, in action as if in a motion picture.

II. Basic Components of Wind-Powered Elec-
trical Systems
   A. Rotor   (motionless)
   B. Generator
   C. Tower

III. Basic Operation of Wind-Powered Electri-
cal Systems
   A. Wind Energy into Mechanical Energy
   B. Mechanical Energy into Electrical   (in motion)
       Energy
   C. Stabilization of Electrical Energy
   D. Conversion to Household Current

• Some outlines move from a *specific, close-up focus* to a more *general, pano-ramic focus*. They seem to start with a microscope, examining the minute details of a subject, and end with a telescope, considering the subject from a distance in relation to other things. (This pattern can also be reversed.)

I. Introduction

II. Characteristics of Municipal Solid Waste
(MSW)

III. Methods of Disposal of MSW   (microscope)

IV. Processing MSW

V. Plant Modifications for Cocombustion

VI. Advantages of Cocombusting MSW
   A. Environmental Advantages
   B. Economic Advantages   (telescope)

VII. Case Studies of Three Cocombustion
Plants

In this next outline the focus broadens after part III, changing to aspects related to computerized voice-recognition technology:

I. Introduction

II. Human Voice Production
   A. The Generation of Sound
   B. Factors Affecting the Human Voice   (microscope)

III. Components of the Isolated Word Recog-
nition System
   A. The Preprocessor
   B. The Feature Extractor
   C. Components in the Classification
       Phase
   D. Decision Algorithms

IV. Problems with Computerized Speech
    Recognition
    A. Accuracy
    B. Limited Vocabulary Size
    C. Privacy

V. Applications of Voice-Recognition
    Systems
    A. Data Entry
    B. Mobility
    C. Security
    D. Telephone Access
    E. Devices for the Handicapped   (telescope)

VI. Current Availability of Speech-Recogni-
    tion Systems

VII. The Future of the Computerized Speech-
    Recognition Industry

• Elements in outlines can also be arranged *rhetorically*, in other words, according to what is most effective for the reader. Here are some examples of rhetorical patterns:

  • Simple to complex
  • Least important to most important (or vice versa)
  • Least controversial to most controversial
  • Most convincing to least convincing (or vice versa)
  • Most interesting to least interesting

This list is by no means complete, but you can see that elements in it are arranged according to impact on the reader—that is, the impact the writer would like to have. Here are some excerpts of outlines where these patterns are used:

—If you have ever studied computer programming, you know that commands like PRINT are simple; variable assignment commands (like LET A = 30), less simple; and FOR-NEXT loop statements, rather complex. If you were outlining a report on fundamental BASIC commands for the beginner, you'd probably start with the simple ones and work your way to the complex:

Simple-to-Complex Order

III. USEFUL BASIC COMMANDS
    A. PRINT
    B. LET
    C. IF-THEN
    D. FOR-NEXT
    E. DIM

—If you were writing a report on cocombustion of municipal solid waste (MSW) for a city concerned about skyrocketing coal costs, you could arrange your advantages section two ways: (a) save "reduction of coal use" for last in order to build up to a climax, or (b) introduce it right away to grab the citizens' attention:

Climax Order (least to most important)	Attention-Getting Order (most to least important)
A. Recovery of revenue from recyclable MSW	A. Reduction of coal use and related costs
B. Reduction of landfill use, costs, and other related problems	B. Reduction of landfill use, costs, and other related problems
C. Reduction of coal use and related costs	C. Recovery of revenue from recyclable MSW

• An obvious outlining principle is *to avoid creating interruptions* within an outline sequence. Here's an example:

Outline Excerpt with Interruption

I. Municipal Solid Waste Generated in the United States
  A. Total Amounts of MSW
    1. Increases since 1950
    2. Projected increases to the year 2000
  B. Processing MSW for Cocombustion
    1. Primary storage
    2. Grinding
    3. Air sorting
    4. Magnetic separating
    5. Screening
    6. Secondary storage
  C. Characteristics of MSW
    1. Composition of MSW
      a. Food waste
      b. Paper and other rubbish
      c. Noncombustibles
    2. Factors Affecting Energy Content
      a. Moisture content
      b. Areas of MSW origination

II. Power-Plant Modifications for Cocombustion

Revised Outline Excerpt

I.   Municipal Solid Waste Generated in the United States
    A. Total Amounts of MSW
        1. Increases since 1950
        2. Projected increases to the year 2000
    B. Characteristics of MSW
        1. Composition of MSW
           a. Food Waste
           b. Paper and other rubbish
           c. Noncombustibles
        2. Factors Affecting Energy Content
           a. Moisture content
           b. Areas of MSW origination

II. Processing MSW for Cocombustion
    A. Primary Storage
    B. Grinding
    C. Air Sorting
    D. Magnetic Separating
    E. Screening
    F. Secondary Storage

III. Power-Plant Modifications for Cocombustion

In the problem version, the municipal solid waste discussion is interrupted by the MSW-processing discussion. A better arrangement would be to discuss MSW fully before going on to the discussion of how it is processed.

Use these common arrangement principles to get your topic list into an initial rough order. The rearranged version of the topic list shown in Figure 8–3 might look like the outline in Figure 8–6.

STEP 7.   Arrange the topics you selected in step 5 using the strategies discussed in the preceding section, and then identify the patterns (for example, chronological or simple-to-complex) you've used.

Elaborating the Rough Outline

When you elaborate a rough outline, you divide and subdivide the items already listed. Even without having done much research, you'll have a fair idea of what these second- and third-level items will be.

1. Historical background
   rising costs of conventional fuels
   problems with conventional MSW disposal
   alternatives

Rough Outline

1. Historical background
   --rising energy, utility costs
   --search for alternatives (review)

2. Composition of MSW

3. Special components of the cocombustion plant

4. Steps in the cocombustion of MSW

5. Economics
   --cost to build or convert
   --cost to operate
   --cost of produced electricity

6. Advantages
   --less coal used
   --reduction of utility rates
   --less landfill used
   --reduction of landfill costs and needs

7. Disadvantages
   --expense of converting existing facilities
   --handling MSW
   --increased emissions

FIGURE 8—6. Rough outline based on topics in Figure 8—3

2. Composition of MSW
   properties
   sources
   energy content
   . . .

3. Special components of the cocombustion plant
   component 1
   component 2
   component 3
   . . .

4. Steps in the process of cocombustion with coal
   step 1
   step 2
   step 3
   . . .

Notice how the basic kinds of writing and organizational patterns (covered in Part I) are used in elaborating the rough outline. With an elaborated outline you can begin to read and take notes; each item represents a question mark that you need to get information on. As you get this information, you can make the wording of outline items more specific: for example, "Component 1" would change to "Collection receptacles." Here's an excerpt from the preceding outline, but much more fully developed:

3. Special components of the cocombustion plant
   a. Collection receptacles
   b. Power compaction unit
   c. Storage pits
   d. Incinerator feed system
      1. Gravity chute
      2. Ram feeder
      3. Hopper
      4. Furnace
      5. Charging gate

Elaborating the rough outline is essentially a process of dividing that outline using two basic principles:

• Division into similar elements. Many elements in a rough outline can be divided into groups of similar elements:

Elements of Discussion	Subdivisions
An object or mechanism	Parts, components, or characteristics
A process or event	Steps, phases, or stages
A classification	Types, kinds, or sorts
A comparison	Points of similarity or difference
Causal discussions	Causes, effects, benefits, problems, or solutions

Thus, a discussion of the main element "incinerator feed system" in a rough outline could be elaborated this way—into parts:

Rough Outline	Elaborated Outline
3. Special components of cocombustion plant	3. Special components of a cocombustion plant a. Collection receptacles b. Power compaction unit c. Storage pits d. Incinerator feed system

• Division into elements related topically. Elements in an outline can subdivide by topics that are all related but that are not similar to each other:

Rough Outline	Elaborated Outline
(d. Incinerator feed system)	(d. Incinerator feed system)
4. Furnace	4. Furnace
5. Charging gate	a. Purpose
	b. Main types
	c. Main components
	d. Materials
	e. Dimensions
	f. Design problems
	5. Charging gate

As a result of elaborating procedures like these, an excerpt of a more detailed outline of the cocombustion report might look like the one in Figure 8–7.

With an outline this well developed, the next step is to begin doing some serious reading, researching, investigating, and note taking. During this next phase, however, the outline will continue to change as new and different information turns up.

STEP 8.   Use the strategies just described to elaborate the rough outline you developed in step 7.

Finishing the Outline

You need not be concerned about the finishing touches for your outline until after you've written and revised the rough draft. Writing the rough draft is the true test of an outline: during that stage you are likely to discover parts of the outline that don't work, are out of place, or do not belong at all. When you "fine tune" an outline after writing the rough draft, however, you are actually transforming it into a table of contents that you can use in the finished, bound copy of the report. Here are some specific things to look for in your final work on an outline:

• *Comparing the outline to the rough draft.* Even the most carefully prepared outlines rarely match the resulting rough drafts. Even the most straightforward of technical subjects can take off in their own unexpected directions. Therefore, you must compare your completed rough draft to the original outline in the following ways:

1. A good way to start is to insert the outline phrases into your rough draft; in other words, insert the headings into your report, if you have not already done so.
2. Make sure that the sequence of items in the outline matches the sequence of topics in the rough draft of the report.
3. Check to see if any items in the outline did not get discussed at all.
4. Check to see if any new topics cropped up in your rough draft but do not appear in your outline.

    I. Municipal Solid Waste Generated in the United States
        A. Total Amounts of MSW
            1. Increases since 1950
            2. Projected increases to the year 2000
        B. Characteristics of MSW
            1. Composition of MSW
                a. Food waste
                b. Paper and other rubbish
                c. Noncombustibles
            2. Factors affecting enery content
                a. Moisture content
                b. Areas of MSW origination
    II. Processing MSW for Cocombustion
        A. Primary Storage
        B. Grinding
        C. Air Sorting
        D. Magnetic Separating
        E. Screening
        F. Secondary Storage
   III. Power-Plant Modifications for Cocombustion
        A. Storage Areas
        B. Conveyor Lines
        C. Boiler Modifications
        D. Air-Control Equipment
    IV. Advantages of Cocombustion
        A. Environmental Advantages
            1. Reduction of landfill needs
            2. Reduction of coal use
            3. Recovery of recyclable materials
        B. Economic Advantages
            1. Reduction of MSW disposal costs
            2. Revenue from recyclables
            3. Reduction of utility bills
    V. Disadvantages of Cocombustion
        A. Potential for Increased Air Pollution
        B. Problems with Processing MSW

FIGURE 8—7. Example of a more detailed outline

5. Look for longer-than-usual sections in your rough draft for which there are few outline items. Try to find additional outline items within those pages. Figure 8–8 contains an example of a longer section; notice that in the original version, there is only one outline item (or heading) whereas there are seven in the revised version.

STEP 9.   When you have written a rough draft of your report, compare it to your outline, and update your outline using the suggestions just discussed.

Passage without Headings

II. SOLID WASTE GENERATED

This country is a great producer of solid waste. In the United States in 1980, each person will produce about 8 pounds of solid waste a day, whereas in Europe the average production rate is 3 to 4 pounds per person per day. An added difference is that in Europe there 243 facilities to utilize solid waste (although none are for the production of electricity), whereas in the United States there are only about 20.

As can be seen in Table 8–8a, this country has increased the generation of waste from 1970 to 1980 by 50 percent, and will increase another 50 percent from 1980 to 2000. These quantities represent only that portion which is collected; there is another 5 to 10 percent that is not collected. These percentages add up to an undeniably large quantity of potential energy that goes almost totally unused in the United States.

TABLE 8–8a.   Quantities of Municipal Waste Generated in the United States

Year	Lbs/person/day	Tons/year $\times 10^6$
1950	3.5	102
1965	4.5	156
1970	5.3	199
1980	8.0	314
2000	12.0	526

(continued)

FIGURE 8–8.   An example of using rough drafts to elaborate outlines

Disposal of solid waste is by far the most useless method of eliminating the refuse. Most methods of disposal currently employed do not utilize the waste material. Disposal costs in this country amount to over $1.02 billion per year.

Sanitary landfills involve the placement of solid waste in valleys, ravines, or other natural depressions in the earth. The waste is placed in the landfill in 18- to 24-inch layers and then covered with soil. This process is repeated until the hole is full and a new location is needed. The average life of a landfill is 5 to 10 years. The cost of a landfill varies from $1.35 to $2.70 per ton of refuse. This rate involves disposal costs only; collection costs are omitted.

Land spreading is a method of waste disposal in which waste is placed in a field and then is plowed into the soil. This method is used only when small quantities of waste are generated because large land areas are required for such operations. The process is a clean one, but the life of such facilities is only 2 to 5 years. Disposal costs range from $0.60 to $4.05 per ton of waste, depending on the quality of the land.

Open dumping, one of the most undesirable of all methods of disposal of solid waste, involves placing the waste in open pits or on level areas. The refuse is constantly exposed and is a haven for vermin. Open dumping costs from $0.65 to $1.00 per ton of refuse and is illegal in most areas.

Incineration in which no energy is recovered is the most commonly used method of solid waste disposal in the United States. The primary purpose of incineration is to reduce the volume of the waste before it is carried to a landfill. The cost of incineration ranges from $6.75 to $20.00 per ton of waste and represents an enormous waste of both money and energy.

Revised Outline

II. SOLID WASTE GENERATED
    A. Quantities of Solid Waste
    B. Methods of Solid-Waste Disposal
        1. Sanitary landfills
        2. Land spreading

FIGURE 8–8. (cont.)

3. Open dumping
4. Incineration

Passage Revised with Headings
(to indicate new outline items)

II. SOLID WASTE GENERATED

This country is a great producer of solid waste. In the United States in 1980, each person will produce about 8 pounds ...

Quantities of MSW Generated
As can be seen in Table 8–8a, this country has increased the generation of waste from 1970 to 1980 by 50 percent. ...

Methods of Solid-Waste Disposal
Disposal of solid waste is by far the most useless method of eliminating the refuse. Most methods of disposal currently employed do not utilize the waste material. Disposal costs in this country amount to over $1.02 billion per year.

Sanitary Landfills.   Sanitary landfills involve the placement of solid waste in valleys, ravines, or other natural depressions in the earth. The waste is placed ...

Land Spreading.   Land spreading is a method of waste disposal in which waste is placed in a field and then is plowed into the soil. This method is used only when ...

Open Dumping.   Open dumping, one of the most undesirable of all methods of disposal of solid waste ...

Incineration.   Incineration in which no energy is recovered is the most commonly used method of solid-waste disposal in the United States. The primary purpose of incineration is to ...

FIGURE 8–8.   **(cont.)**

• *Eliminating one-item outline entries.* Here is an excerpt of an outline with a one-item entry:

Outline with One-Item Entry

II. Characteristics of Municipal Solid Waste
    A. Composition
        1. Food waste
        2. Paper
        3. Other rubbish
III. Current Methods of Disposal

In this example there is no *B* to go along with the *A*. To fix this problem, either (a) insert additional items, or (b) delete the single item by combining some of its phrasing into the preceding item, as in the suggested revision.

Revised Outline

II. Characteristics and Composition of MSW
    A. Food waste
    B. Paper
    C. Other rubbish
III. Current Methods of Disposal

To insert additional items into the outline, you try to add at least a *B* for any unaccompanied *A*; at least a *2* for any unaccompanied *1*; at least a *b* for any unaccompanied *a*. Of course, any *C*s, *D*s, *3*s, *4*s, *c*s, *d*s, and so on are also welcome. Figure 8–9 contains an example of a one-item entry and its corresponding report section.

One way to revise the problem in Figure 8–9 would have been to delete "A. Energy Content" altogether and rephrase the preceding item as "IV. Solid Waste: Characteristics and Energy Content." But another and usually better way to handle the problem is to scan the corresponding passage for at least one other item, in this case, "Energy Content."

• *Adjusting items in an outline.* You should also make sure that items in your outline are on the right level. Here is an example of this problem and a revision:

Unadjusted Outline	*Revised Outline*

A. Plant Modifications for Cocombustion
   1. Storage areas
   2. Conveyor lines
   3. Boiler modifications
   4. Air-control equipment
B. Economic Benefits
C. Environmental Benefits
	A. Plant Modifications for Cocombustion
	   1. Storage areas
	   2. Conveyor lines
	   3. Boiler modifications
	   4. Air-control equipment
	B. Benefits of Cocombustion
	   1. Economic benefits
	   2. Environmental benefits

One-Item Outline-Entry Problem and Corresponding Report Excerpt

IV. Solid-Waste Characteristics
    A. Composition

V. Processing Solid Waste

IV. SOLID-WASTE CHARACTERISTICS

The amount and characteristics of solid waste vary considerably over a year and in different locations. In the fall, for example, leaves change the nature of solid waste in a significant way. The figures that follow are averages that account for both the variations in time and in location.

Composition

    Municipal refuse is composed of a vast array of products that have lost their usefulness. These wastes include home wastes, commercial wastes, and city wastes. While home and commercial wastes are usually placed in receptacles for periodic removal by collection agencies to landfills or incinerators, city wastes usually collect elsewhere and require special handling and disposal.

    Home wastes include such diverse products as glass bottles, cans, plastic toys, cellophane, paper, cardboard, nails, small appliances, tools, light bulbs, clothes, rubber products, and wood and food items. If these wastes are not separated into classes, such as metal, glass, and paper, they are described as "heterogeneous" wastes.

    Commercial wastes are generated by retail businesses and institutions such as hospitals, banks, and schools. Although these wastes are also considered heterogeneous, they contain high percentages of office waste and packing materials....

    Energy content is often referred to in British Thermal Units (BTUs) per pound of waste. A BTU is the amount of energy required to raise one gram of water one degree centigrade. With moisture present in the material, the energy content decreases in the heating value by approximately 30 to 40 percent. The range in energy content of typical municipal solid waste is from 3000 to 60,000 BTUs per pound, with an average value of 4500 BTUs per pound. This last figure assumes a

(continued)

FIGURE 8–9. Solving the one-time outline-entry problem

moisture content of from 15 to 40 percent and an average of 20 percent.

In comparison, coal has an average heating value of 1100 BTUs per pound and a moisture content of 20 percent on the average.

V. PROCESSING SOLID WASTE

Processing MSW involves certain modifications to existing incinerator designs....

F.R. Jackson, Recycling and Reclaiming Municipal Solid Wastes (Park Ridge, N.J.: Noyes Data, 1975), 3. Reprinted by permission.

Revised Outline and Corresponding Passage
(with headings revised to show the new outline item)

IV. Solid-Waste Characteristics
   A. Composition
   B. Energy Content
V. Processing Solid Waste

IV. SOLID-WASTE CHARACTERISTICS

The amount and characteristics of solid waste vary considerably over a year and in different locations. In the fall ...

Composition
Municipal refuse is composed of a vast array of products that have lost their usefulness. These wastes include ...

Energy Content
Energy content is often referred to in British Thermal Units (BTUs) per pound of waste. A BTU is the amount of energy ...

V. PROCESSING SOLID WASTE

Processing MSW involves certain modifications to existing incinerator designs....

FIGURE 8–9. (cont.)

In this revision the problem was solved by adding a more general item ("Benefits of Cocombustion") and downshifting the original "B" and "C" items. Now, here's another example:

Unadjusted Outline	*Revised Outline*
B. Environmental Benefits	B. Environmental Benefits
C. Reduction of Landfill Needs	1. Reduction of landfill needs
D. Economic Benefits	2. Reduction of coal consumption
	C. Economic Benefits

Here, "Reduction of landfill needs" is really a subdivision of "Environmental Benefits". Downshifting it to a "1" creates a one-item entry, however. Therefore, we might add a second item like "Reduction of coal consumption."

• *Checking for parallel phrasing.* The phrasing of any related group of outline items must be parallel. To be related, the items must be on the same level and make up a separate group of items. Parallelism is explained in Appendix D, but essentially it means sticking with similar kinds of phrasing in related outline items. In the example of a nonparallel outline in Figure 8–10, note that

• Items I and II are related and must be parallel to each other.
• Under I, items A and B are related and must be parallel to each other.
• Under IB, items 1, 2, and 3 are related.

Nonparallel Outline Excerpt	Parallel Version
I. Municipal Solid Waste Generated in the United States	I. Municipal Solid Waste Generated in the United States
A. What Is the Total Output?	A. Total Output of MSW
B. Disposal Methods	B. Disposal Methods
1. Sanitary landfills	1. Sanitary landfills
2. Spreading MSW in open fields and plowing it under	2. Open spreading
3. Open dumping	3. Open dumping
II. What Are the Characteristics of MSW?	II. Characteristics of MSW

FIGURE 8–10. Revising for parallelism in outlines

• *Making outlines self-explanatory.* The wording of outline items should clearly indicate the content of the corresponding sections. Items like the following simply don't say enough about the contents of the sections that they represent:

Background	Discussion
Applications	Technical Discussion
Description	Function
The Future	Operation
Economics	Review

Here is an outline excerpt revised with much more self-explanatory phrasing:

Weak Outline Phrasing	Revised Outline Phrasing
I. Background	I. Background: Rising Utility Costs
II. Composition	II. Composition of MSW
III. Processes	III. Processes in Cocombusting MSW with Coal
IV. Components	IV. Basic Components of Cocombustion Plant Facilities
V. Economics	V. Economics of Cocombustion: Construction, Conversion, Operation, Return

• *Adjusting the graphics.* The final step in outlining is to make the numbering, lettering, spacing, and capitalizing—the graphics of the outline—consistent. (See Figure 8–7.)

• Use a consistent style of capitalization.
• Use consistent indentation.
• Skip lines between outline items in a consistent manner.

STEP 10.   Use the preceding strategies to (a) locate and eliminate one-item outline entries, (b) make sure that the items in your outline are on the right level, (c) make the items in your outline parallel, (d) locate and rephrase items that are not fully self-explanatory, and (e) make the graphics of your outline consistent.

EXERCISES

1. Pick any report topic from the list in Figure 8–1 or pick a topic of your own, decide on an audience and purpose for a report on that topic, and then use the Invention Checklist for Reports (Figure 8–2) for brainstorming the topic (jot your ideas on scratch paper).

2. Imagine that you have an audience of real estate developers and sales representatives for whom you are writing an informational report on solar devices, which they are considering as options on housing within a new development. Decide which of the

following topics you'd select for the report for this specific audience and how you'd discuss the selected topics:

Basic components of a solar device

Current research in solar-device technology

Costs to purchase, operate, and maintain solar devices

Historical background on the use of solar power

Architectural considerations in using solar devices

How to determine angle of inclination for a collector

Basic operation of a solar device

A survey of solar-device manufacturers

Results of consumer tests on solar devices

Economics of solar power

Dynamics of heat transfer

Tax programs to benefit users of solar power

Comparison with other common energy sources

3. Revise the outline here using the finishing-up suggestions discussed in this chapter.

A Report on Weather Forecasting

I. Historical
 A. Weather Lore
  1. what phase the moon is in
  2. reactions of people to weather
  3. reactions of animals to weather
  4. optical phenomena
  5. Rainbows
  6. Certain sequences of weather conditions
 B. Technological advances have changed weather-forecasting practices.
  1. predicting storms was the early concern.
  2. use of radio to collect information
  3. Radiosondes for upper-atmosphere information
  4. computers

II. BASIC PRACTICES
 A. Observations and Reports
  1. reports of land stations once or twice a day to a central bureau
 B. Analyzing weather charts
  1. Examination of well-defined pressure systems
   i. low-pressure areas
   ii. high-pressure areas
   iii. troughs of low pressure
   iv. ridges of high pressure
   v. cols, or saddle-backed regions

III. Techniques Used in Short-Range Forecasting
 A. Computation of Displacements
 B. Forecasting Based on Physical Theory
 C. Analogues and types
 D. Regression equations and diagrams
 E. Time-series analyses
 F. Success rate of time-series analyses

IV. Extended-Range Forecasts
   A. The Namias chart
      1. use of several days' averages
      2. comparisons to long-term normals
      3. limited usually to thirty days
 V. SPECIAL WEATHER FORECASTS

4. Find an encyclopedia article of at least three pages or more on a subject you know something about or have an interest in, and create an outline of that article. Include as many levels of detail in your outline as possible.

5. Outline one of the following descriptions of a report project. Beware, however: the ideas are scattered, mixed up, and fragmentary.

A Report on the Greenhouse Effect

This report is concerned with the greenhouse effect, the way in which atmospheric carbon dioxide is increasing and leading to a group of potentially catastrophic consequences for this planet. It discusses the climatic effects of increased carbon dioxide which include changes in local weather patterns, drought, increased tropical-storm activity, and sea-level increases. The report uses the 1930s as an analogue, or model of comparison; the 1930s was a period of unusually higher temperature. The report also discusses what can be done if anything about the greenhouse effect, such as reducing fossil-fuel use, reduction of the burning of wood and other substances, use of cleaner fossil fuels, development of solar and nuclear power resources, massive reforestation on a global scale, and further research into the carbon cycle. The report discusses the basic steps in the natural greenhouse effect, in which a certain amount of carbon dioxide is trapped in the atmosphere, causing higher global temperatures than there would be without the effect. The report discusses the major contributors to increased concentrations of carbon dioxide: deforestation, burning of fossil fuels, burning of wood, etc., and it also discusses how there is a positive feedback mechanism in which increased carbon dioxide in the atmosphere increases the trapping of more carbon dioxide.

A Report on the Saccharine Controversy

In this report the controversy over saccharine as a cancer-causing substance is discussed. Important in the report is the discussion of a number of carcinogenicity studies, in particular, the Canadian rat studies which nearly led to the ban on saccharine in the 1970s, the Ames test for mutagens, and a group of studies generally referred to as promotion studies. One section of the report discusses health risks associated with saccharine such as bladder cancer; risks of other cancers such as uterus, ovary, breast, and lung cancers are also reviewed. The health benefits of saccharine are also discussed; these include reducing sugar intake, which is helpful or necessary to the overweight or diabetic. The clinical aspects of the studies and the risks and benefits that they found are also discussed—how the studies were run, their findings, the implications of those findings, and their reliability. The report discusses the original synthesis of saccharine in 1879, the chemical structure of the substance, its metabolic effects. The report also discusses what the legislation has been on saccharine—the Food, Drug and Cosmetics Act of 1938 and the Food Additives Amendment of 1958 (this amendment contained the Delaney Clause, which states that no substance found to be carcinogenic to man or animal can be added to food). The report goes into the history of the proposed ban on saccharine in 1977 upon publication of the Canadian rat studies and then the postponement of that ban a few weeks later after public outcry, lobbying—lobbying in particular by the Calorie Control Council, a group of Japanese and American manufacturers of saccharine.

6. If you are asked to write a memo proposing a report topic, consider doing the following:
   a. Briefly describe your topic and your interest in it.
   b. Discuss how much or how little you know about the topic and estimate how much you'll need to do to prepare.
   c. Describe the context of the report, the report-writing situation including the audience and purpose.
   d. Explain how you will narrow the report subject.
   e. Make sure that the library has adequate materials on your subject or that you can get adequate information outside the library. Discuss any problems you foresee in gathering information.
   f. Explain which kinds of graphic aids you'll need in your report. Describe the actual content of these graphic aids as specifically as you can.
   g. Provide a tentative outline of your report, even if it is only five or six items long.

Here's an example of a memorandum that proposes a report topic.

Model 8-1:   Example Report-Topic Proposal (Memo)

MEMORANDUM

To: David A. McMurrey
From: Richard Dean Todd
Date: 30 January 19XX
Subj.:   Description of my report project

Here is the information on my report project that you requested. I've included a brief discussion of what I plan to include in the report, who the audience of the report will be, what my own background on the topic is, and what graphic aids will be needed in the final report. A tentative outline concludes this memo.

The Topic and Report Contents
I plan to do a general feasibility study of the preservation of meat by ionizing radiation. The report will investigate the possibility of ionizing radiation as a replacement for present-day chemical preservatives in meat products. I plan to show that radiation processes can be more effective for killing bacteria, preserving the food for longer periods of time, and making the food more wholesome and safe overall. The report will also compare and suggest which types of irradiation are best for meat preservation. The equipment needed in the process will be discussed in addition to any possible dangers this new process may present to humans. I'll also review cost comparisons. In the introduction there will be a brief history of food preservation and of early uses of radiation for preservation.

Audience and Purpose of the Report

This study will be directed toward the meat-packing industry in an effort to encourage it to change its present preservation methods. I will try to show meat-packing companies that, with several important criteria, irradiation is preferable to current methods.

My Background and Library Sources on the Topic

At this point, I know only the basics of radiation chemistry, and I will need to research food preservation and apply my chemistry background in this area. Having begun my preliminary library search, I'm sure that there are plenty of printed resources on the topic, both in and out of the library. The biggest problem I foresee is finding specific costs of the irradiation process, but with letters of inquiry to organizations involved in this new preservation method, I expect to overcome this problem.

Graphic Aids Needed in the Report

There will be no problem finding and using graphic aids for this report. Most of the graphics will be comparison charts showing the advantages and disadvantages of various sources of radiation. Other charts will compare this new method of food preservation to older methods, focusing on bacteria growth, length of storage time, color of meat, and other characteristics of effective meat preservation. I will also include pictures of the process at various stages and the different equipment used.

Tentative Outline of the Project

Here is a tentative outline of the report; I'll keep you informed of changes in it as they occur:

    I. History of food preservation and use of radiation in this field

    II. Comparison of chemical to radiation preservation

    III. Effectiveness of radiation preservation

    IV. Sources of radiation

    V. Installation of radiation equipment in factories

    VI. Cost of the new process compared to the old

    VII. Safety and consumer acceptance of radiation preservation

Richard Dean Todd, University of Texas, 1984.

CHAPTER 9

Finding Information for Reports: Library and Nonlibrary Sources

Chapter Objectives

Developing a Research Strategy

Broad Categories of Information
  Sources

Specific Categories of Information
  Sources

Selecting Information Sources

Finding the Right Subject Headings

Bibliography Cards

Selecting Books, Articles, and
  Reports

Finding Information in Libraries

Finding Books

Finding Articles

Finding Reference Works

Finding Government Documents

Finding Trade and Association
  Literature

Using Computerized Information
  Retrieval

**Sources of Information Outside
  the Library**

Site Inspections and Measurements

Calculations

Business Literature

Interviews

Surveys and Questionnaires

Government Sources

Letters of Inquiry

A Note on Collecting Nonlibrary
  Information

Exercises

Chapter Objectives

After you read this chapter, study the examples, and work the steps, you should be able to:

- List the different strategies for finding books on report topics.
- Explain how to use the *Library of Congress Subject Headings*.
- List the different strategies for finding articles on report topics.
- Explain how to find and use periodical indexes and subject guides.
- List the main indexing sources for finding government documents.
- List some of the best sources for finding trade and association literature.
- List the common nonlibrary sources of information for reports.
- Find businesses involved in a specific kind of manufacturing or service, using *Thomas Register* or some similar source.

If you have developed as detailed an outline of your report as you can (using the steps in Chapter 8, if necessary), your next step is to begin locating sources of information to use in writing your report.* Your job at this stage should be simply to *locate* the sources—not to read or take notes on them just yet. Before you begin locating the individual books, reports, and articles, plan a general *research strategy*, a kind of map of the sources of information to consult.

Developing a Research Strategy

A research strategy is a plan concerning which information sources you should emphasize and in what order to access them. Having a good research strategy speeds up the process of finding the right sources and the right information. It ensures that you don't overlook important sources and that you don't duplicate sources. In other words, a good research strategy makes your information finding fast and thorough.

Broad Categories of Information Sources

The first step in determining that strategy is to figure out whether the bulk of your information will come from one or the other of the two broad and overlapping categories of information sources: those usually found *inside libraries* and those usually found *outside of libraries:*

---

*Much of the content and the organization of this chapter are the result of the help of Kay Nichols, MLS.

Library Sources	Nonlibrary Sources
Encyclopedias and other reference sources	Site inspections and measurements
Books	Calculations
Articles	Business literature
U.S. government documents	Interviews
State and local government documents	Surveys and questionnaires
Computer-based information sources	Government sources of information
	Letters of inquiry

For example, if you plan to write a proposal to build municipal ball parks, your sources will probably be mostly outside the library. If you're writing about some aspect of current cancer research and don't live near a major cancer research center, your sources are likely to be mostly inside the library. Guard against assuming that your sources are either all library or all nonlibrary, however: the library may help you in the municipal ball park proposal, and there may be local nonlibrary sources that can help you write the cancer research report. To be safe, always assume that both categories may supply information to your report and should be investigated. Figure 9–1 contains some suggestions about information from both library and nonlibrary sources.

Specific Categories of Information Sources

The next step in developing your research strategy is to identify which of the main sources in the two broad categories you'll be depending on most heavily. You may decide that your current cancer research report will depend mostly on recent journal articles and government documents. If you are new to library searching, you may wonder how it's possible to identify which sources you'll use ahead of time. Naturally, you cannot know for sure, but you can have an idea which ones you'll rely heavily on and which ones you can just quickly check. This general idea will save you time and ensure that you miss nothing important.

The guidelines in Figure 9–2 should give you a better idea of which sources to investigate carefully and which just to check quickly.

STEP 1.   On your report worksheet explain which of the broad and specific categories of information sources you think you'll get most of your report information from and why.

Selecting Information Sources

Which of these sources you select depends not only on your report project, but also on the following:

• *How much you already know about the subject.* Do you need to start with the basics, or can you leap over them to the intermediate and advanced information on your subject?

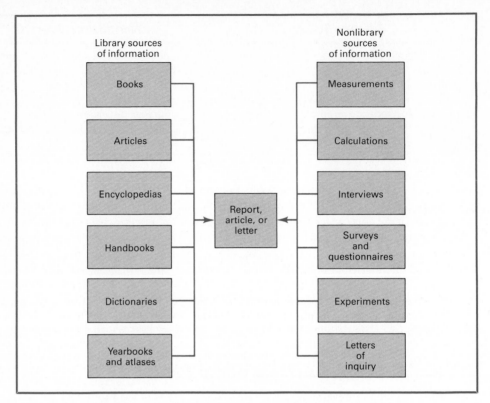

FIGURE 9–1.   Library and nonlibrary sources of information for technical-writing projects

• *How many topics related to your report subject you intend to cover.* The scope of your report will determine how many information sources you use and how much you use them.

• *How technically or specifically you discuss each topic.* The more specific and technical the information you must include in your report, the wider the range of sources you may have to investigate.

• *What audience level you plan to write for.* If your audience is nonspecialist, you may prefer general, fundamental information and avoid the highly specialized or technical. However, if you intend to bring highly technical information to nonspecialists in language that they can understand, then you may need more advanced material.

• *What the historical scope of your report is.* If you want to present historical background, you must draw on different sources of information than you would ordinarily.

• *How much time you have.* If you are not pressed for time, quickly review many different sources to make sure that you miss nothing; if you are rushed, look only at those sources that are definitely essential to your report.

Encyclopedias and other reference books	Certain kinds of reference books such as *indexes* contain information to help you find books, articles, reports, and other reference books. On the other hand, *encyclopedias, atlases, handbooks,* and *yearbooks* provide basic, well-established information to give you an overview of a field and familiarize you with the major terms, concepts, names, and events in that field. *Fact-finding tools* provide specific bits of information rather than conceptual background: for example, barrels of crude oil imported by the United States.
Books	Books provide extensive, in-depth information on a topic. Use the title, table of contents, headings within chapters, bibliography, footnotes, and the index to find out if the book has the information you need. However, in rapidly changing fields, books often go out of date; you must supplement them with the current information in articles.
Magazine and journal articles	Articles found in magazines and journals can give you the most current, detailed information on a technical subject. For example, a book on solar-heating devices may spend only a page on a specific device, while an article might provide detailed design, performance, and economic data on that specific device.
U.S. government documents	The U.S. government publishes books, reports, and articles on a wide range of technical subjects. In government documents you can find survey data, research results, performance and safety information on new technologies, reports on accidents and disasters, and even procedural information on operating certain mechanisms. Take a look at last year's volume of *Government Reports and Announcements: Annual Index* to get an idea of the potential of this resource.

(continued)

FIGURE 9–2. Library and nonlibrary sources of information for reports

State and local government documents	City, county, and state governments also publish technical reports, for example, on local growth patterns or on local water supplies in your area, and usually in great technical detail.
Site inspections, measurements, and calculations	Some reports require you to get out in the field and do site inspections and measurements yourself: for example, for a proposal to build municipal ball parks, you must visit sites, measure the proposed property, and calculate costs for construction materials.
Business literature	Some information only businesses can supply, specifically, product brochures, annual reports, press releases, or articles from in-house periodicals.
Trade and association literature	Trade associations, private-interest groups, and similar organizations collect or publish information that can prove useful in reports. For example, there are plenty of groups supporting certain causes: recycling, biofuels, nuclear power, and solar power. Plenty of trade organizations have publications devoted to their interests: for example, beekeeping, data processing, nursing, soybean growing, auto repair, and city planning.
Interviews and inquiry letters	Some information for your report may only be available directly from specialists, technicians, and executives who are daily involved with some aspect of your subject. Arrange to interview them if they are local, or write inquiry letters to them if they are not.
Surveys and questionnaires	For reports requiring information on public opinion or about the public, you may need to conduct surveys. Because they can be so time-consuming, first check to see if the information is already available in published form.

FIGURE 9–2.   (cont.)

| Other primary research | Primary research refers to any method used to gather original, unpublished information: for example, your own private experiment on the performance of three solar-equipped homes or on different designs for your own solar device. |
| Computerized information retrieval | The computer does not provide information different from that provided by books, reports, and articles; instead, it is another way of obtaining published information—for example, lists of books, reports, and articles available on your subject. Also, computerized databases can be used as fact-finding tools to gather specific pieces of information. |

FIGURE 9–2.   (cont.)

With your information sources identified, think about the order in which you'll use them. For example, don't write inquiry letters or conduct interviews until you've done a thorough job of locating library-based sources of information first and have familiarized yourself with the subject that way. Also, put off reading technical journal articles on an unfamiliar subject until you've developed a more basic understanding.

Finding the Right Subject Headings

A key to finding library information is to identify the subject headings under which you'll find books in the card catalog and under which you'll find articles in periodical indexes. Make a list of these headings, and refer to them often during your library search. Here is a technical subject and the subject headings under which you'd find books, reports, and articles on it:

Subject Matter	Subject Headings
Solar-powered devices	Solar collectors
	Space vehicles–solar engines–collectors
	Solar energy
	Solar heating
	Photovoltaic power generation
	Satellite solar-power stations
	Solar air conditioning
	Solar engines
	Power resources
	Renewable energy resources
	Solar radiation

To find such headings, use the *Library of Congress Subject Headings*. Any term in either boldface or preceded by "xx" or "sa" is an actual subject heading that you can look up in the card catalog. (Whether it is in your library's card catalog depends on the size and specialty of that library.) The subject headings you find in *Library of Congress Subject Headings* will also give you an idea of how to find magazine articles on your topic in periodical indexes.

When you have a list of headings, put them in order from general to specific, and begin searching in the card catalog with the most specific first. This approach reduces the amount of searching you must do: you might find only one book under "solar water heaters," but hundreds of books under "energy."

STEP 2.   On your report worksheet write the subject headings that you may use to find books and articles on your report subject.

Bibliography Cards

Another important element in your research strategy is to keep bibliography cards on *all* of your sources of information, that is, one for each book, article, and report. Make bibliography cards for as many of your nonlibrary sources as you can: for example, make a card on each individual you interview. You'll probably make more bibliography cards than you'll be able to use; don't worry—that's normal. Get a large packet of index cards, and get into the habit of making a bibliography card for *each* source you find. (You'll find examples of bibliography cards in each of the following sections.)

Selecting Books, Articles, and Reports

During your search, you must be selective about the books, reports, and articles to make bibliography cards for. For some technical subjects you'll be amazed at the number of bibliography cards you can collect. To avoid spending all of your time just writing out bibliography cards, use the following ideas:

- Copy only the more recent titles if certain books or articles seem to duplicate each other. (If there are important earlier works, you'll find them by other means.)
- Use the titles of books, reports, and articles to help you decide whether the materials are important to your report.
- Watch for duplicate books, reports, and articles. When you see them, choose the more recent publication, or take a quick look to see which is a better choice.
- Where possible, use the table of contents of books to help you decide which to make bibliography cards for.

Finding Information in Libraries

If you've never done a thorough library search on a technical subject, you'll probably be amazed at just how much technical information libraries store. Being able to get at that information can save you much of the time you would use in consulting nonlibrary sources. To get the most out of this chapter, have a report topic in mind, and try as many of the sources as you have time for. You'll learn much about libraries; you may find materials you might have missed otherwise.

Many resources in the library do not contain the technical information you need but point the way to ones that do. Good examples are the library's card catalog and periodical indexes; they enable you to find books and articles, respectively. Using library sources of information is conceptually illustrated in Figure 9–3.

Finding Books

You are probably familiar with finding books in the card catalog in the library. Here are a few additional strategies to help you make a more thorough search.

Consulting the *Library of Congress Subject Headings*.   Begin your search for books by getting a list of related subject headings from the *Library of Congress Subject Headings*. If you were looking for books on computer graphics, you'd find these subject headings:

> digital incremental patterns
> light pens

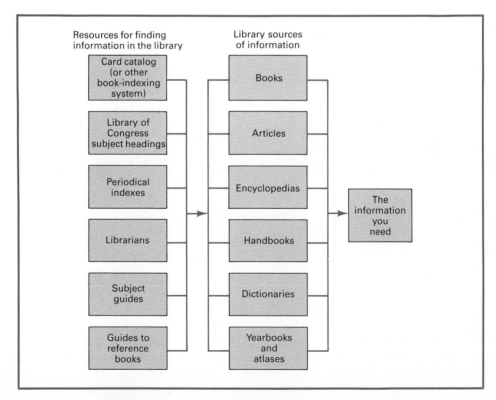

FIGURE 9–3.   Using library resources to find books, articles, reports, and other information sources

automated drafting
graphic data processing
computer graphics
computerized drawing
computer animation

Using the Subject Card Catalog.   At the card catalog, start with the subject section, using the headings you found in *LCSH*. Figure 9–4 contains an example of what you'll see.

As you locate books in the card catalog, make a bibliography card for each one. It's not necessary to copy all of the information onto your bibliography card; the minimum is shown in Figure 9–5.

While you are at the card catalog, here are a few other ideas to help you locate additional books:

- Look under *all* of the subject headings related to your subject. For example, if your report is on computer graphics, look under all of the headings suggested earlier.
- If certain authors' names appear more than once, they may be important in your report field. Check to see if they have written other books useful to your

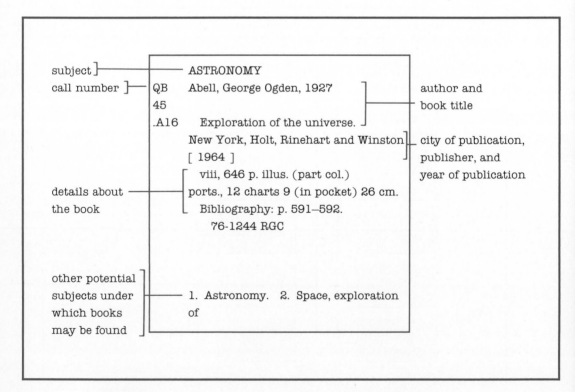

FIGURE 9–4.   **Example of a subject card from the card catalog**

Duncan Burn, Nuclear Power and the Energy Crisis. New York: New York University Press, 1978.

FIGURE 9–5.   Example of a bibliography card for a book

report. (Another way to determine the important names in a field is to consult *Citation Index;* ask your librarian for help in using this book.)
- Check the listing of subject headings on the cards for the books in the card catalog you've already found. (See Figure 9–4.) These may give you a clue as to other subject headings.

Browsing the Stacks.   During or after your work in the card catalog, go to the stacks—the shelves where the books are kept—and do several things:

- Evaluate the books you've made bibliography cards for: check the table of contents and quickly thumb through the pages to see if each book is one you need.
- Compare books that seem to duplicate each other, and choose the better ones. (Don't throw the bibliography cards away, however; just put an *X* on them and keep them with the rest.)
- Browse in areas of the stacks where call numbers on your bibliography cards cluster. You may see other useful books that for some reason did not show up in your card-catalog search.

Checking Bibliographies and References.   While you are browsing or when you are scanning your books, be alert for references to other useful books listed in bibliographies, footnotes, or other references. If your card-catalog search turns up only a few books, take this step as soon as you can.

- Check the ends of chapters and the ends of books for lists of other books. Make bibliography cards on any books that seem potentially useful.

• Check the footnotes at the bottom of pages within books for references to other potentially useful books.

Take the bibliography cards you've made, and return to the card catalog to see if the library has these titles. If not, ask you librarian about getting them through interlibrary loan.

• Check the footnotes, bibliographies, or other references in standard reference books such as encyclopedias, yearbooks, or handbooks (see the section on "Finding Reference Works"). The books listed in sources like these are usually the classics, the ones that experts in the related fields consider to be authoritative. (Look at the bibliography for "robotics" in *The McGraw-Hill Encyclopedia of Science and Technology*, for example.)

Checking Books-in-Print Sources.   For the latest information on your subject, check a books-in-print type of reference such as *Books in Print*. There are also specialized ones, for example:

> *Subject Guide to Books in Print*
> *Technical Book Review Index*
> *Technical and Scientific Books in Print*
> *Medical Books in Print*

The books you find in these sources may not yet be available in your library. Talk to your librarian, instructors, or specialists in the field about locating them.

Consulting Instructors and Specialists.   If you have a list of books unavailable in your library, visit with instructors or specialists in the related field. They may not have the books either, but they may suggest ways to get them or other important titles that you've missed.

STEP 3.   Use the suggestions in the preceding section to locate potentially useful books for your report, and make a bibliography card for each.

Finding Articles

When you begin your search for journal and magazine articles for your report, you use an equivalent of the card catalog: periodical indexes. A periodical index lists articles by subject and author. For example, you might find a dozen or so articles listed under "solar energy" in one volume of a periodical index. You may already be familiar with *Reader's Guide to Periodical Literature* or *Magazine Index*. However, for most technical reports, you cannot rely solely on *Reader's Guide* or *Magazine Index*. They index articles mostly from general-audience, nonspecialist periodicals like *Better Homes and Gardens, Esquire, Field and Stream, Forbes, National Geographic, Working Woman,* and *Sports Illustrated*. These may provide a good start, but you need more specialized indexes. To locate periodical indexes, follow these steps.

Getting a List of *LCSH* Subject Headings.   If you've not already done so, get a list of subject headings from the *Library of Congress Subject Headings*. They may not exactly correspond, but they should give you a good idea of how to locate articles in indexes. (See the section in this chapter on "Consulting the *Library of Congress Subject Headings*" for help on using *LCSH*.)

Checking *Reader's Guide* or *Magazine Index*.   For starters, check for articles in *Reader's Guide* or *Magazine Index*. Remember: for each usable article you find, make a bibliography card similar to the one in Figure 9–6. Notice that on a bibliography card for an article you include the name of the magazine or journal, the date of the specific issue in which your article is found, the volume and issue number if it is supplied in the index, and the page range.

STEP 4.   Check one or two volumes of *Magazine Index* or *Reader's Guide* for general-audience articles related to your report topic, and make a bibliogaphy card for each.

Check *Applied Science and Technology Index*.   Another good place to start your search for articles is an index entitled *Applied Science and Technology Index* (ASTI). It indexes articles from quite an assortment of journals, for example, *Industrial Wastes*, *Industrial Robots*, *Journal of Engineering for Power*, *Journal of Metals*, *Food Technology*, *Computer Design*, *Automotive Engineering*, *Robotics Age*, *Welding Journal*, *Datamation*, and *Nuclear and Chemical Waste Management*. Figure 9–7 contains a typical page from *ASTI*.

---

*S. D. Freedman, "The Future of the Nuclear Option." Environment,
    25: 12–16 (September 1983).*

FIGURE 9–6.   **Example of a bibliography card for an article**

1054   APPLIED SCIENCE & TECHNOLOGY INDEX 1981

HEARING—Testing—*Continued*
Effective hearing protection. J. L. Northern. il diag Plant Eng 35:203-7 Ja 22 '81
Effects of steady-state noise upon human hearing sensitivity from 8000 to 20 000 hz. D. A. Erickson and others. bibl diag Am Ind Hygiene Assn J 41:427-32 Je '80
Hearing conservation equipment buyer's guide. Sound & Vib 15:21 Ja '81
New design concept for an audio dosimeter. E. M. Clark. bibl diag Am Ind Hygiene Assn J 41:700-3 O '80
Noisy leisure time activities in teenage boys. A. Axelsson, and others. bibl Am Ind Hygiene Assn J 42:229-33 Mr '81
Permanent effects of noise exposure on results of a battery of hearing tests. G. R. Bienvenue and P. L. Michael. bibl Am Ind Hygiene Assn J 41:535-41 Ag '80
Representative hearing levels by race and sex in North Carolina industry. L. H. Royster and others. bibl Acoust Soc Am J 68:551-66 Ag '80
Temporary threshold shifts induced by vibratory stimulation. J. E. Kile and W. F. Wurzbach. bibl il diag Sound & Vib 14:26-9 My '80

HEARING aids
Study of multichannel amplitude compression and linear amplification for persons with sensorineural hearing loss. R. P. Lippmann and others. bibl diag Acoust Soc Am J 69:524-34 F '81

Testing
Multidimensional scaling of quality judgments of speech signals processed by hearing aids. J. L. Punch and others. bibl Acoust Soc Am J 68:458-66 Ag '80

HEART
See also
Electrocardiograph

Brain, lung, and heart functions during diving and recovery. P. W. Hochachka. bibl Science 212:509-14 My 1 '81
Chemical modification and functional properties of acylated beef heart myofibrillar proteins. T. A. Eisele and C. J. Brekke. bibl J Food Sci 46:1095-102 Jl/Ag '81
Cytochrome aa_3 electron-transfer reactions; kinetics of hexaammineruthenium(II) reduction of the beef heart enzyme. R. A. Scott and H. B. Gray. bibl Am Chem Soc J 102:3219-24 Ap 23 '80
Heart valve may last a lifetime. N Scientist 89:75 Ja 8 '81

Intrinsic birefringence signal preceding the onset of contraction in heart muscle. R. Weiss and M. Morad. bibl il Science 213:663-6 Ag 7 '81
Myocardial infarct imaging of antibodies to canine cardiac myosin with indium-111-diethylenetriamine pentaacetic acid. B. A. Khaw and others. bibl il diag Science 209:295-7 Jl 11 '80
Original hydraulic system. E. Heath. diag Hydraul & Pneum 34:20 Mr '81
Potassium chloride versus voltage clamp contractures in ventricular muscle. M. Morad and others. bibl diags Science 211:485-7 Ja 30 '81
Relationship between collagen and ultrasonic backscatter in myocardial tissue. M. O'Donnell and others. bibl diag Acoust Soc Am J 69: 580-8 F '81
Sodium-calcium exchange in rabbit heart muscle cells; direct measurement of sarcoplasmic Ca^{2+} activity. C. O. Lee and others. bibl Science 209:699-701 Ag 8 '80

Diseases
Assessment of phamacological treatment of myocardial infarction by phosphorus-31 NMR with surface coils. R. L. Nunnally and P. A. Bottomley. bibl diag Science 211:177-80 Ja 9 '81
Coronary treatment assessed. G. B. Kolata. il Science 213:195 Jl 10 '81
Does drinking water hardness affect cardiovascular disease? M. Joyce. bibl J Environ Health 43:134-9 N/D '80
Drug cuts risk of second heart attack. Chem & Eng N 59:7 Je 8 '81
Exercise and alcohol bring out cholesterol's protection. N Scientist 89:19 Ja 1 '81
Exercise does reduce heart attacks. N Scientist 89:142 Ja 15 '81

Surgery
Consensus on bypass surgery. G. B. Kolata. Science 211:42-3 Ja 2 '81

Transplantation
Heart transplants; to pay or not to pay. R. A. Knox. il Science 209:570-2+ Ag 1 '80
Mass. General; no heart transplants here. Science 209:574 Ag 1 '80

HEART, Artificial
Rare-earth magnets power artificial-heart device. il Mach Design 53:18 Je 11 '81
Total artificial heart. R. K. Jarvik. diags Sci Am 244:74-80 Ja '81

FIGURE 9–7. Example of a section from *Applied Science and Technology Index*

Applied Science and Technology Index, Copyright © 1981, 1982 by The H. W. Wilson Company. Material reproduced by permission of the publisher.

STEP 5.   Check one or two volumes of *Applied Science and Technology Index* for more specialized articles related to your report topic, and make a bibliography card for each.

Finding Specialized Indexes.   After *Reader's Guide* and *ASTI,* use one of the following methods to find *specialized* periodical indexes (ones that index articles only in specialized fields or professions):

- Return to the card catalog, and look under your report subject headings for "Periodical Indexes." Use the indexes you find listed there the same way you would *Reader's Guide* or *ASTI.*
- Find Sheehy's *Guide to Reference Books* or a similar reference book, locate the subsection related to your subject, and then look for "Periodical Indexes," "Indexes," or "Abstract Indexes." (For more on Sheehy's *Guide,* see "Guides to Reference Books" in this chapter.)
- Find a guide to the literature of the field related to your report subject, and use it to find the right specialized periodical index. (For more on these guides, see "Subject Guides and Style Guides.")

Unless your subject has an unusual history, three to four years of index volumes should be sufficient. Of course, some topics, for example, polio, Legionnaires' disease, AIDS, the energy crisis, or the space shuttle, burst into public awareness at some point in time and then fade out of it. Periodical indexes reflect that growing and fading awareness: a volume for one year may have no articles on the subject; the next year, it may have dozens:

Subject Matter	Reader's Guide Volume and Year	Number of Articles Listed
Halley's comet	Vol. 39 (1979–1980)	1
	Vol. 40 (1980–1981)	2
	Vol. 41 (1981–1982)	4
	Vol. 42 (1982–1983)	6
	Vol. 43 (1983–1984)	8
	Vol. 44 (1984–1985)	18

Use encyclopedia yearbooks to find out which are the critical years for your subject, and take notes on the important dates:

Report Subject		Important Dates
Nuclear generation of electricity	1946	Creation of the Atomic Energy Act
	1951	Amendments to allow commercial nuclear power
	1954	First breeder reactor to demonstrate production of electricity

Report Subject	Important Dates
	1957 Price-Anderson Act: private and government indemnity
	1965 First commercial license for a commercial breeder reactor
	1973 AEC requires an environmental impact statement
	1974 AEC is formed; Nuclear Regulatory Commission and Energy Research and Development Administration created
	1979 Three Mile Island nuclear power plant: failure of a cooling system

STEP 6.   Using the preceding suggestions, locate one or more specialized periodical indexes related to your report topic, and write their names on your worksheet.

Checking the Bibliographies and Other References.   As you did for books, check your books, articles, and reports for references to potentially useful articles.

- Check bibliographies at the ends of chapters and at the ends of books.
- Check bibliographies at the ends of articles.
- Check bibliographies at the ends of encyclopedia entries.
- Check footnotes or other references within the pages of books, reports, and articles.

Consulting Instructors and Specialists.   Again as with books, visit instructors or specialists, and ask for help in locating articles. They may know of some titles you've missed or be able to help you find ones that you have bibliography cards for.

STEP 7.   Use any of the general or specialized periodical indexes to locate articles on your report topic, and make a bibliography card for each.

Finding Reference Works

Reference books either help you find books, reports, articles, or other reference books (such as periodical indexes), or they provide you with the information you need in a handy, condensed, quick-reference form (such as encyclopedias). In most cases, there are *general* and *specialized* versions of each of these kinds of reference tools.

Guides to Reference Books.   Some reference books help you find other reference books. For a report on some aspect of medicine, one of these books would have a whole section on medicine, listing related specialized guides to literature, encyclopedias, dictionaries, and periodical indexes. One such reference tool is Sheehy's *Guide to Reference Books*. Some of its main groupings are "pure and applied sciences," "social sciences," and "humanities," each of which is subdivided into more specific areas such as "petroleum engineering," "computer science," or "insurance." For some report projects you need several sections of Sheehy's: for example, for a report on solar-heating devices, you'd look under air conditioning and heating, electrical engineering, and energy resources.

STEP 8.   In Sheehy's *Guide to Reference Books,* or some other similar reference book, locate the subject areas that relate to your report. On your worksheet, copy the names of these subject areas and any useful reference books that you notice there.

Subject Guides and Style Guides.   An excellent reference tool is the subject guide, or guide to the literature of a specific profession or field of knowledge. In some cases this reference is called a bibliography. It works like a guide to reference books, but for one specific field only, for example, nursing, electrical engineering, or agriculture. Here are some examples:

> *Mechanical Engineering: Sources of Information*
> *How to Use a Medical Library*
> *The Literature of Agricultural Research*
> *Cybernetics, Automation, Computers, Control, Ergonomics, Information Theory, and Machine Translation: A Subject Guide*
> *A Guide to Computer Literature: An Introductory Survey of the Sources of Information*
> *A Guide to Materials on Crime and Criminal Justice*
> *The Use of Biological Literature*
> *Searching the Chemical Literature*
> *How to Find Out About Engineering*
> *A Guide to Information Sources in Space Science and Technology*

You can find subject guides in two ways: (1) by looking up your report subject in the card catalog and finding a subheading entitled "subject guide," "guide to the literature," or something similar; (2) or you can consult the subsection entitled "Guides" in Sheehy's *Guide to Reference Books.*

A style guide to a specific field tells you about special rules concerning footnoting, capitalization, abbreviations, symbols, and other such tricky problems *in that particular field:*

> *Council of Biological Editors, Commission on Form and Style*
> *Mathematics in Type*
> *Guide to Medical Writing: A Practical Manual for Physicians, Dentists, Nurses, and Pharmacists*

STEP 9.   Use any of the suggestions in the preceding section to locate one or more subject guides and style guides related to your report topic, and make a bibliography card for each.

Periodical Indexes.   Periodical indexes help you locate articles. Indexes are bound by the year, and some also come out in monthly or even biweekly issues so that if your topic is really "hot" you can find out what has been published on it in the last few months.

General Indexes.   *Reader's Guide* and *Magazine Index*, of course, are the standard nonspecialist indexes. However, you can also use *Social Sciences Index* and *Public Affairs Information Service*, which are more scholarly indexes, for the same purpose.

Specialized Indexes.   A specialized index lists articles for a specific field only. For example, *Sociological Abstracts* lists articles published in sociology; *Indexus Medicus* lists articles in medicine; *Business Periodicals Index* can be used to find business-related articles. *Applied Science and Technology Index* lists articles from many scientific and technical fields (see Figure 9–7 for a sample, and see the section on "Subject Guides and Style Guides" for a list of some specialized periodical indexes).

Encyclopedias.   Encyclopedias are alphabetized repositories of a wide range of human knowledge, as is the case in the *Britannica* for example, or of a specific area of knowledge, as is the case in *The Encyclopedia of Biological Sciences*. If you are new to the field related to your technical report, start by reading articles in general-audience encyclopedias like the *Americana* or *Collier's;* then move on to specialized ones like the *McGraw-Hill Encyclopedia of Science and Technology*. To find specialized encyclopedias, look (1) in a subsection under your report subject entitled "Encyclopedias" in the card catalog; (2) in a guide to reference books like Sheehy's; or (3) in a subject guide to the literature of the field related to your report. Here are some examples of more specialized encyclopedias:

Condensed Computer Encyclopedia
International Petroleum Encyclopedia
Encyclopedic Guide to Nursing
Encyclopedia of Chemistry
Encyclopedia of Engineering
The Encyclopedia of Oceanography
Encyclopedia of Criminology
The New Space Encyclopedia: A Guide to Astronomy and Space Exploration

When you find a useful article in an encyclopedia, make a bibliography card like the one in Figure 9–8.

STEP 10.   Use the preceding suggestions to locate specialized indexes and encyclopedias related to your report topic, and make a bibliography card for each.

Yearbooks.   Yearbooks are usually yearly updates of encyclopedias. Most of the general encyclopedias—and many of the specialized or technical ones—have them. The yearbook that accompanies the *Britannica*, for example, catches you up on a wide range of things such as national and international political events, the latest scientific discoveries, and the newest technological breakthroughs and applications.

Martin J. Steindler, "Nuclear fuel cycle." McGraw-Hill Encyclopedia of Science and Technology, 5th ed., vol. 9, pp. 228–29.

FIGURE 9–8.   Bibliography card for an encyclopedia article

Some yearbooks are published independently of encyclopedias and focus on the year's events within a single field of knowledge, as does *Computer Yearbook*. If you report on a historical event such as the Mount St. Helen's eruption or a space mission or on a rapidly changing subject, yearbooks can help. Here are some examples:

Aerospace Yearbook
Yearbook of Agriculture
Yearbook of Labor Statistics
Computer Yearbook

You can find yearbooks through the card catalog, a guide to reference books, or a subject guide.

Handbooks.   Handbooks typically cover the fundamental knowledge within a field in an in-depth, chapter-by-chapter way. *The Handbook of Engineering Fundamentals,* for example, has sections on mathematical tables, units, and standards; mechanics of rigid and deformable bodies; aerodynamics; engineering thermodynamics; electricity and magnetism; radiation, light, and acoustics; chemistry; and metallic and nonmetallic materials. They are generally intended for quick reference and are not a good way of familiarizing yourself with a new field. Here are some examples:

American Electrician's Handbook: A Reference Book for the Practical Electrical Man

Handbook of Industrial Engineering and Management
Petroleum Exploration Handbook
Agricultural Engineer's Handbook
A Field Guide to Rocks and Minerals
Handbook of Engineering Fundamentals
Standard Handbook for Civil Engineers

To find handbooks for specific fields, check the card catalog, a guide to reference books, or a subject guide.

Dictionaries.   Practically every field has one or more specialized dictionaries for terminology specific to that field. Here are some examples:

The Automotive Dictionary
A Dictionary of the Social Sciences
Technical Dictionary of Automotive Engineering
The Dictionary of the Biological Sciences
Technical Dictionary of Data Processing, Computers, and Office Machines

Atlases.   Atlases are not merely map collections; many are excellent sources of statistical information. In fact, they are often lumped together with statistical guides in Sheehy's. People in business and marketing use Rand-McNally's *Commercial Atlas and Marketing Guide,* which contains much information on manufacturing, trade, business, population, and transportation in the United States.

STEP 11.   Use any of the preceding suggestions to locate general or specialized yearbooks, handbooks, dictionaries, and atlases that might be useful in your report project, and make bibliography cards for each.

Finding Government Documents

The U.S. government, the largest publisher in the world, produces documents on practically every conceivable technical subject. Most of what it prints cannot be found through the usual means, and only libraries designated as "government depositories" store government documents. Even if you have access to one of these libraries, you must send away and pay a small fee to get some government documents. Also different about government documents are the indexing tools you use to find them:

Congressional Indexing Service
Government Reports and Announcements: Annual Index
American Statistics Index
Index to U.S. Government Periodicals
Cumulative Index to the Monthly Catalogue

Congressional Indexing Service.   The *Congressional Indexing Service,* or *CIS,* is one of the most useful tools for locating government documents, since most government-depository libraries possess all of the documents indexed in it. It provides an index and abstract of the documents. The illustrations in Figure 9–9 show

Media impact on alcohol use and abuse, S541–47

"Network for Continuing Medical Education Videocassette Library," catalog of available TV programs, S721–30

Network programming and syndication, H521–31.13

News program tapes for archives, H521–32.9

Sports broadcasting regulation, H963–8

Translator station ops, S261–31

TV and FM radio translator stations regulation revisions, H501–63, H503–33, S263–43, PL94–335

TV blackouts of homegame sporting events, S261–39

TV broadcasting of homegame sporting events, permanent requirement, H501–7

TV broadcasting of 1975 homegame sporting events, FCC rpt, S262–11

TV programming impact on children, S261–32

see also Cable television

see also Educational broadcasting

see also Political broadcasting

see also Public broadcasting

Television News, Inc.

Ops and Joseph Coors mgmt, S261–19

Kiddy, Thomas D.

SSN 688 class submarine procurement revisions, S181–32.3

Kidnapping

Child abduction by parent, Fed criminal code revision, H521–42, PL96–611

Crime, kidnapping and prison related laws, compilation, 57th-96th Congress, H940–12

Human rights violations in Guatemala, H381–90.3

Kidney diseases

End-stage renal disease program, medicare coverage, S362–34

Medical technologies cost-effectiveness analysis, renal disease policy formulation case study, J952–14

Medicare program cost reduction proposals, H781–49

Natl Inst of Arthritis, Diabetes, and Digestive and Kidney Diseases programs, FY82 approp, H181–89.7, S181–27.7

Kidney, Joyce

HUD housing and community dev programs, extension and revision, H241–27.5

Kiefer, Linda

Veterans and military personnel educ assistance programs, extension and revision, H761–28.3

FIGURE 9–9a. A section from the CIS Index

S362–33   **STAFF DATA AND MATERIALS RELATED TO SOCIAL SECURITY FINANCING.**
Sept. 1981. 97-1.
v + 88 p. il. $3.75
S/N 052-070-05640-1.
CIS/MF/3
●Item 1038-A; 1038-B.
°Y4.F49:Sol/44/981.
LC 81-603666.
Committee Print No. 97-8. Staff study evaluating short- and long-term status of social security programs based on current financing methods. Describes possible solutions to social security financing problems, including Administration proposals.
Includes tables and graphs throughout.

S362–34   **END-STAGE RENAL DISEASE (ESRD) PROGRAM UNDER MEDICARE.**
Sept. 1981. 97-1.
v + 51 p. il. † CIS/MF/3
●Item 1038-A; 1038-B.
°Y4.F49:R29/4.
LC 81-604026.
Committee Print No. 97-9. Staff report, prepared with assistance of Glenn R. Markus and Richard J. Price (CRS), reviewing background and status of End-Stage Renal Disease (ESRD) Program under medicare, including benefits for dialysis and kidney transplantation, extent and location of ESRD facilities and networks (tables, p. 41-51), reimbursement policies, and program participation experience.

S261–31.3: Jan. 21, 1976. p. 29-37.
Witness: KNAUER, Leon, counsel, Natl Translator Assn.

Statement and Discussion: (Also covers discussion under S261-31.2.) Support for S. 2847; explanation of and need for translator station operations.

S261–32   **IMPACT OF TELEVISION ON CHILDREN.**
Feb. 13, 1976. 94-2.
iii + 62 p. † CIS/MF/3
●Item 1041. Y4.C73/2:94-62.
MC 76-3614. LC 76-601642.
Committee Serial No. 94-62. Hearing held in Salt Lake City, Utah, before the *Subcom on Communications* to investigate the impact of TV on children and to review programming for young persons.
Includes submitted statements (p. 49-52), and program listings (p. 53-62) for young viewers in Salt Lake City.

S261–32.1: Feb. 13, 1976. p. 34-49.
Witnesses: LLOYD, Jay, vp and station mgr, KSL Inc; member, bd of dirs, Utah Broadcasters Assn.

FIGURE 9–9b. A section from the CIS Abstracts

FIGURE 9–9. Excerpts from *Congressional Indexing Service*

a section from a typical page of the *CIS Index* and a section from a typical page of the *CIS Abstracts*.

American Statistics Index.   As its title suggests, the *American Statistics Index,* or *ASI,* is useful for finding statistical information rapidly. *ASI* works the same way as *CIS.*

Government Reports and Announcements.   This government document resource is a thick volume of indexes and abstracts that comes out every two weeks; it also has the *Annual Index,* an accumulation of the whole year's indexed documents. In many ways, it can be the most exciting of government-document resources, but not all of the documents it indexes are sent to government-depository libraries; instead, you must send away for many of them. For an idea of the range of subject categories indexed in *Government Reports and Announcements,* take a look at its table of contents in Figure 9–10.

Index to U.S. Government Periodicals.   As in *Reader's Guide,* you look up your report topic in the yearly volumes of the *Index to U.S. Government Periodicals* to find useful articles, and then check to see if the journals are kept in government-depository libraries. You'll be surprised how many periodicals are published by the U.S. government and what a vast array of fields they cover: for example, *Naval Aviation News, Solar Law Reporter,* and *Weekly Weather and Crop Bulletin.*

1. Aerodynamics
2. Agriculture
3. Astronomy and Astrophysics
4. Atmospheric Sciences
5. Behavioral and Social Sciences
6. Biological and Medical Sciences
7. Chemistry
8. Earth Sciences and Oceanography
9. Electronics and Electrical Engineering
10. Energy Conversion
11. Materials
12. Mathematical Sciences
13. Mechanical, Industrial, Civil, and Marine Engineering
14. Methods and Equipment
15. Military Sciences
16. Missile Technology
17. Navigation, Communications, Detection Countermeasures
18. Nuclear Science and Technology
19. Ordnance
20. Physics
21. Propulsion and Fuels
22. Space Technology

FIGURE 9–10.   The table of contents of *Government Reports and Announcements*

Other Government Document Resources. There are other indexing sources to government documents, in particular, the *Cumulative Index to the Monthly Catalog* and a number of resources directly related to the president and the Congress: *The Federal Register, The Congressional Record,* and *The Congressional Index.* Use these last three if your report topic is the object of some political controversy and public concern.

When you find a useful government document, make a bibliography card for it similar to the one in Figure 9–11.

STEP 12.   Use any of the preceding suggestions to locate government documents related to your report topic, and make a bibliography card for each. (For starters, look for your topic in a volume of *Government Reports and Announcements: Annual Index.*)

Finding Trade and Association Literature

Another large area of literature—books, pamphlets, articles, brochures, buying guides and catalogs—is not cataloged or indexed in any way in most libraries.

• Private organizations and corporations publish in-house newsletters and magazines for employees, stockholders, and other people in the same area of business or trade. Radio Shack, for example, publishes a monthly called *Radio Shack Intercom;* Exxon, a periodical entitled *The Lamp;* and IBM, a periodical called *Think.*

Department of Defense, Air Force Weapons Lab.   Overview of Reactor Concepts: A   Survey of Reactor Design. L. W. Lee and J. Huff. February 1985.

FIGURE 9–11.   Bibliography card for a government report

• Professions, trades, and specific industries publish potentially useful information, as these examples from *Working Press of the Nation: Volume 2, Magazine Directory* show:

Refrigerated Transporter	*Laundry News*
American Tool, Die, and Stamping News	*Metals Week*
	Motorcycle Product News
Recycling Today	*Occupational Health Nursing*
Modern Machine Shop	*Broom, Brush, and Mop*
Boating Industry	*Meat Plant Magazine*
Athletic Training	*Health Care News*
Hearing Aid Journal	*Coal Energy News*
Today's Office	*American Pigeon Journal*
Pet Business	*Petfood Industry*
Photographic Trade News	*Technical Photography*
Reuse/Recycle	*Camping Magazine*
Coach and Athlete	*Fishing Tackle Trade News*
Bowlers Journal	*Golf Shop Operators*
Lab Animal	*American Bee Journal*
Soybean Digest	*Greenhouse Grower*
The Peanut Farmer	*Avocado Grower*
Co-Op Country News	*Organic Gardening and Farming*
Wyoming Stockman-Farmer	*Cattle Business*
Calf News	*Turkey World*
Horse and Horseman	*Solar Age*

• Interest groups—groups advocating a certain cause, for example, increased use of biofuels, opposition to nuclear power, or support of solar-power use—also publish technical information, although of a partisan nature. Write these organizations and request reprints of articles and other information they are willing to send.

To find these organizations, consult *Gebbie House Magazine Directory*, which has sections called "industry breakdown" and "subjects requested" for locating specific trade magazines. Or, consult *The Magazine Industry Market Place*, which indexes magazines in the table of contents by "associations/organizations," "house organ/company," "trade," as well as by subject matter. Volume 5 of *The Working Papers of the Nation*, entitled *Internal Publications*, is another source for finding trade and association magazines.

Thomas Register.   In your technical report you may need information on certain products or services that only specific companies can provide. The *Thomas Register* enables you to find these companies and their addresses. For example, if you were doing a technical report on some new medical technology and wanted to read the brochures of companies that manufacture it, you would look up "medical technology." For an example of what you'll see in the *Thomas Register*, see Figure 9–12.

Interest Groups.   Also unindexed and sometimes difficult to find are the names of interest groups that might send you information on your topic. For example, an association of farmers out in the Midwest advocating the use of gasohol may be

SCOPES: CENTERING (Contd)

MA: BOSTON
BERGER INSTRUMENTS, DIV. OF HIGH VOLTAGE ENGINEERING CORP. 4T River St., P.O. Box 277 (ZIP 02126) (Out Of State Call Toll Free: 800-343-6853) .... 1M+
NY: EAST ROCHESTER
Amarel Precision Instruments, Inc. Techniplex Mall .... NR
NY: PLAINVIEW
C & H Precision Tool, Co. 44-T Newtown Plaza (Angle & Radius Dressers, Diamond Related Tools; Air Bearings For Jigs & Fixtures) 1/4M–
NY: ROCHESTER
Spectra Services P.O. Box 23682-T .... NR
PA: TREVOSE
LENOX INSTRUMENT CO. 267 Andrews Rd., Scottsville Industrial Park (ZIP 19047) (215—322-9990) .... 1M+
(See Our Full Page Ads At Borescopes)

SCOPES: RIFLE
(see Sights: Firearm)

SCOPES: SPOTTING

CA: FOSTER CITY
Technipol International Corp. 1181 Chess Dr., Bldg. A (Rifle) .... NR
FL: BRANDON
MDS Incorporated P.O. Box 1441F (Rigid & Flexible Borescopes & Fiberscopes, Kits & Accessories) 1/4M–
MT: WOLF POINT
WOOD'S POWR-GRIP CO., INC. 233-T Cascade (ZIP 59201) (Vacuum-Attaching Base For Spotting Scopes & High-Powered Binoculars) (Out Of State Call Toll Free: 800-548-9737) .... NR
NJ: BARRINGTON
EDMUND SCIENTIFIC CO. A415 Edscorp Bldg. (ZIP 08007) (609—547-3488) .... 10M+
NY: ORANGEBURG
MACHIDA AMERICA, INC. 40 Ramland Rd. (ZIP 10962) (Custom Design, Manufacture & Service Of Flexible Borescopes, Etc.) (914—365-0600) .... 1M+
NY: ROCHESTER
BAUSCH & LOMB INC., VISION ACCESSORIES DEPT. 1400 N Goodman St. (ZIP 14692) (Rifle) (716—338-8398) .... 50M+
PA: PITTSBURGH
STAR-TRON TECHNOLOGY CORP. 900 Freeport Rd. (ZIP 15238) (Night Vision Scopes) (412—781-7667) .... 1/2M+
PA: TREVOSE
LENOX INSTRUMENT CO. 267 Andrews Rd., Scottsville Industrial Park (ZIP 19047) (215—322-9990) .... 1M+
(See Our Full Page Ads At Borescopes)
VA: HERNDON
AIMPOINT, INC. 203 Elden St., Ste. 302T (ZIP 22070) (Electronic Sighting Devices) (Out Of State Call Toll Free: 800-336-0185) .... 10M+
WA: REDMOND
Meyers, B.E. & Co., Inc. Dept. TR, 17525 N.E. 67th Court (Night Vision) .... 1M+
WA: SPOKANE
Apollo Optics S. 323 Grant .... 5M+

SCOPOLAMINE

MO: ST. LOUIS
Inland Alkaloid Co. 4200-T Laclede Ave. (Hydrobromide, Hydrochloride Methyl Bromide Alkaloid) .... 1M+
NY: NEW YORK
Academy Chemical Corp. 150-4 W. 28 St. .... 1/4M+

SCOREBOARDS

IL: CHICAGO
STEWART-WARNER ELECTRONICS DIVISION 1300 N. Kostner Ave. (ZIP 60651) (312—292-3000) 50M+
(See Our Company Profile Under Stewart-Warner Corp.)
IL: DANVILLE
Time-O-Matic Inc. P.O. Box 850 .... 1/2M+
IL: GREENVILLE
NEVCO SCOREBOARD CO. 301 E. Harris Ave. (ZIP 62246) (Sports Scoreboards) (618—664-0360) .... NR

SPECTRUM SCOREBOARDS

FOOTBALL SOFTBALL/BASEBALL BASKETBALL

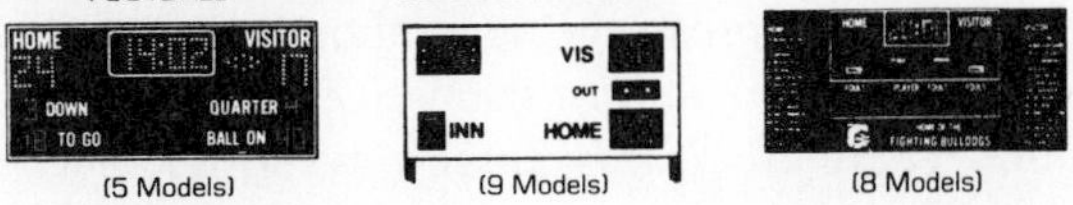

(5 Models) (9 Models) (8 Models)

ALL SPORTS CUSTOM DESIGNS
★ Porcelain/Steel Finish ★ Dependable Operation
★ Reliable Construction ★ Superior Technology
★ 40 Colors

SPECTRUM CORPORATION
10048-T Easthaven, Houston, TX 77075
(713) 944-6200

IL: PALATINE
Davenport, A. C., & Son Co. 308-T E. Hellen Rd. (Changeable) .... 5M+
IA: DES MOINES
FAIR-PLAY SCOREBOARDS, DIV. FAIRTRON CORP. P.O. Box 1847-T (ZIP 50306) (Solid State & Electro-Mechanical Score Boards & Timers For All Indoor & Outdoor Sports) (515—265-5305) .... 1M+
IA: WEBSTER CITY
Naden Industries, Inc. 505-T Fair Ave. (Electric; Football, Hockey, Swimming, Basketball & Baseball) .... 1M+
MI: FERNDALE
MODERN MESSAGE SIGN CO. 2858 Horton (ZIP 48220) (Moving Message Signs & Displays, Time/Temperature Displays. Combination Sign & Message Units. Scoreboards, Remote Controlled Message Systems) (Call Toll Free: 1-800-345-1781) .... 1/4M+
(See Our Full Page Ad At Signs: Advertising)
MI: NILES
Score-Tyme Mfg. Co. P.O. Box 247 .... 1/4M–
NE: GRAND ISLAND
ELECTRONIC DISPLAY SYSTEMS 2809 E. Hwy. 30 (ZIP 68801) (Microprocessor Based Electronic Digital Readout) (Out Of State Call Toll Free: 800-445-9206) .... NR
NY: BELLMORE
Austin Athletic Equipment Corp. 705-T Bedford Ave., Box 423 .... 1M+
NY: BUFFALO
Emed Co., Inc. Box 369, 332-T Greene St. (Safety) .... 1M+
NY: NEW YORK
National Time Recording Equipment Co. 62-64-A Reade St. .... 1M+
NY: UNIONDALE
Uneeda Sign Service 855-T Nassau Rd. (Church Boards, Directory Boards, Chalk Boards, Cork Boards, Etc.) .... 5M+
OH: AKRON
Mayer, Charles, Studios, Inc. 168-TR E. Market St. .... 5M+
OK: TULSA
Ashcoft Specialty Co. 8510-T E. 41st. St. .... NR
PA: WARMINSTER
Franklin Instrument Co. Inc. P.O. Box 2949 (Electronic, Sports-Schools, Colleges) .... 1/4M+
SD: BROOKINGS
DAKTRONICS INC. 331 Thirty-Second Ave., P.O. Box 128 (ZIP 57006) (605—692-6145) .... NR
TN: MEMPHIS
Monotag Corp. 3430-T Winchester (Football & Basketball) .... 1/4M+
Peck Sign Industries Inc. 1429-T Riverside Blvd. .... 10M+
TX: DALLAS
Vaughan & Associates, Inc. 1225 Round Table Dr. (All Sports) .... 1/2M+
TX: HOUSTON
SPECTRUM CORP. 10048-T Easthaven (ZIP 77075) (All Sports; Standard & Custom Designs; Porcelain Finish, 40 Colors) (713—944-6200) .... 5M+
WA: SPOKANE
American Sign & Indicator Corp. N. 2310 Fancher Way, P.O. Drawer 2727 .... 1M+
WI: PARDEEVILLE
General Indicator Corp. 413-T S. Main St., P.O. Box 97 (Electric) .... 50M+
CANADA: B.C., RICHMOND
Adtronics Div. Of Sign-O-Lite Plastics Ltd. 2771-T Simpson Rd. .... NR
CANADA: ONT., MISSISSAUGA
Rotomatic Display Products Ltd. 1600-T Aimco Blvd. (Electronic) .... NR
CANADA: WINNIPEG, MAN.
Kodiak Industries Ltd. 49-T Adelaide St. (Electronic) .... NR

SCORIFIERS

CO: CANON CITY
DFC CERAMICS, INC. P.O. Box 110-T (ZIP 81212) (Metallurgical Clay Grade Scorifiers Available In 1/2" Increments 2-3 1/2" Bart Or Regular Style) (303—275-7525) .... 1M+
CO: DENVER
Cosco-Colorado Scientific Instruments & Supply Co., Inc. 900 N. Broadway .... 1/2M+
KS: KANSAS CITY
Goldblatt Tool Co. 511-T Osage (Mortar, Plasterers) .... 1M+

SCOURERS: CEREAL MILL
(see also Machy.: Flour Mill)

NY: BROCTON
Huntley Mfg. Inc. Buckholtz Rd. (Barley, Corn, Grain, Maize, Rye, Wheat) .... 1/2M+
NY: SILVER CREEK
Howes, S., Co., Inc. 1974 Miller St. 1/4M–

SCRAMBLERS: VOICE

CA: EL SEGUNDO
Hughes Aircraft Co. 200 N. Sepulveda Blvd., P.O. Box 1042 .... 50M+
CA: SAN FRANCISCO
Fargo Co. 577-T 10th St. .... 1/4M+
Saber Laboratories 577-T 10th St. (Counterespionage Systems) .... 1/4M+
CA: SANTA CLARA
Clifford Technologies, Inc. 973T Shulman Ave. .... NR
CT: BETHEL
Franchal Associates 751/2-T Wooster St. 1/4M
CT: STAMFORD
Information Security Associates, Inc. 350 Fairfield Ave., P.O. Box 3272 .... NR
MD: COCKEYSVILLE
MIECO Div., LSA Scientific Corp. 109-T Beaver Court, P.O. Box 737 .... 1/2M+
MA: CONCORD
Technical Communications Corp. 100-T Domino Dr. (Voice & Data Privacy) .... 1M+
MA: WESTFORD
Controlonics Corp. 5 Lyberty Way, Box 555 (Mobile, Marine) .... 5M+
NJ: FAIRFIELD
INTELLIGENCE DEVICES CORP. 125-T Passaic Ave. (ZIP 07006) (Sophisticated Electronic Intelligence Devices For Law Enforcement, Governmental Intelligence Agencies & Security Industries, Computer Software For Law Enforcement) (201—882-9023) .... 1M+
➧ *See our catalog in* THOMCAT vols. 15-21
NJ: METUCHEN
Security Technology Corp. 416-T Main St. .... NR
NY: BUFFALO
Bell Aerospace Textron, Div.-Textron Inc. P.O. Box 1-TR .... 50M+
NY: ITHACA
Sutton Designs Inc. 300-T N. Tioga .... 1/2M+
NY: NEW YORK
CCS Communications Control Inc. 633 Third Ave., Dept. TR .... 10M+
H.L.B. Security Electronics, Ltd. 211-A E. 43rd St. .... NR
NC: RALEIGH
SIRCHIE GROUP, THE Dept. T, P.O. Box 30576 (ZIP 27622) (For Radio & Telephone) (919—781-3120) .... 5M+
PA: CONSHOHOCKEN
Criminal Research Products, Inc. P.O. Box 408-TR .... 5M+
PA: SOUTHAMPTON
SHERWOOD COMMUNICATIONS ASSOCIATES, LTD. 1310 Industrial Hwy., Dept. J (ZIP 18966) (Advanced Electronic Security, Surveillance & Detection Equip.; Exec. Protection, Encryption, Bomb Detection, Communications, Crowd Control, Countermeasures, Optical Armor, Night Vision Devices, Police & Law Enforcement Equip., Mobile Surveillance Vehicles) (215—357-9065) .... NR
➧ *See our catalog in* THOMCAT vols. 15-21
VA: ALEXANDRIA
CYCOMM CORPORATION 85 S. Bragg St. (ZIP 23212) (Radio Or Telephone) (Out Of State Call Toll Free: 800-523-8636; In VA Call: 703-658-2350) .... 1M+
(See Our Company Profile in Volume 13)
➧ *See our catalog in* THOMCAT vols. 15-21

Better features make Nevco a better scoreboard.

Model 2250 Basketball/ Volleyball/ Wrestling

Make us prove our points.

MPC-3 Micro-processor Operator's Control

Nevco's "next possession" feature lets fans know where to look for the action... and it's more proof that, feature for feature, you just can't buy a better scoreboard. Write or call today for full details.

- Includes MPC-3 Operator's Control
- **Five Year** Guarantee
- Easy to Install
- Solid State Circuitry
- UL Listed/CSA Certified

Toll Free
800-851-4040
FAX: (618 664-0398)

NEVCO

NEVCO SCOREBOARD COMPANY
301 East Harris Avenue
Greenville, Illinois 62246 USA
(618) 664-0360
Canada office: Orillia, Ontario

CYCOMM

Voice Security

- High security
- Excellent voice quality
- Compatible with most telephones and radios
- Built-in key management

SEE OUR CATALOG IN *THOMCAT.*

6665 SW Hampton, Portland, OR 97223
(503) 620-1024 Outside Oregon (800) 523-8636

(Complete Company Information, see Volumes 13 & 14) **16909/SCR**

FIGURE 9–12. Excerpt from the *Thomas Register*
Reprinted by permission of Thomas Publishing Company.

delighted to send you loads of free information for your report on gasohol, because they want to spread the news about gasohol. There are hundreds of interest groups like these; they concern themselves with practically every issue, including technical ones. There are at least three ways to find such interest groups:

• Consult subject guides, for example, the *Guide to Ecology Information and Organizations*. Its title in fact tips you off. Not all subject guides, of course, list interest groups, as does this example. (See "Subject Guides and Style Guides" on how to find subject guides.)

• Use Sheehy's *Guide to Reference Books* to locate titles that specifically indicate associations, organizations, or interest groups. For example, you might find this title: *Energy: A Guide to Organizations and Information Sources in the U.S.* In it you would find the name and address of a group in Boston advocating the increased use of wind energy, for example. You'd see information on several organizations promoting the recovery of energy from municipal solid wastes.

• One final means of locating associations related to your report topic is a reference work entitled the *Encyclopedia of Associations*. This book lists associations by subject and provides addresses and descriptions of the associations it indexes. Figure 9–13 contains two examples from this source.

STEP 13.   Use *Thomas Register* to locate companies that offer products or services related to your report topic, and copy the information you find on a bibliography card. Use the *Encyclopedia of Associations* to locate organizations related to your report topic, and make a bibliography card for each of them. Use any of the other preceding suggestions to locate trade, association, or interest-group literature.

Using Computerized Information Retrieval

Another way to go about a library search is to use the computer. Almost every field of knowledge now has one or more facilities for computerized searches for articles and books as well as other kinds of literature. How desirable a computerized literature search can be depends on two things. First, you usually have to pay for the search to be done. For an ordinary thirty-page report, the average cost seems to be around thirty dollars. Second, it also depends on the database being used for the search. When you use a computerized literature search, you get a printout of a bibliography of the books, reports, and articles related to your topic. You give the computer several descriptors to enable it to locate those specific titles.

Another type of computer-based information-retrieval facility actually gets you the information you need: the actual statistics, names, dates, concepts, and other such details. For example:

MINPROC	Metallurgy
IBSEDEX	Construction industry and related professions
IALINE	Food sciences and nutrition
CITIBASE	U.S. economics
AGRISTAT	Agricultural industry
SOLO	Health care
VININFO	Wines

5065 NATIONAL OLD TIMERS' ASSO-CIATION OF THE ENERGY INDUSTRY (NOTAEI)
P.O. Box 168   Phone: (516) 431-4668
Mineola, NY 11501   John M. Sibarium, Chm.
Founded: 1926. **Members:** 1000. **Staff:** 1. Previous and present officers and presidents with a minimum of ten years in a national or regional association in the energy industry. Objectives are: to explore new areas of education and inter-leadership in the energy industry; to promote greater coordination on joint projects; to recommend research and development among member groups; to work with governmental agencies to develop new trends in training programs. Activities include printing manuals for educational distribution to trade schools, maintaining a speakers program on technical subjects, serving on governmental agency advisory councils to make recommendations, and working within trade associations on research and development. Bestows "Hall of Fame" award. **Committees:** Air Pollution; Awards; Educational; Energy Conservation; Engineering; Speakers; Who's Who. **Publications:** (1) Hour Glass (newsletter), 6/year; (2) Technical Manuals, 5/year; (3) Who's Who in Energy Industry, quinquennial. **Formerly:** (1974) Old Timers' Club of the Oilburners Industry. **Convention/Meeting:** semiannual - (next) 1982 Oct. 25-28, Absecon, NJ.

5066 NATURAL POWWER (Energy)
6031 St. Clair Ave.   Phone: (216) 361-3156
Cleveland, OH 44103   Irwin Friedman, Chm.
Founded: 1975. **Members:** 200. **Regional Groups:** 1. **State Groups:** 1. **Local Groups:** 1. Engineers, businessmen, solar scientists and developers, environmental activists and others advocating the replacement of toxic fuels and nuclear power with natural energy forces such as the sun, waves, wind, tides and currents. (The acronym POWWER stands for Power of World Wide Energy Resources.) Supports researchers and experimenters. Influences public officials through letters and petitions; informs the public of energy and environmental issues by participating in talk shows and providing speakers for interested groups. Produces educational packets, which include simple

experiments, for elementary and high school students. Serves as information exchange center. Bestows awards. Publishes newsletter and articles.

5067 OAK RIDGE ASSOCIATED UNI-VERSITIES (Energy) (ORAU)
P.O. Box 117   Phone: (615) 576-3151
Oak Ridge, TN 37830
Founded: 1946. **Members:** 51. **Staff:** 500. Research, education, training and information corporation of 51 universities, operating under direct contract with the U.S. Department of Energy. Maintains diverse programs designed to further the cause of science and science education from the precollege through the postdoctoral level; to improve the quality of science and science teaching nationally; to disseminate information about U.S. energy programs. Also conducts programs for private industry, National Science Foundation (see separate entry), Environmental Protection Agency, National Institutes of Health, U.S. Department of Labor and others. Activities include: research in nuclear and occupational medicine; training in use of radioisotopes in research; research in health physics; research participation programs at DOE and other federal laboratory installations for college and university faculty members and graduate and undergraduate students; long-range energy analysis; public education on energy; high school traveling lecture-demonstration program. Maintains medical and energy libraries. Sponsors University Isotope Separator at Oak Ridge (UNISOR) research program. **Departments:** Fiscal and Management Services; Information Services; Personnel Services; Safety and Health; Technical Services. **Divisions:** Comparative Animal Research Laboratory; Energy Education; Institute for Energy Analysis; Manpower Education Research and Training; Medical and Health Sciences. **Publications:** (1) Annual Report; (2) Medical and Energy Research Reports, annual; also publishes technical reports and policy studies related to energy, health and the environment. **Affiliated with:** American Association for Advancement of Science. **Formerly:** (1966) Oak Ridge Institute of Nuclear Studies.

FIGURE 9–13. Section from *Encyclopedia of Associations* Reprinted from *Encyclopedia of Associations 1984*, edited by Denise S. Akey (Copyright © 1959, 1961, 1964, 1968, 1970, 1972, 1973, 1975, 1976, 1977, 1978, 1979, 1980, 1981, 1982, 1983 by Gale Research Company; reprinted by permission of the publisher), 18th edition, Gale, 1984.

TRIS	Transportation and the transportation industry
MICROLINE	Computers and the computer industry
AUTONET	Automobiles and the automotive industry

If you are interested in finding out about computer-based information retrieval, discuss this resource with your librarian. Also, you can find the database that corresponds to your report topic by consulting one of these guides to computerized library searches:

Online Bibliographic Databases
LUCIS Guide to Computer-Based Information Sources

Sources of Information Outside the Library

Even though libraries can provide useful information for most report projects, certain information for certain reports can only be gained outside the library. When that happens, these are the typical sources to use:

Site inspections and measurements   Interviews
Calculations   Governmental sources
Business literature   Surveys and questionnaires
                                         Letters of inquiry

Imagine that you and some friends feel that your city needs softball and baseball parks on city-owned property. To get city administrators to accept the plan, you would have to gather all appropriate supporting information and prepare a report.

Site Inspections and Measurements

For some report projects you must go out and do certain direct measurements. Building municipal ball parks would require these measurements, plus others:

Dimensions of the land needed
Dimensions of city property suitable for the parks
Terrain of suitable city property
Dimensions of the bleachers to be built
Amount of lumber and other materials needed to build the bleachers and the fences
Dimensions and materials for the concession stand

Other reports might require you to weigh things, run tests, take samples, and the like.

STEP 14.   On your report worksheet describe the site inspections and measurements you may have to conduct in order to write your report.

Calculations

Closely tied to the measurements required by a report project are calculations. Some of the measurements just listed can only be determined by means of several calculations. In the municipal ball-parks report, you would need to calculate:

Total amount of lumber needed to build bleachers, fences, dugouts, concession stands, and so on
Cost of this lumber once you've calculated how much is needed
Amount of dirt, gravel, and so forth needed to landscape the field properly
Amount of electricity required by the park's lighting system
Cost of that electricity use

STEP 15.   On your worksheet explain the calculations you'll need to make in your report work and the information you'll need in order to do those calculations.

Business Literature

An important source of information external to most libraries is business literature, the brochures and information pamphlets that businesses supply customers concerning their products and services. Libraries usually do not and cannot collect this sort of literature.

In the municipal ball-parks project, you might also want to investigate the cost of an electric scoreboard. You could make phone calls for prices of common construction materials, but what would you do for descriptions and costs of such out-of-the-ordinary items as special lighting equipment and electric scoreboards? How do you locate this sort of information? Chances are there are no manufacturers of electric scoreboards in your city. The answer is *Thomas Register*, a wonderful resource for any businessperson or report writer (and there are other such directories of businesses, some for specific fields). In it, under the name of the product or service you need are listed company names, addresses, phone numbers, asset size, and sometimes a list of specific products or services offered. Look again at Figure 9–12 for an example of the kind of listing offered by the *Register*. Once you've located several likely companies, call or write a letter of inquiry (illustrated in Figure 9–15 and discussed in Chapter 11).

STEP 16.   Using *Thomas Register* or some other similar source, locate companies offering products or services related to your report project, and list information about them on your report worksheet.

Interviews

One of the easiest ways to gather information for a report is simply to talk to people who have the facts you need. Remember, however, to do as much of your own homework as you can on the report *before* you bother people with interviews. In the ball-park proposal, it would be wise to interview city officials who could give you advice on this project rather than trying to figure out bureaucratic channels and strategies yourself.

When you start thinking about interviews, remember to prepare for the interviews and to avoid asking questions that can be answered in any basic textbook on the subject: for example, asking the chief engineer of a nuclear power plant about the basic types of plant designs; such information is readily available in a variety of nonspecialist encyclopedias.

Before or during the interview, remember to do several things:

- Call ahead to schedule the interview date and time.
- Think carefully about the questions you'll ask, and list them on paper ahead of time. In the ball-park project, you might ask:

   What agencies or departments within city government must approve the plan?
   What characteristics should a report on this project have?
   At what point is the report reviewed by the council?
   What problems are there in asking to use city-owned land?
   What kinds of supporting evidence are city officials likely to expect?
   What typical snags are likely to occur, and how can we avoid them?

- At the beginning of an interview, introduce yourself, and explain the project you are working on or why you need the information you seek from the interviewee.
- Be ready with photocopying money if you are offered documents to copy.

STEP 17.   On your report worksheet, list the people or the occupations of the people you may need to interview, and describe the information you would want to get from them.

Surveys and Questionnaires

Another important source of information outside the library is the questionnaire or survey. The project to build baseball and softball parks on city-owned property might necessitate such a survey. Because this kind of information-gathering is so time-consuming, you must decide beforehand whether you really can get the necessary information from a survey and whether the same information has not already been published. The design of a questionnaire and the interpretation of the results are areas of great expertise, so you should seek the advice and help of people experienced in this sort of work. Still, a survey of local opinion might be just what you need. Some excerpts of questionnaires that could be used in the municipal ball-park proposal appear in Figure 9–14.

STEP 18.   On your worksheet describe the survey your report project might require and the information you'd want to get.

Governmental Sources

At practically all levels, government organizations can supply you with information through (1) interviews, (2) letters of inquiry, or (3) printed literature. If you are interested in geological information on your area, county and state agencies may have the reports you need. If you need statistics on transportation problems in your community, city and county agencies may have the reports you need. Most states have strong, active agricultural agencies, for example, that readily provide information on a wide variety of subjects.

City Government.   If, for example, you need information on the zoning restrictions associated with city-owned property proposed for the ball parks, you can find the related agencies in city government quickly from the phone book, which usually lists major agencies and departments and gives a number for general information. If you are writing to agencies in other cities, for example, to find out about their recycling programs, find those cities' phone books in the library, or check the *Municipal Yearbook* published each year by the International City Managers Association.

State Government.   If you think that agencies of state government may have the information you need, the phone book will again be the place to start. Otherwise,

Dichotomous Questions

I have played or currently play in city softball leagues	yes	no
Facilities in this city are inadequate for outdoor recreation	yes	no
More recreational areas are needed	yes	no
I use city parks at least once a month	yes	no
Overcrowding has kept me from using city parks	yes	no

Multiple-choice Questions

	Strongly Agree	Agree	No Opinion	Disagree	Strongly Disagree
I use city parks often (twice a month or more)	5	4	3	2	1
Our city needs more park facilities	5	4	3	2	1
Overcrowded conditions have kept me from using city parks more often	5	4	3	2	1
I support use of city property for the construction of additional recreational facilities	5	4	3	2	1

FIGURE 9–14.   Example of questionnaire formats

look for a book called *State Administrative Officials Classified by Functions,* a directory that is available in many libraries.

County Government.   If your report subject matter is more a county-level concern (roads, bridges, or lakes, for example), check phone books for the names of these county agencies also. No separate directory of county governments currently exists, but they are included in *The National Directory of Addresses and Phone Numbers,* available in many libraries.

STEP 19.   On your worksheet explain which federal, state, county, or city government agencies might have useful information for your report, and describe the information that you'd want to get from them.

Letters of Inquiry

Some of your sources of information may be in other cities or states, necessitating letters of inquiry that request the needed information. Chapter 11 covers this type of letter in detail, but here an example is given in Figure 9–15.

3500 West Anderson Lane #323
Luckenbach, Texas 78767
June 24, 19XX

Mr. Fred R. Smith, President
Seguin City League Softball Assoc.
13001 Vista Drive
Seguin, California 90034

Dear Mr. Smith:

From conversations I've had with people here in Luckenbach, I've learned that your association there in Seguin was quite successful in lobbying for additional park facilities. Because we are just beginning the same kind of effort here in Luckenbach, I thought it would be a good idea to write and ask you a few questions:

1. Did you conduct a survey of citizen opinion as a way of proving the need for additional facilities?
2. For any survey you did, what was your response rate? What percentage of support did you and/or the city council consider to be sufficient? What percentage did you actually get?
3. How did you approach city government? Which departments or officials did you approach first?
4. How difficult was it to work with city government? What problems did you encounter?
5. What form or kind of written document did you put together in order to promote your plan? How, when, and to whom did you present the report? What were the important areas of discussion

---

FIGURE 9–15. A letter of inquiry

in that report? Do you have a copy of the report that you can
send?
6. How was the project funded--entirely through city funds? Did
members of your association donate their time?

Your answers or opinions--and any other advice you can share--will
help us avoid many of the pitfalls that are no doubt common in
projects of this sort. Please let me know if there is any way that I
can make your job of answering these questions easier--for example,
by covering your copying and mailing costs or by discussing these
questions on the phone.

Again, thanks for any help and advice that you can send our way.

Sincerely,

Juan J. Juarez, Secretary
Luckenbach Municipal Softball Assoc.
4400 Anderson Lane #343
Luckenbach, Texas 78767
May 17, 19XX

FIGURE 9–15.   (cont.)

STEP 20.   Make a list of inquiry letters that you may have to write in order to get
certain kinds of information for your report. Follow the steps in Chapter 11 in
writing these letters.

A Note on Collecting Nonlibrary Information

Carefully plan how you will collect and save your nonlibrary information. Otherwise, you may end up with scraps of information scattered everywhere from your
house or apartment to your car to your briefcase or backpack. No matter how or
where you store this information—in an old suitcase, a special backpack, a large
envelope, a special notebook with pockets, or a reserved desk drawer—make sure
you have a central place to keep everything: photos, cassette tapes, diskettes, photocopied pages, pamphlets, and so on. As you collect nonlibrary information, remember also to record dates, full names and titles of people, precise locations, and
exact names of places and things.

EXERCISES

1. Select any three technical topics (using the list in Chapter 8 if necessary), and explain whether most of the information for each of the topics would come from library or nonlibrary sources.

2. Select any three technical topics (preferably from widely different fields) and do the following:
   a. Use the *Library of Congress Subject Headings* to make a list of the subject headings you'd use to locate books in the card catalog on each of those topics.
   b. Find a guide to the literature of the subject or field closely related to each of those topics.
   c. Find a specialized periodical index you'd use to locate articles for each of the topics.
   d. Find a specialized encyclopedia, dictionary, and handbook for each of those topics.
   e. Locate at least two companies and two associations involved in some way with each of the topics.
   f. List the titles of trade magazines involved in some way with each of the topics.
   g. Locate at least two government documents on each of the topics you've selected.

3. Select one of the following report projects, and list the nonlibrary sources of information that would be necessary in order to do the project. Also, explain what information you'd expect to get from each of the necessary sources.

Construction of city bike lanes	Plan to begin recycling municipal solid
Proposal to close off a city block for	waste
an annual fair	Plan to use robots in a company's
Changing zoning ordinances in a	manufacturing process
certain area	Plan to institute a variety of special
Study on ways citizens can reduce	facilities and services for the elderly
energy consumption	

4. For the project that you selected in exercise 3, list the specific site inspections, measurements, and calculations that would be necessary. If the project that you selected in exercise 3 does not require this nonlibrary information, choose another one from exercise 3 that does.

5. For the project that you selected in exercise 3, list the specific products for which you'd need to consult business literature. (Choose another report project in exercise 3 to do this exercise if necessary.) Use *Thomas Register* to locate information on companies that manufacture those products, and make a list of them.

6. For the project that you selected in exercise 3, list the people whom you'd need to interview and describe their positions or background. (Choose another report project from exercise 3 if necessary.) Now, make a list of the specific questions that you'd ask one of these individuals.

7. For the report project that you selected in exercise 3, or some other project requiring a survey, explain the nature of the survey needed and the reasons for conducting it. Make a list of the questions that you'd want to include.

8. For the report project that you selected in exercise 3, or some project requiring inquiry letters, make a list of and describe the letters of inquiry that you'd need to write. Next, make a list of the questions that you'd ask in one of these letters.

CHAPTER 10

Developing Reports: Notes, Drafts, and Final Packaging

Chapter Objectives
The Traditional Note-Taking System
  Developing the Rough Outline
  Information on the Bibliography Cards
  Information on the Notecards
  Methods of Recording Information on
    Notecards
  Updating the Outline
  Final Stages in the Note-Taking
    Process
  Other Systems of Note Taking
Rough Drafting
  Preparations
  Sample Rough Draft with Notecards

Revising
  Planning a Revision Strategy
  Identifying Potential Problem Areas
  Grouping the Problem Categories
  Problem-Spotting Strategies
Final Packaging of the Report
  Typing the Final Copy
  Taping in Illustrations
  Proofreading the Final Typed Copy
  Making a Good Photocopy
  Binding the Report
  Attaching the Cover Label
Exercises

─────────────── *Chapter Objectives* ───────────────

After you read this chapter, study the examples, and work the steps, you should be able to:

- List the main steps in the traditional note-taking system.
- Identify common problems in the use of direct quotations.
- List reasons for using paraphrases and summaries as opposed to direct quotations.
- Document any borrowed information correctly.
- Define plagiarism.
- Explain the strategy for rough drafting reports.
- Identify problems in different categories in the revising stage.
- Use one or more strategies for spotting problems in report drafts.
- Produce a professional-looking final report using the appropriate final-packaging techniques.

When you've located the right sources of information for your report, it's time to start gathering the right information from them and developing that into a report. In other words, it's time to start reading, summarizing, paraphrasing, interviewing, measuring, calculating, and developing information any other way your report project requires. The technical report may be one of the largest writing projects that you've ever tackled: you may wonder how you are going to do all that reading and remember all that information. Concerning the reading, here are several suggestions:

- Develop as specific an *outline* as you can: it shows you what information you must gather and, more importantly, what information you can ignore.
- Use the *indexes, tables of contents,* and *headings* within chapters to read books selectively for just the information you need.
- Divide your work into manageable, *hour-long chunks* (make steady progress rather than relying on big blocks of weekend or vacation time).

As for remembering the information you gather for your report, the most practical suggestion is to use some form of note taking. *Note taking* refers to *any* system for collecting and storing information until you can use it in the report. Note taking involves the skills of summarizing, paraphrasing, or quoting. A good system of note taking is one that enables you to gather a large amount of information over a long period of time and to be able to use that information *without having forgotten it or lost it in the meantime.*

The Traditional Note-Taking Process

In the traditional system of taking notes for a long report, you

1. Develop a rough outline.
2. Do any preliminary reading necessary to construct a rough outline.
3. Locate your information sources, and make bibliography cards for each source.

4. Take the actual notes on index cards.
5. Label each notecard according to its place in the outline.
6. Provide bibliographic information on each notecard.
7. Change or add extra detail to the outline as the note-taking process continues.
8. Check off the areas of the outline for which sufficient notes have been taken.

When you have taken sufficient notes to cover all parts of an outline, you transcribe the information from the notecards into a rough draft, filling in details, adding transitions, and providing your own acquired understanding of the subject as you write. Naturally, you may discover gaps in your notes and have to go back and take more notes.

Developing the Rough Outline

As Chapter 8 on outlining emphasizes, you must have a working outline *before* you begin gathering information. The rough outline shows you which specific topics to gather information on and which ones to ignore. Think of the outline as a series of questions, as indicated in Figure 10–1.

If you don't have a good, specific outline, the sky is the limit on how many notes you can take. Think of the outline as a set of boxes that you fill up with the information you collect as you do your research for the report, a process illustrated in Figure 10–2.

STEP 1.   If you have not already done so, use the suggestions here or the steps in Chapter 8 on outlining to create as detailed a rough outline of your report project as you can.

Information on the Bibliography Cards

On the bibliography cards you should record information that enables you or your readers to locate the books, articles, reports, and other sources. Remember that you'll use this information to create the bibliography or list of references for your report. Chapter 9 contains examples of bibliography cards for books, magazine articles, encyclopedias, and government documents; Appendix A contains details on the information to record on many different types of sources, but remember these general guidelines:

• For books, record the facts of publication: the city of publication, the publisher, and the date of publication.
• For magazines, record the title of the magazine, the date of issue of the specific magazine, and the beginning and ending page numbers of the article.
• For encyclopedia articles, record the edition number and date of the encyclopedia, and look up the authors' initials.
• For government documents, disregard the authors' names, use the department, administration, or agency name as the author, and copy the cataloging number.
• For any private sources of information you use, for example, interviews or letters, record the date of the communication, the source's full name, title, and organization with which he or she is affiliated.

Rough Outline for a Report on Light-Water Nuclear Reactors	Questions Generated by the Outline

I. Pressurized-Water Reactors
   A. Major Components
   B. Basic Operation
	What are the main differences? What are the main components? What are the materials? Design? Dimensions? How many are in operation? Where? Who designed them?

II. Boiling-Water Reactors
   A. Major Components
   B. Basic Operation
	How do they differ from PWRs? What are the main components? What are the materials? Design? Dimensions? Designers? Where used? How many?

III. Safety Measures
   A. Pressurized-Water Reactor
   B. Boiling-Water Reactors
   C. Role of the Nuclear Regulatory Commission
	What are the chief dangers? What are the dangers and safety measures associated with PWRs? What are the dangers and safety measures associated with BWRs? How does the NRC regulate nuclear power plants? What standards does it enforce? How?

IV. Economic Aspects of Light-Water Reactors
   A. Construction Costs
   B. Operation and Maintenance Costs
   C. Operating Capacity
	What are the construction, operation, maintenance, and fuel costs? What about the availability of fuel? How do these costs compare to output? How do the PWR and the BWR compare in terms of costs and output? How much electricity can a LWR generate at full capacity?

FIGURE 10–1. Viewing an outline as a series of questions

Information on the Notecards

In the traditional note-taking system, a notecard typically looks like the example in Figure 10–3, which has the following features:

• A word, phrase, or number (top right) that indicates where it fits into the outline (the locator).

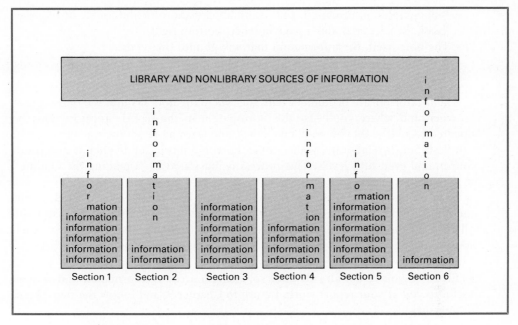

FIGURE 10–2. Gathering information and taking notes: gather information from the various sources until all the boxes are filled

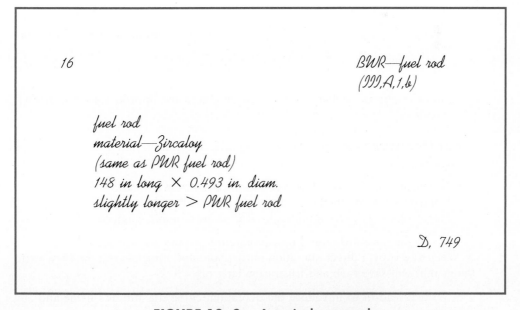

FIGURE 10–3. A typical notecard

- Bibliographic information: that is, an abbreviation for the source of the note (book, article, etc.) and a page number (bottom right).
- The note itself, the information that will go into the report.
- A number that indicates the notecard's place in the final arrangement of all the notecards (top left).

The locator phrase or number tells you where the note fits into the outline, that is, when and where you'll use this information in the report. Locators must be updated regularly. As you read, take notes, and learn more about your subject, you can flesh out, or elaborate, your outline more and more, subdividing it into third, fourth, and even fifth levels. This process is illustrated in "Updating the Outline" in Chapter 8.

Each notecard must also contain bibliographic information, those details about the source of the note: the author, title, page number, and so on. Rather than write all such information on each notecard, use abbreviations: assign a letter to each source, and keep track of the sources on bibliography cards, as shown earlier.

STEP 2.   If you've not already done so, locate sources of information that may be useful to you in your report work. Return to Chapter 9, and follow the steps there, if necessary.

Methods of Recording Information on Notecards

The actual information that you record on the index card is rather small: a few statistics or a sentence or two, and not much else. You take such small bits of information to make it easier to shuffle your notecards into the sequence in which you'll use them in writing the rough draft. There are three ways of recording the information on notecards:

- *Directly quoting* it, copying the information directly from the source word-for-word
- *Paraphrasing* it, retaining the full detail of the information but in your own words
- *Summarizing* it, condensing the main points in the information in your own words

Direct Quotation.   In most technical reports, direct quotation is needed only for the following situations:

- Statements by important or well-known authorities or leaders
- Controversial statements you do not want attributed to you
- Statements expressed in unusual, vivid, or memorable language

Look at the notecard with direct quotation in Figure 10–4.

When you copy a direct quotation onto a notecard, remember to do a few extra things that will save time and frustration later on:

- Write a lead-in to introduce the quotation, citing the author's name and any other important information about the author.

Myers, author of The Nuclear Power Debate *and somewhat of a supporter of nuclear, emphs heavy inspect and penalties:*

During the period between July 1, 1975 and September 30, 1976 the NRC listed 1,611 items of noncompliance. Only six of these were considered serious violations, 923 were classified as infractions, and 682 were noted as deficiencies. The NRC issued fines to ten utilities totaling $172,250 between July 1, 1975 and December 15, 1976. NRC officials report that the limited use of fines and the efforts to get industry to regulate itself have worked. "By and large," one NRC official told IRRC, I think our enforcement program is working."

H, 46

FIGURE 10—4. Original passage and notecard with direct quotation

Desaix Myers III. *The Nuclear Power Debate.* (New York: Praeger, 1977), 46. Quoted by permission of Praeger Publishers.

- Write a brief explanation, interpretation, or comment on the quotation you've just copied.

There are essentially two types of direct quotation: *block* quotations and *running* quotations. Figure 10–5 contains an example of a block quotation—any quotation over three lines long, which is indented.

Running quotations are direct quotations that are trimmed down and worked into the regular sentences of a report. In Figure 10–6 notice how much smoother and more efficient the running quotation is after revision of the paragraph.

Guide for Using Direct Quotations

When you use direct quotations in your report, keep these guidelines in mind.

- Never use free-floating quotations in reports. Always attribute direct quotations; that is, explain who made the quoted statement. Notice how this is done in Figure 10–6.

- Always provide adequate introduction for direct quotations and explain their meaning and importance to your readers. Notice how the block quotation in Figure 10-5 (a) prepares the reader for the quotation, and, afterwards, (b) provides interpretive comment, on the meaning of the word *stigma* in particular.

In Myers's view, the nuclear power industry has every reason to comply with the NRC's regulations to the very letter:

> The NRC issues an order to shut down or imposes civil fines only after repeated violations have indicated what the NRC considers "a pattern of noncompliance." The NRC argues that, particularly with power plants, civil penalties are unnecessary for the most part. "The greatest penalty," one official said, "is to require the plant to shut down, forcing it to buy replacement power (often at a cost of $100,000 to $200,000 per day) elsewhere. A civil penalty's largest cost--the NRC is limited to a $5,000-per-violation ceiling per 30 days--is the stigma attached to it."

The "stigma" refers to the fact that, once a nuclear power plant is fined, it will likely be the target of public concern and even more stringent and frequent NRC inspection.

FIGURE 10–5. Block quotation and running quotations

Ineffective Direct Quotation

There are two types of light water reactors: the pressurized-water reactor and the boiling-water reactor. "LWRs of both types convert heat to electricity with an efficiency of about 32 percent—significantly less than the best fossil-fueled plants, although about equal to the national average for all thermal electricity generation." (13:438). As for harnessing the energy potential of uranium, LWRs are estimated to average only between 0.5 and 1.0 percent.

Revision with Running Quotation

There are two types of light water reactors: the pressurized-water reactor and the boiling-water reactor. According to Paul Ehrlich, who has been a consistent critic of nuclear power, both these types of LWRs "convert heat to electricity with an efficiency of about 32 percent—significantly less than the best fossil-fueled plants, although about equal to the national average for all thermal electricity generation." (13:438). As for harnessing the energy potential of uranium, LWRs are estimated to average only between 0.5 and 1.0 percent.

FIGURE 10–6. An ineffective block quotation revised as a running quotation

• Use indented, or block, quotations whenever a direct quotation goes over three lines long. With any lengthy quotation, make sure that it is important enough to merit direct quotation.

• Whenever possible, trim the quotation so that it will fit into your own writing. Notice how the words that are less important are omitted in Figure 10–6.

• Punctuate direct quotations correctly. Rules for punctuating direct quotations are explained in Appendix D. Here are some examples of the most common ways to punctuate quotations:

> According to Desaix Myers in his *The Nuclear Power Debate*, "The NRC has nearly 400 staff members assigned to inspect nuclear plants now operating or under construction.
>
> NRC officials also inspect nuclear power plants "an average of 50 times during the period before operation" when they are under construction and "a minimum of four times a year" after the plants go into operation.
>
> Myers points out that standardization of nuclear power plant design is an important next step: "The NRC estimates that by standardizing plants . . . , the time between a decision to go nuclear and start-up of plant operations can be reduced from 11 to 6 years."

• Use ellipses to shorten direct quotations. When you do, however, make sure that the resulting quotation reads well. Look at the an example passage in Figure 10–7. The three dots, or ellipses, show that words are omitted from the sentence. The brackets "[ ]" indicate changes made by the writer using the quotation so that it would read well and make sense.

Ehrlich, Ehrlich, and Holdren argue that a mistaken notion of the breeder reactor has been promoted in the United States:

> [Although breeder reactors] can harness so much more of the potential energy in uranium and thorium than nonbreeders[, i]t is worth emphasizing that a breeder does not get something for nothing. . . .*

The authors go on to argue that breeder reactors are ...

Excerpted from Ecoscience: Population, Resources, and Environment by Paul R. Ehrlich et al. Copyright © 1971, 1972 W. H. Freeman and Company. Reprinted with permission.

FIGURE 10–7. **Using ellipses in direct quotations**

• Use direct quotations only when necessary: if the passage doesn't fit one of the reasons for direct quotation cited at the beginning of this section, paraphrase or summarize it instead.

Paraphrasing.   In technical-report writing, usually the better approach to note taking is to paraphrase. When you paraphrase, you convey the information fact-by-fact, idea-by-idea, and point-by-point in your own words. The writer of the original passage ought to be able to read your paraphrase and say that it is precisely what she or he had meant. Some examples of paraphrased notecards appear in Figure 10–8.

BWR--fuel assembly
(999,A,1,3)

fuel assembly—63 f rods spaced, supported in a sq (8 × 8)
   arrangement by upper + lower plate
      3 kinds: (a) tie rods; (b) water rod; (c) stand f rods
      3d, 6th f rods on a bundle's outer edge act as tie rods
      the 8 tie rods screw into castg of lower tie plate water
      rod: acts as spacer support rod, as source of moderator
      material close to the center of f bundle

K, 2001

BWR--fuel assem
(999,A,1,3)

fuel channel—enclosure for f bundle; f bundle + f channel
   make up fuel assem is a tube with a square shape, made of
   Zircaloy dimensions: 5.518 in. × 5.518 in. × 166.9 in.
   function: channel core coolt thru f bundle and guide control
   rods

K, 2001

FIGURE 10–8.   Paraphrased notecards

Paraphrases are necessary and preferable for a number of reasons:

- You paraphrase because the content of the passage is so important to your report that you need every bit of it.
- When you paraphrase, you adjust the wording of the original to meet the needs of your audience, the purpose of your report, and your own writing style. In other words, you translate other writers' material into your own.
- A report of mostly direct quotations would be hard to read.
- Readers tend to skip over direct quotations, particularly long ones.
- One final reason for paraphrasing: you are actually writing bits of the rough draft of your report as you paraphrase.

Figure 10–9 contains an example of an original passage and its paraphrases, with the unique wording of the original (which must be changed in the paraphrase) underlined.

Original Passage

About a third of light-water reactors <u>operating or under construction</u> in the United States are boiling-water reactors. <u>The distinguishing characteristic</u> of a BWR is that the reactor vessel <u>itself serves as the boiler</u> of the nuclear steam supply system. This vessel is <u>by far the major</u> component in the reactor building, and the steam it <u>produces passes directly</u> to the turbogenerator. The reactor building <u>also contains</u> emergency core cooling equipment, <u>a major part of which</u> is the pressure suppression pool which is <u>an integral part of the containment structure</u>. ... Earlier BWRs utilized a <u>somewhat different</u> containment and pressure suppression system. <u>All the commercial BWRs sold</u> in the United States have been designed and built by General Electric.

Several types of reactors that use boiling water in pressure tubes <u>have been considered, designed, or built</u>. In a sense, <u>they are similar</u> to the CANDU which uses pressure tubes and separates the coolant and moderator. The CANDU <u>itself can be designed to use</u> boiling light water as its coolant. The British steam-generating heavy-water reactor <u>has such a system</u>. Finally, <u>the principal reactor type now being constructed</u>

(continued)

FIGURE 10–9. Avoiding the original wording in paraphrases

in the Soviet Union uses a boiling-water pressure tube design, but with carbon moderator.

Anthony V. Nero, A Guidebook to Nuclear Reactors (Berkeley: Univ. of California Press, 1979), 232. © 1979 The Regents of the University of California.

Paraphrased Version

According to Anthony V. Nero in A Guidebook to Nuclear Reactors, boiling-water reactors, either completed or constructed, make up about one-third of the light-water reactors in the United States. The most important design feature of the BWR is that the reactor vessel itself acts as the nuclear steam supply system. The steam this important component generates goes directly to the turbogenerator. Important too in this design is the emergency core cooling equipment, which is housed with the reactor vessel in the reactor building. One of the main components of this equipment is the pressure suppression pool. The containment and pressure suppression system currently used in BWRs has evolved since the early BWR designs. General Electric is the sole designer and builder of these BWRs in the United States.

The different kinds of reactors that use boiling water in pressure tubes are similar to the CANDU, which separates coolant and moderator and uses pressure tubes also. CANDU can also use boiling light water as a coolant. The British have designed a reactor-generated steam from heavy water that uses just such a system. Also, the Soviets have developed and are now building as their main type of reactor a boiling-water pressure tube design that uses carbon as the moderator. (12:232)*

*Source 12 in "Literature Cited" would be Nero's *A Guidebook to Nuclear Reactors*.

FIGURE 10–9. (cont.)

Guide for Writing and Using Paraphrases

Here are some guidelines to remember when paraphrasing:

- In most cases, paraphrase rather than use direct quotation.
- Avoid the distinctive wording of the original passage.

- Do not interpret, criticize, or select from the original passage.
- Include bibliographic information on the author, source, and page numbers.
- In the rough draft cite the author's name and other important details about her or him just as you would if you were quoting directly. In Figure 10–9, notice how the paraphrased author's name is given early.
- Refer to the paraphrased author in such a way to make it clear where the paraphrase begins and ends. (See Figure 10–9.)
- Document a paraphrase just as you would a direct quotation. Mark the area of the paraphrase by citing the paraphrased author's name at the beginning of the paraphrase and by inserting a footnote or parenthetical reference at the end.

Summary.   Summaries are usually much shorter than their originals. A summary concentrates on only those points or ideas in a passage that are important. Unlike in a paraphrase, the information in a summary can be rearranged. Here is a passage from which summaries in Figure 10–10 have been developed:

Numerous systems are available for controlling abnormalities [in boiling-water reactors]. In the event that control rods cannot be inserted, liquid neutron absorber (containing a boron compound) may be injected into the reactor to shut down the chain reaction. Heat removal systems are available for cooling the core in the event the drywell is isolated from the main cooling systems. Closely related to the heat-removal systems are injection systems for coping with decreases in coolant inventory.

Both abnormalities associated with the turbine system and actual loss of coolant accidents can lead to closing of the steam and feedwater lines, effectively isolating the reactor vessel within the drywell. Whenever the vessel is isolated, and indeed whenever feedwater is lost, a reactor core isolation cooling system is available to maintain coolant inventory by pumping water into the reactor via connections in the pressure vessel head. This system operates at normal pressures and initially draws water from tanks that store condensate from the turbine, from condensate from the residual heat removal [RHR] system, or if necessary, from the suppression pool.

(continued)

FIGURE 10–10.   Passage to be summarized

A network of systems performs specific ECC [emergency core cooling] functions to cope with LOCAs [loss-of-coolant accidents]. (See Figure 10–10a.) These all depend on signals indicating low water level in the pressure vessel or high pressure in the drywell, or both.

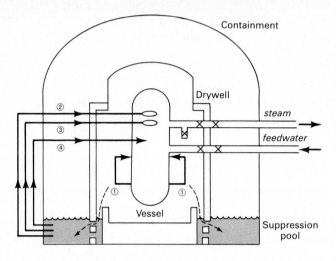

Emergency core cooling functions:
   ① Overpressure injection into pressure suppression pool
   ② High-pressure core spray
   ③ Low-pressure core spray
   ④ Low-pressure coolant injection
  (X = valves)

Figure 10–10a.   BWR emergency core cooling systems

The systems include low-pressure injection, utilization of the RHR system, and high- and low-pressure core spray systems. The high-pressure core spray is intended to lower the pressure within the pressure vessel and provide makeup water in the event of a LOCA. In the event the core is uncovered, the spray can directly cool the fuel assemblies. Water is taken from the condensate tanks and from the suppression pool. On the other hand, should it become necessary to use low-pressure systems, the vessel must be depressurized. This can be accomplished by opening relief valves to blow down the vessel contents into the drywell (and hence the suppression pool). Once this

FIGURE 10–10.   **(cont.)**

is done, the low-pressure core spray may be used to cool the fuel assemblies (drawing water from the suppression pool) or RHR low-pressure injection (again from the suppression pool) may be initiated, or both. The RHR system may also be used simply to cool the suppression pool. (Two other functions of the RHR are to provide decay heat removal under ordinary shutdown conditions and, when necessary, to supplement the cooling system for the spent fuel pool and the upper containment pool.)

Anthony V. Nero, A Guidebook to Nuclear Reactors (Berkeley: Univ. of California Press, 1979), 104–7. © 1979 The Regents of the University of California.

FIGURE 10–10. (cont.)

Sentence-length Summaries. Often summaries are only a sentence long. To create sentence-length summaries, use one or a combination of the following methods:

• Locate a sentence or two in the original passage that summarizes the information that you want, and simply rewrite it in your own words. Find the sentence in the third paragraph in Figure 10–10 that is the basis for this summary:

BWR—safety sys
(IV,B,2)

The systems that perform emergency core cooling functions in loss-of-coolant accidents include low-pressure injection, utilization of the RHR system, and high- and low-pressure core spray systems.

I, 104

• If no individual sentence will work, locate several sentences that contain the right information, and combine them. (This summary sentence is built from paragraphs 1 and 2 of Figure 10–10.)

BWR—safety sys
(IV,B,2)

In case of problems with control rods or loss of coolant, BWRs use an absorber to stop the reaction or emergency systems to replenish and maintain coolant around the reactor core, respectively.

I, 104–7

• Sometimes, the summary sentence is like a new sentence, scarcely resembling any in the original. Here is a different summary sentence on the passage; notice how new it seems:

BWR—safety sys
(IV,B,2)

If the control rods malfunction, a substance can be introduced to shut down the reaction altogether, and if water is prevented from reaching the reactor core, BWRs are equipped with backup sources of coolant that can be sprayed or injected into the pressure vessel.

I, 104–7

Extended Summaries.   A summary can be longer than a single sentence because of the important information contained in the original passage. (Remember, however, that a paraphrase is a point-by-point recap of the original, whereas the summary is a selection, reordering, and condensation of the original.) Here's an extended summary of the passage on BWR emergency safety systems in Figure 10–10:

BWR-safety sys
(IV.B.2)

Boiling-water reactors use numerous systems to control abnormalities in reactor operations. If a problem with control rods occurs, a liquid neutron absorber can be injected to halt the chain reaction. If coolant is cut off from the reactor core, a reactor core isolation cooling system can maintain coolant inventory by pumping water from various storage areas. This system includes low-pressure injection, the residual heat removal system, and the high- and low-pressure core spray systems. The water supply for these various emergency systems ultimately comes from the suppression pool.

J, 104-107

Guide for Using Summaries

Whenever you summarize, you must handle the resulting summary the same way you would a direct quotation or paraphrase.

- Cite the name of the author and other important information about that author.
- Document that summary using whichever system is appropriate for your report.
- If it is an extended summary, make it clear where that summary begins and ends, for example, by referring to the author's name at the beginning and placing a footnote or parenthetical reference at the end.

STEP 3.   With the note-taking system just described, take at least 10 notes using the following steps: (a) find information that you want to summarize, paraphrase, or directly quote; (b) take each note on a separate index card; (c) key each notecard to your outline; and (d) include bibliographic information on each card.

Plagiarism.   If you follow the guidelines presented thus far, *plagiarism* should not be a problem at all, but make sure you understand what it is. Plagiarism refers to two kinds of theft:

- Plagiarism is the practice—whether deliberate or not—in which a writer borrows other people's facts, ideas, or concepts and presents them as if they were her or his own.
- Plagiarism is also the practice—again whether deliberate or not—in which a writer uses other writers' exact words without quotation marks.
- In all cases, plagiarism is the lack of proper documentation: documentation refers to *any* system of footnoting or reference that indicates the author and source of the borrowed information.

Reports with plagiarized information are often easy to spot for several reasons:

- A reader may recognize the ideas or facts in the report as those of someone else. An expert in a field of knowledge can spot this theft of information right away.
- A reader may realize that the report writer could not possibly have developed certain information in the report. If a writer who is at the beginning of his studies sounds like an advanced physicist, something is fishy.
- Most readers can also spot a sudden change in the style or tone of the language of a report. Most people's writing style is as readily identifiable as their voices over the telephone.

Plagiarism is bad business: the plagiarizer can fail an academic course or lose his or her reputation among business and professional associates. It only takes simple documentation to transform a report with plagiarized material in it into one with legally borrowed material. Appendix A explains these procedures in detail.

Updating the Outline

As you take notes, you must regularly update the locators on all your notecards because as you read, take notes, and learn more about your technical subject, your outline may either change or become more specific. Imagine that you started with the excerpt in Figure 10–11 of a rough outline and had the notecards in that figure. As you took these notecards, you would update your outline periodically; at the end, the outline might look like the one in Figure 10–12.

Notice that all five of the notecards in Figure 10–11 are about "IV. B. Boiling-Water Reactor Safety Systems." Notecard 1 divides this safety system into the drywell and the emergency core cooling systems. This division produces *1* and *2* under *B.* Notecards 3 through 5, about the subsystems making up the emergency systems, produce *a, b,* and *c* under *2.*

Rough-Sketch Outline

IV. Safety Measures
    A. Pressurized-Water Reactor Safety Measures
    B. Boiling-Water Reactor Safety Systems
    C. Role of the Nuclear Regulatory Commission

Corresponding Notecards

> 1
>
> *BWR—safety sys (IV,B)*
>
> *safety sys incl control rods, containmt bldg, resid heat removl sys*
> *these work like ones in PWR*
> *unique to BWR: drywell, emergency core coolg sys*
>
> *I, 100*

> 2
>
> *BWR—safety sys (IV,B)*
>
> *drywell—encloses react vess + assoc equip (includes recirc sys, press relief valves on main steam lines)*
>
> *I, 100*

(continued)

FIGURE 10–11. Notecards and the corresponding outline before updating

3
                                                 BWR—safety sys
                                               (IV,B)

emergency core coolg sys—handles loss-of-coolt accidents;
   includes reactor core iso sys, hi-press core spray sys, lo-
   press core spray sys (figure for this, p. 106)

                                           I, 105–6

4
                                               BWR—safety sys
                                               (IV,B)

react core iso coolg sys: if loss-of-coolt accidt (causg closing of
   steam lines, feedwtr lines to react vessel), RCICS activated
   (maintains coolt inventory by pumpg water to reactor via
   connex in press vess head

                                           I, 104

5
                                               BWR—safety sys
                                               (IV,B)

hi-press core spray: lowers press w/in press vessel, provides
   suppl water in loss-of-coolt accidt.

   with uncovered cores, spray directly cools fuel assemblies
   (wtr fr condensed wtr storage tanks + suppress pool)

                                           I, 104

FIGURE 10–11. (cont.)

Revised Outline

IV. Safety Measures
    A. Pressurized-Water Reactor Safety Measures
    B. Boiling-Water Reactor Safety Systems
        1. The drywell
        2. Emergency core-cooling systems
            a. Reactor core isolation cooling system
            b. High-pressure core spray

FIGURE 10–12. Updated outline

If you had taken these notes and updated your outline, you would revise the locators on the individual notecards like this:

Notecard No.	Original Locators	Updated Locators	Alternate Locators
1	IV. B	same	Safety/Boil.Wtr.React.
2	IV. B	IV. B. 1	Safety/BWR/drywell
3	IV. B	IV. B. 2	Safety/BWR/Em.Cor.Cool.
4	IV. B	IV. B. 2. a	Saf./BWR/Em.Cor.Cool/ React.Cor.Cool.
5	IV. B	IV. B. 2. b	Saf./BWR/Em.Cor.Cool./ Hi.Pres.Cor.Spray

Remember that if you don't like the number combinations as locators, you can substitute short phrases, as is shown in the alternate locators in the preceding example.

STEP 4. Review the notes you took in step 3, compare them to your report outline, and update your outline as necessary.

Final Stages in the Note-Taking Process

As you take notes, check off sections of your outline for which you have gathered sufficient information, as in the outline excerpt in Figure 10–13. In this example the writer has taken sufficient notes for much of IV. B. but still needs information for the rest of the outline.

III. Boiling-Water Reactors
    A. Description of the Basic Components
        1. Core
            a. Core
            b. Fuel
            c. Fuel rod
            d. Fuel assembly
        2. Control rods
        3. Core shrouds and reactor vessel
        4. Recirculation system
        5. Steam separators
        6. Steam dryers
    B. Production of Electricity
        1. Circulating water
        2. Separating steam
        3. Drying the steam
        4. Producing electricity
IV. Safety Measures
    A. Pressurized Water Reactor Safety Measures
        1. Residual heat removal system
        2. Emergency core cooling systems
            a. Passive system
            b. Low-pressure injection systems
            c. High-pressure injection systems
        3. Containment building
    B. Boiling Water Reactor Safety Systems
        1. The drywell
        2. Emergency core cooling systems
            a. Reactor core isolation cooling system
            b. High-pressure core spray
            c. Low-pressure core spray
    C. Role of the Nuclear Regulatory Commission

V. Economic Aspects of Light-Water Reactors
    A. Busbar Cost
        1. Construction costs
        2. Operation and maintenance costs
        3. Fuel costs
    B. Operating Capacity
        1. Availability factor
        2. Capacity factor

FIGURE 10—13. An outline for which note taking is partially complete

STEP 5.   Review the notes you've taken to see whether you can cross off any items in your outline. Once you've done this, return to step 3, and repeat the process until you've gathered enough information.

In the final step in note taking, you arrange the notecards in the order that you'll use them as you write the rough draft. Read through your cards several times to make sure that the sequence is right and that there are no gaps in the information you've gathered. When you're sure that the order is correct, write sequence numbers on each of the cards to preserve the order (see the sequence numbers on the note-cards in Figures 10–11 and 10–15). With the notecards in the right order and numbered, you are ready to write the first draft, which is discussed in the section in this chapter on "Rough Drafting."

STEP 6.   Put the notes that you've taken in the preceding steps into a proper sequence, and number them.

Other Systems of Note Taking

There are plenty of other ways to take notes. The main point of any form of note taking, of course, is to make your report work easier and less time-consuming. You may prefer some other note-taking system because of your own work style or because of your report project. Or, you may end up using some other system in combination with the traditional one. *Any* system that enables you to get your work done efficiently is a good one.

• *Mental note taking.* With short reports it is possible to remember all the information and not write any of it down. But few of us are able to remember all of the information for long, highly technical reports.

• *Bookmarks.* If you use only a few articles or books, you can mark the important passages with slips of paper and write the rough draft with them. If you have many books and articles, this approach can get to be quite chaotic.

• *Photocopying.* You can also photocopy everything you think you need in your report. With the photocopied pages you highlight the important passages or cut out the important passages and paste them on notecards. Two problems with this approach are that (a) you may photocopy many unnecessary pages and waste money and (b) you still have the job of paraphrasing and summarizing ahead of you. Still, this is a system some report writers use occasionally to supplement their more traditional note-taking procedures.

• *Exploratory drafts.* If you are already familiar with your report subject, you can try writing a rough skeletal draft to discover what information you need. You may discover that all you lack is specific names, statistics, or terminology. You can take notes and plug the information into the draft (especially if you have computerized word processing). Writing the exploratory draft shows you what you know and don't know.

• *Note taking by the source.* If you have only a few sources, you can also use one other fairly common system of note taking:

1. You take notes from individual sources onto long sheets of paper rather than onto notecards.
2. You take all the information you need from the source onto as many sheets of paper as necessary; you don't split it up into bits of information on separate notecards.
3. At the top of each notesheet you give full bibliographic information on the book or article.
4. Throughout each notesheet you indicate the exact pages the information comes from.
5. Also, you label these pages of notes with locators, the letter-number combinations from the outline.
6. You mark off sections of the outline as you gather sufficient information for them.
7. In some cases, you can cut up these full-page notes and actually handle them as if they were notecards.

Figure 10–14 contains a note sheet using this approach.

In this system, the source (book, article, report, etc.) is indicated at the top of the page; the page numbers are indicated down the right margin in parentheses; and the sheet of notes is keyed to the outline down the left margin in parentheses.

When you've gathered enough information and know your report subject well enough, it's time for the last three major steps in writing a technical report: writing the rough draft, revising and editing, and doing the final packaging.

Rough Drafting

Writing a rough draft, at its simplest, is like copying your notecards onto regular sheets of paper: more specifically, like copying the information from your notes, phrasing it in complete sentences, and filling in the gaps with transitions and with your own understanding of the subject. If you have taken as complete a set of notes as you can, and if you have paraphrased and summarized most of them, your rough drafting may go rapidly.

Preparations

Here are some rather mechanical matters to keep in mind as you start the rough draft:

- Use pencils (instead of pens) to make corrections easier.
- Write on only one side of the paper so that you can cut and paste, if necessary.
- Skip every other line in your rough draft to make insertions or revisions easier.
- Insert headings *as* you write rather than afterwards (see Chapter 6 if you need information on headings).
- Write your first draft rapidly: don't worry about getting every word and comma exactly right this time.

Outline Area	Source: J	Pages
	1. <u>BWR core</u>—large nbr of fuel assembls	(94)
	ea one a sq array 7 × 7 or 8 × 8	
III. A. 1.	fuel pin: active length 12 ft	
	contains water rod (providg moderator w/	
	in f bundles)	(95)
	large BWR contains 764 assems w	
III. A. 2.	40-50,000 f rods + about 180 tons of	
	uran. diox	
	2. <u>reactor vessel</u>—contains core and assoc	(99-100)
	equip, also control rods above core, steam	
	separators/dryers	
	3. <u>vessel dimensions:</u> 72 ft high, 21 ft	
	diam	(100)
	material: carbon steel, 6-7 in. thick clad w	
	1/8 in. stainls steel	
III. A. 3.	withstands 1000 psi at operatg temps	
	4. <u>coolant</u>—recirculates w/in react vessel	(101)
	of BWR	
	no external loop	
IV. B. 2.–3.	jet pumps in annulus	
	pump: reactor inlet nozzles	

FIGURE 10–14. Sample notesheet: taking notes by the source

- If you can't get started, find another section of your report to begin with.
- If you get stuck, start on another section and come back later.
- If you don't particularly like how a section is sounding, go ahead and keep writing. Consider it a rehearsal.
- Use a typewriter, if possible, to get a sense of how your report will look in its finished form and to make revising easier. Again, don't worry about grammar or typos; type rapidly.

Sample Rough Draft with Notecards

An excerpt from a report draft with the corresponding notecards appears in Figure 10–15. Notice how much discussion the writer has put into the paragraphs without the aid of notecards.

Outline Excerpt

  I. Introduction

 II. Amount of Oil Drilled

III. The Condeep Drilling Platform
   A. The Hull
   B. The Deck

IV. The Effects of Spilled Oil on Marine Organisms
   A. Impact on Zooplankton
   B. Impact on Fish
   C. Impact on Marine Birds
   D. Impact on Marine Mammals

 V. Procedure in Cleaning Up Offshore Spills
   A. Preliminary Inspection of ...

Notecards

8   III. drillg pltfm: intro

movement to drill Outer Contl. Shelf
water depths in this region—2-3,000 ft.
convention. steel-jacket platform too expensive

FIGURE 10–15   Outline, notecards, and rough-draft excerpt

9   *III. drillg pltfm: ballast tanks*

water up to 1000 ft (twice ht. of Wash. Monument)
submersibles designed for waters up to 600 ft or more
massive buoyant base or hull flooded after the unit is stationed
water pumped out & replaced w/ oil as need. from well or
  satellite wells

                                    Earney, pp. 124-31

---

10   *III. drillg pltfm: ballast tanks*

usually have base casted in a graving dock & moved into deep
  waters where sunk by ballasting while its ht is increased (1st
  one built holds 1 mill. bbls)
may also use differential hydrostatic pressure (suction); base
  forms suction seep when situated on ocean bottom; water
  pumped out of pores beneath the rig to lower hydrost. press.
  inside.
sand and clay seabeds lend themselves to this technique
stream currents can sheer stress these loose

                                    Earney, pp. 124-31

(continued)

FIGURE 10–15. (cont.)

10   *III. drillg pltfm: ballast tanks*

tanks: shaped like lab. oxy. tanks
vol: 30,000-60,000 bbls
(0.9 to 1.8 mill. gals)

Earney, pp. 124-31

11   *III. drillg pltfm: suppt pilngs*

3 of the ball. tanks convert to supp. pilings for platfm deck
typically 300 ft long—whatever length to keep deck 15 ft above
  avg water level fully ballasted

pilings connected at top w/connecting rods, enorm steel girders,
  10 ft diam; support rig deck
conduits inside supp. plgs—drillg bits, pipes for o & g flow,
  drlg fluids
protective sacrific. annode & packg material to prevent leak in
  case of damage to plgs.

Earney, pp 124-31

FIGURE 10—15.   (cont.)

Rough-Draft Excerpt

III. THE CONDEEP DRILLING PLATFORM

In recent years there has been a strong movement among the world's oil producers toward drilling on the Outer Continental Shelf. Typical water depths in this region are 2000 to 3000 ft. At these depths, the conventional steel-jacket platform has a prohibitive cost-to-benefit ratio. A number of new concepts in drilling and production rigs have been developed in attempts to reduce the costs of deepwater drilling. The Condeep submersible rig, depicted in Figure 10–15a, is one of the most promising of those developed so far.

The Condeep consists of two major sections, the hull and the deck.

The Hull

The underwater part of the platform is known as the hull. The hull in turn consists of support pilings and ballast tanks.

The Ballast Tanks.   The ballast tanks contain most of the bulk of the hull. These are built at a graving dock. A typical arrangement consists of 19 tanks built in a giant hexagon. All but three of the tanks are used as ballast tanks. The remaining are converted into support pillars for the rig deck.

The ballast tanks serve a dual purpose. Each tank is equipped with ballasting valves and pumps. The valves may be opened to admit seawater as ballast for the rig. In the early stages of the operation of the rig, these seawater-filled tanks serve as mooring for the platform. When fully ballasted, these tanks rest on the ocean bottom. These tanks may be pumped free of seawater and used as storage for oil produced by the rig or its neighboring rigs.

If the platform is intended to operate in areas where the ocean bottom is exceptionally loose or porous (e.g., composed of sand or clay), then additional mooring support is usually needed. This additional mooring is usually added in the form of pumps attached to

(continued)

FIGURE 10–15.   (cont.)

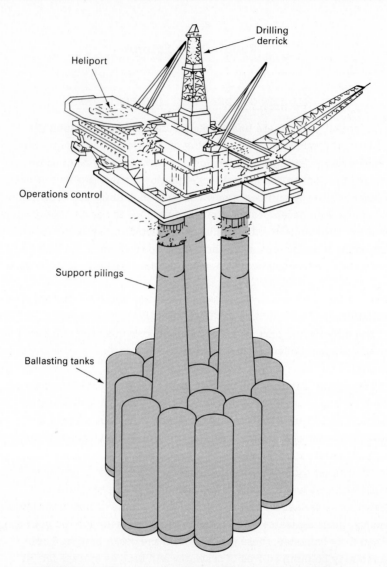

Drilling
derrick

Heliport

Operations control

Support pilings

Ballasting tanks

FIGURE 10—15a.   The Condeep offshore drilling platform

the bottom of the ballast tanks. These pumps provide a differential
hydrostatic pressure by evacuating the pores in the floor under the
tanks. This pressure creates a suction that serves as additional
mooring for the rig.

As for the individual tanks themselves, they are shaped like

FIGURE 10—15.   (cont.)

standard laboratory oxygen tanks. They have a round flat bottom, a cylindrical shaft, and a hemispherical top. Typically, they have a volume of from 30,000 to 60,000 barrels each (i.e., 900,000 to 1,800,000 gallons each). The bottom and shaft are cast in one piece, and the dome with its ballasting valves and pumps is added later.

The Support Pilings.   Three of the ballasting tanks are converted into support pilings for the platform deck. These pilings are located toward the center of the platform. The support pilings are typically about 300 ft long but may be however long is necessary to maintain the deck at about 15 ft above the average water level when the tanks are fully ballasted. The pilings are rounded like cylinders but are tapered toward the top ...

Robert S. Arnold, The Environmental Impact of Drilling on the Outer Continental Shelf (Austin: Univ. of Texas, 1984), 12-15. Reprinted by permission.

FIGURE 10–15.   (cont.)

STEP 7.   If you have developed a good outline and have as complete a set of notecards as you can get, use the preceding suggestions and write a rough draft of your report, or some portion of it. (If you are collaborating on a technical report, see the Introduction for ideas and suggestions on working together during the rough-drafting phase.)

Revising

When you complete the rough draft, set it aside for a while so that when you return, you can see it with fresh eyes. Then begins the critical phase of revising and editing: you become an editor rather than a writer of your work. Most important in being a good editor of your own work is to have that uncanny knack of looking at your work objectively, as if through the eyes of a stranger.

This section gives you a broad overview of revising and editing strategies and brings together the other techniques and skills you've read about in this book. The main idea here is to get a clear view of the full range and scope of things you should look for when you revise. The specific nuts and bolts of revising paragraphs and sentences are covered in Chapter 7, Appendix C, and Appendix D. If you've not read Chapter 7 yet, you might want to do so now before going on.

Planning a Revision Strategy

Good revision work means more than hunting down all the spelling and comma errors; it means being ready to spot problems at any level of writing. Although they overlap to a certain extent, problem areas in reports include the following:

audience problems   sentence problems
paragraph problems   content problems
organizational problems   logic problems
graphics problems

Figure 10–16 contains a conceptual illustration of some of the different ways in which you analyze a report draft during the revision process.

If you are not used to in-depth revising, consider reading your report several times with only a few of the problem categories in mind each time.

Study your report draft for audience problems (see Chapter 5 for a detailed discussion):

Audience Problems

- For whom or for what audience have you written your report?
- What is that audience's specific need or use for the report?
- What technical background or knowledge must that audience have to read your report?
- What additional explanatory discussion must you provide to enable your audience to understand your report?

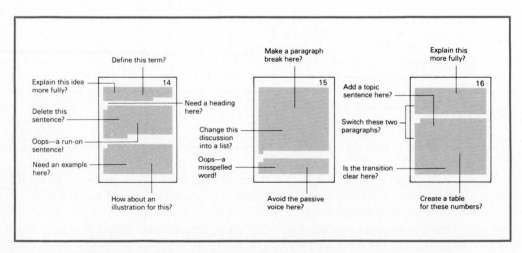

FIGURE 10–16.   Revising the report draft: asking yourself questions about all levels of the rough draft

- Are there technical terms you have not defined? Are there areas of technical discussion requiring further elaboration?
- Does the audience need more introductory discussion in order to understand the main part of the report?
- Will your report meet the needs of its audience?

Also reread your rough draft for organizational problems, asking yourself questions like these (see Chapter 7 or 8 for a detailed discussion):

Organizational Problems

- Are the topics of discussion in the paragraphs, sections, and chapters arranged in an appropriate order?
- Does the arrangement of the topics of discussion (in a paragraph, section, or chapter) follow a pattern? What is that pattern?
- Are any sections in your report either out of order or out of sequence?
- Are there any topics of discussion that can be eliminated?

Use these questions to think about content-related problems in your report (see Chapter 8 for more details also):

Content Problems

- Does the report supply all the right content to accomplish its purpose?
- Is any of the content unnecessary to the purpose or audience?
- Has any important content been left out?
- Does the report supply enough "hard facts," for example, statistics, numbers, terms, or names?
- Does the report supply enough examples, definitions, comparisons, and other such explanatory material?

When you study your rough draft for paragraph problems, ask yourself questions like these (if you are not sure about some of these terms, use the index to find the right pages in Chapter 7 and Appendix C):

Paragraph-Level Problems

- Do you need topic sentences to provide clarity and direction for readers?
- Are the paragraphs sufficiently developed; is more explanatory detail needed?
- Are the paragraphs coherent; are better transitions needed?
- Are the paragraphs well organized; is the sequence of ideas logical?
- Are there adequate transitions between paragraphs and between sections?

Review the graphic aids in your rough draft or your plans for them (see Chapter 6 for detailed discussion):

Graphics Problems

- Do you provide adequate graphic aids throughout your report?
- Do you provide the right kind of graphic aids?
- Are there any passages where you could have provided graphic aids but did not?
- Are there any passages in which the content could be repeated graphically (for example, a discussion of a process that could be shown as a flowchart or a discussion of statistics that could be presented as a table)?
- Do the graphic aids you use provide the right amount of detail? Do you have too much for the readers' needs, or too little?
- In nearby text do you refer to, explain, interpret, or help the readers in some way to understand the graphic aids you use?
- Are your graphic aids properly numbered, titled, labeled, and documented?

Also, study your rough draft for problems involving the logic or reasoning of your discussion. Although logic problems involve the technical aspects of your report subject, there are some general problems you can watch out for:

Logic Problems

- Do you provide sufficient supporting evidence and discussion to prove your main points, conclusions, or recommendations?
- Could the reader look at your facts and arrive at a different conclusion?
- Do you explain how you obtained the supporting discussion?
- Do you compare alternatives and show how yours is best?
- Do you list your conclusions separately?
- Do you explain and justify the criteria you used?
- Might anyone think that you've jumped to a hasty conclusion?
- Do you discuss the situation or problem from all possible angles in order to show the reader that you have been thorough?
- What are the possible logic problems or fallacies in your report? Do you avoid them successfully?

When you reread your report for sentence problems, ask yourself such questions as the following (if you are not sure about some of these terms, use the index to find the right pages in Chapter 7 and Appendix D):

Sentence-Level Problems

- Overly long, awkwardly worded, or unclear sentences
- Unnecessarily specialized or technical vocabulary
- Slanted, too-informal, or too-formal word choice
- Passages of short, choppy sentences
- Unnecessary use of the passive voice
- Unnecessary use of expletives (*there is, it is*, etc.)
- Agreement problems between subjects and verbs

- Unclear reference for pronouns
- Incorrect commas, colons, semicolons, and apostrophes
- Parallelism problems
- Modifier problems with phrases
- Misspelled words

Faced with all these categories and questions, you may rightly wonder how people revise and edit written work without rereading report drafts dozens and dozens of times. Experienced revisers and editors do reread their work several times, but not dozens, and not with a single category at a time in mind. Instead, they are simply alert to any sort of problem.

If you are new to in-depth revising and editing, (a) make a list of potential problem areas in your report, and (b) make two or three groups of the problem areas just described and read your draft with one of these groups in mind at a time.

Identifying Potential Problem Areas

Before you plunge into a close reading of your rough draft, stand back from it a moment, and try to imagine some of the potential problems it may have.

- If you describe a mechanism, the reader may not be able to visualize it easily.
- If you propose the purchase of some new technology, your discussion may not make a convincing case for the expenditure.
- If you explain how to do something, you'd want to make sure that you had left nothing out of the instructions.
- If you explain how a new technology for use in nuclear fusion reactors works, you'd want to make sure that the highly technical discussion could be understood by the audience.

You should be able to make a list of up to a dozen potential problem areas that your report faces. This kind of forethought will make you much more alert when you read your rough draft.

STEP 8.   On your worksheet, list and briefly describe the problems that you think your report may contain.

Grouping the Problem Categories

Also, make two or three groups of the problem categories just discussed, and read your draft with one group in mind at a time, disregarding all other categories. Here's one possible grouping:

1. *Audience, organizational, logic* problems
2. *Paragraph* problems and *content* problems
3. *Sentence* problems and *graphics* problems

There is nothing magical about this grouping, but remember to worry about the sentence problems last; after all, if you omit a whole section, what's the point of correcting misspelled words or fixing comma errors in it?

Problem-Spotting Strategies

Equipped with the smartest of revision strategies, anyone can still miss the most obvious problems in a rough draft. Why? When you write something, you sometimes develop a strange blindness to the most obvious problems because you are so close to your work. What can you do about this editorial blindness? Here are some useful strategies:

• Put your rough draft away for a time in order to get some distance from it. When you return, it will seem less familiar, and you may see things you'd have missed otherwise.

• Read the rough draft of the report out loud at a very deliberate tempo, making sure to pronounce and think about every word, sentence, paragraph, and section.

• Ask a friend to read your rough draft or, in fact, read it back to you. Ask your friend to mark problem areas; listen for areas during which your friend hesitates when reading aloud.

• Scramble your reading of the rough draft in some way: for example, begin at the end and read backwards line by line, sentence by sentence, or paragraph by paragraph. Such reading forces you to puzzle out the order and logic.

• Try recopying parts of your rough draft, particularly the highly technical ones or ones that you had a hard time writing initially. This tactic may prompt you to make changes you wouldn't have thought of otherwise.

• Get a typewritten copy of your report draft. Seeing it in a different format may help you spot problems you might have overlooked in the handwritten version.

• Use the strategies for revising paragraph and sentence problems presented in Chapter 7 on areas of your report draft that are highly technical or that were difficult to write.

STEP 9.   Use any of the revision strategies discussed in the preceding section to look for ways to improve your report rough draft, and, on your worksheet, list and briefly describe what you find. (If you are collaborating on a technical report, see the Introduction for ideas and suggestions on working together during the revision stage.)

Final Packaging of the Report

When you finish revising, your next job is to put the report in a neat, professional-looking package. Remember, however, that different report-writing situations require different kinds of packaging. A short, informal report written for people you know may not need the packaging described here. The only way to be sure is to check around in your organization.

For more formal reports over 8 or 10 pages, use the packaging suggestions described here. This should give a report the neatest, cleanest, most professional-looking appearance possible. How a report looks has a great influence on how readily it is received, considered, understood, and acted upon.

Good packaging for your report also protects it from becoming worn or soiled. Good reports are often carried about, tossed around, and passed about among a number of readers. For such use, something more durable than ordinary paper covers and a staple is necessary.

The most important considerations in the final packaging of a report include:

1. Typing the final copy
2. Inserting the illustrations into the final copy
3. Making a good photocopy of the final product
4. Binding and labeling the report

Typing the Final Copy

If you do your own typing, remember several things:

• With high-quality photocopiers, submitting neatly copied reports, instead of originals, is not only acceptable but preferable in many ways. Being able to submit a photocopied report enables you to take advantage of many shortcuts.

• If you plan to submit the original typed copy instead, avoid the sticky erasable, crinkly or pebbly parchmentlike, and cheap, see-through, lightweight kinds of paper. Use standard 10 percent cotton paper.

• When you get ready to type, make sure you have the following:

A new or relatively new typing ribbon (don't change in the middle of the typing job!)
A good pair of scissors
A bottle of liquid paper ("white-out")
"Magic" or "frosty" tape (not the yellowish kind)

• Use shortcuts to avoid having to type whole pages over again. Use liquid paper for typos: it won't show up in the photocopy. Use scissors and tape rather than retype whole lines or paragraphs: careful taping and photocopying don't show. When you use liquid paper, scissors, and tape, keep these guidelines in mind:

1. Use the "magic" or "frosty" tape just described: the yellowish kind will show on the photocopied version.
2. Align your inserted item carefully with the rest of the material already on the page.
3. Cover *all* the edges of the taped insertion with the tape; let none of the seams show.

• Use a common type style (or font); avoid the strange, overly large, overly small ones, and don't change fonts within a report. Some of the most commonly used fonts are listed in Figure 10–17.

Letter Gothic	Dual Gothic
Scribe	Artisan 12
Courier 12	Courier 72
Prestige 72	Prestige Elite 72
Pica 72	Delegate
Symbol 10 or 12	Light Italic

FIGURE 10–17. List of common type styles (or fonts)

• Plan your margins and other spacing carefully and be consistent with it throughout your report. Leave extra space on the left margin for binding (how much to leave depends on the type of binding).

• Plan to double-space your report's main text unless there is some special reason not to do so. Certain elements, like the letter of transmittal, references, and table of contents can use other kinds of spacing (see the model report excerpts in Chapters 12 and 13).

• Proofread each page *before* you pull it out of the typewriter to avoid having to realign the page if it has a typo. If you do have to reinsert a page, get into the habit of always loading paper into the typewriter flush against the left-margin paper guide to ensure right-to-left alignment. To get the up-and-down alignment right, align the paper as best you can, type a test letter out in the margin, use a straightedge to see if it is properly aligned, try again until it is, type your corrections, and then white-out the test letters in the margin.

Special Note about Hired Typists.   If you get someone else to type your report, make sure the typist has all necessary instructions.

• Double-space your handwritten report; often typists charge extra for cramped, single-spaced work.

• Make it absolutely clear where every insertion goes. Use a different color to mark areas for insertions, and label the items to be inserted.

• Don't assume the typist will type out abbreviations, fill out phrasings you didn't have time to finish, or correct mechanical problems in your handwritten manuscript.

• Provide samples or models of how you want such things as headings in your report; provide a sample page or two of critical or typical areas.

• Always proofread your typed report on receipt from the typist: too many technical-report writers have been sabotaged by typo-ladened finished reports that they submitted without proofreading.

Special Note about Word Processors and Text Editors. If you are fortunate enough to have access to word processing, you'll be able to produce your report much more efficiently. But writing electronically does have its potential for problems—big problems!

• On some text editors, make sure that you are in the "insert" mode; otherwise, you can lose everything you type.

• Save your material occasionally; don't type for hours and hours only to let a stray keystroke obliterate everything you've written.

• Make a backup copy of your work regularly in case something terrible happens to your working copy. However, make sure that you add new material to the working copy *only*.

• Watch out for global changes or deletions; make sure that no unexpected changes are made. Consider doing such changes with prompts so that you know what you're changing.

• Don't completely trust software that checks spelling for you. Remember that computers are not (or at least not yet) capable of distinguishing between homonyms, for example, *affect/effect, principle/principal,* or *to/too.*

• When you change a sentence, read the whole section or passage in which the change occurs: make sure that your first change does not necessitate other changes.

• Watch out for numbered items (for example, figure numbers) and forward and backward references that may need to be changed because you have shifted text around.

• Never assume that you can insert or delete sentences or paragraphs without making minor changes on the nearby text. Always go back and reread passages where you've made changes.

• Make a test print of several pages of your report early on: don't assume it will look exactly as you expect it will.

• Set all the formating values such as tabs, margins, and line spacing *before* you begin. Make sure that you like the way the printed pages look before you type too much text.

• Think about little details such as hyphens: if your word-processing program automatically reformats lines, will your hyphenated words end up in the middle of lines?

• Watch for "widowed" or "orphaned" material in your print-out: a heading may be at the bottom of one page and the section it introduces at the top of the next. Watch out for figure titles getting separated from the figures themselves by page breaks.

• Avoid printing your report too often (for the sake of the trees), but print at least once before the final copy. Edit the printed, or hard, copy: you'll see things you might have missed on the 25-line display screen. Also, it's easier to get a sense of the whole report when you can spread pages out and flip through them rapidly.

Taping in Illustrations

Advice for taping in illustrations is the same as in the previous section on typing reports.

- Use the kind of frosted tape described earlier.

- Make a good photocopy of any illustration that you plan to borrow from another source.

- Trim off the original figure number, title, and other material accompanying the original illustration.

- Remember to document the source of your illustration as shown in Appendix A, "Common Systems for Documenting Reports."

- Make photocopies of hand-drawn illustrations, and tape them in to your report; they look better photocopied.

- Align your inserted illustration carefully.

- Cover all the edges of your inserted illustrations with tape; let no seams show.

If you align and tape your illustrations carefully, you won't be able to tell that those illustrations were taped in; it will look like a professional print job!

Proofreading the Final Typed Copy

With a complete typed copy of your report and with all the illustrations taped in, proofread the report at least one last time before you copy, bind, and submit it. Now, however, it is too late for the larger problems of organization, audience, and logic. Instead, you must look for mechanical problems such as spelling, punctuation, and typos. For simple proofreading, consider using some of these tricks:

- Use a straightedge on each line, and run your eyes across each line more than once.

- Anticipate specific kinds of problems: for example, if you use capital letter, scrutinize it carefully for correctness and consistency; if the word *effect* or *affect* appears, make sure that it is correct.

- Rescan your copy sentence-by-sentence or paragraph-by-paragraph backwards in order to break up your rapid flow of reading.

- Softly pronounce each word as you read in order to force yourself to concentrate on the text.

- Put your copy away for several hours or a day and read it again when you are rested.

- Watch for *omitted* words: it's easy enough to be alert for problems with words that are on the page, but you need to stay alert to words you may have left out.

Making a Good Photocopy

A critical stage in the final packaging of a report is getting a good photocopy. Photocopying is so good now that a photocopied version of your report is actually better looking than the original. Find a good-quality machine, however. The ones in libraries, drugstores, or other heavy-traffic areas usually do not produce good copies. Why ruin your hard work because of a cheap, worn-out copy machine? Instead, find a store that specializes in photocopying, and ask the attendant for help if necessary. Also, here are some basic precautions to take:

- Use a paper towel to wipe off the glass; often stray specks accumulate on the glass and can show up on *every* page.
- Sometimes a clean white sheet of paper behind (on top of) your original pages enhances the quality of your copies.
- Request use of 10 percent cotton paper or some other high-quality paper in the machine.
- Make a few test copies of key pages from your report to make sure they look right.
- Don't expect photographs to copy well. If they are crucial to your report, make your own and glue them into your report directly.
- Photocopy your *entire* report; don't submit a mixture of different kinds of paper. Also, don't submit a report with taped-in illustrations (other than glued-in photographs, as just mentioned).

If you have never scissored and taped and photocopied written work in this way before, you'll probably be amazed, elated, and proud to see how good and professional-looking your photocopied report looks. It's like an unexpected, but well-deserved reward after long hours of hard work.

Binding the Report

Several kinds of bindings and covers are commonly available for reports (see Figure 10–18).

- One of the most common is the metal brad binder (A); pages of the report require two holes in the left margin and an extra half-inch margin on that side.
- Another type (B) is a plastic-spiral binder, particularly attractive in that it takes up little of the left margin and lies flat when open.
- Small-ring binders (C) are usually not necessary for reports under 50 pages long; they are unnecessarily bulky.
- Avoid the plastic strip binder with the clear, sometimes colored covers: generally, this type is associated with high school and college term papers rather than technical reports.

As for the covers, usually some sort of colored, heavy-duty paper is appropriate. However, do not use the gaudy varieties of covers with the gold trim or simulated leather texture. Just make it plain, simple, and honest!

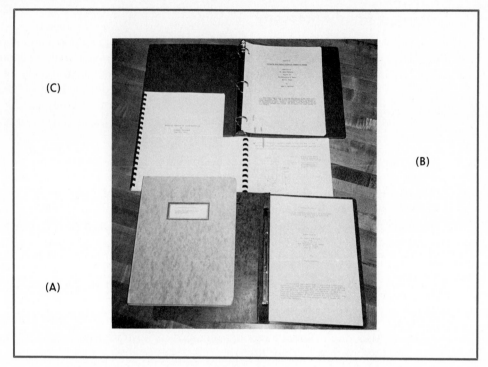

FIGURE 10–18.   Commonly used report bindings (Photo courtesy of Phoebe Hughes McMurrey.)

Attaching the Cover Label

With the report all typed, taped, copied, and bound, are you all done? No, not quite: don't forget that simple but important finishing touch—the label on the cover. Notice that all the reports in Figure 10–18 have cover labels. Usually, the cover label has only the title of the report, the author's name, a date, and possibly the intended recipient. (See Chapter 6 for details on cover labels.) Make sure the label has good adhesive and won't fall off the next day. Also, avoid haphazardly scissoring a label from a piece of typing paper and taping or gluing it on: the result is messy and tacky looking.

With the report complete, bound, and labeled, you are ready to send or deliver it. If you have followed the final-packaging recommendations here, congratulations; you should have an excellent, professional-looking report. Be proud of it; show it off! Keep a copy of it for future employment hunting or work negotiations; it shows what high-quality work you are capable of.

EXERCISES

1. Trade the outlines and an unnumbered set of notecards with a fellow student, decide what part of the outline the notecards belong to and what order these notecards should

be placed in, and number them accordingly. When you've done this, write a double-spaced rough draft of the section of the report corresponding to these notecards.

2. Using materials for paraphrasing practice that you get from a fellow student, paraphrase a passage to fit into the student's report excerpt.

3. Using the materials for summarizing practice that you get from a fellow student, summarize a passage to fit into the student's report excerpt.

4. Using the direct quotations and the report excerpts that you get from a fellow student, combine them
   a. Using only the appropriate parts of the direct quotations
   b. Including one block quotation
   c. Including one or more running quotations
   d. Using the proper documentation (see Appendix A).

5. Using the sample notecards and accompanying outline that you get from a fellow student, do the following:
   a. Locate where in the outline the notecards belong.
   b. On the notecards write the topic identifiers and number-letter combinations.
   c. Make the necessary additions or phrasing changes to the outline.

6. Using the sample passages and accompanying outline that you get from a fellow student, do the following:
   a. Make a set of bibliography cards for those passages.
   b. Take at least four notecards in which the information should be summarized.
   c. Take at least four notecards in which the information should be paraphrased.
   d. Take at least four notecards in which the information should be directly quoted.

7. Interview other report writers concerning their note-taking systems. Find out why they use them and the problems they have had with them. With this information, try to determine what factors (report length, nature of the information, or audience and purpose of the report) influence the type of note-taking system used and its success or failure.

8. Trade copies of an unrevised report with a fellow student, and follow the steps in this chapter to revise and edit it. Mark the problems you find, and write in your own revisions of them.

PART IV

Processes for Correspondence, Reports, and Articles

Chapter **11.** **Corresponding with Business and Professional Associates**

Chapter **12.** **Designing and Writing Informational Reports**

Chapter **13.** **Writing Effective Instructions**

Chapter **14.** **Designing Proposals and Feasibility Reports**

Chapter **15.** **Writing Popular Science Articles**

Chapter **16.** **Preparing and Delivering Oral Reports**

Introduction

The chapters in this part of the book are what Parts I, II, and III all lead up to: the actual day-to-day uses of technical reporting, the real-world applications. Use the discussion, examples, models, and steps in these Part IV chapters to guide you in preparing these often-used applications of technical reporting:

Applications Covered in Part IV	Chapter
Business letters and memoranda	11
Resumes	11
Progress reports	12
Primary research reports	12
Information reports	12
Technical-background reports	12
Written technical instructions	13
Proposals	14
Feasibility reports	14
Popular science articles	15
Oral reports	16

In the chapters of Part IV you draw upon all of the skills and techniques discussed in the earlier parts of this book:

Main Contents	Parts of This Book
Organizing and writing the main kinds of technical writing, the building blocks: process, causal discussions, descriptions, comparisons, definitions, classifications, introductions, conclusions, and summaries	I
Analyzing or inventing an audience for the report Translating technical discussions for nonspecialists Incorporating graphic aids and textual aids in reports Making paragraphs and sentences well-organized and readable	II
Finding and narrowing a report topic Creating a detailed outline for a report Finding information in library and nonlibrary sources Taking notes for the report Rough drafting, editing, and final packaging the report	III

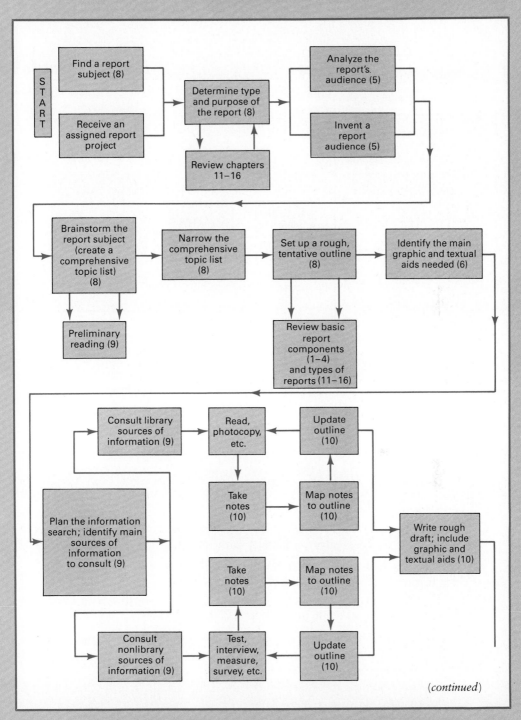

Figure IV–1. Flowchart illustrating the typical steps in report-writing projects and the interrelationships of the chapters of this book

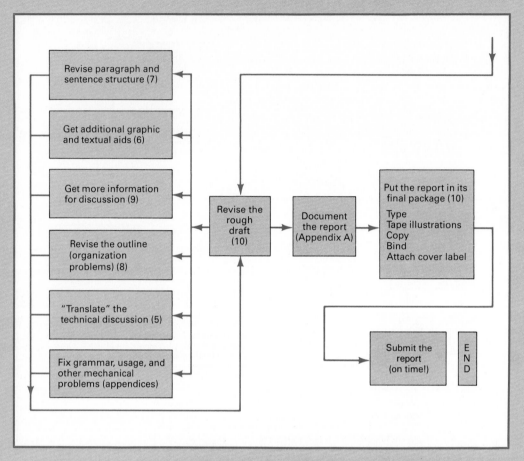

FIGURE IV–1. (cont.)

To get the grand view of how all these chapters and parts work together, study for a moment the flowchart of this book provided in Figure IV–1; the numbers in the boxes in parentheses refer to chapters in this book.

The chapters here in Part IV often refer to techniques in technical reporting covered in earlier parts of the book. However, those techniques are not explained here in Part IV. To use the chapters of Parts I, II, and III together with these Part IV chapters, you can take one of two approaches:

- If you have read none of the earlier chapters in this book, follow the steps that direct you back to them: read the discussion and follow the steps there, and then return here to the Part IV chapter you are working on.
- If you have studied the chapters of Parts I, II, and III, return to them for a quick review.

As mentioned in the introductions to the previous parts of this book, these chapters are designed to be "modular": that is, you can use them in almost any order and combination you require.

CHAPTER 11

Corresponding with Business and Professional Associates

Chapter Objectives
Common Types of Business Letters
  Inquiry Letters
  Letters of Complaint and
    Adjustment
  Order Letters
  Query Letters for Publishing
  Application Letters
Resumes
  Gathering the Information
  Designing the Resume Format
  Drafting and Finishing
    the Resume

Components and Formats for
  Business Correspondence
  Components of Business
    Correspondence
  Business-Letter Formats
  Memoranda
Tips on Writing Business Letters and
  Memos
Finishing Business Letters and Memos
  Revising
  Final Packaging: Originals and
    Photocopies
Exercises

──────────────────── *Chapter Objectives* ────────────────────

After you read this chapter, study the examples, work the steps, and do the practice writing, you should be able to:

- Explain why business letters are sometimes preferable to conversations in person or over the phone.
- Define the common types of business letters.
- Define the purpose of the resume and identify its contents.
- Identify the main parts of resumes and sketch the different ways to present information in each of these parts.
- Explain the purpose and content of each of the main formal features of business letters.
- List the main techniques for producing professional-looking business letters.
- Define the memorandum, list its main purposes and types, and state the main strategies for writing effective memos.

Despite the commercials that show sophisticated telephone equipment as the only communication tool necessary in the modern business environment, the business letter remains a critical tool in the worlds of business, industry, government, and the professions. Despite phone-company claims, the business letter provides certain advantages that the phone call simply cannot.

- A business letter provides a permanent record of a communication, while phone conversations cannot.
- The writer of a business letter does not have to contend with busy signals, no answers, long holds, or recipients who are constantly out of the office.
- Business letters provide a greater opportunity to explain a case, present more facts, and provide reasons.
- Business letters can, if clearly written, provide greater clarity of explanation simply because recipients can read them over again.

Certainly, plenty of other reasons keep the business letter as an essential tool in the electronic world. The types of letters discussed in this chapter are not the whole range: they are simply the most common, and knowing how to write them will aid you in writing letters for many different situations. This chapter covers not only five of the most common types of business letters but resumes and memoranda as well. If you are about to write a resume, go to that section now, but if you are interested in letters or memoranda, continue with the next section.

STEP 1.   Describe the situation in which you are writing your business letter, or if you already know, explain what type of business letter you are writing. (If you are not sure yet, keep reading, and come back to this step later.) If you are writing a resume, go straight to that section now. (Steps for each of the different types of letters and for the resume end in a different letter; steps ending without letters are common to all.)

Common Types of Business Letters

Some of the most common types of business letters include the inquiry letter (and the response to it), the complaint letter (and responses to it), the order letter, the query letter, the application letter (and follow-up letters to it). This chapter discusses these types of letters as well as resumes, an important element in business correspondence for job hunters.

STEP 2.   Now go directly to the discussion in this section on the type of letter that you are writing, and follow the steps at the end of that section.

Inquiry Letters

The letter of inquiry is useful when you need information, advice, names, or directions. Be careful, however, not to ask for too much information or for information that you could easily obtain in some other way, for example, by a quick trip to the library. There are two types of inquiry letters: solicited and unsolicited.

You write a *solicited* letter of inquiry when a business or agency advertises its products or services. For example, if a software manufacturer advertises some new package it has developed and you can't inspect it locally, write a solicited letter to that manufacturer asking specific questions. If you cannot find any information on a technical subject, an inquiry letter to a company involved in that subject may put you on the right track. In fact, that company may supply much more help than you had expected (provided of course that you write a good inquiry letter). If you need to find the names and addresses of businesses related to your report subject, see Chapter 9.

Your letter of inquiry is *unsolicited* if the recipient has done nothing to prompt your inquiry. For example, if you read an article by an expert, you may have further questions or want more information. You seek help from these people in a slightly different form of inquiry letter.

As the steps and guidelines for both types of inquiry letters show, you must construct the unsolicited type more carefully, because recipients of unsolicited letters of inquiry are not ordinarily prepared to handle such inquiries. Figure 11–1 provides an example of a well-developed unsolicited letter of inquiry.

STEP 3A.   Preparing the inquiry letter:

1. Early in the letter identify the purpose—to obtain help or information (if it's a solicited letter, information about an advertised product, service, or program). On your worksheet explain why your inquiry letter is solicited or unsolicited, and list the specific items of information you need or the specific questions you need answered.
2. In an unsolicited letter identify who you are, what you are working on, why you need the requested information, and how you found out about the individual. In an unsolicited letter, also identify the source that prompted your inquiry, for example, a magazine advertisement. On your worksheet, list this information.

1102 West 30th
Lawrence, KS 66321
August 4, 19XX

Dr. Maria Gomez-Salinas
Director of the Diabetes Clinic
St. David's Hospital
1000 Greenberg Lane
Wichita, KS 66780

Dear Dr. Gomez-Salinas:

I am writing you in hopes of finding out more about the new Glucoscan II blood glucose monitoring system, which a representative at Lifescan informed me that your clinic is currently using.

Originally, I saw Lifescan's advertisement of this new device in the January 19XX issue of Diabetes Forecast and became very interested in it. I wrote the company and got much useful information but was recommended to write several current users of the system as well.

For a technical report that I am writing for a technical-writing class at Johnson County Junior College, I need some help with the following questions:

1. How often does the Glucoscan II need to be calibrated in practical, everyday-use conditions?
2. How accurate is the Glucoscan II compared to other similar systems that your patients have used?
3. What problems do your patients experience with this new device?

The Lifescan representative indicated that your clinic is one of the leaders in implementing new technology for diabetics, and therefore I am eager to hear from you. In the report I will acknowledge your contributions, and I will send you a copy of the completed report if you wish.

Thank you for your time, and I hope to hear from you soon.

Sincerely,

Anita Teller
Student, Medical Technology
Johnson County Junior College

Figure 11–1. Example of unsolicited letter of inquiry (semiblock format)

3. In the letter, list questions or information needed in a clear, specific, and easy-to-read format. If you have quite a number of questions, consider making a questionnaire and including a stamped, self-addressed envelope. On your worksheet, explain what format you'll use to request the information.

5. In an unsolicited letter try to find some way to compensate the recipient for the trouble, for example, by offering to pay copying and mailing costs, to accept a collect call, to acknowledge the recipient in your report, or to send him or her a copy of your report. In a solicited letter suggest that the recipient send brochures or catalogs. On your worksheet explain how you can make the recipient's job of answering your inquiry letter easier.

6. In closing an unsolicited letter express gratitude for any help that the recipient can provide you, acknowledge the inconvenience of your request, but do not thank the recipient "in advance." In an unsolicited letter tactfully suggest that the recipient will benefit by helping you (for example, through future purchases from the recipient's company). On your worksheet explain how you will acknowledge the recipient's help.

7. On your worksheet write the first sentence of the inquiry letter, making sure that it states the main business of the letter. Next, use the notes on your worksheet to write a first draft of the letter.

8. If you have written the draft of the inquiry letter, turn now to step 4, and study the section that precedes it.

Letters of Complaint and Adjustment

A complaint letter requests some sort of compensation for defective or damaged merchandise or for inadequate or delayed services. Although many complaints can be made in person, some circumstances require formal business letters. The complaint may be so complex that a phone call may not effectively resolve the problem; or the writer may prefer the permanence, formality, and seriousness of a business letter. The essential rule in writing a complaint letter is to maintain your poise and diplomacy, no matter how justified your gripe is. Avoid making the recipient an adversary. Look at the example in Figure 11–2.

STEP 3B. Preparing the complaint letter:

1. Early in the letter identify the reason you are writing—to register a complaint and to ask for some kind of compensation. Avoid leaping into the details of the problem in the first sentence. On your worksheet write a sentence explaining your reason for writing.

2. In the letter state exactly what compensation you desire, either before or after the discussion of the problem or the reasons for granting the compensation. (It may be more tactful and less antagonizing to delay this statement in some cases.) Briefly describe this compensation on your worksheet.

3. In the letter provide a fully detailed narrative or description of the problem. This is the evidence for your point. On your worksheet write a rough-draft narrative or description of the problem to be discussed in your complaint letter.

4. In the letter explain why your request should be granted. Presenting the evidence

206C Park Lane
Austin, Texas 78705
11 February 19XX

Director of Consumer Relations
American Airways
Mail Drop 4F13
P.O. Box 56989
DFW Airport
Dallas, Texas 75441—4545

Dear Director:

I am writing you concerning a round-trip flight from Austin, Texas, to
Detroit, Michigan, I made on 10 December 19XX. Travel demands
have made me a consistent patron of American for the past six years.
In that time, service on your airlines has always been good to excellent.
But an interruption in service on the flight mentioned above has
prompted my request for a 50 percent reduction in airfare on my next
flight.

Here is what happened on 10 December. While changing planes during
the return trip at DFW Airport, I was informed that our flight would
be delayed. After two hours' delay, we boarded the plane we had just
left in order to meet our Chicago connection in Dallas. After takeoff
from DFW, our pilot casually informed us that we should be impressed
by the fact that the Dallas Cowboys football team had just left our
seats. This was the only explanation of our inconvenience.

I believe that this rerouting was done purely for promotional gain and
was in no way mechanically or technically necessary. As a loyal
patron of American Airways, at least until this point, I have every
confidence that the compensation I request above will be provided,
considering the high standard of service and consideration your
company has demonstrated toward its customers in the past.

Sincerely,

Scott Woodrow

SAW: rrw
encl.: copy of ticket

**FIGURE 11—2. Example of a complaint letter
(semiblock format)**

is not enough: state the reasons why this evidence indicates your request should be granted. On your worksheet number and discuss your reasons for believing that the compensation you request should be granted.

5. In the letter suggest why it is in the recipient's best interest to grant your request: appeal to the recipient's sense of fairness and desire for continued business, but don't threaten. Find some way to view the problem as an honest mistake. Don't imply that the recipient deliberately committed the error or that the company has no concern for the customer. Toward the end of the letter, express confidence that the recipient will grant your request. On your worksheet explain how you are going to try to keep from antagonizing the recipient of your complaint.

6. Write the first sentence of the complaint letter on your worksheet, making sure that you state the main business and purpose of the letter. Next, write a first draft of the body of the complaint letter.

7. When you've written a draft of the complaint letter, turn to step 4, and study the section preceding it.

Replies to complaint letters, often called letters of adjustment, must be handled carefully when the requested compensation cannot be granted. Refusal of compensation tests your diplomacy and tact as a writer. Here are some suggestions that may help you write either type of adjustment letter.

1. Begin with a reference to the date of the original letter of complaint and to the purpose of your letter. If you deny the request, don't state the refusal right away unless you can do so tactfully.

2. Express your concern over the writer's troubles and your appreciation that he has written you.

3. If you deny the request, explain the reasons why the request cannot be granted in as cordial and noncombative a manner as possible. If you grant the request, don't sound as if you are doing so in a begrudging way.

4. In denial letters, only after you have presented your reasons for the refusal should you directly state the denial.

5. If you grant the request, explain the problem from the point of view of your company and defend the company's competence, attention to detail, and care for its customers.

6. If you deny the request, try to offer some partial or substitute compensation or offer some friendly advice (to take the sting out of the denial).

7. Conclude the letter cordially, perhaps expressing confidence that you and the writer will continue doing business.

Figure 11–3 contains an example of an adjustment letter granting the requested compensation.

Order Letters

An order letter makes a formal order for specific products or services to a specific company. It is preferable to a personal visit or phone call when the order is long, detailed, or complicated. Look at the example in Figure 11–4.

Green Tree Freight Co., Inc.
Columbus, Ohio 45453
(315) 565–6789

March 29, 19XX

Complete Table, Inc.
P.O. Box 3132
Austin, TX 78703

Subj.: March 24 letter about damaged freight

Dear Mrs. Hughes:

I have just received your March 24 letter about the damaged shipment
you received through Green Tree Freight and regret the inconvenience
that it has caused you.

From your account of the problem, I am quite sure that your request
for the $240 adjustment on the damage to the two crates of Valjean
Cristal stemware will be granted. A certain amount of breakage of this
sort does unavoidably occur in cross-country shipping; I am sorry that
it was your company that had to be the one to suffer the delay.

I must remind you to keep the damaged crates in the same condition
in which you received them until one of our representatives can
inspect them. That inspection should take place within two weeks.

If all is in order, as it sounds to be in your letter, you can expect the
full reimbursement within two weeks after our representative's
inspection. I hope this unfortunate accident will not keep you from
having merchandise shipped by Green Tree Freight in the future.

Sincerely,

David F. Morgan, Customer Relations
Green Tree Freight Co., Inc.
Columbus, Ohio 45453
(315) 565-6789

**FIGURE 11–3. An adjustment letter: compensation
granted (alternative block format)**

City of Austin

Founded by Congress, Republic of Texas, 1839
Municipal Building, Eighth at Colorado, P.O. Box 1088, Austin, Texas 78767

February 14, 19XX

Lindsay Office Products
P.O. Box 1879
Spokane, Washington 98989

Subject: Furniture and equipment order

Please ship the following items from your sales catalog dated January 31, 19XX:

Item	Catalog #	Color	Qty	Price
Conference Desk	HN–33080–WB	Sandalwood	2	$478.60 ea.
Credenza	HN–36887–WK	Sandalwood	2	431.40 ea.
Executive Chair	HP–56563–SE	Toasted Tan	4	422.00 ea.
File Cabinet	HN–5344C–K	Beige	2	135.90 ea.
Letter Tray	K5–299907–A	Black	6	16.95 ea.

The items ordered above should be shipped C.O.D. to this address:

CLAIMS DIVISION, LAW DEPARTMENT

City of Austin

P.O. Box 96

Austin, Texas 78767–0096

The costs above reflect a discount of 50/10, with net due in 30 days after the invoice date. The merchandise is to be shipped by your company's own truck line at a rate of 7 percent of the total net cost.

(continued)

FIGURE 11–4.   Example of an order letter (simplified format)

We are remodeling our offices and have a target completion date of March 30, 19XX. If there is any reason you see that you cannot keep your part of this schedule, please let me know immediately.

Sincerely,

Berenice Chamala
Supervisor, Clerical Services

BKC: amm

FIGURE 11–4. (cont.)

STEP 3C.   Preparing the order letter:

1. In the letter begin with the purpose—to order products or services from the company.
2. In the letter describe the items you want: if there are many, list in vertical columns their important descriptive characteristics, such as the exact names, quantities, sizes, colors, lengths, widths, catalog numbers, model numbers, and prices. On your worksheet, list the items and their details.
3. In the letter indicate the method of payment. A common one is the 1/10, net/30 arrangement in which the recipient can deduct 10 percent of the total by paying within 30 days. On your worksheet, explain what payment plan you'll use.
4. In the letter also indicate the method of delivery (postal service or rail, truck, or air delivery) and the date of delivery. If the order needs to be rushed to you, state this need clearly. On your worksheet, explain how you want the goods sent and when you want them delivered.
5. On your worksheet write the first sentence of the letter, making sure that it states the main purpose. Next, write a first draft of the body of the order letter.
6. When you've written a first draft of the order letter, turn to step 4, and study the section that precedes it.

Query Letters for Publishing

You write query letters to find out if a publisher is interested in your idea for an article, book, or some other kind of publication. (See Chapter 15 for more on the other aspects of writing articles.) If, for example, you have an idea for an article, you can write query letters to the editors of magazines who might be interested. See the example in Figure 11–5.

22215 Tipton St.
Austin, Texas 78795
February 21, 19XX

Acquisitions Editor
RN
Oradell, NJ 07649

Dear Editor:

I have just completed an article that I believe the readers of RN will find useful and interesting. I would like to tell you about the article and to request any information you have on guidelines for writers. I am currently developing an in-service series about the transport of high-risk neonates to a regional center for use in an orientation program and believe that an abridged version of it would be just right for RN.

The article describes the levels of care and the classifications of the different neonatal units. The article also illustrates some of the forms that must be filled out for most centers, reviews the types of maternal/fetal and neonatal transport, explains when to call the referral center and what information the staff needs, reviews the methods of stabilizing the neonate until the transport team arrives, and lists the equipment needed. The article also discusses the problem of parent-infant bonding, which is disrupted by such crises, and the ways in which this problem can be minimized.

I have been working in intensive care for four years and last year received my CCRN certification in critical care. Of these four years, I have worked one year in a regional neonatal center in Illinois and one year in a Level III facility in Texas. During this time, I have helped to orient new nurses to the centers. Because so many nurses have little knowledge of how to care for the high-risk neonate, I think your readers will find my article very important.

I'll look forward to receiving any guidelines for your writers that you can send me and to hearing your thoughts on my article.

Sincerely yours,

Mary Marconi, RN, CCRN

FIGURE 11—5. Example of a query letter (block format)

STEP 3D.   Preparing the query letter:

1. In the letter make sure that the first sentence states the purpose—to tell about the idea you have for an article. Briefly describe the idea. Include details about the expertise the audience needs to read the article. On your worksheet describe your article and its audience.
2. On your worksheet write the name of the magazine(s) that you want to publish your article (see Chapter 15 for more on finding magazines). Next, describe the kinds of articles that the magazine usually publishes and the sorts of people that you think usually read the magazine.
3. In the letter explain why readers of the magazine will be interested in your article. List, number, and discuss the specific reasons why you think your article will be a good one and why readers will find it enjoyable or informative. On your worksheet, list these reasons.
4. In the letter explain why you think your article is right for the magazine you hope to publish it in. Express a willingness to modify the article, but don't imply that you are prepared to make wholesale changes to your article; stand by your basic ideas. On your worksheet, list reasons for publishing your article.
5. In the letter briefly explain anything about yourself, your background, education, or work experience that relates to your article. On your worksheet briefly list this information.
6. Now, write the first sentence of the query letter on your worksheet, making sure that it states the main purpose of the letter. After that, write a first draft of the body of the letter.
7. Close the query letter by indicating when you expect or hope to hear from the editor.
8. With the first draft of the body of the query letter written, turn to step 4, and study the section preceding it.

Application Letters

You write a letter of application to begin the process of applying for certain jobs. Although not always necessary, it is the first step toward many kinds of jobs: through it, you seek an interview with the prospective employer. At the end of the process, if all goes well, you have been offered a job. A condensed, comprehensive listing of your main qualifications, called the resume or data sheet, often accompanies the application letter.

In the letter of application you do several important things; among them to

- Identify the kind of work you want.
- Highlight your best qualifications with details of your education and work experience.
- Demonstrate your interest and enthusiasm concerning the job, the work, or the company.
- Show how your background makes you right for the job.
- Encourage the prospective employer to contact you for an interview and possibly suggest a convenient time.

Three examples of well-planned letters of application appear in Figure 11–6.

3005 Cedar Creek #2402
Austin, TX 78714
April 19, 19XX

Haskins Electrical Co.
4141 Thomasson Lane
Austin, Texas 78714

Dear Sir:

I am writing for the job of journeyman electrician as advertised in the classified section of the *Austin American-Statesman.* I have considerable work experience as an electrician and believe that I am qualified for this position.

I have worked as an electrician in the Kansas City, Missouri, area for about five years. Since 19XX I have been licensed by Kansas City as an electrical contractor qualified to undertake commercial and industrial work as well as residential work.

I have had formal vocational training as an electrician. I have completed an electrical program offered by Rich Creek Community College in 19XX. This program emphasized installation planning as well as the basics of wiring.

As you will see from my enclosed resume, I am currently attending college. I will be available for full-time employment when the semester ends May 11. I do intend to continue my education but in the future will do so part-time as my employment permits. I would welcome the opportunity to talk further with you at your convenience.

Sincerely,

Eugene S. Lamb

Enclosure: Resume

(continued)

FIGURE 11–6. Example of job-application letters

801 East 54th Street #101
Austin, Texas 78715
February 17, 19XX

Director of Personnel
Automation Associates
7805 Pearl Creek Drive
Austin, Texas 78706

Dear Director of Personnel:

Will you please consider me as an applicant for the position of electronic technician there at Automation Associates? Mr. Eddie Aronson, components engineer at TRW, suggested that I write you because he believes that I have the necessary qualifications for the position.

On May 11, I shall graduate from Austin Community College with an Associate in Science degree with a major in digital electronics. My overall grade point average is 3.2, and I have developed to a superior level the troubleshooting skills necessary for work as an electronic technician.

I am presently employed on a part-time basis as a senior assembler for the hybrid circuits division of Texas Instruments. This position has provided me with excellent opportunities to use my skills in solving some of the diverse problems a technician encounters.

You will find enclosed with this letter a personal data sheet, which will give you more complete information about my background and qualifications. At your convenience, I shall be glad to come to your office to discuss my experience and interests and the position with you. I can be reached by phone at (512) 954–1899 after 5 P.M.

Sincerely yours,

Harold Glidden

Encl.: Personal Data Sheet

FIGURE 11–6. (cont.)

P.O. Box 5285
Austin, Texas 78721

Office Manager
808C Guadalupe
Austin, Texas 78721

Dear Sir:

I am writing about your newspaper ad in the October 21 *Chronicle* concerning your need for a dependable, experienced, full-time legal secretary. I have these qualifications and plenty of experience with word processors, which your ad also mentions.

I have been a legal secretary for the past five years with Steen and Gross until last year when I took off to attend Austin Community College full-time. Well established now in my degree program, I hope to return to full-time work and to attend night classes in data processing.

As you can see from my resume, I have had experience in criminal, corporate, and civil law as a legal secretary. If all my qualifications meet your requirements, I would be pleased to meet with you any time at your convenience.

Cordially,

Rose Marie Guerra

enclosure: resume

FIGURE 11–6. (cont.)

STEP 3E.   Preparing the letter of application:

1. In the letter begin by identifying the purpose—to apply for a job. Avoid plunging directly into a discussion of your background without introducing the purpose of the letter. On your worksheet describe what you know about the job that you are seeking and the company for whom you would be doing that job.

2. In the first paragraph explain how you found out about the job—for example, through the newspaper or by word of mouth. On your worksheet, list and discuss the requirements or qualifications that one would need to do the job that you are seeking.

3. In the first paragraph make use of some attention-getting device; here are four common ones (some of which are used in combination in the preceding application letters):
   - Briefly refer to your most important qualification, that one credential that you think should get you hired.
   - Mention some bit of knowledge you have about the company to which you are applying for the job, something that shows you know about the company.
   - Mention the name of an individual who knows both you and people in the company to which you are applying, an individual who is willing to speak or write in your support to the prospective employer.
   - Ask the prospective employer a direct question concerning his or her needs, and explain that you can fulfill those needs.

   On your worksheet explain which, if any, of these attention-getting devices might work in your letter.

4. In the second paragraph of the application letter discuss the highlights of your qualifications—details of your education, work experience, or both. Leave less-important details to the resume. The application letter must be relatively short: a single page-length letter is preferable. On your worksheet, list those aspects of your education and work experience that relate to the job and that may help you get that job.

5. In the letter you can split the discussion of your experience and education into two paragraphs: one for education and one for work experience (whichever is your best qualification comes first). On your worksheet explain how you'll handle experience and education sections.

6. In the highlights paragraphs, show how your education, experience, or career goals fit the prospective employer's needs. Don't just state your best qualifications; show how they make you right for the job. On your worksheet explain which aspects of your education and work experience may prevent you from being hired and how you'll overcome these problems in the letter.

7. In the highlights paragraphs, discuss your career or occupational goals to show that you are serious about your work and your future. Use this strategy especially if you have little solid work experience and are at the start of your career. On your worksheet describe these goals.

8. At some point, mention that your resume accompanies the letter.

9. In the last paragraph encourage the prospective employer to arrange an interview (but do not demand an interview). Often, you can prompt the prospective

employer to schedule an interview in the same sentence that you explain how to contact you and when you are available. On your worksheet explain how you'll conclude the letter.

10. With the preceding steps completed, write a first draft of the body of the application letter. When you've done this, turn to step 4, and study the section preceding it.

Follow-up Letters.   Write a follow-up letter (a) when you've had no word for at least two weeks, (b) after you've had an interview, (c) when you want to acknowledge a refusal of a job offer, or (d) when you must either accept or reject a job offer. Use the following suggestions to write the follow-up letter if after two weeks you've received no response:

1. Identify the purpose of the letter—to ask what has happened to your application.
2. Give the date of the letter and specify the position that you have applied for.
3. Suggest that the letter was misplaced either by the post office or somewhere in the recipient's own company.
4. Enclose a copy of the original letter and resume that you sent, and mention that you've enclosed these items.
5. Encourage the recipient as tactfully as you can to let you know of the decision about the job, perhaps by indicating that your own decisions are dependent upon it.

Figure 11–7 contains an example of a follow-up letter written after the job hunter has had no response from the company.

Resumes

The resume, sometimes called the data sheet, is a record of your qualifications, experience, background, and any other information that might be useful to potential employers. Many different styles and formats for resumes are used, but the variety you'll see here covers many of the common types.

Gathering the Information

If it's your first resume, spend some time just gathering information about yourself. A good way to start is to set up a resume worksheet. It should include practically everything in your background, abilities, education, and character even remotely related to your job or career. Use the resume worksheet to explore your education and work experiences. You'll select information from it for the resume.

Education.   Provide information for any of the following categories that seem relevant. Try to think of other categories as well. Include information on high schools you have attended also.

Name of the institution	Degree received (or to be received)
Dates attended	Grade point average

801 East 54th Street #101
Austin, Texas 78715
March 3, 19XX

Director of Personnel
Automation Associates
7805 Pearl Creek Drive
Austin, Texas 78706

Dear Director of Personnel:

On February 17, I applied for a position as electronic technician with
your firm. Not having heard from you in the past two weeks since I
wrote the letter, I'm concerned that perhaps my letter has been lost.

Attached to this letter is a copy of the original letter that I sent on
February 17. As you will see, it details my work experience, education,
and my sincere interest in working for your company.

If you have made a decision about my application for the position, I
would appreciate hearing from you. My availability for the position and
my interest in it continue, and I look forward to the chance to discuss
the job and my background with you in person.

Sincerely,

Harold Glidden

Encl.: Copy of 2/17 letter and data sheet

FIGURE 11–7. Follow-up letter to an application
letter (block format)

All courses	Special projects
Major	Major emphasis of study
Major courses	Percent of expenses earned
Minor	Extracurricular activities (clubs, etc.)
Brief description	Honors and awards
Important courses	

Work Experience.   Provide the following information suggested on past jobs. If you don't have a great deal of work experience, list part-time jobs, even if they are not directly related to the work you are seeking.

Name and address of the organization	Name and address of supervisor
Brief description of the organization	Promotions
Dates you worked there	Title(s) of position(s) held
Brief list and description of duties	Major accomplishments

Military Experience.   Military experience is usually treated as a separate section in resumes. Provide information such as:

Branch of the military	Rank
Military occupation	Skills obtained
Years that you served	Area(s) stationed
Duties	

Occupational Goals.   As some of the examples of resumes show, career or occupational goals can be stated in the most eye-catching spot on the resume. (Do not include career objectives, however, if they might actually reduce your chances of being hired.) If you want an area like this on your resume, here is a list of what you can supply:

Short-range objectives	Kind of organization you want to work for
Long-range objectives	Position desired
Specific kind of work desired	

Most Important Qualifications.   You can also place your most important qualifications in the most strategic, eye-catching area of the resume. Here is the kind of information to provide:

Most important aspects of education
Most important positions held
Most important duties performed
Number of years positions held, duties performed
Most important accomplishments, awards, licenses, certificates, degrees
Most important skills, training, etc.

Special Skills or Licenses.   List your special skills, abilities, licenses, certificates, and equipment you know how to operate:

Special skills or licenses you have
When you received the certificate or license
How long you have used the skill

Where you learned the skill
Where you obtained the license
Equipment you've operated

Personal Background.   You may be surprised to learn that certain kinds of personal information on the resume can benefit you in your job hunt, even if the information is not related to the work you seek. Personal information rounds out the picture of you that the resume conveys; it shows that you are a human being, and it can cause potential employers to remember you. Because of antidiscrimination laws, certain information, such as information on your age, sex, marital status, or race, is no longer included. Information on health, weight, height, and so on also tends to be omitted. In the personal information section of your resume worksheet, list your interests and activities, but don't make up suspicious-looking interests such as "reading books on prestressed concrete" or "visiting refineries in the midwest." Here's a list of possibilities:

Interests
Hobbies
Community activities
Travel

Areas where you've lived
Reading interests
Languages

References.   References are the people willing to speak or write in your behalf. They can be both people who know your work and people who know you personally. Before you list these people as references, ask their permission:

Full name
Business or home address
Business or home phone number

Position or title
Organization

Designing the Resume Format

Once you've completed your resume worksheet, the next step is to design the format. In this phase, choose the overall order or arrangement of the major sections of the resume, and decide on the detailed format for the specific information in each of those sections. For ideas look at the example in Figure 11–8.

• *Overall order.* Although there is no standard order for the major sections, keep these guidelines in mind:

1. Your name, address, and phone number go first, at the top.
2. If you want a section on your most important qualifications, your career, or

both, place that section just below your name and address. Information a fourth to a third of the way down the page is usually what the reader sees first.

3. If your work experience is more relevant to the job you seek or if it is your strongest qualification, present it before your education. Present your education first if the reverse is true.

4. Personal information is usually placed toward the end of the resume, just before the references.

5. References are almost always presented last.

When you've decided on an overall arrangement, make a sketch of how your resume will look. (Refer to Figure 11–8.)

• *Detail formats.* A detail format is the way in which specific information within the sections of the resume is arranged on the page. These formats vary according to whether they are used in the heading, the education/experience section, or the concluding section. Study the examples that follow for detail formats that best present your qualifications.

FIGURE 11–8.   Sketches of resume designs

Headings. The heading of the resume contains elements such as your name, address, the position you are seeking, occupation or profession, career objectives, main qualifications, personal information, willingness to relocate, and the date of the preparation of the resume. Several examples of headings appear in Figure 11–9.

Education and Experience Sections. The middle portion of the resume summarizes your education and work experience. Here, the format for details is critical. Some of the detail formats in Figure 11–10 are *space savers*, which enable you to

Resume
of
SHARON E. PRICE
3341 Jolliffe Dr.
Shreveport, LA 70011
Phone: (816) 676-2323

Resume
of
BETTY S. NESLON

Address (until Jan. 1, 19XX)
1801 Oak Lane
Bloomington, IN 56560
(707) 192-8367

Address (after Jan. 1, 19XX)
1710 Humble Street
Lawrence, KS 66336
(613) 123-4567

Resume of

MARGARET M. HUGHES

1567 West 34th
Charlotte, NC 23546
(404) 876-0987

Age: 23
Marital status: single
Willing to relocate

FIGURE 11–9. Examples of resume headings

VIRGIL P. STEEN
  3535 Avenue F
  Ames, Iowa 69911   DENTAL HYGIENIST
  Phone: (818) 345-0987

OBJECTIVE: To gain experience as a dental hygienist with
emphasis in dental hygiene education as part of job
responsibilities.

Professional Training and Experience

of

MARIANA N. MARCONI

Medical Technologist
(ASCP Certification)

4611 Pleasant Dr.
Pittsburgh, PA 23440   Marital status: married,
                                 one son

Phone: (216) 787-9900 (work)   Willing to relocate
        (216) 784-2233 (home)   Available immediately

OBJECTIVE: To advance into ultrasound specialization in a large
metropolitan hospital with access to an AMA-approved
training institution.

EXPERIENCE: Six years of general medical technology experience in
private laboratories and clinics.

(continued)

FIGURE 11–9. (cont.)

EDUCATION: Foothill College, Los Altos Hills, CA 94022
             Degree: Associate in Science, summer of 1983
             Major: digital electronics

             3345th Tech School, Air Force, Chanute A.F.B., Ill.
             Specialization: graduate in Aerospace Ground Equip-
                               ment Repair, February 1981

EDUCATION

1983-present   Austin Community College, Austin, TX
                  Course work toward BA in Business

1981-1982   College of DuPage, Glen Ellyn, Ill.
                  Evening course work toward BA in Business

1976-1978   Ray Vogue Schools, Chicago, Ill.
                  Diploma with Honors, Interior Design

1974-1975   Virginia Polytechnic Institute and State University,
                     Blacksburg, Va.

1981-1985   The University of Texas at Austin

             Will graduate in May 19XX with a B.S. degree in
             Chemical Engineering, having a GPA of 3.2

Representative Courses   Descriptions

Chemical Engineering   Applied technical-writing
   Fundamentals Lab   background by writing a
                                       25-page report every 2 weeks.

Chemical Reactor Design   In one major project, researched
                                       and compiled 35-page
                                       technical design report.

FIGURE 11–10.   Education and experience sections
of resumes

Chemical Engineering Process
  Plant Design

Four major projects
  accompanied by 18 to 25-page
  reports.

WORK EXPERIENCE

January 1983
to June 1983

Accents and Interiors, Inc., Lawrence, KS
Store Manager.
Full range of retail sales functions: all floor
sales, design, and maintenance of store
displays; placement and follow-up on
special orders; maintenance of
manufacturer catalogs and samples.

August 1980
to June 1983

Creighton Corporation, St. Paul, Minn.
Design Consultant.
Assisting customers in coordinating fixture
styles and colors for kitchens and baths,
quoting selections to contractors, placing
and following up on same orders, arranging
and maintaining showroom displays.

WORK HISTORY

3/15/80 to
8/19/80

Brown & Root, P.O. Box 345, Seadrift, TX 77643
Job Title: Instrument Fitter
Duties: Installation of pneumatic control lines and
other control lines; left to obtain degree.

1/24/79 to
1/24/80

TWR/Vidor, 34 Bluff Ridge, Kansas City, MO 60003
Job Title: Documentation Specialist
Duties: Maintained electronic-parts data library and
published vendors' lists for the Material
Standards Engineering Department.

(continued)

FIGURE 11–10. (cont.)

WORK EXPERIENCE

April 1982-Present   City of San Diego, Law Department, Claims
                           Division

                           Duties

* Supervise, train, plan, and assign clerical duties
* Prepare correspondence for debts due
* Prepare monthly reports for the department
* Monitor and maintain accounts-receivable ledger

July 1980-   Lackland Federal Credit Union
April 1982

                           Duties

* Assist collection supervisor in maintaining accounts
* Collect and control loan accounts
* Prepare correspondence for debts due
* Research loan accounts

FIGURE 11–10.   (cont.)

present lots of information about yourself without overcrowding the page and causing reading problems. Other detail formats are *space users,* which enable you to
use up more space and to avoid having a skimpy-looking resume. If you are at the
beginning of your career, you may need space users to avoid emphasizing your lack
of experience.

In the examples in Figure 11–10 notice how individual jobs or phases of education are presented in *reverse chronological order* and how the first parts of sentences (usually "I") are omitted.

Concluding Sections.   In the concluding section, list personal data, interests,
professional and honorary memberships, special skills, community activities, licenses, references, and the date of the preparation of the resume. Some examples are
provided in Figure 11–11.

PERSONAL INFORMATION

Interests: music, cooking, sewing, painting
Organization: Phi Chi Theta Business Fraternity,
University Pre-Law Association,
International Business Association, Student
Involvement Committee

REFERENCES: provided on request   January 24, 19XX

Personal Information

High School Honor Graduate, Member of National Honor Society,
University Accounting Association, University Finance Club,
Association of Real Estate Majors

Interests include piano, martial arts, cooking, jogging, crafts

References

Available upon request

May 19XX

PERSONAL INFORMATION

Academic Achievements: Oklahoma Achievement Award, Jones
Engineering Scholar, OU Engineering Dean's List (fall/spring 1981-82
and 1983-84), National Honor Society.

Organizations and Clubs: American Institute of Chemical Engineers,
Oklahoma Relays Committee, American Diabetics Association member.

Activities and Interests: health- and fitness-oriented interests; sports,
including marathon running, tennis, gymnastics. Enjoy ballet recitals,
musicals, and cats.

REFERENCES PROVIDED ON REQUEST   January 1, 19XX

(continued)

FIGURE 11–11. Concluding sections of resumes

AFFILIATIONS:

Registered Nurse License for Indiana, North Dakota, and Maine
American Association for Critical Care Nurses, member certification:
CCRN

SPECIAL INTERESTS:

Sewing, ceramics, music, traveling, language study (4 years of Spanish
and 3 semesters each in French and German)

SKILLS TRAINING:

IBM 8775 Word Processor	PBX Switchboard
Manual & electric typewriters	CRT terminals
Key punch machines	Adding Machines

PROFESSIONAL SOCIETIES:

San Diego Society for Public Administration

REFERENCES:

James S. Harding	Julio X. Ramirez
Deputy Director of Personnel	Director of Administrative
City of San Diego	Services
P.O. Box 1880	San Diego Police Dept.
San Diego, CA 98886	San Diego, CA 98885
Phone: (919) 234-0987	Phone: (919) 678-5432

February 12, 19XX

FIGURE 11–11.   (cont.)

Drafting and Finishing the Resume

When you've done the preceding preparations, it's time to type a rough draft to get a sense of how your resume will look. If necessary, use scissors and tape to cut out the sections and try different arrangements to achieve balance or symmetry. Leave as much white space around the sections of the resume as possible, and make the resume fit the page properly.

When you type the final copy of the resume, do as neat and careful a job as possible. Once you have the final copy the way that you want it, you are ready to make photocopies. (See Chapter 10 on final-packaging techniques.) Figure 11–12 contains an example of a finished resume.

HAROLD D. GLIDDEN

108 W. 43 St., Apt. #110
Austin, Texas 78751
(512) 444-7878

EMPLOYMENT OBJECTIVE: Obtain an entry-level electronic technician position affording opportunities to learn and progress. Seeking long-term employment.

EDUCATION   Baker University, Baldwin City, Kansas 66006
Degree: Associate in Science, summer 1983
Major: Digital electronics

Attended North Valley College, Saratoga, Kansas, 9/77 to 1/78. Studied general subjects.

Graduate of 3345th Tech School, Chanute A.F.B., Illinois.
Specialization: Aerospace ground equipment repair, February 1971.

WORK HISTORY

Mar. 1980   Brown & Root, Inc., P.O. Box 567, Old Ocean,
  to   Texas 77463
Aug. 1980   Job title: Instrument fitter
                   Duties: Installation of pneumatic control lines
                   and pressure gauges. (Left to obtain degree.)

(continued)

FIGURE 11–12.   Example of a finished resume

Jan. 1979   TRW/Vidar, 77 Ortega Ave., Mountain View,
   to   California 94040
Jan. 1980   Job title: Documentation specialist
                 Duties: Maintained electronic-parts data
                          library and published the vendors' list
                          for the Material Standards Engineering
                          Dept. (Left for degree.)

Sept. 1976   Dynamic Valves, Inc., 923 Industrial Ave.,
   to   Palo Alto, California 94303
May 1977   Job title: Hydraulic lab technician
                 Duties: Assembly, inspection, and repair of
                          electrohydraulic servo controls. (Left to
                          attend school.)

REFERENCES AVAILABLE ON REQUEST   September 1983

FIGURE 11–12.   (cont.)

STEP 3F.   Preparing the resume:

1. Begin a resume worksheet like the one just described. Set up sections for each of the relevant categories listed, and fill them in with information about your background.
2. Write out a rough sketch of your resume as suggested for the worksheet. Decide whether the section on your work experience or the section on your education should go first.
3. On your resume worksheet circle or highlight the elements you want in the heading of your resume, and then sketch out this heading on your resume worksheet.
4. On your worksheet circle or highlight elements of work experience or education you want to include in the resume; select a detail format in which to incorporate that information; and write a rough draft of this part of your resume.
5. On your resume worksheet circle or highlight the personal information you want in the concluding section.
6. Now, rough type a complete draft of your resume to see how the format works. Use scissors and tape to try out different arrangements if you don't like the way your resume looks.
7. Type and make photocopies of the finished resume according to the guidelines suggested in the final-packaging section of Chapter 10.

Components and Formats for Business Correspondence

To this point in the chapter you've considered the content and organization of business correspondence: this section is concerned with the mechanical and physical details. When you have a rough draft of your letter or memo, the next steps are to select a format, revise, and do the final typing.

Components of Business Correspondence

To understand the discussion of formats that follows, you need to know the terms for the main components, which are shown in the example in Figure 11–13.

• *Heading.* The heading contains the writer's address and the date of the letter. The writer's name is not included, and only a date is needed in headings on letter-head stationery.

• *Inside address.* The inside address shows the name and address of the recipient of the letter. This information helps prevent confusion. Also, if the recipient has moved, the inside address helps to determine what to do with the letter. In the inside address include the appropriate title of respect for the recipient, and copy the name of the company exactly as that company writes it.

• *Salutation.* The salutation, the "Dear Sir or Madam" of the letter, is followed by a colon (except when a friendly, familiar, sociable tone is intended, in which case a comma is used). Notice that in the simplified-letter format (see Figure 11–4), the salutation line is eliminated altogether. If you don't know whether the recipient is a man or woman, traditionally you write "Dear Sir" or "Dear Sirs" and just not worry about it. More recently, however, salutations such as "Dear Sir or Madam," "Dear Ladies and Gentlemen," "Dear Friends," or "Dear People" have been recommended. Deleting the salutation line altogether or inserting "To Whom It May Concern," in its place, however, is not always a good solution; this approach is quite impersonal.

Try to get a person's name within the organizaton; make a quick, anonymous phone call to get a name. Or, address the salutation to a department name, committee name, or a position name: "Dear Customer Relations Department," or "Dear Recruitment Committee," "Dear Chairperson," or "Dear Director of Financial Aid," for example.

When you do have the names of individuals, remember to address them appropriately: Mrs., Ms., Mr., Dr., and so on. If you are not sure what is correct for an individual, try to find out how that individual signs letters or consult the forms-of-address section in a dictionary.

• *Subject or reference line.* As shown in Figures 11–3 and 11–4, the subject line replaces the salutation or is included with it. The subject line announces the main business of the letter.

• *Body of the letter.* The actual message, of course, is contained in the body of the letter, the paragraphs between the salutation and the complimentary close.

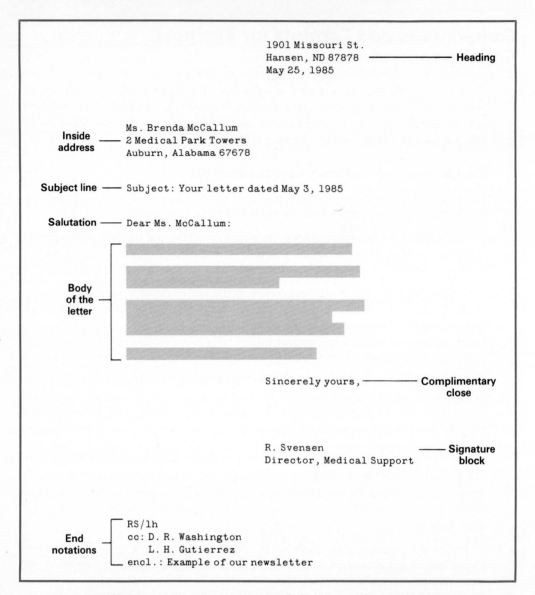

1901 Missouri St.
Hansen, ND 87878 ———————— **Heading**
May 25, 1985

Inside ——— Ms. Brenda McCallum
address   2 Medical Park Towers
Auburn, Alabama 67678

Subject line ——— Subject: Your letter dated May 3, 1985

Salutation ——— Dear Ms. McCallum:

**Body
of the
letter**

Sincerely yours, ———————— **Complimentary
close**

R. Svensen ——————— **Signature
Director, Medical Support   block**

**End
notations**   RS/lh
cc: D. R. Washington
L. H. Gutierrez
encl.: Example of our newsletter

FIGURE 11—13. Components of the typical business letter

Strategies for writing the body of the letter are discussed in "Tips on Writing
Business Letters."

• *Complimentary close.* The "Sincerely" element of the business letter is called
the complimentary close. Other common ones are "Sincerely yours," "Cordially,"
"Respectfully," or "Respectfully yours." You can design your own, but be careful
not to create florid or wordy ones. Notice that only the first letter is capitalized,
and the close is always followed by a comma.

• *Signature block*. Usually, you type your name four lines below the complimentary close, and sign your name in between. If you are a woman and want to make your marital status clear, use Miss, Ms., or Mrs. in parentheses before the typed version of your first name. Whenever possible, include your title or the name of the position you hold just below your name. For example, "Technical writing student," "Sophomore data-processing major," or "Tarrant County Community College Student" are perfectly acceptable.

• *End notations*. Just below the signature block are often several abbreviations or phrases that have important functions.

—*Initials*. The initials in all capital letters in Figure 11–2 are those of the writer of the letter, and the ones in lowercase letters just after the colon are those of the typist.

—*Enclosures*. To make sure that the recipient knows that items accompany the letter in the same envelope, use such indications as "Enclosure," "Encl.," "Enclosures (2)." For example, if you send a resume and writing sample with your application letter, you'd do this: "Encl.: Resume and Writing Sample." If the enclosure is lost, the recipient will know.

—*Copies*. If you send copies of a letter to others, indicate this fact among the end notations also. If, for example, you were upset by a local merchant's handling of your repair problems and were sending a copy of your letter to the Better Business Bureau, you'd write this: "cc: Better Business Bureau." If you plan to send a copy to your lawyer, write something like this: "cc: Mr. Raymond Mason, Attorney."

• *Following pages*. If your letter is longer than one page, the heading at the top of subsequent pages can be handled in one of the ways shown in Figure 11–14. If you use letterhead stationery, remember *not* to use it for subsequent pages. However, you must use blank paper of the same quality, weight, and texture as the letterhead paper (usually, letterhead stationery comes with matching blank paper).

Mr. Raymond Mason	-2-	October 19, 1984
Mrs. Raymond Mason	October 19, 1984	Page 2

Mr. Raymond Mason
October 19, 1984
Page 2

FIGURE 11–14. Three formats for following pages in business letters

• *Envelope.* As illustrated in Figure 11–15, the envelope contains the recipient's address and the sender's address. Traditionally, you do not put your name on the envelope, but it can facilitate the return of a letter within large organizations if handling problems occur. Normally, business-letter envelopes are the long, 8½-inch kind.

STEP 4.   On your worksheet write or list the information you need in your letter: the (a) heading, (b) inside address, (c) subject/reference line, (d) salutation, (e) complimentary close, (f) signature block (specifically, your title), (g) end notations as needed, (h) the heading for following pages if needed, and (i) the information on the envelope. If you are writing a memo, write (a) the name of the person to whom it is addressed and (b) the subject of the memo.

Business-Letter Formats

If you are writing a business letter, select one of the common formats as shown in the preceding examples. These include the block letter, the semiblock letter, the alternative block letter, and the simplified letter.

- For the block letter, see Figures 11–5 and 11–7.
- For the semiblock letter, see Figures 11–1 and 11–2.
- For the alternative block letter, see Figure 11–3.
- For the simplified letter, see Figure 11–4.

P. H. Murray
1103 Rundberg
Provo, Utah 86772

Mr. Julio X. Ramirez
Director of Administrative Services
San Diego Police Department
San Diego, CA 98881

FIGURE 11–15.   Envelope format for business letters

Which of these formats to use depends on the ones commonly used in your organization or the situation in which you are writing. Use the simplified letter if you lack the name of an individual or department to write to.

Memoranda

If you are writing a memo, the format is generally the same in most cases. Because the memorandum resembles the business letter in many ways, most of the advice on writing business letters in this chapter applies. Memos are often preferable to conversations for generally the same reasons business letters are: the memo, like the letter, becomes a permanent record that does not vanish from sight or mind as easily as a conversation in the hallway. The advice in this chapter on writing effective business letters, therefore, applies generally to memos:

- State the business or purpose of the memo right away.
- If you are responding to another memo, identify that memo by date and subject early.
- Keep the paragraphs short.
- Compartmentalize the contents of the memo in paragraphs.
- Locate words or phrases that indicate the main subject or purpose of a paragraph in the first sentence.
- List or enumerate whenever possible.
- Place important information in the emphasis, or high-visibility, points of paragraphs and less-positive or detrimental information in areas of less emphasis.
- Try to find positive ways to express bad news whenever possible.
- Try to focus on the reader's needs, purposes, or interests rather than on your own.
- Avoid pompous, inflated, legal-sounding phrasing.
- Use action-oriented endings to let readers know what to do.

The common types of memos generally resemble the common types of business letters and some of the common types of reports:

- Many memos request information and thus resemble letters of inquiry.
- Many memos convey information and thus resemble information reports or responses to inquiry letters.
- Memos are often written to order supplies or equipment and thus resemble order letters.
- Memos often communicate instructions on procedures to follow in operating equipment.
- Finally, memos often propose or recommend in the same way that report-length proposals and feasibility studies do.

Memos differ from business letters particularly in format. In the examples in Figure 11–16, notice that instead of the familiar heading, inside address, salutation, and signature block, the memo has lines for the recipient of the memo, "TO," for the sender, "FROM," and for the subject of the memo, "SUBJ." or "RE."

Memos are also more direct than most business letters because the recipients are likely to be acquainted with the writers, closer at hand, and familiar with the subject matter already.

To: Supplies Department
From: Jane Allen Murray, Personnel
Subj.: Desk supplies for new secretary

Please deliver the supplies listed below to Room 3.303A to John Cullen, a new secretary in our office:

Cat. No.	Description	Quantity	Unit Cost	Costs
K4-85677	Desk Blotter	1	25.00	25.00
YA-234	Three-Hole Punch	2	13.95	27.90
T5-1256	Bulletin Board	1	30.00	30.00
Y15-457	Stapler	2	7.25	14.50
			TOTAL	97.40

Bill these items to our department as usual.

TO: Ellen Vracek, Records   March 3, 19XX
FROM: Avery Hunt
SUBJ.: Info on real estate

At your earliest convenience, please send me the following information on Lot 47A in Bastrop Meadows subdivision, Smithville County, Texas:

1. Last sales price
2. Square footage
3. Amenities
4. Date of last sale

If we have a complete description of the property on file, please let me know. Thanks again.

FIGURE 11—16. Examples of memoranda

TO: Mayor and Councilmembers
FROM: Nancy Jensen, City Manager
DATE: April 23, 19XX

SUBJECT: Wheeler Park

The staff recommends that the Capital Improvements Project be amended for Wheeler Park to perform restoration work in the park including the improvement of retaining walls and play areas. For the following reasons it is not recommended that the streets adjacent to this park be closed:

1. There is substantial difference of opinion on the closure, and the CIP was dependent on neighborhood agreement.
2. The closure will not add substantially to the green space in the park.
3. The Urban Transportation Department has taken steps to address the traffic concerns that have been expressed by the residents of the area.

The full text of the staff's study and recommendations is available in my office, or I will be glad to send you a copy.

FIGURE 11–16. (cont.)

STEP 5.   Select a format for your business correspondence, explain which you plan to use on your correspondence worksheet (if it's a letter, also explain which letter format you'll use, and why).

Tips on Writing Business Letters and Memos

Writing business letters and memos differs in certain important ways from writing reports. Keep the following advice in mind when you write and especially when you revise your business letters or memos.

• *State the main business, purpose, or subject matter of your letter in the first sentence if at all possible.* Let the reader know from the very first sentence what your letter is about. If you are writing to apply for a job, begin with something like this: "I am writing to apply for the position you currently have open. . . ." If you have bad news for someone, you need not spill all of it in the first sentence. Here is an example of how to avoid negative phrasing: "I am writing in response to your letter of July 24, 1984, in which you discuss problems you have had with an electronic spreadsheet purchased from our company." This opener still announces what is to be the subject of the letter.

Remember that when businesspeople open a letter, their first concern is to know what the letter is about, what its purpose is, and why they must spend their time reading it. Therefore, avoid roundabout beginnings in business letters such as this one (the main business has been underscored):

Business Letter with a Problem Opener

Dear Sir:

On June 1 of this year I purchased a McCallum Model 311 chainsaw from your company. I had difficulties with the saw from the very beginning. After checking with your company, I took the saw to a local repair shop, H & H Lawn and Garden, here in Santa Barbara, for warranty service. The problem, a misaligned chain assembly, was corrected in one day. About three weeks later, however, I again had problems. I took the saw back to H & H. The repairman there said he would have to order parts for the carburetor, so I left the saw there, expecting it to be ready in about a week.

However, four weeks went by, and H & H was still unable to get the needed parts. At this time, I had an out-of-town project that called for a dependable chainsaw, so I rented a saw for a total of $35. When I returned to Santa Barbara, I found out that the reason for the delay was that your company had lost H & H's parts order.

As a result of this inconvenience and expense, <u>I am writing you to request reimbursement</u> on the rental charges I paid for a dependable chain saw <u>and a brand-new replacement for the chainsaw that I originally bought.</u>

Revision

Dear Sir:

I am writing this letter to describe problems that I have had over the past five months with one of your chainsaws and to request reimbursement for rental charges that I incurred during that time and for a new replacement saw.

Problems with the McCallum Model 311 chainsaw began from the very beginning when I bought it on June 1. After checking with your company, I took the saw to a local repair shop, H & H Lawn and Garden, here in Santa Barbara....

• *If you are responding to a letter, identify that letter by its subject and date in the first paragraph or sentence.* Busy recipients who write many letters themselves may not remember their letters to you. To avoid problems, identify the date and subject of the letter to which you respond:

Dear Mr. Stout:

I am writing in response to your 1 September 19XX letter in which you describe problems that you've had with one of our chainsaws. I regret that you've suffered this inconvenience and expense and....

Dear Ms. Cohen:

I have just received your 4 August 19XX letter in which you list names and other sources from which I can get additional information on the manufacture and use of plastic bottles in the soft-drink industry....

• *Keep the paragraphs of most business letters short.* The paragraphs of business letters tend to be short, some only a sentence long. Business letters are not read the same way as articles, reports, or books. Usually, they are read rapidly. Big, thick, dense paragraphs over ten lines, which require much concentration, may not be read carefully—or read at all.

To enable the recipient to read your letters more rapidly and to comprehend and remember the important facts or ideas, create relatively short paragraphs of between three and eight lines long. In business letters, paragraphs that are made up of only a single sentence are common and perfectly acceptable. Throughout this chapter you'll see examples of the shorter paragraphs commonly used in business letters.

• *Compartmentalize the contents of your letter.* When you compartmentalize the contents of a business letter, you place each different segment of the discussion— each different topic of the letter—in its own paragraph. If you were writing a complaint letter concerning problems with the system unit of your personal computer, you might have these paragraphs:

• A description of the problems you've had with it
• The ineffective repair jobs you've had
• The compensation you think you deserve and why

Study each paragraph of your letters for its purpose, content, or function. When you locate a paragraph that does more than one thing, consider splitting it into two paragraphs. If you discover two short, separate paragraphs that do the same thing, consider joining them into one. Analyze some of the letters you see in this chapter in terms of the contents or purpose of their individual paragraphs.

• *In the first sentence of any paragraph within the body of a business letter, try to locate a word or phrase that indicates the topic of that paragraph.* If a paragraph discusses your problems with a personal computer, work the word *problems* or the phrase *problems with my personal computer* into the first sentence. Doing this gives recipients a clear sense of the content and purpose of each paragraph. Here is an excerpt before and after topic indicators have been incorporated:

Problem Version: No Topic Indication

I have worked as an electrician in the Decatur, Illinois, area for about six years. Since 1980 I have been licensed by the city of Decatur as an electrical contractor qualified to undertake commercial and industrial work as well as residential work.

Revision

As for *my work experience,* I have worked as an electrician in the Decatur, Illinois, area for about six years. Since 1980 I have been licensed by the city of Decatur as an electrical contractor qualified to undertake commercial and industrial work as well as residential work. [italics not in the original]

• *List or itemize whenever possible in a business letter.* Listing spreads out the text of the letter, making it easier to pick up the important points rapidly. Lists can be handled in several ways, as explained in Chapter 6. For examples of lists in business correspondence, see Figures 11–1 and 11–4.

• *Place important information at emphasis, or high-visibility, points in your business letters.* Information in the first and last lines of paragraphs tends to be read and remembered more readily. Information buried in the middle of long paragraphs is easily overlooked or forgotten. Therefore, place important information in high-visibility points. For example, in application letters which must convince potential employers that you are right for a job, locate information on appealing qualities at the beginning or end of paragraphs for greater emphasis. Here is a paragraph in which the writer seeks a technical-writing job and a revision of the paragraph for emphasis (italics have been added to show what must be emphasized):

Problem Version: Emphasis Lacking

In July I will graduate from the University of Kansas with a Bachelor of Science in Nutrition and Dietetics. Over the past four years in which I have pursued this degree, I have worked as a lab assistant to Dr. Alison Laszlo and have been active in two related organizations, the Student Dietetic Association and the American Home Economics Association. In my nutritional biochemistry and food science labs, *I have written many technical reports* and scientific papers. I have also been serving as a diet aide at St. David's Hospital in Lawrence the past year and a half.

Revision

In my education at the University of Kansas, *I have had substantial experience writing technical reports* and scientific papers. Most of these reports and papers have been in the field of nutrition and dietetics, in which I will be receiving my Bachelor of Science degree this July. During my four years at the university I have also handled plenty of paperwork as a lab assistant for Dr. Alison Laszlo; as a member of two related organizations, the Student Dietetic Association and the American Home Economics Association; and as a dietetic aide at St. David's Hospital in Lawrence in the past year and a half.

• *Place less-positive or detrimental information in less visible points in your business letters.* The reverse of the preceding strategy is to use the middle of paragraphs for points that are to receive less attention. If you have some difficult things to say, a good (and honest) strategy is to deemphasize them in areas of less emphasis. If a job requires three years of experience and you only have one, bury this fact in the middle or the lower half of a paragraph in the body of the application letter. The resulting letter will be honest and complete; it just won't emphasize weak points unnecessarily. Here's a pair of paragraphs, the second version of which not only relocates negative information in low-visibility areas but finds an almost positive way of saying it (emphasis has been added):

Problem Version: Unwanted Emphasis

To date, *I have done no independent building inspection on my own.* I have been working the past two years under the supervision of Mr. Robert Packwood, who has often given me primary responsibility for walk-throughs and property inspections. It was Mr. Packwood who encouraged me to apply for this position. I have also done some refurbishing of older houses on a contract basis and have some experience in industrial construction as a welder and as a clerk in a nuclear construction site.

Revision

As for my work experience, I have done numerous building walk-throughs and property inspections under the supervision of Mr. Robert Packwood over the past two years. Mr. Packwood, who encouraged me to apply for this position, has often given me primary responsibility for many inspection jobs. I have also done some refurbishing of older houses on a contract basis and have some experience in industrial construction as a welder and as a clerk in a nuclear construction site.

• *Try to find positive ways to express bad news in your business letters.* Often, business letters must convey bad news: a broken computer keyboard cannot be replaced, or an individual cannot be hired. Such bad news can be conveyed in a tactful way. Doing so reduces the chances that business relations with the recipients of the bad news will end. To convey bad news positively, avoid such words as *cannot, forbid, fail, impossible, refuse, prohibit, restrict,* and *deny* as much as possible. The first versions of the examples are phrased in a rather cold and unfriendly negative manner; the second version is much more positive, cordial, and tactful:

Problem Negative Phrasing

Because of the amount of information you request in your letter, I simply cannot help you without seriously disrupting my work schedule.

If you do not complete and return this advertisement contract by July 1, 19XX, you will not receive your advertising space in this year's *Capitol Lines.* If we have not heard from you by this deadline, we will sell your advertisement space to some other client.

While I am willing to discuss changes in specific aspects of this article or ideas on additional areas to cover, I am not prepared to change the basic theme of the article: the usability of the Victor microcomputer system.

Revisions

In your letter you ask for a good amount of information, which I would like to help you locate. Because of my busy work schedule, however, I am going to be able to answer only a few of the questions. . . .

Please complete the enclosed contract and return it to us by July 1, 19XX. After this deadline, we will begin selling any unrenewed advertisement space in this year's *Capitol Lines,* so I hope we hear from you before then.

I am certainly open to suggestions and comments about specific aspects of this article, or any of your thoughts on additional areas that you think I should cover. I do want, however, to retain the basic theme of the article: the usability of the Victor microcomputer system.

• *Try to focus on the recipient's needs, purposes, or interests rather than exclusively on your own.* Avoid a self-centered focusing on your own concerns rather than those of the recipient. Even if you must talk about yourself in a business letter a great deal, do so in a way that relates your concerns to those of the recipient. This recipient-oriented style is often called the "you-attitude," which does not mean using more *you*'s but making the recipient the main focus of the letter.

Problem Version: Focus on the Writer Rather than the Recipient

I am writing you about a change in our pricing policy that will save our company time and money. In an operation like ours, it costs us a great amount of labor time (and thus expense) to scrape and rinse our used tableware when it comes back from large parties. Also, we have incurred great expense on replacement of linens that have been ruined by stains that could have been soaked promptly after the party and saved.

For these reasons, our new policy, effective September 1, 19XX, will be to charge an additional 15% on unrinsed tableware and 75% of the wholesale value of stained linens that have not been soaked.

Revisions

I am writing to inform you of a new policy that we are beginning, effective September 1, 19XX, that will enable us to serve your large-party needs more often and without delay. In an operation like ours in which we supply for parties of up to 500, turnaround time is critical; unscraped and unrinsed tableware causes us delays in cleanup time and, more importantly, less frequent and less prompt service to you, the customer. Also, linens ruined by stains that could have been avoided by immediate soaking after the party cause you to have to pay more in rental fees.

Therefore, in order to enable us to supply your large-party needs promptly and whenever you require, we will begin charging 15% on all unrinsed tableware and 75% of the wholesale value of stained linens that have not been soaked. This policy, we hope, will encourage our customers' kitchen help to do the quick and simple rinsing and/or soaking at the end of large parties that will ensure faster and less expensive service.

• *Avoid pompous, inflated, legal-sounding phrasing.* Watch out for puffed-up, important-sounding language. This kind of language may seem businesslike at first; it's actually ridiculous. When you write a business letter, picture yourself as a plain-talking, commonsense, down-to-earth person (but avoid slang). Here is an example of a wordy, inflated passage and a revision:

Problem Version: Pompous, Inflated Language

The Capital Improvements Project (hereinafter to be designated as CIP) for the fiscal year 1982–1983 stipulated budget allocations in the amount not exceeding $20,000 to be designated for utilization by a program under the nomination of the 23rd Street Renaissance Market. The purpose and aim of the aforesaid program is to provide and permit basic pedestrian amenities and conveniences for a marketplace devoted to the commerce of arts and crafts to the maximum extent possible. In consideration of these dictates, the CIP has mandated that there be a geographical extension of the sidewalk no greater than fifteen feet in a northerly direction. The said extension would continue to permit an opening of approximately fifteen feet for the orderly flow and passage of vehicular traffic.

The city council in 1982 issued directives that mandated the temporary closure of the above named street for a period not to exceed one calendar year. In April of the ensuing year it was directed by the city council that this closure remain in full effect for a period not exceeding an additional six months.

Revision

The Capital Improvements Program (CIP) in 1982–1983 included the amount of $20,000 for the 23rd Street Renaissance Market to provide sidewalks for an arts-and-crafts marketplace. The detailed plans of the CIP called for an extension of the sidewalk fifteen feet north, with a fifteen-foot opening for automobiles.

In 1982 the city council temporarily closed 23rd Street for a one-year period. In April of 1983, the council extended that closure for an additional six-month period, which will end in October 1983.

• *Give your business letter an action-oriented ending whenever appropriate.* An action-oriented ending makes clear what the writer of the letter expects the recipient to do and when. Ineffective conclusions to business letters often end with rather limp, noncommittal statements such as "Hope to hear from you soon" or "Let me know if I can be of any further assistance." Instead—or in addition—specify the action the recipient should take and the schedule for that action. If, for example, you are writing a query letter, ask the editor politely to let you know of his decision if at all possible in a month. If you are writing an application letter, subtly try to set up a date and time for an interview. Here are some examples:

As soon as you approve this plan, I'll begin contacting sales representatives at once to arrange for purchase and delivery of the microcomputers. May I expect to hear from you within the week?

I am free after 2:00 P.M. on most days. Can we set up an appointment to discuss my background and this position further? I look forward to hearing from you.

Finishing Business Letters and Memos

This section covers the finishing stages critical in letter and memo writing in particular. For other revising and proofreading strategies, see Chapters 7 and 10.

Revising

When you have written the rough draft of your letter, spend some time rereading it carefully for the full range of potential problems. Naturally, you want to spot grammar, punctuation, and spelling errors; they stand out in a business letter. But you'll also want to think carefully about the tone, content, and organization of your letter.

STEP 6.   Revise the rough draft of your letter or memo, using the advice in Chapter 7 and in Chapter 10 and the guidelines presented in the preceding section "Tips on Writing Business Letters and Memos."

Final Packaging: Originals and Photocopies

The physical or mechanical details of business letters can be just as important as format and prose style. Not only must your letter be written well; it must also be neat and professional-looking. If you've not already done so, read Chapter 10 for final-packaging tips on the following:

Kind and quality of paper to use
Typing suggestions
Correction techniques
Photocopying precautions

Here are some suggestions that relate specifically to business letters:

- Sending a photocopied letter is much less acceptable than sending photocopied reports.
- When you send the original, make a good clean typing job of it: take care not to smudge the paper or to crumple the pages.
- If you correct a typo with liquid paper, make as small a dot of it over the error as you can; a big blob is unsightly.
- If there are many typos to correct, resign yourself to retyping the page. A heavily corrected letter does not reflect well on you or create a good impression of your ability or work.
- Position the contents of your letter carefully on the page. Avoid jamming the whole letter into the top third or quarter of the page or having only one or two lines appear on a final page. Compare the poorly aligned letter in Figure 11–17 to the better version in Figure 11–7.

STEP 7.   If you are ready to produce the final copy of your letter, make sure that you have the necessary materials (good paper, adequate ribbon, liquid paper, etc.) before you begin. As you finish each page, check for typos and positioning of the letter on the page.

EXERCISES

1. Schedule interviews with people in business, industry, and government, and ask them these questions about the business letters they write and receive:
   - What are the audience, purpose, and content of your typical letters?
   - What adjustments in style, tone, or content do you have to make in certain cases?
   - Which types of letters do you write and receive?
   - What makes some letters effective and others ineffective?
   - Why do you write letters as opposed to conducting your business on the phone or in person?
2. Pretend you have just opened a small business and must write these letters:
   - A letter to your banker reviewing a recent discussion of your need for a loan to purchase more inventory
   - An order letter for supplies or other inventory
   - A general sales letter seeking business for your company
   - A complaint letter about problems you had with the products or services of a company other than your own

801 East 54th Street #101
Austin, Texas 78715
March 3, 19XX

Director of Personnel
Automation Associates
7805 Pearl Creek Drive
Austin, Texas 78706

Dear Director of Personnel:

On February 17 I applied for a position as electronic technician with
your firm. Not having heard from you in the past two weeks since I
wrote the letter, I'm concerned that perhaps my letter has been lost.
Attached to this letter is a copy of the original letter that I sent on
February 17. If you have made a decision, I would appreciate hearing
from you. I look forward to the chance to discuss the job and my
background with you in person.

Sincerely,

Harold Glidden

Encl.: Copy of 2/17 letter and data sheet

FIGURE 11–17. Example of a poorly positioned business letter

- An adjustment letter either in response to the preceding letter or in response to a customer who has had problems with the products or services of your company
- A letter of application and a resume from someone seeking employment with your company
- An inquiry letter to your company seeking information about your products or services or to some other company seeking information about its products or services
- A response to the preceding letter

Use the steps in this chapter to write these letters.

3. Schedule an interview with a person whose work occasionally requires her or him to read letters of application and resumes. Ask questions such as these:
    - What makes some of the letters and resumes effective and others ineffective?
    - What are some of the specific problems that cause the ineffective ones to fail?
    - What strategies or techniques do the good letters and resumes use?
    - What strategies can the person with only minimal work experience use in the letter of application and resume?

4. Schedule an interview with a person in business, industry, or government, and discuss the memoranda that he or she typically writes and receives. Ask the same general questions as are listed in exercise 1.

5. If you have a friendly, inside connection with someone in business, industry or government, ask to see a sampling of the letters and memos that person receives or writes. Evaluate them according to the guidelines presented here in this chapter. Make a list of the differences that you discover and a list of the problems that you notice. Also, keep a list of the strategies or techniques that are not covered here.

CHAPTER 12

Designing and Writing Informational Reports

Chapter Objectives
Progress Reports
  Reasons for Progress Reports
  Ideas for Progress Reports
  Timing and Format of Progress Reports
  Organizational Patterns for Progress Reports
  Gathering Information for Progress Reports
  Other Parts of Progress Reports
Primary-Research Reports
  Problem or Question
  Purpose, Objectives, and Scope
  Review of Literature
  Materials, Equipment, and Facilities
  Methods and Procedures
  Results or Findings
  Discussions, Conclusions, and Recommendations
Technical-Background Report
  Finding a Report Topic
  Analyzing or Creating a Report Situation
  Narrowing the Report Topic
  Developing a Rough Outline

Determining the Kinds of Writing Needed
Identifying Sources of Information
Gathering Information and Taking Notes
Other Informational Reports
  Site-Inspection and Field-Trip Reports
  Work Estimates
  Survey Results
  Minutes of Meetings
Finishing Informational Reports
Exercises
Models
  12–1 Progress on Technical-Background Report on Computer Structures and Logic Design (progress report)
  12–2 Altering the Spawning Cycle of Rainbow Trout by Manipulating Water Temperature (primary-research report)
  12–3 Report on Light-Water Nuclear Reactors (excerpt from a technical-background report)

--------------------- *Chapter Objectives* ---------------------

After you read this chapter, study the examples, work the steps, and do the practice writing, you should be able to:

- Explain what an informational report is.
- List the common ways to design a progress report.
- Explain the function of progress reports and primary research reports.
- List the typical parts of progress reports and primary research reports.
- List the typical steps in writing a technical-background report.
- Identify the common content and purpose of site-inspection and field-trip reports.
- Identify the common elements of work estimates, survey results, and minutes of meetings.

When you write an informational report, your goal is to provide readers with the information that they need. For example, if you are an expert on computer-based instructional materials for public schools, a school district might hire you to prepare an *informational* report on which instructional programs are available for its specific needs. If the district asked you to recommend a certain package of educational software, you'd write a different kind of report, a feasibility report, discussed in Chapter 14.

The same would be the case if you were an energy consultant for public utilities: if city planners asked you to provide information on the different technologies, operational characteristics, economics, and environmental considerations related to new emissions-control systems for coal-fired utility plants, you'd write an informational report. If they asked you to report on the feasibility (technological and economic practicality) of this system, again you'd write the kind of report discussed in Chapter 14.

The informational report also differs from instructional writing. If you, as an expert on computer-based instruction, were asked to write a guide for schools explaining how to select the right hardware and software for computer-based educational facilities, you'd be writing instructions, discussed in Chapter 13. If you, as an energy consultant, were asked to write a manual on the operation, maintenance, and repair of new emissions-control equipment associated with a coal-fired generator, you'd be writing instructions.

Here are some additional examples of these types of reports:

Informational Report	Instructional Report	Feasibility Report
New methods of diabetes control	How to use the new insulin-infusion device for diabetes control	Whether diabetics can effectively and safely use the new insulin-infusion device
Survey of recycling in U.S. cities	How to promote recycling at neighborhood meetings	Whether citizens will accept and participate in recycling; whether the program will generate revenue
Main differences between BASIC, Pascal, and FORTRAN	How to choose the right high-level programming language	Whether the company should develop its own record-keeping program or get a commercially available one

There are many types of informational reports, and they go by a wide variety of labels:

investigation reports	analytical reports
physical research reports	informal reports
reading reports	periodic reports
occurrence reports	field-trip reports
laboratory reports	empirical research reports
survey reports	decision-making reports
executive technical reports	formal reports

Don't be concerned about having to learn strategies and organizational patterns for each of these: once you've studied the common types covered in this chapter and once you understand the audience and purpose of your report, you'll have the skills to construct effective informational reports by any name.

STEP 1.   On your worksheet explain why your report project is informative (rather than an instruction or feasibility report), explain which type of informational report you plan to write, and go to that section in this chapter. (If you are thinking about collaborating with someone else on your informational report, see "Collaborating on Technical Reports" in the Introduction for ideas and suggestions.)

Note: In this chapter the letters following the step numbers refer to the type of report: all the progress-report steps, for example, end in *A*; all of the steps for the primary-research report end in *B*.

Progress Reports

You write a progress report to inform a supervisor, associate, or customer about progress you've made on a project over a certain period of time. The project can be the design, construction, or repair of something; the study or research of a problem or question; or the gathering of information on a technical subject. You write progress reports when it takes well over three or four months to complete a project. In the progress report, you explain any or all of the following:

How much of the work is complete
What part of the work is currently in progress
What work remains to be done
What problems or unexpected things, if any, have arisen
How the project is going in general

Reasons for Writing Progress Reports

Progress reports have several important functions; they:

- Reassure recipients that you are making progress, that the project is going smoothly, and that it will be complete by the expected date.
- Provide their recipients with a brief look at some of the findings or some of the work of the project.
- Give their recipients a chance to evaluate your work on the project and to request changes.
- Give you a chance to discuss problems in the project and thus to forewarn recipients.
- Force you to establish a work schedule so that you'll complete the project on time.

Ideas for Progress Reports

If you are not sure what to write a progress report on, think of any goal toward which you may be working right now. In your technical-writing course you may have a semester-long report. In your work toward a degree you have another possibility for a progress report.

STEP 2A.   On your worksheet briefly describe the project on which you will write a progress report and its audience (for more on audiences, see Chapter 5).

Timing and Format of Progress Reports

In a year-long project there are customarily three progress reports, one after three, six, and nine months. Depending on the size of the progress report, the length and importance of the project, and the recipient, the progress report can take the following forms:

Memo	A short, informal report to someone within your organization
Letter	A short, informal report sent to someone outside your organization
Formal report	A long, formal report sent to someone outside your organization

STEP 3A.   Explain which format (memo, letter, or report) you will use for your progress report and why.

Organizational Patterns for Progress Reports

The recipient of a progress report wants to see what you've accomplished on the project, what you are working on now, what you plan to work on next, and how the project is going in general. To report this information, you combine two of these organizational strategies: time periods, project tasks, or report topics.

Time Periods.   A progress report usually summarizes each of the following:

Work accomplished in the preceding period(s)
Work currently being performed
Work planned for the next period(s)

Project Tasks.   Practically every project breaks down into individual tasks:

Project	Individual Tasks
Building municipal ball parks on city-owned land	Measuring community interest Locating suitable property Clearing the property Designing the bleachers, fences, etc.
Writing a report	Studying the assignment Selecting a topic Identifying the audience of the report Narrowing the topic Developing a rough outline Gathering information Writing one or more rough drafts Documenting the report Revising and editing the report draft Typing and proofreading the report Putting the report in its final package

Report Topics.   You can also organize your progress report according to the work done on the sections of the final report. In the project on cocombusting municipal solid waste discussed in Chapter 10, you would need information on these topics:

Topics to Be Covered in the Final Report

1. The total amount of MSW produced
   - locally
   - nationally
2. The energy potential of MSW, factors affecting its energy potential
3. Costs to modify city utilities in order to change to cocombustion

For each of these topics, you'd explain the work you have done, the work you are currently doing, and the work you have planned.

A progress report is a combination of two of these organizational strategies. The following outline excerpts give you an idea of how they combine:

Progress Report A	*Progress Report B*	*Progress Report C*
Task 1	Work Completed	Topic 1
Work completed	Task 1	Work completed
Current work	Task 2	Current work
Planned work	Task 3	Planned work
Task 2	Current Work	Topic 2
Work completed	Task 1	Work completed
Current work	Task 2	Current work
Planned work	Task 3	Planned work
Task 3	Planned Work	Topic 3
Work completed	Task 1	Work completed
Current work	Task 2	Current work
Planned work	Task 3	Planned work

Figure 12–1 contains an example of the project-tasks approach with subheadings for time periods.

An example of time-period approach with subheadings for report topics is provided in Figure 12–2.

STEP 4A.   Select one of the organizational patterns for progress reports, and on your worksheet explain why you've chosen it. Next, sketch an outline of the body of your progress report.

<u>Brine Drainage Tube Modifications</u>

During this period we have continued to work on problems associated with the brine drainage tubes.

<u>Previous Period.</u>   After minor adjustments during a month of operation, the drainage tubes and the counterwasher have performed better but still not completely satisfactorily. The screen sections of these tubes, as you know, are located at variable distances along the height of the washer.

<u>Current Period.</u>   The screen portion of the brine drainage tubes has been moved to within 5 feet of the top of the pack. So far, no change in counterwasher performance has been observed. Production statistics at the end of this month (February) should give us a clearer idea of the effect of this modification.

<u>Next Period.</u>   Depending on the continued performance of the screen in its current position in relation to the top of the pack, we may move the screen to within 3 feet of the top of the pack in the next period of testing. Although the wash ratio was greater with greater screen height, the washing efficiency seems to remain relatively constant as the production versus compressor KW data for all screen locations so far has seemed to follow the same linear curve.

FIGURE 12–1.   Progress report organized by project tasks and time periods

Gathering Information for Progress Reports

To gather information on the progress you've made, consider using one of the charts in Figure 12–3 (use either "tasks" or "topics," and fill in the task or topic just after the number).

STEP 5A.   On your worksheet, design an information-gathering chart like one of the ones in Figure 12–3, and use it to take notes on the work you've done on your project.

WORK COMPLETED

As of this time, I have completed almost all of the research work and am putting the sections together. Here is a breakdown of the work that I have done so far.

Development of the Soft-Drink Bottle

In the development section of my report I have written a technical description of a typical PET soft-drink bottle. It is very complete and gives the reader a good idea of what the product should look like and be able to accomplish.

Favorable Properties

The section describing the properties of PET is completely finished. I have chosen four physical properties that many raw materials containers are tested for, and I have shown how PET withstands these various tests.

Manufacture

For the section on manufacturing processes I have done research to help me recommend one particular production method for PET bottles. Here, I have described this chosen method and have explained exactly how a plastic bottle is produced on an assembly line.

Economics

I have finished work on half of the economics section. So far, I have written an economic comparison of the use of plastic and glass bottles.

PRESENT WORK

Right now I am mainly involved in determining just which areas of my report are lacking information. Also, I am continuing my work in locating financial information on PET bottles.

Manufacture

In the manufacture section I am currently searching for information to....

FIGURE 12–2. Progress report organized by time periods and report topics

Task/Topic	Work Completed in Preceding Period(s)	Work in Progress Currently	Work Planned for Future Period(s)
1.			
2.			
3.			
4.			
etc.			

Periods	Task 1	Task 2	Task 3	Task 4
Work completed				
Work in progress				
Work planned				

Periods	Topic 1	Topic 2	Topic 3	Topic 4
Work completed				
Work in progress				
Work planned				

FIGURE 12–3.   Three information-gathering charts for progress reports

Other Parts of Progress Reports

In your progress report you also need (a) an introduction that reviews the history of the project's beginnings as well as the purpose and scope of the work, (b) a detailed description of your project, and (c) an overall appraisal of the project to date, which usually acts as the conclusion. (For a complete progress report, see the model at the end of this chapter.)

Introduction.   Review the details of your project's purpose, scope, and activities. This will aid recipients who are unfamiliar with the project, who do not remember certain details, or who want to doublecheck your approach to the project. The introduction can contain the following:

Purpose of the project
Specific objectives of the project
Scope, or limits, of the project
Date the project began
Date the project is scheduled to be completed
People or organization working on the project

People or organization for whom the project is being done
Overview of the contents of the progress report
Other background information about the project

Figure 12–4 contains an example of an introduction to a progress report.

Project Description.   In most progress reports, include a project description to review the details of your project for the recipients, as in Figure 12–5.

STEP 6A.   On your worksheet write one or more sentences for each of the items in the preceding checklist for introductions that apply to your progress report. Also, write a brief description of the project that is the subject of your progress report. Use the suggested contents and example in Figure 12–5 to guide you.

Conclusion.   The final paragraph or section usually reassures audiences that all is going well and on schedule. It can also alert recipients to unexpected changes or problems in the project.

STEP 7A.   On your worksheet write a brief conclusion to your progress report, commenting on (a) general progress of the project, (b) unexpected variations in the project, (c) problems that may cause delays, or (d) the likelihood of completing the project on schedule. (When you've finished this step, skip to the section entitled "Finishing Informational Reports" and continue.)

Primary Research Reports

When you conduct *primary research*, you run an experiment in a laboratory or conduct surveys in the field, that is, in a real-life setting. Research scientists use the term *primary research* in a very strict sense, but it is used here for contrast to

---

I am now submitting to you a report on the progress that I have made on my research for your company, Ginseng Cola. Immediately following the 15 January 19XX acceptance of my firm's bid to study the advantages of bottling your soft-drink product in plastic bottles, I began investigating all areas of the project.

In the following sections, you will be informed of the work I have already accomplished, the work I am now involved in, the work left to do, and, finally, an overall appraisal of how the project is going.

FIGURE 12–4.   Example of an introduction to a progress report

PROJECT DESCRIPTION

Purpose.   The original investment plan of this corporation included
only long-term, low-risk investment in corporate bonds and U.S.
securities. This project was designed to answer questions about the
potential of short-term, high-dollar investments, particularly those
suited to the future expansion of this company's investment plan.

Scope.   The report will cover basic definitions of stocks and options
as well as reasons for and against these two investment strategies.
The report will be broken into four areas:

1. The mechanics of stocks and options
2. Comparisons of stocks and options
3. Example investment scenarios
4. Recommendations for an investment plan

**FIGURE 12–5.   A project description from
a progress report**

secondary research, which refers to information gathering in libraries. Primary research produces new knowledge, verifies existing knowledge, or disproves existing
knowledge. Usually, this knowledge must be presented in the form of a written
report. Here are some projects involving primary research:

Comparative costs of:
    Standard brake repair
    Realignment
    Tune-up
    Engine overhaul
    Dented fender/door repair
    Gasoline prices
    Utility bills
    Housing prices in different neighborhoods
    House repainting
    House reroofing
    Home/personal computer system

Local opinion on:
    Public transportation system
    Plan to recycle glass, metal, and paper
    Traffic conditions

<u>OVERALL APPRAISAL</u>

The project to recommend PET production is coming along well. I have not run into any major problems and have found plenty of material. However, I have not heard from Mr. Simon Juarez of PET Mfg., who is sending information on the PET production methods used in several plants in the Southwest.

I can foresee no major setbacks that will hinder me from submitting my report to you on the contract date; in fact, I may be able to get it to you a few days earlier than planned. In general, I am finding that the PET bottle is an even more attractive packaging idea than had seemed in our earlier discussions. Full details on this, however, will appear in the final report.

Sincerely,

Steven C. Crosswell
Process Engineer
C & S Engineering Corp.

FIGURE 12–6. Overall appraisal conclusion to a progress report

Recreational facilities
Services of a certain bank
Primary or secondary education (school or system)
Community college
Student opinion concerning certain degree requirements
Statistical information on:
Traffic-flow patterns at an intersection
Traffic-flow patterns on a section of street, road, or highway
Customer-flow patterns at a store, bank, or mall
Students' majors, backgrounds, or other details
Experimentation on:
Effects of different fertilizer on tomato growth
Effects of different artificial lighting on Kentucky Wonder bean growth
Miles per gallon using different kinds of gasoline
Different techniques for getting rid of roaches or ants

Reports on primary research usually have a number of common parts arranged in a certain order. The contents and arrangement of these parts are based on one simple principle: to provide readers with *all* the necessary information so that they can repeat, or replicate, the research for themselves and so that they can interpret the findings for themselves and draw their own conclusions. To do this, most primary-research reports contain the following elements:

- An explanation of the problem, purpose, and scope of the research, including any background necessary
- A review of the existing knowledge or theory (usually contained in books, reports, and articles) on the problem
- A description of the equipment, materials, instruments, and facilities used to conduct the research
- An explanation of the method and the specific steps in the procedure used during the research
- A presentation of the information, or data, obtained from the research
- A discussion of the conclusions, implications, and recommendations arising from the research

A complete primary-research report containing some of these standard parts can be found in the models at the end of this chapter.

Problem or Question

In the introduction or in a separate section, explain the problem or question you are focusing on as well as the background of that problem and the importance of solving it. In the example in Figure 12–7 the problem is the decreasing water supply for an important cash crop, sugar beets.

STEP 2B.   On your worksheet briefly describe the primary research project (experiment, survey, etc.) that you will conduct or have conducted, and then describe the audience of your report (for more on audiences, see Chapter 5).

Purpose, Objectives, and Scope

Either in the introduction or in a separate section, explain the purpose and objectives of your research. Look at the example in Figure 12–8.

STEP 3B.   On your worksheet briefly describe the purpose of your research, the scope of that research, and the background of the problem you are concerned with.

Review of Literature

If necessary, summarize the existing knowledge about the problem you are working on. Locate books, reports, and articles that relate to your research and summarize the content that relates to your project. Call the section either a "review of literature" or "background." An excerpt from such a section (the numbers in parentheses are references to literature cited) is provided in Figure 12–9.

PROBLEM

The combination of hot, dry climate and long growing season results in high irrigation water requirements for sugar beets in the Texas High Plains. The growing season extends from April to October and includes the 6-month interval with the highest potential evapo-transpiration. Emergence irrigating is a common practice, and one or more irrigations may be required to establish a stand. Water use increases quickly during the late spring and early summer, and the sugar beet leaves effectively cover the soil before the potential evapo-transpiration reaches its summer peak. Unlike the water requirement for grain crops, which rapidly declines as the plants approach maturity, evapo-transpiration for sugar beets remains near the potential rate until fall harvesting.

Sugar beets have been grown extensively in the Texas High Plains only since 1964, and irrigation research data are limited. The nearest location where an irrigation water use study has been reported is Garden City, Kansas (1). Because of differences in the length of growing season, the soil, and the climate, the data from Garden City are not representative of the Hereford, Texas, area. Accurate water use data for the Texas High Plains are urgently needed because of the rapidly diminishing groundwater supply. In the three counties where the sugar beet acreage is concentrated, the water table decline from 1962 to 1968 averaged 3.8 feet per year (4). Guidelines for efficient management and use of the diminishing groundwater supply could extend the time that the Ogallala aquifer remains an economical source of irrigation water.

This paper reports sugar beet water use measurements made at the USDA Southwestern Great Plains Research Center at Bushland during the 4-year interval from 1964 to 1967.

Texas A&M University, Agricultural Experiment Station, "Water Use by Irrigated Sugar Beets in the Texas High Plains," MP-935, October 1969.

FIGURE 12–7. Problem section from a primary-research report

STEP 4B.   If applicable, explain the theory or background of your project on your worksheet. (Use the discussion and steps in Chapter 9 to find related books, reports and articles on your topic, if necessary.)

OBJECTIVES

The objectives of the research reported in this paper were (1) to compare the yield and quality of cotton (Gossypium hirsutum L.) irrigated with a mixture of wastewater and pump water with the yield and quality of cotton irrigated with pump water alone, and (2) to compare the quality of a wastewater and pump water mixture with the quality of pump water alone as a source of irrigation water for cotton production.

A. D. Day and J. A. McFadyen, "Yield and Quality Cotton Grown with Wastewater," BioCycle (April 1984), 35. Reprinted by permission.

FIGURE 12—8.   Purpose or objective section of a primary-research report

REVIEW OF RELATED LITERATURE

Paterson and Speights (8) have reported that growing sweet potatoes for 2 years on the same soil reduced the percentage of No. 1 sweet potato roots from approximately 33 to 12 percent of the total yield. Aldrich and Martin (1) found that nitrification of ammonium nitrogen, which accumulated following soil fumigation treatments, began sooner in sandy alkaline soil than in soil which was higher in organic matter. ... According to Davidson and Thiegs (2), it appears that MB, chloropicrin and 1,3-dichloropropene exert a greater effect on soil nitrifying organisms than ethylene dibromide and 1,2-dibromo-3-chloropropane. Newhall (6) reported that chemical treatments reduce the population of nitrifying bacteria ...

Texas A&M University, Agricultural Experiment Station, "Effects of Crop Rotation, Soil Fumigation, Variety and Nitrogen on Yield of Sweet Potatoes," MP-938, December 1969.

FIGURE 12—9.   Review-of-literature section from a primary-research report

Materials, Equipment, and Facilities

Particularly in lab reports, you must list and sometimes describe the equipment and materials used in your research. Include details on the sizes, volumes, amounts, types, brand names, or other dimensions. Readers who want to repeat your research to verify your findings must have this information. (An example of this element common to primary-research reports is combined with a discussion of methods and procedures in the next section.)

STEP 5B.   If applicable, describe on your worksheet the equipment, materials, instruments, and facilities that are necessary in your primary research.

Methods and Procedures

To repeat your research, your readers must have an explanation of the specific steps you took in carrying out the research. Figure 12–10 contains an example of a method and procedures section combined with a section on materials, equipment, and facilities (these sections can be combined or separated according to the requirements of the situation or of the format).

STEP 6B.   On your worksheet describe the method you have used or will use in your research project, and then list the steps in that method.

Results or Findings

At some point after the methods section, you must present the results, data, or findings of your research in charts, tables, or graphs as well as in prose. If you have lots of data, you present a summary of it in the body of the report and present the complete data in appendices. In the results section, you do not interpret or draw conclusions about your findings. Read closely the example in Figure 12–11.

Discussion, Conclusions, and Recommendations

After your section on findings usually come the conclusions. Here, you interpret your findings and discuss their significance. Some primary-research reports end by discussing implications for further research, applications of the findings, or recommendations based on those findings. An example of a discussion section (with the conclusions and recommendations underlined is shown in Figure 12–12 (again, these sections can be combined or separated according to the situation or format).

STEP 7B.   On your worksheet, list and discuss each of the specific conclusions that you draw from your research work. If applicable, list and then briefly explain on your worksheet the recommendations, implications for future research, or applications of your findings. (When you've finished this step, skip to "Finishing Informational Reports" and continue.)

MATERIALS AND METHODS

Experimental Design

Three soil rotation treatments that included land which had been in pasture for 12 years, land that had produced a crop of sweet potatoes 1 year, and land that had produced a crop of sweet potatoes 2 years in succession were assigned to each of the three replications. Each replication was split horizontally and received either Vorlex at 10 gallons per acre (gpa), 1 pound per square feet of MB (methyl bromide) under a 4 mil-thick polyethylene tarp, or no fumigant treatment. In addition, each of the three fumigant treatments was split vertically and nine treatments from all possible combinations of a 3 by 3 variety ... Nitrogen from ammonium nitrate (33.5-0-0) was used at 0, 50, and 100 pounds per acre. Previous experiments at this location gave no yield response to P or K (8).

On May 5, 1961, a mechanical transplanter was used to set transplants of the Puerto Rico (PR), Copperskin Goldrush (CSGR), and Redgold (RG) cultivars approximately 12 inches apart in the row. Each plant received approximately one-half pint of a starter solution consisting of 3 pounds of a soluble 10-52-17 NPK fertilizer per 50 gallons of water. The N was applied as a sidedressing May 18. Harvesting was completed, and the weight of roots in the various grades was recorded October 19.

Texas A&M University, Agricultural Experiment Station, "Effects of Crop Rotation, Soil Fumigation, Variety and Nitrogen on Yield of Sweet Potatoes," MP-938, December 1969.

FIGURE 12–10.   Example of a procedures, equipment, and materials section from a primary-research report

Technical-Background Report

The technical-background report is constructed primarily from published materials available in libraries (and therefore could be called secondary-research reports). For this type of report you gather what is already known about some aspect of a subject

RESULTS

As shown in Table 1, growing sweet potatoes for more than 1 year on the same soil resulted in a highly significant decrease in the yield of No. 1 grade of roots. Growing sweet potatoes for 3 years in the same plot reduced the No. 1 yield another 39 percent. The No. 2 root yield was reduced about 26 percent the second year. Growing sweet potatoes 3 years in succession gave a highly significant reduction in the No. 2 grade of roots.

The use of Vorlex as a soil fumigant increased the yield of No. 1 roots about 11 percent (Table 12–11). MB (methyl bromide) gave a highly significant increase in the yield of No. 1 and a significant increase in the yield of the No. 2 grade. There was little difference between the Vorlex treatment and the control in the yield of No. 2 sweet potatoes.

TABLE 12-11   Effect of Soil Fumigation and Crop Rotation on the Yield and Grade of Sweet Potatoes

| Fumigant | Year | Number of 55-pound Crates per Acre | | | | |
		No. 1	No. 2	Grade Cracked	Cull	Total
Control	1	154	122	52	247	575
Control	2	71	90	95	219	475
Control	3	29	43	105	160	337
	Average	85	85	84	209	463
Vorlex	1	146	118	47	216	527
Vorlex	2	90	74	94	231	489
Vorlex	3	49	59	75	182	365
	Average	95	84	72	210	461
MB	1	167	118	62	258	605
MB	2	101	101	72	257	531
MB	3	79	88	84	185	436
	Average	116	102	73	233	524

(continued)

FIGURE 12–11.   A results section from a primary-research report

| | Fumigant | | Year | |
L.S.D.	No. 1	No. 2	No. 1	No. 2
5 percent	14	15	38	40
1 percent	20		64	

Texas A&M University, Agricultural Experiment Station, "Effects of Crop Rotation, Soil Fumigation, Variety and Nitrogen on Yield of Sweet Potatoes," MP-938, December 1969.

FIGURE 12—11. (cont.)

DISCUSSION

In addition to having a maximum daily water use that can exceed 0.30 inch per day, sugar beets require high daily water use for an extended interval. As Figure 12–12a illustrates, daily water use exceeded 0.25 inch per day for 2 months and 0.20 inch per day for three months. For an irrigation water supply with a nearly constant delivery rate, such as the wells on the Texas High Plains, the maximum daily water use, rather than the total seasonal water use, is the most important consideration in irrigation planning.

The seasonal water use of approximately 40 inches is high in relation to that of other irrigated crops in the Texas High Plains. Several reasons for this are readily shown. The growing season extends for 6 months or more and includes the months having the highest evaporation potential.... [Thus] Efficient irrigation systems, good irrigation practices, and effective use of rainfall are required to furnish the water used by sugar beets with the least possible amount of groundwater depletion.

FIGURE 12—12. A discussion-section excerpt from a primary-research report

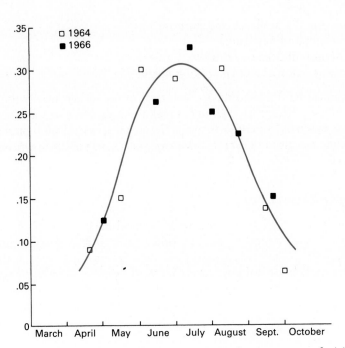

FIGURE 12–12a   Daily water use by sugar beets measured at the
Southwestern Great Plains Research Center at Bushland during
1964 and 1966

The importance of irrigation systems design and management can
be shown ...

Texas A&M University, Agricultural Experiment Station, "Water Use by
Irrigated Sugar Beets in the Texas High Plains," MP-935, October 1969.

FIGURE 12–12. (cont.)

and tailor it to meet the needs of your audience. Such reports usually aid business
and government people who must make decisions but do not have the time to do
the extensive reading themselves. If you are taking a technical-writing course, this
type of report—or an instructional or feasibility report—is probably your major,
semester-long project. (For an example of a technical-background report, see the
excerpt in the models at the end of this chapter.)

Critical points in writing a technical background report include

- Finding a topic
- Identifying the audience and purpose
- Narrowing and outlining
- Identifying information sources
- Gathering information and taking notes

In the technical-background report, you tend to use rather heavily the information sources found in the libraries; good note-taking skills, therefore, are important. And because so much information is available on most technical subjects, narrowing and outlining are also important: these two skills save you from writing impossibly long reports.

Finding a Report Topic

Unless you know about some need for a technical-background report or have been asked to write such a report, you must find a topic to write on. Chapter 8 provides steps for brainstorming and suggests that you look into such areas as the following: your major or area of training, career interests, your current occupation, areas of science and technology that interest you, problems facing you or your community, and local businesses or other kinds of organizations that may have information needs.

STEP 2C.   On your worksheet briefly describe the topic of your technical-background report. (See Chapter 8 for help in finding a topic.)

Analyzing or Creating a Report Situation

You must also identify the specific audience and purpose of your report, in other words, the situation out of which the demand for your report arises. A clear sense of audience and purpose helps you focus, narrow, or limit what to discuss. Put another way, the audience and purpose show you which topics to cover and how much detail to provide on each of those topics. Chapter 5 shows you how to analyze a report audience and define the report purpose and what to do when you do not have a real audience and report-writing situation.

STEP 3C.   On your worksheet describe the audience and purpose (real or invented) of your technical-background report. (Return to Chapter 5 and do the steps involved in analyzing or inventing an audience and purpose, if you need more on analyzing audiences.)

Narrowing the Report Topic

As soon as you select or are assigned a report topic, begin narrowing or focusing that topic. Narrowing can mean two things: (a) discussing fewer aspects of the main report topic, and (b) deciding how detailed and technical the discussion of each topic should be. (Chapter 8 shows you how to narrow a report topic.)

The audience and purpose of your report should help you choose which topics to discuss and which to omit. For example:

Audience and Report	Topics to Discuss	Topics to Omit
Executives: report on computerized graphics	Uses and costs of computer-graphics equipment	History of research and development of the equipment; programming logic
Technicians (operators): intensive-care equipment	Basic operation, safety concerns, maintenance, and troubleshooting tips	Detailed description of components and circuitry
Experts (researchers): emissions-control devices on automobiles	Research on problems in use; new designs and their performance	Basic principles of operation; background on legislation for such devices; effects of uncontrolled emissions

The audience and purpose of your report should also help you decide on the amount of detail and level of technicality. For example:

Report Topic	Specific, Technical Discussion for Specialists	General, Nonspecialist Discussion
Bond election to raise money to build a saltwater conversion plant	Designers, builders, operators	General voting public; investment analysts
Alzheimer's disease	Medical personnel: nurses, doctors, technicians, researchers	General public: victims' families, relatives; legislators, social workers, counselors
Water hyacinth for sewage and other waste treatment	City planners, civil engineers, waste-water-treatment experts	General citizens, city council-members, financial officers, environmentalists

You can also narrow a topic by designing your report as only one in a series. For example:

Large Report Subject	Series of Reports
Desalination: Converting Brackish Water to Fresh Water	I. The History of Desalination Technologies II. Different Types of Desalination Processes Currently Used or Being Developed III. Basic Components and Operation of a Desalination Plant IV. The Economics of Desalination

Because you could not write a report covering all of these topics in one semester, you could present your report as one in a series of reports and cover only one of the preceding numbered items.

Developing a Rough Outline

Early in your report work you should also create a rough outline (or a list of topics to be covered or questions to be answered in the report). This step enables you to narrow the report topic, to decide on the kinds of information you need to locate and take notes on. See Chapter 8 for strategies on developing a rough outline.

STEP 4C.   On your worksheet, list the topics you'll include, explain which you'll discuss in detail or generally, and develop this list into a rough outline. (For more on narrowing and outlining, see the discussion and steps in Chapter 8.)

Determining the Kinds of Writing Needed

Particularly useful in planning a technical-background report is identification of the kinds of writing you'll use. This step will help you add extra detail to your outline, give you a better idea of how to conduct your reading, fieldwork, and note taking, and help you plan and write your report. Look at the example in Figure 12–13.

STEP 5C.   On your worksheet indicate which sections of your report match which kinds of writing presented in Part I. For more on these kinds of writing, see the discussion and steps in Chapters 1 through 4. Also, briefly describe the sections of your report that do not match any of the Part I kinds of writing.

Identifying Sources of Information

Your next step is to think about the sources of information for your report, both library and nonlibrary ones. First, find out what books, reference works, reports, and articles are available in the library on your topic. In this step you assemble a

Rough-Outline Topics	Kinds of Writing Needed
1. Brief history of desalination processes	Process discussion
2. Theory of desalination	Cause-effect
3. Plant description	
a. Hydroconverter	
b. Counterwasher	
c. Heat exchanger	Description
d. Deaerator	
e. Heat removal	
f. Pumping	
4. Component analysis	Comparison
5. Plant operations	Process
6. Economics of desalination	Comparison

FIGURE 12–13. Example of an outline: different kinds of writing used in a typical report

working bibliography, in other words, a list of items that may turn out to be useful in your report. (Chapter 9 shows you the details to record on each of your information sources.)

While you are developing your working bibliography, think about which of the various sources of information external to the library you may need:

Interviews with experts, technicians, government officials, executives, and the public
Surveys of public opinion
Inspection of sites and the facilities on them
Measurements and calculations
Brochures, magazines, reports, and other printed literature available only from businesses and other organizations

STEP 6C.   On your worksheet make a list of books, reports, articles, and other library materials that may be useful when you write your report. Also, list the nonlibrary sources of information that you may need, and explain what information you expect from each. (For more on sources of information, see the discussion and steps in Chapter 9.)

Gathering Information and Taking Notes

With all of the preceding steps completed, you are ready to plunge into the information-gathering stage of your report project. Return to Chapter 10 for a discussion of how to take notes.

STEP 7C.   On your worksheet briefly describe the system that you will use to gather information for your report. (If you have never taken notes before, see the discussion and steps in Chapter 10.) When you complete this step, go to the section entitled "Finishing Informational Reports" and continue.

Other Informational Reports

From time to time you may need to write other kinds of informational reports, usually rather short and informal ones. Although terminology and format for these reports vary, use the guidelines and models here as starting points. Also, remember these guidelines as you plan and write these reports:

- *Always* adjust the content and discussion to the specific audience (see Chapter 5 on analyzing audiences).
- Use plenty of graphic and textual aids, particularly headings and in-sentence and vertical lists (see Chapter 6).
- Provide readers with sufficient details. If you draw a conclusion or make a recommendation, show them the information you used to reach those conclusions. Give them enough information to doublecheck your reasoning.
- Make sure that you understand the purpose of the report you write. Is it supposed to inform, to instruct, to evaluate, or to recommend?
- Ask for a copy of some past report similar to yours, and use it as a model.

Site-Inspection and Field-Trip Reports

In a site-inspection report you provide descriptive information about a place, a piece of property, or the structures and facilities on it. It may also contain evaluative information if the writer or recipient is considering purchasing or using that property in some way. Some form of site-inspection report is used by fire inspectors, for example, to report on fire causes and damages and by insurance agents to report on damage by fire, flood, or other causes. Also, bank officers and real estate people make use of such reports to evaluate and to keep records on property. An example of a site-inspection report is provided in Figure 12–14.

Work Estimates

In a work estimate you provide customers with an itemized list of the costs of a project, the specific steps in the work, the materials to be used and their costs, the totals, and in some cases the schedules. Often written on forms specially prepared for such purposes, work estimates are in some ways like proposals, but they are much less formal and lack many of the elements of the proposal. An example of a work estimate is provided in Figure 12–15.

10023 Manchaca
Austin, TX 78759
June 15, 19XX

Mr. Patrick Hughes Murray
PHM Realtors, Inc.
3001 W. 30
Austin, TX 78767

Subject: Site Inspection--Lot 48D Elgin Meadows

Dear Mr. Murray:

As you requested, I have inspected Lot 48D and its improvements in Elgin, Texas. The following is a description for your records of my observations.

The subject site is located at the intersection of Highway 290 East and FM 1100. It is zoned C-1 "Commercial." The site is irregular in shape with $+/-$ 80 feet of frontage.

Exterior

The subject property is a one-story, 100%-masonry exterior with a 26-gauge metal roof. The building has approximately 1,475 square feet and 2,450 square feet of parking and driveway area. There is a drainage easement at the rear of the property. All utilities are available to the site.

Interior

The interior of the building is arranged to function as a beauty parlor.

(continued)

FIGURE 12—14.   Example of a site-inspection report

<u>Foyer</u>.   The front entrance opens into a small foyer that is separated from the hair-drying and manicuring room by a 5-foot-high wall with 3-inch turnposts. At the end of this foyer and to the right is a coat closet with a clothes pole and hat shelf. Directly to the east of the foyer is a built-in natural-wood reception counter. The entire interior of the beauty parlor is painted drywall except where noted.

<u>Hair-Drying and Manicuring Room</u>.   The hair-drying and manicuring room measures 14'2" x 15'0". The floor is covered with a gold shag carpet. There are two 110-v duplex receptacles for general purposes and ten 110-v outlets for the hair dryers. Also, there are two light switches and a recessed ceiling incandescent light fixture.

<u>Makeup Counter</u>.   Directly north of the hair-drying and manicuring room is the makeup counter. The floor is covered with gold speckled vinyl floor covering. Starting at a height of 4 feet and directly in the center of the makeup counter is a 3-foot x 4-foot mirror. Display cabinets and shelves are located on both sides of the mirror. There are two 110-v duplex receptacles and three recessed ceiling incandescent light fixtures. Separating the makeup counter from the shampoo room are 5-foot-high walls with 3-inch turnposts.

<u>Shampooing</u>.   The shampooing room measures 10'4" x 14'2". The floor covering is vinyl. Directly to the west is a 1'8" x 7'4" storage cabinet. Three sinks and shampoo chairs sit 4 feet apart. There are three 110-v duplex receptacles, three recessed ceiling incandescent light fixtures, and one light switch.

<u>Dispensary</u>.   Directly to the left of the entrance are storage cabinets. There are two swinging wooden doors to the dispensary entrance. The floor is covered with gold speckled vinyl. Appliances include a washer, a dryer, a water heater, a heater, and an air conditioner. The latter two appliances are contained in a closet northwest of the room. Counter tops are plastic-covered. The sink is stainless steel with a garbage disposal. There are three electrical outlets, two light switches, a gas connection, and a recessed fluorescent light panel in the ceiling.

FIGURE 12—14.   (cont.)

<u>Rest Room</u>.   The rest room measures 5′8″ x 6′2″ and has a gold speckled vinyl floor covering. The plumbing fixtures are white and consist of a low-box flush and a built-in 48-inch-long by 3-foot-high vanity. Over the vanity is a surface-mount incandescent light fixture, an electrical outlet, and a light switch. Also, there is an air vent in the ceiling.

<u>Office</u>.   The office walls are covered with natural ash paneling; the floor is covered with gold shag carpet; and the ceiling has a fluorescent light panel. The room measures 10′0″ x 11′4″. Also, there are four electrical outlets, one light switch, and one telephone jack in the office. At the south end of the room there is a double-pane window.

<u>Reception Room</u>.   Six rotating hair-styling chairs, each with a recessed incandescent light fixture directly above it, highlight the 30′0″ × 10′2″ room. Directly to the west of the room is a 5-foot-high dressing table covered with blue formica. Also, there are six electrical outlets, two white ceiling fans, and one light switch in the reception area.

<u>Waiting Room</u>.   Located with access from the foyer is the 9′8″ × 5′8″ waiting room. There is one electrical outlet and one recessed ceiling incandescent light fixture.

<u>Lounge</u>.   Directly north of the waiting room is the 11′4″ × 9′8″ lounge. Located on the north wall is a double-pane window; and, located on the south wall is a one-way 36-inch × 36-inch mirror. The room has gold shag carpet, and the walls have natural ash paneling. There are built-in natural-wood cabinets next to a General Electric refrigerator. In addition, there are four electrical outlets, a light switch, and a recessed fluorescent light panel in the ceiling.

Attached is a floor plan of the property. Thanks for the opportunity to begin this appraisal. Let me know if you have any questions about the details of this inspection.

Respectfully,

Jane Allen Murray

FIGURE 12–14.   (cont.)

KRAEMER TILE CO.

P.O. Box 34230

Austin, Texas 78767

(512) 454-3423

June 18, 19XX

Mr. David A. McMurrey
2000 Sharon Lane
Austin, Texas 78705

Dear Mr. McMurrey:

Having inspected the tile in your bathrooms and kitchen, I have made
the following estimates for repair:

Front Bath Area

Tear-out and reconstruction of water-damaged tub/shower walls
through the installation of standard-grade ceramic tile and grout.

LABOR & MATERIALS.....................$800.00

Removal of tub/shower faucet set and installation of a quality-
constructed brass faucet fixture with chrome-plated shower head and
exterior features.

LABOR & MATERIALS.....................$175.00

Back Bath Area

Tear-out and reconstruction of water-damaged tub/shower walls
through the installation of standard-grade ceramic tile and grout.

LABOR & MATERIALS.....................$800.00

FIGURE 12–15. Example of a work-estimate report

Removal of tub/shower faucet set and installation of a quality-constructed brass faucet fixture with chrome-plated shower head and exterior features.

LABOR & MATERIALS......................$175.00

Kitchen Countertop

Tear-out and reconstruction of water-damaged kitchen countertop through the installation of standard-grade ceramic tile and grout.

LABOR & MATERIALS......................$895.00

TOTAL CONSTRUCTION COST $2845.00

Please note that any wood-damage reconstruction of 2″ × 4″ wall studs because of wood rot will be charged extra at a rate of $38.50/hour.

Kraemer Tile proposes to furnish the above material and labor according to the stated specifications for the amount of two thousand eight hundred forty-five dollars ($2,845).

Sincerely,

Patrick Hughes

PMH/cnn

FIGURE 12–15.   (cont.)

Survey Results

If, for example, you conduct a survey of public opinion or of the prices of a particular product, you'd write a survey-results report. It resembles the primary-research report but does not need the special elements of the latter. Survey reports are often primarily made up of tables, charts, and graphs with introductory and concluding statements. Some discussion on why the information is needed (purpose), how and when it was collected (method), and what it means (conclusions and interpretations) may be provided also. For an example, see Figure 12–16.

July 30, 19XX

To: Roberta James, Project Director
From: Jane Allen Murray, ACSW
Subj: Southern regional costs of raising a child

I have just finished compiling the survey of comparative costs of child-rearing which you requested in September of last year. As I had expected, the U.S. Department of Agriculture and its publication Family Economics Review were excellent resources for the national part of this survey.

Here are the figures for the southern region:

Average Annual Cost of Raising a Child in an Urban Area in the South

Age of Child	Total Costs	Food at Home	Food away from Home	Clothing Costs	Housing Costs	Medical Care	Educ.	Trans.	All Other
Under 1	$4,463	$595	$0	$151	$1,925	$293	$0	$877	$622
1	4,587	719	0	151	1,925	293	0	877	622
2–3	4,298	695	0	235	1,708	293	0	771	596
4–5	4,507	769	135	235	1,708	293	0	771	596
6	4,762	769	161	319	1,627	293	174	771	648
7–9	4,911	918	161	319	1,627	293	174	771	648
10–11	5,109	1,116	161	319	1,627	293	174	771	648
12	5,445	1,116	188	470	1,681	293	174	824	699
13–15	5,594	1,265	188	470	1,681	293	174	824	699
16–17	6,012	1,389	188	604	1,735	293	174	904	725
TOTAL	90,624	17,686	2,364	6,224	30,638	5,274	2,088	14,568	11,762

In the category of food at home are included home-produced foods and school lunches. In the category of housing are included shelter, fuel, utilities, household operations, furnishings, and equipment. In the category of "all other" are included personal-care, recreation, reading, and other miscellaneous expenditures.

FIGURE 12–16. Example of a survey-results report

Minutes of Meetings

In the minutes of a meeting you provide a brief account of the actions and statements that occurred in that meeting. Minutes usually contain a list of those present and a brief summary of the actions taken. Minutes report on the motions made, the discussion of those motions, and the votes on those motions. Minutes become the official record of the organization's activities and are distributed to all members. Figure 12–17 contains an example of minutes of a meeting.

Recording for the Blind

Luckenbach Chapter

Minutes of the Meeting of November 19, 19XX

Members Present

    Murray, Hughes, Steen, Massey, Banks, Alexander, Nelson, Greenberg, Magee, Juarez, Lopez, Sims, and Frontaine.

Agenda

1. The meeting was called to order at 7:00 P.M. by Chairman Greenberg.

2. The minutes of the October 18 meeting were approved as circulated.

3. Chairman Greenberg regretfully announced the resignation of Lauren Jefferson from the Board but informed the Board that Phoebe Murray will serve as Publicity Chairman in her place and that the Nominating Committee will select a Board member to serve as Vice-Chairman for the remaining term.

4. The Chairman stated that employee insurance rates have increased. Also, the rate of the RRW maintenance agreement for the computer will be increasing as of the next billing.

(continued)

FIGURE 12–17. Example of a minutes report

5. Betty Banks presented the studio report: during January, books totaling 114 tape hours were mailed to the master tape library; 345 tape hours were duplicated and mailed to students. There are 78 books in progress currently at the Luckenbach unit.

6. Glenda Greenberg read the donations report: the recent August 20, 19XX, appeal to corporate donors of 300 letters has produced 47 replies, consisting of 25 refusals and 22 contributions totaling $7,450.00. An appeal letter to individual donors has generated $1,140.00. The year-to-date total for individual contributions is $13,568.00. The average is $5.00 per response letter.

7. Discussion ensued on the merits of a second mailing. Although the Board was receptive to a second mailing, it was suggested that time be allowed for updating and increasing the donor list before doing so.

8. The members discussed strategies for increasing the number of volunteer readers. Meghan Sims suggested allowing volunteers to choose the subject matter for their reading. Nancy Magee pointed out that such a policy would make it difficult to continue to record enough books in the technical fields which are less popular with most volunteers. Further discussion of this matter was postponed until the next meeting.

9. The next meeting was scheduled for December 14 at the Community Center—Northwest at 7:30 P.M.

10. The meeting was adjourned at 10:00 P.M.

Respectfully submitted,

Mollie Steen,
Secretary

FIGURE 12–17. (cont.)

Finishing Informational Reports

If you've followed the steps to this point in your work on the informational report, you are ready now to make some final plans and start writing. The following steps take you through these final preparations to write the first draft, revise it, and put it in its final package. The following steps direct you to the chapters of Parts I, II, and III. If you've already studied those chapters and have been through the steps there, you may only want to go back to them for a brief review.

STEP 8.   Follow these steps to write and complete your informational report:

  • *Plan your introductions and conclusions.* For ideas on introductions and conclusions, particularly for technical-background reports, see Chapter 4. If you have not done so already, read Chapter 4, do the steps there, and then return here for the next step.
  • *Analyze your audience.* For direction on audience analysis, read Chapter 5, do the steps there, and then return here for the next step.
  • *Design the graphic aids.* If necessary, read Chapter 6 on locating areas for graphic aids and incorporating them into your report, and return here for the next step.
  • *Use headings and lists.* For help on planning the headings and creating lists for the report, read Chapter 6, do the steps, and return here for the next step.
  • *Write the rough draft.* When you are ready to write a rough draft, read the discussion in Chapter 10, and then return here for the next step.
  • *Write the summaries.* If you must write a descriptive summary or informative summary (or both) for your report, read the discussion and follow the steps in Chapter 4 on this topic.
  • *Revise.* If you need direction on revising your report, read Chapter 10, follow the steps there, and return here.
  • *Plan the additional textual aids.* During or after your revision work, you should also plan the additional textual aids that must be incorporated into your report. These may include the following, depending on the type of report you are writing:

Title page	Pagination
List of figures	List of symbols and abbreviations
Letter of transmittal	Glossary
Table of contents	

Discussion, examples, and steps to help you in designing these elements of your report can be found in Chapter 6.
  • *Proofread and do the final packaging.* When you are ready to type your report, proofread it, and put it in its final package—that is, tape in the illustrations, bind the report, and attach the cover label—read the discussion and follow the steps in Chapter 10.

EXERCISES

1. Contact friends or acquaintances who are in business or government, set up interviews, and find out which of the types of informational reports they write or read. Ask to make copies of examples of these reports, and compare them to the contents and formats of the reports that you see here. Write a memo to your instructor about your findings.

2. Try to locate a site where damage has occurred or where improvements are needed. Prepare a work estimate as if you were going to do the actual work. Supply all the information needed in writing a work estimate. If you are so inclined, create a company name for yourself (with you as the president!), and design a logo for the top of the letterhead.

3. Find something locally on which to do a survey, for example, costs of a product or service or local opinion on some issue. With the information you gather, prepare a memo to an appropriate audience (someone who would have naturally requested such information) and present the information.

4. Attend some local meeting (school board, city council, PTA, church committee, or student government, for example), and take minutes. Follow the model shown in this chapter, and, later, try to have a look at the minutes that the official secretary actually took.

5. Locate an individual involved in the work, occupation, and profession that you hope to enter. Set up an interview and ask questions about that individual's writing such as the following:

   • What kinds of writing does he or she produce?
   • How important is that writing in his or her work?
   • What are some common problems that arise with such writing projects?
   • What are the most important factors in those documents' effectiveness, success, or quality?

> **Model 12–1.   Progress on Technical-Background Report on Computer Structures and Logic Design**
> *(progress report)* *

Mo Kim Cheng
2108 San Gabriel #404
Austin, Texas 78705
29 November 1983

Dr. David A. McMurrey
English Department
Austin Community College
Austin, Texas 78712

Dear Dr. McMurrey:

I am writing to bring you up to date on the progress that I have made on my semester report project. As you know from my 20 September memo, my topic is the fundamentals of computer structures and logic design. I have kept in my mind your advice about narrowing this topic, but I expect to solve this problem and I continue to gather information.

After your approval of my project, I got to work right away gathering detailed information on the four major components of the computer system and the basic technique of logic design.

Dr. David A. McMurrey   -2-   29 November 1986

After nearly two months of research, study, and rough drafting, I have completed about two-thirds of the report project. This letter summarizes my work from 20 September to 27 November.

The report project can be divided into three major tasks:

1. Finding information for the discussion of the four major components of a computer, namely, the central processing unit, the arithmetic and logic unit, the memory unit, and the input/output system.

2. Finding information for the description of the logic design, which includes number systems, Boolean algebra, logic gates, and logic circuits.

*Reprinted with permission from Mo Kim Cheng.

3. Developing graphics that adequately illustrate as well as language that conveys these computer concepts.

My work on task 1 is nearly complete, although I'm still searching for additional examples to present the concepts more clearly. Most of the materials related to task 2 have been gathered, and I'm working on different ways to organize and present this information (logic design). In fact, that is where most of my time on this project seems to be going: how to explain the basic techniques of logic design so that the nonspecialist reader can understand readily.

Dr. David A. McMurrey   -3-   29 November 1986

Project Description

As you requested, here is a review of what my report project is all about.

Subject. The report will discuss the four major components of the computer system as well as the basic techniques of logic design. Logic design is a procedure for designing computer components by using "black boxes" that perform specific functions. The designer is not required to understand the behavior of the actual electronic circuitry.

Purpose. The purpose of this report is to offer the nonspecialist reader and the beginning electrical engineering student an introduction to the fundamentals of computer structures and logic design.

Dr. David A. McMurrey   -4-   29 November 1986

Topic 1: Computer Structures

Work Completed. The library research on computer structures is now complete. Also, I have written a complete draft of the sections of the report involving this topic. The four major components are described in detail; there are numerous examples and illustrations. Several nonspecialists have read the draft and have made suggestions for improving it.
    In this section, you'll learn about the central processing unit, the "brain" of the computer, that part that controls the entire system and processes information. You'll also learn about the arithmetic logic unit, which performs numerical calculations at high speed, and about the memory unit, which stores information to be processed. You'll also see how the computer communicates with the outside world through the input/output devices.

Work Remaining. Based on the suggestions of my test readers, I am still tinkering with finding different ways to explain certain key events in a cycle of computer operation and with developing better graphics.

Dr. David A. McMurrey   -5-   29 November 1986

Topic 2: Basic Techniques of Logic Design

<u>Work Completed</u>. I'm still trying to locate up-to-date information on logic design techniques, but most of the information is in place. At this stage I only have a very rough draft and have not been able to test it out on nonspecialist readers. Much of the writing in this draft is still in specialist language and is going to require a good amount of translating.

<u>Work Remaining</u>. Currently, I am in the process of rewriting the part of the report on logic design techniques. This may entail some major reorganization; also I still must find or create good examples and illustrations for some of the areas of this part. I am particularly concerned about presenting Boolean algebra in the clearest and the most concise way possible, since it is one of the keys to understanding the operations of a computer.

Dr. David A. McMurrey   -6-   29 November 1986

Enclosed is a two-page outline of my report as it stands now. If you have any suggestions about it or if you would be interested in looking at the rough draft in its current state, please let me know. Otherwise, everything is moving along well, and you should have the report by or before the scheduled date.

Respectfully yours,

Mo Kim Cheng
Electronics major, ACC

Enclosure

Model 12–2. Altering the Spawning Cycle of Rainbow Trout by Manipulating Water Temperature*
(primary-research report)

John K. Morrison and Charlie E. Smith

U.S. Fish and Wildlife Service

Fish Technology Center

Bozeman, Montana 59715

It is often desirable to provide eggs or fry from a particular strain of rainbow trout (Salmo gairdneri) over an extended period of time. Availability can be prolonged by incubating eggs in cold water and thus slowing embryonic development. However, an experiment conducted at the Bozeman Fish Cultural Development Center in which rainbow trout eggs were exposed to temperatures of 13, 10, 6, and 3° C (55.5, 50, 43, 37.5° F) showed a significant reduction in the percentage of eyed eggs and the survivability of eggs held at the lowest temperatures (unpublished data). Published studies on egg incubation of various salmonid species indicate that temperatures below 4.5° C (40° F) are detrimental (Davis 1953; Combs and Burrows 1957; Combs 1965; Hokanson et al. 1973; Leitritz and Lewis 1976). Another possible method of extending egg availability is to hold broodstock in cold water, and thus delay egg and sperm development. The present study was designed to compare spawning time and egg quality of rainbow trout broodstock maintained in cold creek water with those of broodstock maintained in constant temperature spring water.

The facilities at the Bozeman Center offer the opportunity to use Bridger Creek or spring water in the raceways. Chemical characteristics of the water supplies are similar. Alkalinity and total hardness (both in mg/L as $CaCO_3$) and pH of the creek water were 189, 203, and 8.2, respectively (Russo and Thurston 1974); values for spring water were 181, 207, and 7.6 (analysis by Water Chemistry Laboratory, Montana State University, Bozeman, Montana).

METHODS

Two hundred fifty, 3-year-old, Winthrop strain rainbow trout were held in each of two outdoor raceways measuring 1.8 × 18 × 0.6 m (6 × 60 × 2 ft). The trout had been reared in spring water and the raceways were initially provided with this water. In early September, creek water was introduced into one raceway; the other continued to receive spring water at 10 ± 1° C (50 ± 1° F). Water inflow for each raceway was approximately 570 L/min (150 gal/min). Fish were checked weekly beginning in December and artificially spawned by manually stripping when ripe. The initial spawn from each group was discarded; egg quality was believed to be poor because optimum spawning time was missed.

Fish were anesthetized in a 1% salt solution containing 50 mg/l of MS 222 and

*Reprinted by permission of the American Fisheries Society.

then checked for ripeness. Ripe females were rinsed with fresh water and the eggs spawned into a strainer to drain off excess fluid. Eggs were then placed in a pan and fertilized. On each spawning day, 9 to 18 females were spawned separately and fertilized with sperm from separate males. If additional females were spawned, eggs from three fish were pooled and fertilized with sperm from two males. Eggs were incubated in individual and pooled lots in Heath incubator trays supplied with spring water at the rate of 19 L/min (5 gal/min). Eggs were treated daily with formulin at a concentration of 1:600 for 15 min to control fungus. When eyed, eggs were counted with a Veeder-Root electronic counter. Dead eggs were picked out by hand with a suction bulb and glass tube.

Data collected for individual fish included female weight, total number of eggs per kilogram of body weight, and percent of eyes eggs (Table 1). A comparison of two samples test (t-test) was used to statistically analyze the data (Snedecor and Cochran 1967).

TABLE 1.   Egg Production of Rainbow Trout Broodstock Held in Spring Water at 10° C (50° F) and Bridger Creek at Lower Temperatures.

Water Source	Weight of Female (kg)	Fecundity		Weight per 1,000 Eggs (g)[a]	Eyed Eggs (%)
		Eggs per Female	Eggs per kg/Female		
Spring	1.99[b]	2,992	1,527	75	86
Creek	1.75	3,094	1,793[b]	72	86

[a]Data for all fishes, pooled.
[b]Value significantly higher ($p < 0.05$) than the other value in the same column.

Results

Average weekly temperatures of the creek water ranged from 2° C (35° F) to 14° C (57° F) (Figure 1). Fish held in spring water were spawned from December 12, 1977, to February 9, 1978, and fish held in creek water from March 29 to April 20, 1978 (Figure 2). When fish held in creek water were ready to spawn, water temperature was about 7° C (45° F) and rising rapidly. At this time, the creek water became heavily silted and was replaced with spring water.

A total of 39 females were spawned from the creek water and 66 females from the spring water. Gross observations such as "blood in eggs" or "some bad eggs" were made when spawn was taken. Fish observed with these conditions were not considered in the individual comparisons, because these eggs would normally be discarded. However, the data were included when overall egg weight per thousand eyed eggs was calculated (Table 1).

Fish held in spring water were significantly larger at spawning time than those held in creek water, a difference directly related to increased food intake and higher metabolism at the higher water temperatures. Fish held in creek water produced more eggs per kilogram of body weight than did those in spring water, but the eggs were smaller; consequently, there was no significant difference in weight of eggs per kilogram of fish between groups. Neither was there a significant difference in total number of eggs per female or in percent eyed eggs between the fish held in spring water and those held in creek water (Table 1).

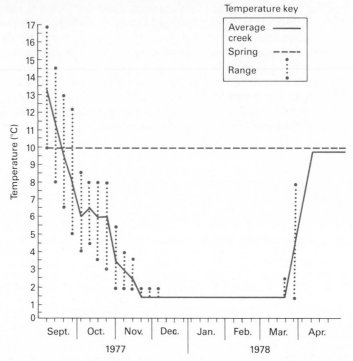

FIGURE 1. Average temperature and ranges for creek versus spring water, beginning 6 September 1977 (week 1).

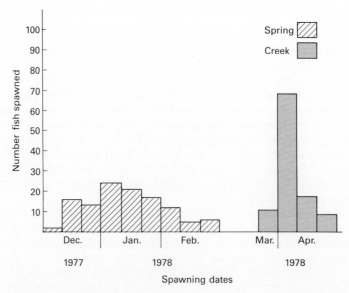

FIGURE 2.   Number of rainbow trout held in spring water or creek water, spawned on different dates.

This study suggests that, if late-season rainbow trout eggs are desired, broodfish (at least of the Winthrop strain, and perhaps other late fall and winter strains) can be held in cold water to delay spawning without affecting egg quality. We also demonstrated that a domestic hatchery strain of fish that spawns in early winter in a hatchery environment can revert to typical spring spawning when exposed to temperatures experienced in the wild.

ACKNOWLEDGMENT

We thank C. Kaya, Montana State University, Bozeman, for reviewing this manuscript.

REFERENCES

Combs, B. D. 1965. Effects of temperature on the development of salmon eggs. Progressive Fish-Culturist 27:134–137.

Combs, B. D., and R. E. Burrows. 1957. Threshold temperatures for the normal development of chinook salmon eggs. Progressive Fish-Culturist 19:3–6.

Davis, H. S. 1953. Culture and disease of game fishes. University of California Press, Berkeley.

Hokanson, K. F. R., J. H. McCormick, B. R. Jones, and J. H. Tucker. 1973. Thermal requirements for maturation, spawning, and embryo survival of the brook trout, Salvelinus fontinalis. Journal of the Fisheries Research Board of Canada 30:975–984.

Leifritz, E., and R. C. Lewis. 1976. Trout and salmon culture (hatchery methods). California Department of Fish and Game, Fish Bulletin 164.

Russo, R. C., and R. V. Thurston. 1974. Water analysis of Bridger Creek (Gallatin County) Montana 1973. Montana State University, Fisheries Bioassay Laboratory, Technical Report 74-3, Bozeman.

Snedecor, G. W., and W. G. Cochran. 1967. Statistical methods. Iowa State University Press, Ames.

Model 12–3. Report on Light-Water Nuclear Reactors
(excerpt from a technical-background report)*

1092 Willowcreek Dr.
Austin, Texas 78741
April 27, 19XX

Mr. David A. McMurrey
Department of English
Austin Community College
Austin, Texas 78712

Dear Mr. McMurrey:

In keeping with our January 22 agreement, I am submitting the accompanying technical-background report entitled Light-Water Nuclear Reactors.

The purpose of this report is to provide introductory information to city council members who are considering membership in a regional consortium. This report provides an explanation of how each type of light-water reactor operates. In addition, the report discusses some of the basic safety mechanisms used in this type of reactor. The report concludes with a review of the economic aspects of nuclear power plants.

I hope this report will prove to be satisfactory.

Respectfully yours,

Jeffrey De La Cruz

Encl.   Technical-background report on light-water reactors

*Jeffrey De La Cruz. Report on Light-Water Nuclear Reactors (Austin: Univ. of Texas, 1984). Reprinted by permission.

Report on

LIGHT-WATER NUCLEAR REACTORS

submitted to

Dr. David A. McMurrey
Department of English
Austin Community College
Austin, Texas
April 27, 19XX

by

Jeffrey De La Cruz

This report examines light-water reactors as a possible alternative source of energy for Luckenbach, Texas. Both types of light-water reactors are described, and an explanation of how each reactor produces electricity is presented. Safety systems and economic aspects conclude the main discussion of the report.

i

TABLE OF CONTENTS

LIST OF ILLUSTRATIONS   iv

LIST OF TABLES   iv

ABSTRACT   v

   I. INTRODUCTION   1

  II. PRESSURIZED-WATER REACTORS (PWR)   2

     Description of Major Parts   2

      Core   3

       Fuel   3

       Fuel Rod   3

       Fuel Assembly   3

      Control Rods   3

      Reactor Vessel   4

      Steam Generators   6

       Heat Exchangers   6

       Steam Drum   6

      Pressurizer   7

     Production of Electricity   8

      Circulating Water to Primary System   8

      Producing Steam in Secondary System   8

      Separating the Steam   8

      Producing the Electricity   9

 III. BOILING-WATER REACTORS (BWR)   10

     Description of Major Parts   10

      Core   10

       Fuel   11

       Fuel Rod   11

       Fuel Assembly   11

      Control Rods   11

      Core Shroud and Reactor Vessel   12

      Recirculation System   13

      Steam Separators   13

      Steam Dryers   14

     Production of Electricity   15

      Circulating Water   15

      Separating Steam   15

      Drying the Steam   15

      Producing Electricity   16

  IV. SAFETY MEASURES   17

     Measures Used in the PWR   18

      Residual Heat-Removal System   18

      Emergency Core-Cooling System   18

       Passive System   19

       Low-Pressure Injection Systems   20

High-Pressure Injection Systems 20
Containment Building 20
Measures Used in the BWR 20
Drywell 21
Emergency Core-Cooling System 21
Reactor Core Isolation Cooling 22
High-Pressure Core Spray 22
Low-Pressure Core Spray 22
Nuclear Regulatory Commission's Role 22

V. ECONOMIC ASPECTS 24
Busbar Costs 24
Construction Costs 24
Operation and Maintenance Costs 25
Fuel Costs 25
Operating Capacity 26
Availability Factor 26
Capacity Factor 26

VI. CONCLUSION 28

APPENDIX 29

Literature Cited 30

LIST OF ILLUSTRATIONS

Figure   Page
1. Schematic of a Pressurized-Water Reactor 3
2. Pressurized-Water Reactor Core 4
3. Control Rod of a Pressurized-Water Reactor 5
4. Heat Exchangers 6
5. Pressurizer 7
6. Schematic of a Boiling-Water Reactor 10
7. Control Rod 12
8. Recirculation System 13
9. Steam Separators 14
10. Steam Dryer 14
11. PWR Emergency Core-Cooling System 19
12. BWR Emergency Core-Cooling System 21

LIST OF TABLES

1. Busbar Costs 24
2. Economic Data from Other Consortia 25

ABSTRACT

Light-water reactors are a category of nuclear power reactor in which water is used as both a coolant and a moderator. There are two types of light-water reactors: the pressurized-water reactor and the boiling-water reactor. In a pressurized-water reactor, steam is produced in a secondary system. The main components of a pressurized-water reactor are the core, control rods, reactor vessel, steam generators, and pressurizer. The core contains fuel assemblies that contain fuel rods filled with fuel pellets. The coolant flows through the core, where it is heated at high pressure. Then coolant flows to a series of steam generators, where the coolant flows through the heat exchangers and the steam drum. The pressure is lowered and the steam that is allowed to form then flows to a turbogenerator where electricity is produced. The control rods control the amount of nuclear fission reactions in the core, while the pressurizer maintains the operating pressure in the reactor coolant system. The reactor vessel contains the fuel elements, the control elements, and the core monitoring instruments.

In a boiling-water reactor, steam is allowed to form directly in the core. The main components of a boiling-water reactor are the core control rods, the core shroud and reactor vessel, the recirculation system, the steam separators, and the steam dryers. The core of a boiling-water reactor is slightly larger than that of a pressurized-water reactor but contains the same elements. The coolant is circulated through the system by the recirculation system, which consists of two loops containing pumps external to the reactor vessel and jet pumps inside the vessel. After steam is formed in the reactor vessel, it flows to a series of steam separators, where it is separated from the coolant. The steam then flows through steam dryers where additional drying is done, and then it turns a turbogenerator. The control rods and reactor vessel function in the same way as in the pressurized-water reactor.

Safety systems are designed to prevent meltdown in both types of light-water reactors. The safety systems in a pressurized-water reactor include the residual heat-removal system, the emergency core-cooling systems, and the containment building. The residual heat-removal system removes decay heat from the primary coolant system during plant shutdown. The emergency core-cooling systems are designed to deal with loss-of-coolant accidents. The passive system consists of accumulators which inject coolant into the vessel when an accident occurs. The low-pressure injection systems and the high-pressure injection systems also provide make-up water. The safety systems of a boiling-water reactor include the drywell and emergency core-cooling systems. The reactor core isolation cooling system pumps water into the reactor during a loss-of-coolant accident, while the low- and high-pressure core spray systems provide make-up water. The drywell encloses the reactor vessel, and the containment vessel encloses all the components of the reactor. The Nuclear Regulatory Commission inspects all nuclear power plants to ensure that these safety systems are adequate.

The economics of a nuclear power plant are determined by the busbar cost and the operating capacity costs. The busbar cost is determined by the construction cost, the cost of operating and maintaining the plant, and the cost of the fuel. The operating capacity costs are determined by the availability of fuel and the capacity of the plant.

Report on

LIGHT-WATER NUCLEAR REACTORS

I. INTRODUCTION

There are approximately five hundred nuclear power plants in operation or under construction worldwide. These plants can produce as much as 370,000 megawatts of electricity. These nuclear power plants can be categorized into four types: (1) light-water reactors, (2) heavy-water reactors, (2) gas-cooled reactors, and (4) breeder reactors. Basically, a nuclear power reactor operates by having a central unit, called the core, in which nuclear fission reactions take place and produce heat. A liquid, called the coolant, flows through the system and absorbs the heat produced in the core. The liquid is then converted into steam that drives a turbogenerator to produce electricity.

The purpose of this report is to present the basic design, operation, and safety measures of light-water reactors to the city council. The city council is currently investigating the possibility of membership in a regional consortium as an alternative to increased coal-fired production of electricity. This report will explain how the two types of light-water reactors, the design to be used by the consortium, operate and present the key safety and economic aspects of these reactors. Although the operations of nuclear power reactors do involve complex chemistry and physics, these aspects of the discussion have been avoided; only an introductory discussion of the mechanical operation of the reactor is presented.

The four parts of this report discuss (1) the design and operation of pressurized-water reactors, (2) the design and operation of boiling-water reactors, (3) safety measures employed in these reactors, and (4) economic aspects of these reactors' operation. The sections on the two types of light-water reactors describe the components and explain their operation. The section on safety measures discusses the causes of meltdown, safety systems used in both types of reactors, and the role the Nuclear Regulatory Commission plays to ensure the safety of these reactors. The final section reviews the various costs involved in the construction and operation of a nuclear power plant.

II. PRESSURIZED-WATER REACTORS

This section of the report describes the key components of the pressurized light-water reactor and explains their operation in the production of electricity.

Description of the Major Parts

In a pressurized-water reactor (see Figure 1), the reactor cooling water entering the core is highly pressurized so that it remains below the boiling point. The water leaves the reactor to pass through steam generators, where a secondary coolant is allowed to boil and produce steam to drive the turbine.

1

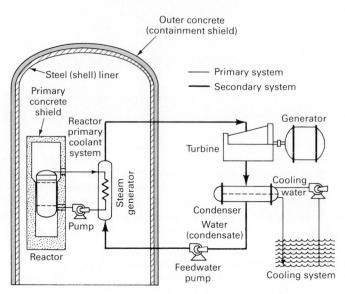

FIGURE 1.   Schematic of a pressurized-water reactor

Source: Anthony V. Nero, *A Guidebook to Nuclear Reactors* (Berkeley, CA: Univ. of California Press, 1979), 78. © 1979 The Regents of the University of California.

The key components in this process are the core, the control rods, the reactor vessel, the steam generators, and the pressurizer.

Core.   The core is the active portion of the reactor providing heat to the system. The core contains fuel assemblies that contain fuel rods filled with fuel pellets.

Fuel.   The fuel in the pressurized-water reactor consists of cylindrical pellets of slightly enriched uranium dioxide with a diameter of 0.325 in. by 0.39 in. The pellets are dished at the ends to allow for thermal expansion (12:2004).

Fuel Rod.   A fuel rod consists of a cylindrical tube made of Zircalloy, a steel-gray alloy that is highly resistant to corrosion. This tube is 13 ft long with an outer diameter of 0.39 in. and a 0.025-in. thick wall. The tube is filled with fuel pellets and is sealed (10:122).

Fuel Assembly.   A fuel assembly is formed when about 230 of the fuel rods are grouped in a bundle. The fuel assembly is about 8 in. on a side and 177 in. long (10:122). The reactor core is formed when about 240 of these assemblies are arranged in a cylindrical array. These assemblies are supported between upper and lower grid plates and are surrounded by a stainless-steel shroud. The grid plates consist of an assembly of spring clips interlocked to form an egg-crate arrangement providing rigid support and spacing of the fuel rods (3:259).

Control Rods.   Control rods provide a means of changing the amount of heat produced in the core ...

V. ECONOMIC ASPECTS

This section presents some of the key costs that determine the economics of a nuclear power plant. These costs will be compared to those associated with other energy-producing systems, primarily those involving coal. Costs are determined by the busbar cost and the operating capacity costs.

Busbar Cost

The busbar cost is the total cost of electricity leaving the power station. The busbar cost consists of several factors: (1) construction cost, (2) operation and maintenance costs, and (3) cost of the fuel. The per-kilowatt cost of electricity estimated by the Energy Research and Development Administration, generated from 1000-megawatt nuclear, coal, and oil plants beginning operation in 1980 is as shown in Table 1.

TABLE 1. Busbar Costs

Costs	Electricity Costs (in mills* per kilowatt hour)		
	Nuclear	Coal	Oil
Capital costs	18.7	15.2	10.5
Fuel costs	5.8	13.7	25.7
Operation and maintenance costs	2.8	3.3	2.2
TOTAL COSTS	27.3	32.2	38.4

*A mill is ¹⁄₁₀ of a cent ($0.001).

Construction Cost.   The construction costs include the hardware, labor, original capital borrowed, interest generated on that capital, and inflation of capital costs. The construction costs for a nuclear power plant are 18.7 mills per kilowatt hour, whereas those of coal are 15.2 mills per kilowatt hour (8:20). However, there is evidence to show that complete or nearly complete nuclear power plants cost about twice as much in real dollars as they do at the time they are ordered (1:1). This inflation is the result of additional quality-assurance, inspection, and documentation requirements. The rise in costs can also be attributed to increases in the costs of engineering manpower and of materials such as concrete, steel, and wire (11:113). However, the actual cost of a nuclear steam supply system and the turbine generator together amount to only 15% of the total cost (11:117). Most of the cost of a nuclear plant can be attributed to interest on capital during construction. Industry experts hope that reducing the time between initial plans for and operation of nuclear power plants will cut these costs (8:23).

Operation and Maintenance Costs.   The operation and maintenance costs for a nuclear power plant are 2.8 mills per kilowatt hour compared to 3.3 mills per kilowatt hour for a coal power plant. The difference can be attributed to recent requirements for installation of environmental-protection scrubbing equipment in coal plants. Another factor ...

LITERATURE CITED

1. Bupp, Irwin C., Jr., and Robert Trietel. 1976. The Economics of Nuclear Power. Boston: MIT.
2. Burn, Duncan. 1978. Nuclear Power and the Energy Crisis. New York: New York University Press.
3. Cameron, I. R. 1980. Nuclear Fission Reactors. New York: McGraw-Hill.
4. Glasstone, Samuel, and Alexander Sesonske. Nuclear Reactor Engineering. Princeton, N.J.: D. Van Nostrand.
5. Kessler, G. 1983. Nuclear Fission Reactors. New York: Springer-Verlag Wien.
6. Lahey, R. T., and F. J. Moody. 1977. The Thermal-Hydraulics of a Boiling Water Nuclear Reactor. American Nuclear Society.
7. Murray, Raymond I. 1974. Nuclear Energy. New York: Pergamon.
8. Myers, Desaix III. 1977. The Nuclear Power Debate. New York: Praeger.
9. Naval Reactors Branch, Division of Reactor Development, United States Atomic Energy Commission. 1958. The Shippingport Pressurized Water Reactor. Reading, Mass.: Addison Wesley.
10. Nero, Anthony V. 1979. A Guidebook to Nuclear Reactors. Berkeley, Calif.: University of California Press.
11. The Nuclear Energy Policy Study Group. 1977. Nuclear Power Issues and Choices. Cambridge, Mass.: Ballinger.
12. "Nuclear Reactor." 1980 ed. Van Nostrand's Scientific Encyclopedia. Vol. 2.
13. Pickard, James K., ed. 1957. Nuclear Power Reactors. Princeton, N.J.: D. Van Nostrand.

CHAPTER 13

Writing Effective Instructions

Chapter Objectives
Preparing to Write Instructions
    Finding a Topic
    Identifying the Audience
    Narrowing the Topic
    Locating Information Sources
Identifying the Elements of the
        Procedure
    End Product
    Tools
    Resources
    Steps
Planning Your Instructions
    Simple Instructions
    Complex Instructions
    Organization
Identifying and Explaining the
        Individual Steps
Supplementary Sections
    Equipment and Materials

Related Theory and Principles of
    Operation
Guidelines, Cautions, and Warnings
Troubleshooting and Maintenance
    Charts
Introductions
Graphic and Textual Aids for
    Instructions
    Illustrations
    Textual Aids
Finishing Instructions
Testing Your Written Instructions
Exercises
Models
    13–1. Installing Your Ceiling Fan
          (excerpts from simple, fixed-
          order steps instructions)
    13–2. Operating the Weston AM/FM
          Electronic Digital Clock Radio
          (excerpts from complex, task-
          oriented instructions)

——————————————— *Chapter Objectives* ———————————————

After you read this chapter, study the examples, work the steps, and do the practice writing, you should be able to:

- Identify situations where written instructions are needed.
- Identify the end product, tools, resources, and steps in an instructional process.
- Identify the features and capabilities of the tools used in the process.
- Define and organize task-oriented and tool-oriented instructions.
- Identify the supplementary sections necessary to a set of instructions.
- Use the critical points in the instructional process and the critical parts of the equipment used in the process to plan illustrations for instructions.
- Set up a test to make sure your written instructions work.

If you look around you, you'll notice that we live in a world flooded with instructions—instructions on how to build or assemble things, instructions on how to operate things, and instructions on how to maintain or repair things. Instructions are everywhere: on the back of boxes, on little slips of paper inserted in product packaging, in stenciled lettering on the sides of machinery, and in pamphlets or even whole books that accompany equipment. Often, however, instructions are difficult, confusing, and frustrating to try to follow. Instructions often fail to do their job because

- The reader hurries through them or does not read them at all, which of course is not a fault of the instructions.
- Some procedures are just difficult to explain in writing, without in-person demonstrations and guidance.
- Writers sometimes do not carefully plan and write their instructions.
- Inadequate format and illustrations can prevent rapid reading or easy understanding.
- Sometimes, instructions are not tested. Even the most carefully written instructions can omit an important explanation or be unclear at certain points.

This chapter should guide you in writing clear, understandable instructions that avoid some of these problems. If you have read Chapter 1, "Process and Causal Discussions," you already know about one of the basics in instruction writing: dividing the procedure into steps.

Preparing to Write Instructions

In the early stages, writing instructions is much the same as writing any of the other applications discussed here in Part IV. You must make some preliminary decisions before diving into the actual writing.

Finding a Topic

If you want to write an instructional report but need to find a topic, keep these two bits of advice in mind:

- Avoid simplistic procedures: explaining how to change a flat tire, for example, is not much of a challenge to you as a writer.
- Avoid large, complex procedures: trying to explain how to program in Pascal, for example, will cause you big problems. If you are interested in such a topic, try narrowing it to a more manageable size.

STEP 1.   On your worksheet briefly explain the instructions you are going to write. For ideas for instruction-writing projects, see Chapter 8 as well as exercise 1 at the end of Chapter 1. (If you are thinking about collaborating with someone else on your written instructions, see "Collaborating on Technical Reports" in the Introduction for ideas and suggestions.)

Identifying the Audience

As with any report, identifying the audience is critical: Who will be reading your instructions and trying to follow them? Use the strategies in Chapter 5 to help you identify and analyze the audience for your instructions. Understanding your audience will enable you to know

- Which topics to emphasize
- Which topics to summarize
- Which topics to delete.

Narrowing the Topic

Narrowing means covering only a limited portion of a topic—not the whole thing. As the following examples show, you can provide instructions within limited areas: as opposed to explaining how to program anything in Pascal, you could provide instructions on how to write home-budget programs or metric-conversion programs.

Oversized Topics	Narrowed Topics
How to program in Pascal	Home-budget programs in Pascal
Overhauling an automobile engine	Cleaning and adjusting a carburetor
How to use a text-editor program on a computer	Copying, moving, and deleting large blocks of text
Planting a garden	How to raise tomatoes

Locating Information Sources

Instructional reports generally require less library work; most of your information comes from direct, hands-on experience, rehearsal, and observation of the activity. Still, the library may provide you with some useful information to make your instructions even better:

- Check *Consumer Reports* and other product-evaluation literature (see Chapter 9 on finding these information sources). These sources may alert you to problems others have found in the product you are giving instructions for.

- Check business and industry directories such as the *Thomas Register*; consider writing for product-information and user's guides. Use this information to add depth to your own instructions.
- Locate other instructions on procedures like yours; study how they explain things, evaluate their effectiveness, avoid their mistakes, and use their good points.

STEP 2.   If necessary, return to the discussion and steps for analyzing audiences and translating technical subjects in Chapter 5; for brainstorming, narrowing, and outlining in Chapter 8; for locating library and nonlibrary sources of information in Chapter 9; and for note taking in Chapter 10.

Identifying the Elements of the Procedure

The simplest instructions are those that have one fixed goal (a baked cake, a fixed flat, a grafted fruit tree, or a blood-pressure reading) and have a fixed, unchanging order of steps. Not all instructions, however, have a fixed goal and a fixed sequence of steps. Understanding the basic components of an instructional process can aid you in writing more organized instructions, regardless of their complexity. Before you begin writing your instructions, analyze the four basic components of your instructional process: the end product, the tools, the resources, and the steps.

End Product

Most important in your instructions is the end product that you want the reader to achieve. Understanding the end product will help you organize and write the rest of your instructions. Two types of end products have a direct bearing on the organization of your instructions: the fixed end product and the variable end product.

Fixed End Product.   When you have one clear, unchanging goal in a set of instructions, it is a fixed end product: a baked cake, a changed tire, or a grafted fruit tree are examples. There may be some minor variation—for example, a different flavor of icing—but the goal is relatively unchanging. Here are some other examples:

Instructional Processes with Fixed End Products

Converting an electric typewriter to a computer output device	Rebinding a worn hardback book
Overhauling a carburetor	Installing a ceiling fan
Properly trimming trees in residential areas	Starting an intravenous device
Putting a new roof on your home	Repairing brakes on an automobile
Downloading files from a Model 2330 mainframe to a Kiwi personal computer	Sending files to others by asynchronous phone communications

Variable End Product.   When you write a set of instructions to enable the reader to do a variety of things, the end product is variable. For example, if you were writing a brief guide on how to use a typewriter or a text-editing program, how to cook with a wok, how to use a food processor, or how to program in BASIC or Pascal, there would be no unique, unchanging goal. Instead, you'd show the reader various ways to use a tool or instrument:

Instructional Processes with Variable End Products

Using special features on the System 3200 electronic typewriter

Using the block text functions on the Friendly Editor

Handling financial and other statistical matters with Hypothesis/33, an electronic spreadsheet

Creating color graphic geometric shapes in BASIC

Using the standard router for a variety of woodworking projects

Using the Microcook 3434 for all your cooking needs

STEP 3.   On your worksheet describe the end product that you want your readers to achieve in using your instructions, and explain whether it is a fixed or variable end product.

Tools

The tools in an instructional process are those things that the reader used to get the job done. In baking a cake, the tools are bowls, eggbeaters, sifters, and the like. Some tools are less obvious than others: for example, in writing a Pascal program, the computer and the Pascal programs are the tools. However, you can't see Pascal and handle it the same way you can an eggbeater or a sifter:

Instructional Process	*Tools*
Changing a tire	Jack Lug wrench
Changing the oil in a car	Pan to catch old oil Oil-filter wrench
Programming in Pascal	Pascal compiler Computer with display, keyboard, and sufficient memory Pascal reference book
Taking a blood-pressure reading	Sphygmomanometer Wrist watch with second hand or readout
Planting tomatoes for a patio garden	Shovel or handspade Large pots Stakes or wire cages

Tools have various *capabilities* and *features*. Some typewriters have a feature known as an erase key that gives you the capability of erasing a letter. Consider these other examples of features:

Tools	Features
Photocopying machine	Automatic feed Paper-size adjustment Automatic collating 10% reduction Lightness and darkness controls Alternate paper selection Reverse-side copy
Text-editor computer program	Block copy, move, delete Global search and replace Margin readjustment Macro definition capability Current file switching Profile modification
Electric drill	Lock-on control Variable speed controls Reverse direction
Baby stroller	Adjustable hood Convertible seat Carry-all compartment Swivel front wheels

Resources

The resources used in an instructional process are those things that are consumed during the process: for example, eggs, flour, sugar, and the like are used up in baking a cake. In writing a Pascal program, electricity and perhaps some paper are all that are consumed. Here are more examples:

Instructional Process	Resources
Changing a tire	New and old tires
Changing the oil in a car	New and old oil New and old oil filters Old rags for cleanup
Programming in Pascal	Paper Electricity Diskettes or disk space
Taking a blood-pressure reading	(Nothing!)

Instructional Process	*Resources*
Planting tomatoes in a patio garden	Dirt
	Fertilizer
	Seeds or plants
	Water
	Twine
	Insecticide or organic insect repellent
	Lemonade

STEP 4.   On your worksheet describe the tools and resources readers will use in following your instructions, and list the features of the tools.

Steps

Another important element of instructions is the actual steps—the groups of action required to get the job done. Before you identify these steps, however, you still need to develop a larger view of the instructional process you are writing about.

Planning Your Instructions

Once you've identified the components of your instructional process and understand which sort of instructions you are writing, the organization of the written instructions is much easier.

Simple Instructions

If the procedure for which you are writing instructions has a fixed end product and a relatively fixed order of steps, it is fairly easy to plan, outline, and then write. In these *simple* instructions, you

- Identify and make a list of the steps
- Make sure you've not omitted any steps
- Watch out for steps that have too many actions in them (steps that are really two or more in one)
- Explain each step using the guidelines discussed in Chapter 1.

Figure 13–1 contains an example of a completed steps discussion; notice that the order and end product of the steps are both fixed.

Complex Instructions

There are two kinds of variable-end-product instructions: *task-oriented* instructions and *tool-oriented* instructions. Both are usually aimed at showing readers how to use an instrument—usually a fairly complex one that has many features and capabilities. In these instructions the end product is widely variable, and there is not necessarily any fixed order in the steps. Here are two contrasting partial outlines that illustrate the difference between these two kinds of complex instructions:

Task-Oriented Instructions	Tool-Oriented Instructions
Reducing copy size	Size key
Collating copies	Collate key
Copying on front and back	Reverse-copy key
Using automatic feed	Auto-feed tray
Changing print quantity	Quantity key
Selecting different paper size	Paper key
Adjusting copy darkness	Light–dark key

The items in the task-oriented list are action oriented; those in the tool-oriented list are feature oriented. Which would be the best way to handle these instructions for a photocopier? Since people are generally familiar with copiers, just a review of the keys and other features—the tool-oriented approach—might be the best route; it would certainly take fewer pages.

Task-Oriented Instructions.   In task-oriented instructions you identify the most common tasks readers must know and then explain the steps for each task separately. Readers can then use these tasks in whatever order or combination necessary to achieve their goal. Task-oriented instructions are actually groups of simple instructions. In task-oriented instructions

- Identify *all* of the important tasks or routines that a reader might need to know about.
- Enable the reader to understand the capability or purpose of each task. For example, if the food processor can whip, chop, grate, puree, and blend, some users might need to understand the difference between these capabilities.
- Provide examples for each of the tasks.
- Design the discussions of the different tasks so that they are interlocking and refer to each other.
- Make the format allow for easy and quick reference by the reader.

If you were writing instructions on how to use an automatic phone-answering device, you'd probably have to write task-oriented instructions because readers want to know how to use the machine in specific ways. In preparation for writing these instructions, you'd identify these common tasks that readers use the answering machine for:

Instructional Process	Individual Tasks
Automatic phone-answering machine	Installing the machine
	Recording your phone message
	Setting the machine to auto-answer
	Reviewing messages from callers
	Monitoring calls without answering
	Erasing old messages
	Recording phone conversations with the machine

Procedures

1. Slides for microscopic smears must always be sparkling clean. They must be stored or dipped in alcohol and polished clean (free of grease) with a tissue or soft cloth.
2. Take three clean slides and with a marking pencil make a circle (about 1½ cm in diameter) in the center. At one end of the slide write the initials of one of the three organisms.
3. Turn the slides over so that the unmarked side is up (when slides are to be stained, wax pencil markings should always be placed on the underside so that the wax will not smear or wash off, or run into the smear itself).
4. Place a loopful of water in the ringed area on the slide. Use the inoculating loop. Mix a small amount of bacteria in the water and spread it out.
5. Allow the smear to air dry. You should be able to see a thin white film. If not, add another loopful of water and more bacteria as in Step 4.
6. Heat-fix the smear by passing the slide rapidly through the Bunsen flame three times.
7. Place the slides on a staining rack and flood them with Loeffler's methylene blue. Leave the stain on for three minutes.
8. Wash each slide gently with distilled water, drain off excess water, blot (do not rub) with bibulous paper, and let the slides dry completely in air.
9. Prepare two more slides as in 1, 2, and 3 above. Place a loopful of distilled water (or sterile saline) in the ringed area on each slide.
10. With the flat end of a toothpick scrape some tartar from the surface of your teeth and around the gums. Emulsify the tartar in the drop of water on one slide. Repeat the procedure on the other slide.
11. Allow both slides to dry in air; then heat-fix them. Stain one with methylene blue for three minutes; the other with safranin also for three minutes.
12. Wash, drain, and dry the slides as in Step 8 above.
13. Examine all slides, including the prepared stained smear with all three microscope objectives. Record your results.

Josephine A. Morello et al., Laboratory Manual and Workbook in Microbiology (New York: Macmillan, 1984), 30–31. Reprinted by permission.

FIGURE 13–1. Simple instructions: fixed-order steps and fixed end product

Now, each of these individual tasks you'd explain in a step-by-step way, as shown in the excerpt from a task-oriented approach to instruction writing in Figure 13–2.

Tool-Oriented Instructions. In tool-oriented instructions you explain the capabilities of each feature of the tool. Readers can then use these features and their capabilities in any order or combination they wish in order to achieve their goal.

- Make sure that you discuss *each* important feature of the mechanism.
- Make sure you explain the capabilities of each feature.
- If necessary, explain how to use certain features step by step.
- Provide examples of the use of each feature.

If you were writing instructions on using a microwave oven or using new BASIC programming software, you might decide that a tool-oriented approach is more effective. In that case, you'd explain how to use the various features of the tools and what their capabilities are, as follows:

Tools	Features	Capabilities
Microwave oven	Defrost key	Enables you to thaw frozen foods easily
	Clock display	Provides the time of day
		Counts down cooking time
	Auto Cook key	Saves you the time of looking up cooking temperatures and times by sensing steam from the food being cooked
BASIC programming	F5 key	Facilitates editing of program lines
		Enables you to copy a program line by typing a new number
	F6 key	Facilitates renumbering of all or part of program statements in a file
		Enables you to renumber portions of a file rather than the whole file

To explain how to use each of these capabilities, you might present an example of its use and present steps:

Features	Examples	Steps
Microwave oven: Defrost key	Thawing frozen minute steaks	1. Place the minute steaks in the oven and close the door. 2. Press the Defrost key. 3. Press 7,0, and 0 on the number pad to indicate 7 minutes of cooking. 4. Press Start. 5. Turn the package over and repeat steps 2, 3, and 4.

Recording Your Phone Messages

Below are instructions on how to record your phone message for friends and associates who call while you are out. Making your recording is easy, so you can change your message as often as necessary. (Refer to Figure 13–2a.)

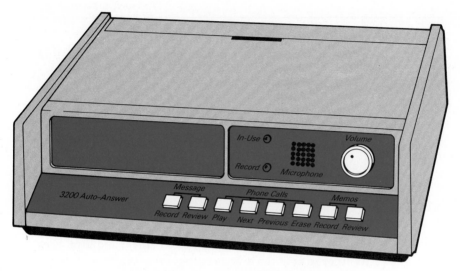

FIGURE 13–2a.   The 3200 Auto-Answer

1. Plug your 3200 in; the green ready light should illuminate immediately.
2. Lift the top panel control cover.
3. Press and hold down the Record Message button.
4. When the In-Use light illuminates, dictate your message into the built-in microphone next to the Volume control. Position yourself about 18 inches away from the microphone.
5. When you finish recording your message, release the Record Message button. A "beep" is automatically placed at the end of your message, and the tape automatically rewinds.
6. To listen to the message that you've just recorded, press and release the Review button on the front panel. Your recorded message will play back through the speaker. Use the Volume control to adjust the volume if necessary.

TO READY THE 3200 AUTO-ANSWER FOR AUTOMATIC ANSWERING, SEE
"Setting the 3200 for Auto-Answering,"
pages 5–6.

FIGURE 13–2.   **Excerpt from task-oriented instructions**

Features	Examples	Steps
BASIC programming language: F6 (renumbering key)	Renumbering only statements 30 to 1000 in a program but not statements 5000–7000.	1. Locate cursor on line 30. 2. Press F6. 3. Move cursor to line 1000. 4. Press F6 again. 5. Now, press Enter.

Figure 13–3 contains an excerpt from a tool-oriented approach to instruction writing:

Special Keys

On the right side of the keyboard you'll find ten keys that provide you with special time-saving functions. When you enter BASIC, these special keys offer you a powerful set of functions:

F1   List the file. This key enables you to review the programming statements in the current file. Press Control and Num Lock together to stop the display output temporarily, and then press any key to continue.

F2   Run the file. This key enables you to run the current file; you do not need to type the program name.

F3   Save the file. This key enables you to save the current file; you must supply a name for the file (the system supplies the extension .BAS).

F4   Load the file. The key enables you to load a file; you must type in the name of the file, but the system takes care of the quotation marks and the .BAS extension for you.

F5   Edit a line. This key simplifies your job of editing lines in a program: position the cursor on the number of the line you want to edit, press F5, make the changes you want, and then press Enter.

F6   Renumber part or all of the file. This key enables you to ...

FIGURE 13–3.   Excerpt from tool-oriented instructions

Organization

Not all instructions have the simple fixed-order sequence that Figure 13–1 does. When the steps do have a fixed order, you simply number them and present them in order. However, if you have complex instructions, you'll have to organize the steps carefully so that readers can find their way around in them.

In a task-oriented approach there are small groupings of steps that readers can use in any order or combination that they wish. How do they locate the tasks that they want? Arrangement of the tasks, headings, and tables of contents are the best ways to help readers find the information they need. In the example in Figure 13–4, the headings on different kinds of cooking enable readers to find the type they want to use.

STEP 5.   If you are writing complex instructions, explain whether you are writing task-oriented or tool-oriented instructions, and then list the tasks or the features according to the type you've chosen.

Identifying and Explaining the Individual Steps

The steps in an instructional process are the actions the reader takes to reach the desired end product: in baking a cake, for example, sifting the flour, beating the eggs, preheating the oven, and so on. There are four types of steps:

• *Fixed-order steps.* In some procedures you must perform the steps in a specified order; otherwise, the results may be a disaster.

Fixed-order steps: Changing the oil in a car

1. Place a pan under the car to catch the old oil.
2. Remove the bolt from the oil pan and let the old oil drain out.
3. Remove the oil filter.
4. Install the new oil filter.
5. Replace the bolt.
6. Put in the new oil.

• *Variable-order steps.* In a few procedures you have relative freedom in the order in which you perform the steps (numbers are not used in this example because they imply a fixed order).

Variable-order steps: Baking bread

• Preheat the oven.
• Start the dried yeast in a small bowl of warm water.
• Measure out 4 cups of flour.
• Prepare a clean, dry surface; sprinkle with flour.
• Put on some good bread-kneading music.

The preceding section "Selecting a Cooking Mode" explains how to choose the best cooking mode for the meals you want to prepare. Read that section in order to understand which of the microwave cooking alternatives is best for you. The following steps explain how to use each of these cooking modes.

TIMED COOKING
1. Place the food in the oven and close the door.
2. Press the Time key.
3. Using the number keypad, enter the amount of time in minutes and seconds that the food is to cook.
4. Press Start.

COOK-CODE COOKING
1. Place the food in the oven and close the door.
2. Press the Cook Code key.
3. Enter the cook code you desire. For example, a recipe calling for 15 minutes of cooking time at power level 8 should be entered as 158; 11 minutes at power level 10, as 1110.
4. Press Start.

AUTOMATIC COOKING
1. Place the food in the oven and close the door.
2. Press the Auto Cook key.
3. Enter the auto-cook code that is right for the food you are preparing.
4. The next step depends on which auto-cook code you've entered:

• If you entered auto-cook code 1, remove the food when the cooking cycle is completed.

   Or

• If you entered auto-cook code 2-7, the oven beeps at the end of the auto-cook cycle, changes to timed cooking, and allows you to check the food, stir, or rotate as necessary. If you want to continue cooking, follow the steps in timed cooking.

FIGURE 13–4. Handling complex instructions

• *Variable steps.* In some procedures, particularly those for variable end products, you use different groups of steps depending on what you are trying to accomplish. In using a typewriter, for example, you might never change the pitch from 10 to 12. Thus, steps themselves can be variable: they may or may not be used every time the process is performed.

Variable steps: Typing on a new typewriter

- Erasing text with the special erase key.
- Changing the type element (ball) for different fonts or characters.
- Resetting margins for special indented text.
- Changing the pitch (8, 10, 12, etc.)
- Altering line spacing (half, single, double, etc.)

• *Alternate steps.* In still other procedures there are different steps readers can follow depending on their tools, resources, or preferences.

Alternate steps: Erasing text with a text editor on a computer

1. Move the cursor to the start of the text you want to erase.
2. Press the Delete key as many times as necessary to delete the letters required.

Or

1. Move the cursor to the start of the text you want to delete.
2. Press Control-B (begin block).
3. Move the cursor to the last letter of the text you want to delete.
4. Press Control-E (end block).
5. Now, press Control-D (delete block).

STEP 6.   On your worksheet, list the steps that readers will follow in your instructions, and identify which type the steps are (fixed order, variable order, variable, or alternate steps).

In addition to discussing the actual steps, you must supplement them with explanations to make them clearer and easier to understand, using the Chapter 1 guidelines summarized here:

- Explain the purpose of each step.
- Define potentially unfamiliar words.
- Use comparisons or examples wherever they help make the discussion more understandable.
- Describe the tools or instruments used in the instructions.
- Describe the objects before and after the actions taken during the step.
- Explain the causes and effects that lie behind the steps being performed.
- Provide cautionary and troubleshooting advice on any step requiring it.
- Divide overly large steps into smaller steps or into substeps.

You won't use all of these types of supplementary discussion for each step, only those that help readers understand. Look at Figure 13–5 for an excerpt from a steps discussion; the supplementary information provides description of the yeast culture, some cautionary advice, and a description of how things should look throughout the process.

STEP 7.   On your worksheet, list which of the kinds of supplementary discussion you think will be needed for each of the steps in your instructions. (For more on supplementary discussion, see Chapter 1.)

Start-Up and Shutdown of an Ethanol Plant

The following is a sequence for starting up and shutting down an ethanol plant.

Preliminaries

For the initial start-up, a yeast culture must be prepared or purchased. The initial yeast culture can use a material such as molasses; later cultures can be grown on recycled silage. Yeast, molasses, and some water should be added to the yeast culture tank to make the culture. Although yeasts function anaerobically, they propagate aerobically, so some oxygen should be introduced by bubbling a small amount of air through the culture tank. The initial yeast culture will take about 24 hours to mature.

At this time, the boiler can be started. Instructions packaged with the specific boiler will detail necessary steps to bring the unit on-line (essentially the boiler is filled with water and the heat source started). These instructions should be carefully followed; otherwise there is the possibility of explosion. The next step is the milling of grain for the cooker/fermenter. Enough grain should be milled for two fermentation batches (about 160 bushels).

Prior to loading the fermenter, it should be cleaned well with a strong detergent, rinsed, decontaminated with a strong disinfectant, and then rinsed with cold water to flush out the disinfectant.

Distillation

Once the beer well in the ethanol plant is full, the distillation system can be started up. This process involves the following steps.

1. Turn on the condenser cooling water.
2. Purge the still with steam. This [procedure] removes oxygen from the system by venting at the top of the second column. When steam is seen coming out of the vent, the steam can be temporarily shut off and the vent closed. Purging the still with steam not only removes oxygen but also helps to preheat the still.
3. Pump beer into the still. The beer is pumped in until it is visible at the top of the sight-glass.

FIGURE 13–5. Steps with supplementary discussion

4. <u>Turn steam on and add beer.</u> This process of adding beer and watching the liquid level movement to adjust the steam level will be repeated several times as the columns are loaded. Initially, steam flows should be set at a low level to prevent overloading the trays, which might require shutdown and restart. During this period the valves in the reflux line are fully opened but the reflux pump is left off until enough liquid has built up in the condensate receiver. This prevents excessive wear on the pump. The reflux line <u>between</u> the two columns should also be opened and that reflux pump should be left off. The liquid level in the bottom of the beer still should be monitored, and when it drops to half way, beer should be fed back into the column to refill the bottom of the still. The liquid level should continue to drop; if it does not, additional steam should be fed into the still bottom.

Solar Energy Research Institute, <u>Fuel from Farms: A Guide to Small-Scale Ethanol Production</u> (Oak Ridge, Tenn.: U.S. Department of Energy, February 1980), 62–68.

FIGURE 13–5.   **(cont.)**

Supplementary Sections

If in writing your instructions you find that you have so much supplementary information that it buries the actual steps and reduces the clarity of the discussion, you can shift some of this supplementary information into separate sections.

These supplementary sections include (1) equipment and materials, (2) discussion of theory, principles of operation, or underlying causes and effects, (3) cautionary statements, (4) troubleshooting guides, and (5) introductions.

Equipment and Materials

In almost any set of instructions where tools, equipment, and materials are needed, you must list those items and often describe important details about them. For long lists requiring several paragraphs of explanation, present the information in a separate section just before the individual steps. Otherwise, the list of equipment and materials can be included in the introduction. Figure 13–6 contains a simple list of materials needed in a lab exercise.

Materials: 4 tubes of nutrient broth
                  4 slants of nutrient agar
                  One 24-hour slant culture of *Escherichia coli*
                  One 24-hour slant culture of *Bacillus subtilis*
                  One 24-hour slant culture of *Serratia marcescens*
                  (pigmented)
                  One 24-hour plate culture of *Serratia marcescens*
                  (pigmented)
                  Wire inoculating loop
                  Bunsen burner (and matches)
                  China-marking pencil (or labels)
                  A short ruler with millimeter markings

FIGURE 13—6. Supplementary section: material and equipment

Figure 13–7 shows a different way to present additional information on equipment and materials needed. This example provides descriptive detail on each piece of equipment. An example of additional discussion that must sometimes accompany the list of equipment appears in Figure 13–8.

Table V-3. Equipment for Representative Ethanol Plant

Equipment	Description
Grain bin	* ground carbon steel * 360 bu. with auger for measuring and loading cooker/fermenter
Back-pressure regulators	* 0-50 in. of water
Back-pressure regulator	* 100-200 psig
Beer storage tank	* 6,000-gal. * carbon steel
Condenser, distiller	* 225-sq.-ft. tube and shell * copper coil (single tube, 1.5-ft. diameter) * steel shell cooled

FIGURE 13—7. Supplementary section providing details on equipment

The Autoclave

The autoclave is a steam pressure sterilizer. It is essentially a large, heavy-walled chamber with a steam inlet and an air outlet (Fig. 13-8a). It can be sealed to force steam accumulation. Steam (being lighter but hotter than air) is admitted through an inlet pipe in the upper part of the rear wall. As it rushes in, it pushes the cool air in the chamber forward and down through an air discharge line in the floor of the chamber at its front. When all the cool air has been pushed down the line, it is followed by hot steam, the temperature of which triggers a thermostatic valve placed in the discharge pipe. The valve closes off the line and now, as steam continues to enter the sealed chamber, pressure and temperature begin to build up quickly.

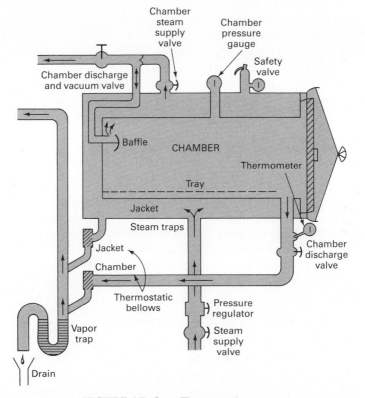

FIGURE 13—8a.   The autoclave

Source: Adrian Delaat, <u>Microbiology for the Allied Health Professions</u>, 2d ed. (Philadelphia: Lea & Febiger, 1979.)

(continued)

FIGURE 13—8.   Supplementary section with extended discussion of important equipment

The barometric pressure of normal atmosphere is about 15 lb to the square inch. Within an autoclave, steam pressure can build to 15 to 30 lb per square inch <u>above</u> atmospheric pressure, bringing the temperature up with it to 121 to 123 degrees centigrade. Steam is wet and penetrative to begin with, even at 100 degrees centigrade. When raised to a high temperature, and driven by high pressure, it penetrates thick substances that would be only superficially bathed by steam at atmospheric pressure. Under autoclave conditions, pressurized steam kills bacterial spores, vegetative bacilli, and other microbial forms quickly and effectively, at temperatures much lower and less destructive to materials than are required in a dry heat oven (160 to 170 degrees centigrade).

Josephine A. Morello et al., <u>Laboratory Manual and Workbook in Microbiology</u> (New York: Macmillan, 1984), 75. Reprinted by permission.

FIGURE 13—8. (cont.)

Related Theory and Principles of Operation

Sometimes, a brief discussion of the theory or principles of operation that lie behind a process can save you much laborious step-by-step explanation. In the example in Figure 13–9, the basic discussion of transmissions gives new mechanics a general understanding that will make the instructions much easier to understand.

Figure 13–10 contains a table of contents showing how a theory section takes up a large part of a manual: the discussion of the theory (Part I) and the discussion of the equipment (Part II) take up about half of the total pages of the manual.

Guidelines, Cautions, and Warnings

Almost all instructions need to include some guidelines, cautions, and warnings. Guidelines and cautions help your readers avoid problems and accomplish their goals. For example, if you're explaining how to use a wok, remind readers to stir the contents briskly; otherwise, their meal will burn. Warnings, on the other hand, have more to do with physical harm to the readers or those around them. For example, in changing a flat tire, the jack must be properly positioned; otherwise, it might fly out and hurt someone. Guidelines, cautions, and warnings are handled several ways:

- They can be explained *in the introduction*, especially if certain guidelines or cautions pertain to the entire procedure. For example, some paints and var-

BASIC THEORY OF MANUAL TRANSMISSION GEARS

The transmission portion of the power train, installed between the engine and the differential, must be capable of transmitting through the differential from the engine to the rear wheels at a variety of speed and torque requirements. This variation is accomplished by using gears of different sizes through which the power flow is changed in torque and speed. The transmission must also provide for a smooth and easy change in direction of the automobile, for the internal combustion engine is not able to reverse its direction without many costly changes in design.

There are two basic transmission designs, the automatic and the manual (standard) transmission. The manual transmission requires that the driver select gear ratios manually, while the automatic transmission selects the proper gear ratio for the driver automatically in some of the forward ranges.

To understand what gears do, we must first review a few principles of physics.

Torque

Torque is a force that produces or tends to produce rotation or torsion. To put it into simpler terms, torque is a force which will rotate or twist an object such as a shaft or bolt. Gears can be used to reduce or increase the amount of torque.

When a small gear drives a larger gear, the result is an increase in torque. Just the opposite occurs when a large gear drives a smaller gear: the torque is reduced....

Gear Ratio

The amount of change in speed or torque through any set of gears, referred to as gear ratio, is directly related to the size of the two gears. Figure 13–9a shows an outline of a drive gear and a driven gear in which the pitch diameter of the drive gear is one-half that of the driven gear. An easy way to determine the gear ratio between two gears is to count the number of teeth on each gear. The drive gear in Figure 13–9a has ten teeth, and the larger driven gear has twenty....

(continued)

FIGURE 13–9. Supplementary section with discussion of related theory

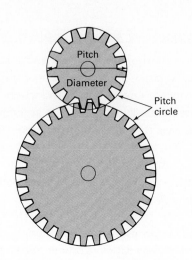

FIGURE 13–9a   Gears with 2:1 gear ratio

Sheldon L. Abbott, <u>Automotive Power Trains</u> (Encino, Calif.: Glencoe, 1978), 37–39. Reprinted by permission.

FIGURE 13–9. (cont.)

nishes cannot be used in full sunlight or used in temperatures above or below certain degrees.
- They can be explained at the point *in the steps discussion* where they become important. The warning about positioning the jack should occur right with the step where that tool is used.
- They can be explained *in a separate section* before or after the steps. If they occur after, they can act as reminders to emphasize certain do's and don'ts.

An example of a cautionary section appears in Figure 13–11.

Troubleshooting and Maintenance Charts

Often instructions are accompanied by troubleshooting and maintenance sections. Troubleshooting sections, of course, list problems, sometimes their potential cause, and their remedy. Look at the example in Figure 13–12.

STEP 8.   On your worksheet explain which of the supplementary sections you think will be necessary in your instructions.

TABLE OF CONTENTS

PART I.   THE THEORY OF HEMODIALYSIS
           Chapter 1. History 1
           Chapter 2. Medical Overview 5
           Chapter 3. Medical Problems in the Patient with
                       Renal Disease 11
           Chapter 4. Principles of Operation 19
           Chapter 5. Bacteriology 25
           Chapter 6. Chemistry 43

PART II.   HEMODIALYSIS EQUIPMENT
           Chapter 1. Access to Circulation 81
           Chapter 2. Dialyzers 85
           Chapter 3. Dialysis Subsystems 89
           Chapter 4. Engineering Subsystems 179

PART III. THE PATIENT AND DIALYSIS
           Chapter 1. Introduction to Dialysis 241
           Chapter 2. Anticoagulation 285
           Chapter 3. Monitoring During Dialysis 293
           Chapter 4. Complications During Dialysis 297
           Chapter 5. Patient Teaching 305

Department of Health, Education and Welfare, Hemodialysis Manual
(Washington, D.C.: GPO, 1971), n.p.

FIGURE 13–10. Table of contents illustrating extended
discussion of related theory

Introductions

You can return to Chapter 4 for general guidelines on introductions, but for instructions in particular, keep these suggestions in mind:

- Provide an overview of the steps about to be performed.
- Explain the purpose of performing the instructions.
- Explain the special conditions for the performance of the instructions (special people, circumstances, etc.).
- Discuss the importance of the procedure, the importance of performing it correctly, or both.

Precautions

Generally speaking, the startup of air systems is considerably easier than liquid systems since the fill/venting procedure is unnecessary. In all other respects, control checks and temperature and power measurements are essentially the same. *Before* actual start-up, follow these precautions:

1. Check the proper mounting of belt-drive motor.
2. Check belt tension.
3. Check pulleys for tightness on shafts.
4. Remove all tools, materials, etc., from inside the unit.
5. Check auxiliary heating unit per manufacturer's recommendations.
6. Activate electrical power to air-handling unit and controller.
7. Check rotation of air-handler blower.
8. Activate electrical power to auxiliary heating unit.
9. Secure all access doors.
10. Check operation of all components and systems per control instructions.

FIGURE 13–11. Supplementary sections: cautions

- Provide general introductory cautions.
- Explain the theory or principle of operation involved in the procedure.
- List the equipment and materials needed.

Of course, you need not use all these elements in any one introduction, and if any element takes up too much space, make a separate section of it. Study the introduction in Figure 13–13 and the model instructions at the end of this chapter to see how these elements combine.

STEP 9.   On your worksheet explain which of the elements you think are needed in the introduction to your instructions.

Graphic and Textual Aids for Instructions

Important in most technical writing, graphic aids become vital in instructions. The same is true for textual aids, particularly lists and headings; they enable readers to find their way around your instructions easily. You can read or review the suggestions for graphic and textual aids in Chapter 6, but for written instructions, keep the following special considerations in mind.

DIAGNOSIS

Differential-Standard and Anti-Spin

Condition	Cause
1. Noise the same in drive or coast.	1. a. Road noise b. Tire noise c. Front wheel bearing noise c. Incorrect drive line angle
2. Noise changes on a different type of road.	2. a. Road noise b. Tire noise
3. Noise tone lowers as car speed is lowered.	3. Tire noise
4. Noise produced with car standing and driving.	4. a. Engine noise b. Transmission noise c. Drive line angle
5. Vibration	5. a. Rough wheel bearing b. Unbalanced or damaged propeller shaft c. Tire imbalance d. Worn universal joint in propeller shaft e. Incorrect drive line angle f. Misindexed propeller shaft at companion flange g. Companion flange runout too great

Sheldon B. Abbott, Automotive Power Trains (Encino, Calif.: Glencoe, 1978), 167. Reprinted by permission.

FIGURE 13–12. Supplementary sections: troubleshooting guide

Illustrations

In graphic aids for instructions, you are primarily illustrating *actions* as well as *tools* and *resources*. You illustrate

- Key *moments* or *points* in a procedure to keep readers from making mistakes
- Key *objects* and *mechanisms* in a procedure to help readers recognize the tools and resources they will use and to find the right parts on the tools.

HUNTING THE WILD HONEY TREE

A honey tree is simply a hollow tree or dead, hollow section of a live tree that has become inhabited by wild honeybees. Locating a honey tree is an old craft that can supply a person who loves the woods with gallons of free, natural sweetener, time out of doors, and a chance to collect bees. Trees providing homes for wild honeybees are not necessarily found deep in the woods; they can also be found in suburbs or even in cities. In the South, the most popular trees for wild honeybees are black gum and live oaks. Up North, colonies of bees are usually found in maples, oaks, or poplar trees. The best time to go on a honey tree hunt is usually early spring when bees are the most ambitious and can replace whatever honey is taken before winter.

There are five steps in a successful honey hunt: (1) baiting the bee, (2) finding the beeline, (3) felling the tree, (4) taking the honey, and (5) bringing the honey tree home. The last two steps are really a choice between taking only the honey or taking both the honey and the bees.

Before tromping off into the woods, the hunter should be sure to take along the following accessories:

A bee bait box, or a 50/50 mixture of sugar and water in a shallow
  bowl with some wood chips to float in the bowl
Chainsaw
4 two-inch wedges
Hammer
Bee smoker
Large metal spoon
Large soft brush
Anise or sweet clover scent
A few light-weight plastic buckets with covers
A few long nails
8 feet of rope
Pick-up truck (if you are going to take the bees home)
Fly screen (if the bees are taken home)
Protective clothing such as two pairs of pants made of sturdy
  material, several shirts, gloves, headnet

FIGURE 13–13. Introduction to written instructions

Avoid wearing dark clothes such as denim or clothes made of wool, felt or other animal fibers as they seem to provoke bees to attack. Be certain that your headnet does not contact the face because the bees may sting through it. In general, people with allergies to bee sting should probably not hunt for wild honey at all, regardless of protective clothing, because a reaction to a bee sting out in the woods can cause serious problems.

In locating the honey tree, the hunter in essence draws a foraging bee to the bait where it will eat and collect its fill of nectar and then return to the hive to communicate to other bees where the source is located. Once the bees begin to work the bait heavily, the hunter can observe the direction of the bees and follow them to the source.

Scott A. Woodward, Austin Community College, April 1984.

FIGURE 13–13.   (cont.)

In other words, you illustrate how the reader is supposed to position an object or hold a tool; how the thing is supposed to look before and after a step. On machinery with several parts, knobs, plugs, sockets, and other features, you illustrate to help readers find the right one.

To plan the illustrations for your instructions, you must identify the *critical points* in the procedure and the *critical parts* of the tools used within the procedure. To do that, ask yourself

- What are the points in the procedure at which the reader can easily get lost, confused, or do the wrong thing?
- What are the parts or features of the tools used in the procedure that the reader might get mixed up about?

When you've identified the critical points and critical parts, you can then plan your illustrations more accurately. Figure 13–14 contains two excerpts from instructions in which the critical parts are carefully identified for the readers.

In many instructions it's equally important to identify the critical points in the procedure. Figure 13–15 has two excerpts in which the process is shown at its important moments.

If you are just starting a vineyard, you should probably begin with a single wire trellis.

The end posts should be at least 7 inches in diameter, 8 feet long, set 3½ feet in the ground, and securely braced. The line posts should be at least 4 inches in diameter, 6½ feet long and set 2 feet in the ground (spaced 20 feet apart in the row). One strand of No. 9 smooth galvanized wire is stretched from end post to end post. The wire is then wrapped around the end posts and tied. After the wire is stretched, staple the wire to the top of the line posts. A span of 600 feet or 30 vines is the maximum safe stress load for No. 9 wire. The following illustration (Figure 13–14a) shows the parts of the trellis and the dimensions.

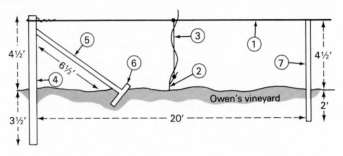

1. No. 9 smooth galvanized wire
2. Vine
3. Sisal twine
4. End post

5. Brace
6. Brace – base block
7. Line post

FIGURE 13–14a.   A single-wire trellis

Vines should be planted exactly halfway between posts and directly under the trellis. When vines reach maturity . . .

In your stock pond, the core of the dam should be filled with clay soil removed from the excavation. The clay core should meet with clay at the base of the dam. The dam on the water side should have at least 3 feet of slope to every foot in the height of the dam, and a 2 to 1 slope on the back side.

The crown or top of the dam should be 5 feet wide plus one-fifth of the height of the dam. Thus, a dam 15 feet high should have a crown at least 8 feet wide. (See Figure 13–14b.)

FIGURE 13–14.   Critical parts illustrated in instructions

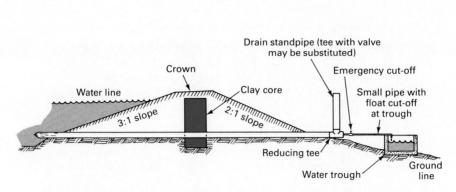

FIGURE 13–14b. Cross section of the dam showing water trough
and drain lines

The spillway should be wide enough to accommodate maximum
flood waters. Few fish will escape over wide spillways with shallow
overflows. Those that escape usually are small, and the loss of a few
small fish will help prevent overstocking. The screening of a properly
consructed spillway is not necessary. In fact, it may prove dangerous
to the dam during floods if screens become choked with brush or other
trash. Dropped inlet structures or drains, as illustrated in Figure
13–14b, or a 4-foot drop over the spillway will prevent undesirable
fish from entering the pond.

Because all ponds eventually need draining, a drain pipe should be
provided through the dam at construction time. Pour a concrete water
seal or install a steel collar around this pipe in the center of the dam
to prevent seepage. Close the end and drill or torch cut sufficient holes
in the projecting portion of the pipe to allow intake of full water
capacity.

The bottom of the pond at the point where the drain pipe projects
into the lake should be the lowest point.

FIGURE 13–14. (cont.)

Textual Aids

Two kinds of textual aids—headings and lists—are quite important in instructions.
Headings help guide readers through complex instructions:

- If you write task-oriented instructions, generally you must use headings to help
  readers find the tasks they need. (See Figures 13–2 and 13–4 for examples of
  this use of headings.)

Use the current season's growth to cut scions, which are the small branches of the desired variety that will be grafted onto a larger piece of the living stock plant. Stock plants are seedlings that are not likely to bear quality fruits or nuts unless they are grafted.

 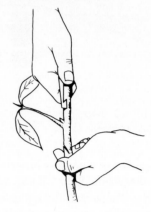

FIGURE 13–15a. To start, choose a suitable bud on a small branch, and make a sloping cut ½ inch below the base of the leaf.

FIGURE 13–15b. Next, make a sloping cut ½ inch above the bud.

1. When an infant needs immediate artificial respiration, you'll have to modify the basic procedure that you'd use on an adult. Obviously, you must still check for a possible airway obstruction and remove it, if you can.

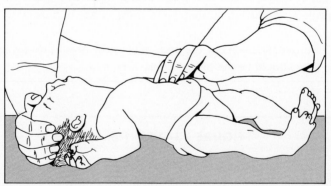

FIGURE 13–15c. Positioning the infant

FIGURE 13–15. Critical points illustrated in instructions

If no obstruction is present and the infant is still not breathing, perform the usual procedure for mouth-to-mouth resuscitation, with the following important changes. Position the infant as indicated in Figure 13–15c.

2. Don't hyperextend the infant's neck as much as you would an adult's. Doing so could seriously damage his spinal cord. Ventilate the infant's lungs by sealing your mouth over both his mouth and nose....

Nursing Photobook: Providing Respiratory Care (Springhouse, PA: Springhouse, 1979), 71. Reprinted by permission of the Springhouse Corporation. All rights reserved.

FIGURE 13–15.   (cont.)

- If you have alternate steps that readers must choose depending on their preferences or their equipment, headings also help. (See Figure 13–4.)
- In almost all cases, numbered lists are used to make the individual steps easy to find, easy to read, and easy to follow. (Almost every example in this chapter has steps in numbered lists, but see Figures 13–1 and 13–2 in particular.)

STEP 10.   On your worksheet, list the critical points in the procedure you're discussing and the critical parts of the equipment used in your instructions, and then briefly describe the illustrations you'll use for them.

Finishing Instructions

If you've followed the steps to this point in planning your instructions, you're ready to start writing. The following steps take you through these final preparations to write the first draft, revise it, and put it in its final package. The following steps direct you to the chapters of Parts I, II, and III. If you've already studied those chapters and have been through the steps there, you may only want to go back to them for a brief review.

STEP 11.   Follow these steps to write and complete your instructions:

   • *Write the rough draft.* If you've not done so already, read the discussion of rough drafting in Chapter 10, follow the steps there, return here for the next step.

• *Revise.* For direction in revising your instructions, read Chapter 10, follow the steps, and then return here for the next step. (After you test your instructions, you may have some additional revision to do.)

• *Plan the additional textual aids.* During or after your revision work, you should also plan the additional textual aids that must be incorporated. These may include the following, depending on the type of instructions you are writing:

Title page	Table of contents
List of figures	Pagination
Letter of transmittal	List of Symbols and Abbreviations
	Glossary

• Discussion, examples, and steps to help you in designing these elements can be found in Chapter 6.

• *Proofread and do the final packaging.* When you're ready to type your instructions, proofread them, and put them in their final package—that is, tape in the illustrations, bind the pages, and attach the cover label (see Chapter 10). Because the testing phase may necessitate changes in your instructions, delay on some of the more elaborate aspects of final packaging.

Testing Your Written Instructions

Writing instructions can be rather like getting dressed and combing your hair in the dark: you're never really sure about your instructions just as you're never really sure about your appearance until you can find a mirror and some light. To check your written instructions, you can do one of several things:

• Set the first draft aside for a time, and then read it for problems.
• Ask a friend to read your instructions and comment on any problems for you.
• Ask a friend to perform the procedures you explain in your instructions, and then have your friend tell you about problems she had, or observe your friend following your instructions (and take notes on any signs of problems).

You can prompt your test readers to be critical by asking them to look for specific problems or weaknesses. Make a list of such potential problem areas for your readers. Here are some example questions; substitute your content for the Xs and Ys:

Is it clear what to do first and why?
Do you understand why X is added and how to add it?
Do you understand why and how X is done?
Do you understand how to adjust X?
Do you understand what principle you are using when you do X?
Is it clear what X should look like after step Y?
Do you understand how to prevent Y from happening?
Did X turn out as you expected?
Were any important steps omitted in the instructions?

STEP 12.   On your worksheet briefly describe how you'll test your instructions. After your test, list the problems, if any, that you discovered in the process. (When you have revised your instructions according to your test findings, return to the "Finishing Instructions" section.)

EXERCISES

1. Find some mechanism that requires written instructions, and follow the steps in this chapter in writing instructions for it.
2. Make a list of the mechanisms or procedures in the typical modern American home or in your workplace for which written instructions are necessary.
3. For one or more of the mechanisms requiring instructions that you just cited, list the main steps that would make up those instructions.
4. Review your list of instructions in exercise 2, and identify which ones would require the following kinds of supplementary sections: (a) list of equipment, materials, or supplies; (b) extended discussion or description of some of those items of equipment or supplies; (c) the principle of operation or theory related to the instructions; (d) guidelines or warnings sections; or (e) troubleshooting sections.
5. Locate a set of instructions (for example, on how to use a home or personal computer or a microwave oven), and test them critically to see if they are clear and thorough. Make a list of any problems or weaknesses that you find, and think of ways to remedy them.

Model 13–1.   *How to Install Your Ceiling Fan (excerpts from simple, fixed-order steps instructions)*

When you unpack your ceiling fan, check to see that you have the following parts:

Partially assembled fan
Four blades
One ceiling cover
Four blade flanges
One pipe-and-ball assembly
One hanger bracket
One loose-parts bag containing:
   two $8/32 \times 1/2$-inch round-head screws
   one set screw
   one $5/32$-inch hex wrench

eight ¹⁰⁄₃₂ × ¾-inch fillister-head screws
twelve ¹⁰⁄₃₂ × ⅝-inch pan-head screws
two knurled knobs
two threaded studs
four wire nuts
four blade trims

Hanging Your Ceiling Fan

CAUTION: The fan must be hung with at least 7 feet of clearance from the floor to the blades. (If you use 3 inches of pipe, there will likely be a total of 12 inches from the ceiling to the bottom of the fan.)

NOTE: Your electrical box must be securely anchored and capable of withstanding a load of at least 50 pounds.

• 1. Securely attach the hanger bracket to the electrical box using the two ⁸⁄₃₂ round-head screws (supplied). See Figure 1.

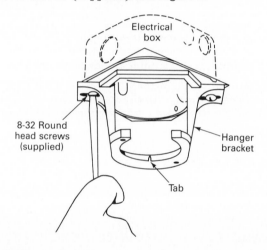

FIGURE 1.   Attaching the hanger bracket to the electrical box

NOTE: If the bracket, the junction, or both are not securely attached, the fan may wobble.

• 2. Carefully lift the fan from the foam pad, and seat the pipe-and-ball assembly that you just attached to the electrical box (see Figure 2). Be sure the groove in the ball is lined up with the tab on the hanger bracket (see Figure 1.)

WARNING: Failure to seat the tab in the groove can cause damage to the electrical wires. Also, be careful not to pinch the wires between the pipe-and-ball assembly and the hanger basket.

Wiring Your Ceiling Fan

If you feel you do not have enough electrical-wiring knowledge or experience, have your fan installed by a licensed electrician.

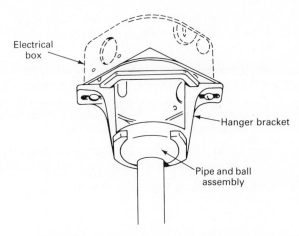

FIGURE 2.   Seating the pipe-and-ball assembly

CAUTION: To avoid possible electrical shock, be sure electricity is turned off at the main fuse box before you begin wiring.

• 1. Make sure the electrical box is properly secured. If Romex cable was used to wire the electrical box, the presence of a third wire connected to the electrical box indicates that the box is grounded. This ground wire may be either a bare wire with no insulating jacket or a green insulated wire. The two supply wires will be white and black insulated wires.

• 2. If the wiring to the electrical box is enclosed in electrical conduit pipe, the ground wire may not be present. The conduit itself can serve as the ground.

NOTE: If you are not sure whether the electrical box is properly grounded, contact a licensed electrician for advice.

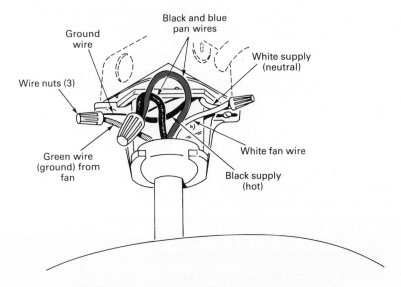

FIGURE 3.   Connecting the ground wire

- 3. If Romex cable was used to wire the electrical box, connect the green ground wire from the fan to the ground wire in the Romex cable using a wire nut (see Figure 3).

- 4. Connect the white fan-motor wire to the supply white (or neutral) wire using a wire nut (Figure 3). Connect the black fan-motor wire and the blue fan-motor wire to the black supply (hot) wire using a wire nut (Figure 3). Your fan is now wired and ready to be turned on and off from the fan switch. Tuck the completed wiring back into the electrical box.

NOTE: Check to see that all connections are tight, including ground wires, and that no bare wire is visible at the wire nuts, except for the ground wire.

- 5. Screw the two threaded studs (provided) into the tapped holes in the hanger bracket (Figure 4).

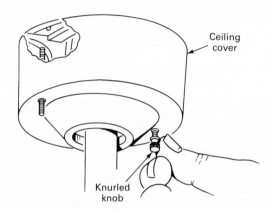

FIGURE 4.   Attaching the ceiling cover

- 6. Lift the ceiling cover up to the threaded studs and turn until the studs protrude through the holes in the ceiling cover (Figure 4).
- 7. Secure the ceiling cover in place by screwing the two knurled knobs (supplied) onto the threaded studs (Figure 4). Tighten the knurled knobs until the ceiling cover is clear of the pipe.

<u>Attaching the Blade Assemblies to the Fan</u>

NOTE: Take care not to scratch the fan housing when installing the blades.

- 1. Place one of the $^{10}\!/_{32} \times {}^{3}\!/_{4}$-inch fillister-head screws (supplied) into one of the recessed holes in the flange of the blade assembly (Figure 5).
- 2. Using a ¼-inch blade screwdriver, hold the screw in place and position the flange of the blade assembly under the motor hub.
- 3. Turn the screw until it mates with the threaded hole in the hub. Do not completely tighten the screw at this time.
- 4. Install the second screw in the same manner.

NOTE: Be sure the two pins on top of the blade flange go into the slot in the bottom of the motor hub (Figure 5).

- 5. Now tighten both screws firmly.
- 6. Install the remaining blade assemblies by repeating the preceding steps.

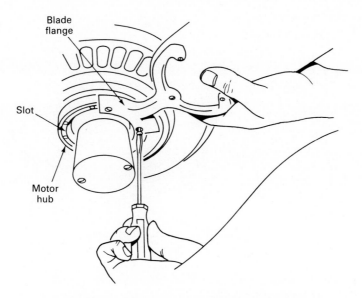

FIGURE 5.   Attaching the fan blade assemblies

Model 13–2.   Operating the Weston AM/FM Electronic Digital Clock Radio (excerpts from complex, task-oriented instructions)

Controls and Power Supply

Use the diagram in Figure 1 to acquaint yourself with the controls on your Weston AM/FM Electronic Digital Clock Radio. Since the cord also serves as an FM antenna, stretch the AC power cord to its full length to ensure best FM reception, and then connect it to an AC outlet supplying 120 volts, 60 Hz.

Note: When the power cord is connected to the AC outlet for the first time, or the AC power returns after a power interruption, the display will blink. Set the time following the steps under "How to Set Time." The blinking of the time display will stop once time is set.

How to Set Time

1. With the **Real Time** set button pressed and held down, press the **Hour** set button until the time display is set to the correct hour. (See Figure 1 for location of buttons.) When the PM indicator is on, the time displayed is PM, and when it is not on, the time is AM.

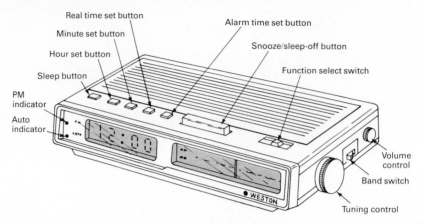

Real time set button
Minute set button
Hour set button
Sleep button
PM indicator
Auto indicator
Alarm time set button
Snooze/sleep-off button
Function select switch
Volume control
Band switch
Tuning control
WESTON

FIGURE 1. Location of controls

2. Release the **Hour** set button.
3. With the **Real Time** set button still held down, press the **Minute** set button to adjust the displayed time to the correct minute.
4. Release the **Minute** and **Real Time** set buttons.
5. Press both the **Alarm** and **Sleep** buttons. The display changes from an hours-and-minutes format to a minutes-and-seconds format. Minutes are displayed with only one digit.
6. With the **Alarm** set button still held down, press the **Hour** set button when you hear a time signal or tone on radio or TV. This will set the seconds display to zero, making your time setting precise to the second.

How to Operate the Radio

1. To turn the radio on, set the **Function** switch to the **On** position.
2. Set the **Band** switch to the desired broadcast band, AM or FM.
3. Turn the **Tuning** control to obtain the desired station on the AM (525–1615 kHz) or FM (88–108 MHz) band.
4. For AM operation, rotate or relocate the unit to a different position to improve reception, if necessary.
5. Adjust the **Volume** control to the desired sound level. To increase the volume, rotate the knob clockwise. To decrease the volume, rotate the knob counterclockwise.
6. To turn the radio off, set the **Function** switch to the **Off** position.

How to Set the Radio Timer

The radio can be set so that it will play for a maximum of 1 hour and 59 minutes and then switch off automatically.

1. Place the **Function** switch in the **Off** or **Auto** position.
2. Press and hold down the **Sleep** button. "0:59" (minutes) will appear, and the radio will begin to play.

Or

If you wish to listen to the radio for more than one hour, press and hold the **Sleep** button, and then press the **Real** and **Hour** buttons once. "1:59" will appear, and the radio will begin to play.

3. With the **Sleep** button still pressed, press the **Minute** set button. The display will count down from "0:59" or "1:59" to "0:00". When the desired time displays, release the **Sleep** and **Minute** set buttons. Now, sleep time is set.
4. The real time will appear on the display.
5. If you want to turn off the radio before it turns off automatically, press the **Snooze/Sleep-Off** button.

CHAPTER 14

Designing Proposals and Feasibility Reports

Chapter Objectives
Proposals
   Ideas for Proposals
   Types of Proposals
   Parts of Proposals
Feasibility Reports
   Ideas for Feasibility Reports
   Phases in a Feasibility Study

Finishing Proposals and Feasibility
   Reports
Exercises
Models
   14–1. Managing Pine Timber
       (proposal)
   14–2. Conversion of a Heating
       System (excerpt from a
       feasibility report)

———————————————— *Chapter Objectives* ————————————————

After you read this chapter, study the examples, work the steps, and do the practice writing, you should be able to:

- Define proposals and feasibility reports.
- Identify situations in which proposals and feasibility reports are required.
- List the different ways to find projects calling for proposals and feasibility reports.
- List the main parts of proposals and feasibility reports, and explain the purpose of these parts.
- Explain why comparison is a key element in feasibility reports.
- Explain the function of criteria in feasibility reports.

When you write a proposal, feasibility report, or similar report, you are attempting to convince readers to do something: to allow you to undertake a project or to accept your recommendations. In contrast to the informational report, the type of report discussed in this chapter is *evaluative* or *persuasive*. In this kind of report, you must supply plenty of information, but you must go one step further and show your readers why that information leads to certain conclusions and recommendations. In other words, you use the information in a proposal or feasibility report to make your point and to convince your readers to take certain actions.

Here are some examples of proposal and feasibility-report projects:

Proposal Projects	*Feasibility-Report Projects*
To study whether stock tanks can be built on certain acreage, where they should be located, and what their design should be	Report on the feasibility of stock tanks on certain acreage, their best location, and design
To investigate the technical and economic feasibility of having certain city officials use electrical vehicles	Report on the technical feasibility and financial savings that would result from certain city officials' use of electrical vehicles
To analyze our city's water-shortage problems and to evaluate different solutions	Presentation of a long-term solution to our city's water shortage
To examine the potential of various alternate energy sources and energy-conservation technologies for saving utility costs in city-owned buildings	Recommendations to the city concerning how to save on utility costs by using certain alternate energy sources and energy-conservation devices in city-owned buildings

STEP 1. On your worksheet explain why your report project is evaluative or persuasive (rather than informational or instructional), and then explain whether

you are writing a proposal or a feasibility report. If you are thinking about collaborating on your proposal or feasibility report with someone else, see "Collaborating on Technical Reports" in the Introduction for ideas and suggestions.)

(Please note that in this chapter all the proposal steps end with *A*; all the feasibility-report steps end with *B*.)

Proposals

When you write a proposal, you offer to do something: to build, research, repair, design, improve, sell, or purchase something, or to solve some problem. If your proposal is accepted, you get to do the work that you proposed to do, and, in addition, you get money, recognition, advancement, course credit, or academic degrees in return for performing the work described in the proposal.

Many businesses depend on the written proposal as their primary means of getting work. For example, a construction company may find out about a college's plan to build a new gymnasium and write a proposal to capture some part of that job. A software company may submit a proposal to produce computerized training programs for an insurance company's new data-processing system.

Proposals are commonly written as offers to conduct research. Businesses often need research done on market or technological questions to help in their decision making. Proposals to do research are also common in colleges and universities. For example, a technical-communications student could propose to research questions such as these: How important are writing skills to graduates of two- and four-year colleges? Are the applications taught in technical-writing classes similar to the kinds of writing actually done in business and industry?

Finally, proposals are commonly written to obtain funding for nonprofit community-level projects. Recycling programs, city bike lanes, outdoor theaters and concerts, and projects to record for the blind, for example, often begin with proposals. (For a complete proposal, see Model 14–1 at the end of this chapter.)

Ideas for Proposals

If you are looking for a topic on which to write a proposal, try some of the following suggestions.

• Start with a subject that interests you, and then imagine it as the subject of a proposal. Are you interested in the potential of electric cars? Then propose to study the feasibility of city or college employee use of electric cars as work vehicles. Does someone you know have a medical problem that you'd like to learn more about? Propose to conduct research on some aspect of that problem or to write a handbook for the victims and their families and friends.

• Browse through local newspapers in search of problems that bother the city: traffic congestion, parking problems, lack of recreational areas, deteriorating schools, increasing utility bills, or inadequate human services for the elderly or the handicapped. Imagine yourself as part of an organization that could alleviate one of those problems, and write a proposal to get your organization hired to do just that.

• Take a drive around your city or area, looking for problems like those just listed. Think about the community organizations you belong to or know about: what are some of their needs?

• Think about your own problems, needs, or desires. Do you want to convert your garage into a rental apartment? How about a swimming pool in your backyard or some place to have a garden? Call a local contractor to do an estimate on adding a room to your house, and then turn the work estimate he gives you into a proposal. Write the proposal as if you were the contractor.

• Take a look at formally published requests for proposals (RFP) such as those in the *Commerce Business Daily*. Make a few phone calls to city and county governments or the chamber of commerce, and request centralized listings of requests for proposals.

• Make a few phone calls to organizations around town, and ask about their problems or needs for which proposals might be written. For example, some of the members of the nearby senior citizens' center may be having difficulty getting to the park because of steep slopes, curbs, and busy streets. Your proposal might offer to design and build facilities or make improvements to enable these citizens to enjoy the park.

STEP 2A.   On your worksheet briefly describe the project on which you want to write a proposal and the audience for that proposal. (For additional ideas on topics, see Chapter 8; for more on audiences, see Chapter 5.)

Types of Proposals

A proposal is basically an offer or bid to do work for someone. Some proposals are quite informal: a local yardman may knock on your door offering to do your yard for a certain amount of money; nothing would need to be written. A work estimate, described in Chapter 12, is less informal: it is written but has few of the elements of the formal proposal. You'd receive a work estimate, for example, if you wanted to convert your garage into a rental apartment. You'd get a few small-time contractors to write estimates on the cost, time to complete, and construction details.

At what point, however, does it become necessary to put proposals into written form? This usually depends on the size of the project and on the individual or organization to whom the proposal is addressed. Some companies specify the format of proposals to be submitted to them; others send printed forms to the proposers; still others do not specify the format, in which case the following guidelines can be used.

Proposals can be categorized in a number of ways. If a company or government agency actively seeks proposals to have work done, it is a *solicited* proposal. If an individual or organization notices a problem or a need or hears about the possibility of work to be done and offers to do it, it is an *unsolicited* proposal.

Businesses find out about solicited proposals through advertisements in newspapers, magazines, journals, and through the mail. Such advertisements are called *requests for proposals*. An important source of requests for proposals from agencies of the federal government is the *Commerce Business Daily*, a good source of ideas for proposals if you are in a technical-writing course. An example of a page from this publication appears in Figure 14–1.

On a more local level, you can find out about requests for proposals by contacting the chamber of commerce and individual departments and agencies in city and county government.

Proposals can also be categorized according to the kind of work that they offer to do:

Kind of Work Proposed	*Example Proposals*
To design or plan something	A data-processing system for a business Plumbing, wiring, air conditioning for a new office building A computer-assisted instruction facility for a community college
To build, maintain, operate, or repair	The city's transit system The city's garbage-collection system An apartment complex Municipal tennis courts
To study or research	Traffic flow in the city City opinion on utility bills Problems in lower-income areas

STEP 3A.   On your worksheet explain which type of proposal you will write and what it will propose to do.

Parts of Proposals

To understand which contents to put in a proposal, imagine what *you* would expect from a proposal if you were prepared to pay for an expensive project:

- You'd expect the proposal writer to demonstrate a full understanding of your problem or need.
- You'd also expect to see a sound plan for solving that problem or meeting that need.
- You'd want to see proof that the writer of the proposal had the capability, experience, and personnel to do the job.
- In some proposals you'd want discussion of the benefits of the project or the likelihood of its success.
- Finally, you'd want details on the cost of the project and the time to complete it.

These essential ingredients correspond to sections typically found in proposals.

Commerce Business Daily

WEDNESDAY, JUNE 6, 1984
Issue No. PSA-8602;

A daily list of U.S. Government procurement invitations, contract awards, subcontracting leads, sales of surplus property and foreign business opportunities

Contracting Officer, Naval Research Laboratory, Washington DC 20375

A — PREPARE SECTIONS OF DEFENSE NUCLEAR AGENCY EM-1 HANDBOOK FOR CHAPTER ENTITLED "EFFECTS OF NUCLEAR WEAPONS ON SPACE SYSTEMS." The contractor will be required to participate in committee meetings, conduct chapter reviews, make comments and recommendations, and provide supplemental material. This effort requires persons who have been responsible for and/or carried out major portions of work in the radiation hardening of actual DOD spacecraft such as DSCSII, FLTSATCOM, or DSC III which have been hardened to the JCS requirements. National stature in the field of spacecraft survivability/radiation hardening is required. A security clearance level of Secret is also required, allowing access to classified info. Negotiations will be conducted with General Electric, Philadelphia, PA 19101. See notes 22 & 68, NRL Ref. 32RC.

A — PREPARE SECTIONS OF DEFENSE NUCLEAR AGENCY EM-1 HANDBOOK FOR CHAPTER ENTITLED "EFFECTS OF NUCLEAR WEAPONS ON SPACE SYSTEMS." The contractor will be required to participate in committee meetings, conduct chapter reviews, make comments and recommendations, and provide supplemental material. This effort requires persons who have been responsible for and/or carried out major portions of work in the radiation hardening of actual DOD spacecraft such as DSCSII, FLTSATCOM, or DSC III which have been hardened to the JSC requirements. National stature in the field of spacecraft survivability/radiation hardening is required. A security clearance level of Secret is also required, allowing access to classified info. Negotiations will be conducted with TRW, Redondo Beach, CA. See notes 22 & 68, NRL Ref. 32RC. (153)

U.S. Dept. of Justice, Procurement and Contracts Staff, Procurement Service, 10th & Constitution Ave. NW, Rm 6328, Washington DC 20530. Attn: Stephen Denny

A — STUDY OF ECONOMIC IMPACT OF PRIVATE ENFORCEMENT OF ANTI TRUST LAWS. The successful contractor will be required to study the cost and disposition of private antitrust litigation; the relationship between government and private litigation; the impact of private litigation on business behavior; and the likely impact on private enforcement of various legislative reforms. Est sol date Jun 15, 1984. Interested firms must send a written request for RFP JFOLP-84-R-0046. Copies of the sol document will be limited and requests filled until supply is exhausted. (153)

Office of Naval Research, 800 N Quincy St., Arlington VA 22117

A — OCEAN MODELING. The contractor will validate the hydrodynamic World Ocean Primitive Equation Model; perform diagnostic calculations for the Gulf Stream ocean mode, create bottom topography fields for ocean basins and compile realistic time varing wire stress data sets for the World Ocean and the Mediterranean. This is a modification to an existing contract. Negotiations are anticipated on a sole-source basis with JAYCOF Alexandria VA due to JAYCOR's extensive experience using Naval Ocean Research and Development Activity's ocean models in numerical modeling of ocean circulation, competitive acquisition is planned for any subsequent work. See note 22. If a statement of interest or capabilities is submitted, compliance with note 68 is requested. Contract Negotiator K Farrington, 202/696-4510. (153)

Chris Davenport (Dept 3824), Martin Marietta Corp, Michoud Div, PO Box 29304; New Orleans, LA 70189

J — REHABILITATION OF FIRE ALARM SYSTEM — Contractor services to rehabilitate the fire alarm system including: 1. Removal of the existing central fire surveillance system and the installation of a new computerized central fire surveillance system. 2. Installation of new fire alarm systems and remote terminal units for Bldgs 101, 102, 103, 130, 173, 207, 220, 221, 301, 420, 450, 451 and 485. 3. The installation of new remote terminal units and modifications to the existing fire alarm systems to interface with the new central fire surveillance system for Bldgs 104, 105, 106, 110, 111, 114, 117, 119, 121, 123, 127, 131, 203, 205, 213, 303, 318, 320, 321, 350, 404, 421, 422, 452 and 480. Estimated value $350,000 to $400,000. Plans and specs are available on June 5, 1984. No bid pkgs will be issued after site inspection. A site inspection for prospective bidders will be held on July 12, 1984 at 9 AM local time. Contact Chris Davenport at 504-255-4594 for arrangements. Sealed bids will be received until Aug. 9, 1984 (154)

Chief Supply Service (663/90C) VA Medical Center, 1660 So Columbian Way, Seattle WA 98108, R E Klein, 206-764-2156

J — COMPUTERIZED ENERGY MANAGEMENT SYSTEM — Concerns having the ability to furnish the following services are requested to give written notification (including the telephone number for a POC) within 30 calendar days from the date of this synopsis: Maintenance/repair services including parts for Computerized Energy Management System, Honeywell Inc. Model "Delta 1000" (A) During non-administrative work hours, i.e.: 4:31 PM to 7:59 AM weekdays, Saturdays, Sundays and holidays for the period Oct. 1, 1984 thru remainder of warranty period, approx June 1985 and (B) 24 hour services including parts for one additional year thereafter. It is the government's belief that services may be available from only Honeywell Inc., 9555 SE 35th Street, Mercer Island, WA 98040. This belief is based on the facts that (1) Honeywell Inc. is manufacturer and supplier of system involving equipment of a highly technical or specialized nature; (2) on-call response time is required within 3 hours after notification due to the impact of down time of system on medical operations as a whole; (3) under warranty provisions of original supply contract, Honeywell Inc. must furnish maintenance/repair services including parts during regularly established administrative work hours, i.e., 8 AM to 4:30 PM Mondays thru Fridays, for one year after acceptance of system; and (4) the warranty provisions of original supply contract would be negotiated if another contractor were allowed to work on system during the warranty period. This is not a formal sol. However, concerns that respond should furnish detailed data concerning their capabilities and may request to receive a copy of the sol when it becomes available. This notice may represent the only official notice of such a sol. (153)

Supply Officer, Naval Air Station, Bldg 10, Corpus Christi, TX 78419

❶ J — UPHOLSTER AND RECONDITION FURNITURE for Public Works Dept. Naval Air Station, Corpus Christi, TX. See notes 24 and 42. RFQ N00216-84-Q-0046, closing date 84 Jul 13. (153)

FIGURE 14—1. Excerpt from the *Commerce Business Daily*

Problem or Need.   In a proposal you must discuss the problem or need in detail to show the recipient that you understand it or to convince the recipient that it exists and ought to be solved. In the excerpt in Figure 14–2, a consultant to a nursing agency reviews the paperwork problems facing that agency.

Related Literature.   In some proposals, particularly those involving research, a review of related literature is often necessary. In a proposal to study some aspect of premenstrual syndrome, the writer must show a knowledge of the related books, articles, and reports on the problem. In a city bike-lanes proposal, there may not be much published literature, but there will be some: professional journals for city planning and transportation people might be the area to check. An example of a related-literature section is provided in Figure 14–3.

STEP 4A.   On your worksheet briefly describe the problem or need that your proposal will focus on. If your proposal requires a review-of-literature section, describe the areas of literature that you must investigate.

Problem Review

As a result of my conversation with you on 18 February, I have a strong sense of the paperwork and related procedural problems facing Community Home Health. Through further discussions with you and your staff as well as through detailed observations, I'll be able to refine this understanding when I begin my work on the project. Basically, however, the problem facing your agency is the enormous increase in paperwork brought on by added documentation required by various levels of government (in particular, by Medicare); specifically, this burden of forms to fill out, file, copy, and so forth has brought about the following problems:

- An enormous amount of time spent by nurses completing mandatory charts as opposed to doing what they're trained and what they want to be doing—nursing
- Tedious, repetitious entering of the same information on different forms for the same individual patient visit
- Reduction of the available time for visiting more patients, and preventing nurses and office staff from completing the paperwork on time
- Undue stress on nurses and resulting burnout, poor working morale, and rather high turnover rates of nurses and staff

FIGURE 14–2.   Problem discussion in a proposal

Related Literature

With the rapid increase of documentation required by all levels of government as well as the insurance industry, the nursing profession has responded with a useful, innovative body of articles, reports, and, in some cases, book-length works exploring various ways to offset the paperwork problem. This information divides into categories:

- Literature that reviews the various regulations passed by the federal government and explores their implications to nurses and nursing agencies
- Literature that reviews the approaches and solutions individual agencies and even individual nurses around the country have used to overcome the problems presented by the new regulations

As a nursing professional, I am quite familiar with this literature as well as with some of the innovative programs that have been devised and plan to draw upon this knowledge and experience in my analysis of Community Home Health's situation. (A brief bibliography of some of the key articles and reports is attached.)

FIGURE 14–3.   Literature-review section in a proposal

Method, Plan, or Procedure.   The heart of any proposal is the explanation of how you intend to solve the problem. In this section you explain such things as the following:

- What procedures will be used to carry out the plan
- How long the work will take and what the schedule will be
- What personnel, facilities, and materials will be needed
- How much the project will cost and how it can be paid for

In the bike-lanes proposal, for example, you would explain how you'd prove the citizens' interest in the bike lanes and how you'd determine the actual locations and routes of the lanes. In the excerpt in Figure 14–4, the nursing consultant lists and describes the steps she'll take in analyzing the agency's problem and arriving at a recommendation:

STEP 5A.   On your worksheet briefly describe the plan or method you will use in doing the work that your proposal offers to do.

Results or Benefits.   In a proposal you must also discuss the results or benefits of the plan and the likelihood of its success. In discussing the results of a project, you are also discussing its scope: you must clearly identify what you will do and what you won't do so that the recipients will have no wrong expectations. In a proposal to study the African or "killer" bee, which threatens domestic beekeeping

Task Breakdown

In my work on the project, I foresee the following tasks:

- Determine the average time spent by nurses on the following:
  —Charting after each patient visit
  —Driving to each patient's home
  —Visiting with each patient
  —Performing other office duties
- Review costs and estimate time savings obtainable through computerizing key phases of agency routines
- Contact other nursing agencies using special forms and adhesive labels and prepare estimates of time and cost savings
- Interview nurses concerning the acceptability of using dictating equipment to record chart information for later transcription by secretaries back in the agency offices
- Interview secretaries concerning the feasibility of transcribing charts from nurses' dictation
- Design a mock recording and transcribing session for several nurses to test how the recording and transcribing of chart information works
- Analyze time savings available through recording and transcribing chart information
- Compare results of the various alternatives for reducing the paperwork load, summarize the findings in a feasibility report, and recommend the best alternative, given the agency's basic requirements and limitations

FIGURE 14–4. Method or plan section in a proposal

in the United States, you would not want to imply that your study would show how to control or eradicate the insect. Related to scope is the discussion of the likely success of a project: the results of some projects cannot be guaranteed. In the bike-lanes proposal, you could not guarantee 100 percent satisfaction with all the routes or immediate heavy usage of them, for example. In the excerpt in Figure 14–5, the nursing consultant lists the specific benefits likely to come from implementing some form of solution to the agency's paperwork overload.

STEP 6A.   On your worksheet briefly list and number what you think will be the results or benefits, or both, of the project described in your proposal.

The Organization or Individual Making the Proposal.   Equally important to practically any proposal is the discussion of the proposing organization's capability, personnel, and experience. Recipients of proposals want to see evidence that the

Feasibility of the Project

As a result of my study of the paperwork routines in Community Home Health, I believe it is feasible to develop and implement solutions that will greatly

- Reduce stress, burnout, and the tedium of paperwork currently besetting nurses
- Reduce the turnover rate of nurses and thus retain talented and committed nurses on the staff of Community Home Health
- Enable nurses to visit more patients, thus increasing the agency's income and enabling nurses to do more of the kind of work they prefer
- Expedite the processing of paperwork in the agency.

FIGURE 14—5. Benefits section in a proposal

proposing organization can handle the work successfully. In this section you can include information such as the following:

- Discussion of your previous experience, particularly experience similar to the proposed work
- Qualifications of your organization's personnel
- References to other companies or agencies that can vouch for the quality of your organization's work
- Exhibits, portfolios, or any kind of example of your past work

In the excerpt in Figure 14–6, the nursing consultant reviews the highlights of her resume that make her an especially good candidate for carrying out the project.

STEP 7A.   On your worksheet, list the qualifications and experience you have or would need to present in your proposal to support your bid to do the proposed work. (When you've done this step, skip to the finish-up section and continue.)

Introduction to the Proposal.   The introduction to the proposal can be quite short if the proposal is a relatively brief letter or memo, or it can be a separate section of one or more pages if the proposal is a longer one. In either case, the introduction should do some combination of the following:

- Identify the problem and its background.
- Identify the memo, letter, or separate report as a proposal.
- Explain the source of your proposal.
- Explain the subject matter of the proposed work.
- Discuss the importance of the work briefly.
- Briefly refer to your qualifications to do the work.
- Provide a brief overview of the contents of the proposal.

Figure 14–7 provides an example of a proposal introduction.

Qualifications and Experience

As my attached resume illustrates in detail, I have had a number of experiences over the past ten years that amply prepare me for this work:

- I have developed recording systems for several nursing agencies in the past five years (see resume for references).
- I have worked as a public health nurse for over ten years, doing basically the same kind of work the nurses on your staff do.
- I have attended and held several time-management workshops for nursing professionals.
- In my master's degree, I specialized in community health issues.
- As my review of literature should indicate, I make every effort to stay current with this area of the profession, in terms of publications, new government regulations, and programs under way at agencies around the country.

FIGURE 14–6. Qualifications section in a proposal

Introduction

Having reviewed my notes from our 18 February conversation in your office and made a few preliminary inquiries, I am submitting this proposal to study the paperwork overload at Community Home Health and to recommend one or more solutions. Enclosed are a review of the problem at the agency, a listing of the steps I'll take in investigating the problem, a summary of the benefits that are likely to result, and aspects of my background and experience that qualify me for this work. As a nurse, as a supervisor, and as a consultant, I am quite familiar with the problems of your agency and believe that I can find ways to help you alleviate some of the burden you and your staff are facing.

FIGURE 14–7. Introduction to a proposal

Feasibility Reports

A feasibility report is a recommendation accompanied by the facts and conclusions that support, prove, or justify that recommendation. The report can recommend:

To build or not to build something
To purchase or not to purchase something
To plan or not to plan something
To design or not to design something
To change or not to change something

Such a report presents a studied decision on whether actions like these are *feasible,* that is, whether they are technically and physically possible and whether they are socially and economically desirable. To put it another way, a feasibility report shows whether a plan is practicable (physically or technologically possible) and whether it is practical (advantageous and economically suitable to people).

Here are some examples of feasibility-report projects:

- Would some form of rapid transit alleviate this city's traffic problems?
- Which form of mass transit is best for this city's needs?
- Would pecan trees planted on a 100-acre tract be a productive use of the land and an economically wise move?
- Is there a practical method to clear algae and duckweed from the lake and keep it cleared?

As you can see in these examples, feasibility reports are addressed to problems, needs, or ideas for improvements. There are essentially two phases of feasibility reports:

- *The decision to change or improve something or to solve a problem.* Any feasibility report passes judgment on some idea that involves change. Monorails for a city transit system or word-processing equipment for the secretarial staff constitute real changes.

- *The review of the different alternatives for solving the problems or making the change or improvement.* Feasibility reports also pass judgment on the alternative products, services, and plans that can be used to make innovations or improvements. In the word-processing example, which system is the best for the staff's needs? For the city's mass-transit system, which type of mass transit is best? Which system of routes in the city will best serve citizens' needs?

Feasibility reports can be written to answer one or both of the preceding questions— whether to make a change and which alternative is preferable if change is wanted.

In large purchases or costly plans for change, feasibility reports are necessary for at least three reasons:

- The writing of a feasibility report forces greater care and thoroughness leading up to the recommendations.
- A written feasibility report enables other people to study and pass judgment on the recommendations in the report.
- Most written feasibility reports contain so much information that they cannot be presented orally.

For a complete feasibility report, see Model 14–2 at the end of this chapter.)

Ideas for Feasibility Reports

You can use the ideas in the preceding section on proposals or those in Chapter 8 to find ideas for feasibility reports. The difference, however, is that you must go beyond merely proposing to do something and actually do something—for example, studying the project idea, determining costs, surveying public need or interest, drawing up designs, and calculating costs of materials. You do this work to pass judgment on the feasibility of the project, and then you write the report to demonstrate that feasibility.

Here are some additional ways of finding feasibility report projects:

- Think of a subject you are interested in, and imagine a situation involving it in which a feasibility report might be written.
- Browse newspapers for local problems; the feasibility report would study possible solutions and pass judgment on the feasibility of one or more of those solutions.
- Drive around looking for problems or possibilities for improvements for which a feasibility report could be written.
- Make phone calls or visits to individuals and organizations asking about their problems, needs, or ideas for improvement. For one of them, write a feasibility report in which you study the problem, find solutions, and investigate the feasibility of those solutions.
- Think of anyone who is considering a large purchase—either in terms of quantity or cost—and help them make that decision by studying the alternatives and making a recommendation.

STEP 2B.   On your worksheet briefly describe the project on which you want to write a feasibility report and the audience for that report. (For additional ideas on topics, see Chapter 8; for more on audiences, see Chapter 5.)

Phases in a Feasibility Study

Before you can write a feasibility report, you must conduct a feasibility *study* to find out whether a solution to a problem or an improvement to a situation is possible and worthwhile. In most cases, the phases of your feasibility study become sections in your feasibility report.

Describing the Problem or Situation.   Every feasibility report concerns itself with a problem for which solutions must be found or with a situation in which improvements might be made. For example, as owner of a small business, your paperwork may have become so burdensome that you can't keep up with it. The city's electrical bills may have increased so sharply that some new approach to generating electricity has to be explored.

Feasibility reports need not necessarily address problems: they can also focus on situations that can be improved. Building bike lanes in the city is not necessarily a solution to any problem, but it's a definite improvement in the quality of life in a community.

In Figure 14–8 is an excerpt of the background discussion concerning a city coliseum in need of extensive improvements.

STEP 3B.   On your worksheet briefly describe the problem that your feasibility report will try to solve or the situation that it will try to improve.

Past Use and Future Potential

The City Coliseum is an arena-type structure built in 1949. It contains bleacher seating for 2,000 which can be supplemented with 1,800 folding chairs, for a total concert seating of 3,800 people. In the past the building has been used year round for all types of civic events, but now it functions primarily during temperate seasons for a limited number of events.

There are three main reasons why the use of the Coliseum has become increasingly limited. First, the building is not climate-controlled. This restricts use of the facility to outdoor-oriented events like livestock shows and circuses or to events that can be held in the moderate fall and spring seasons.

Second, the building is old, and many of its fixtures are outmoded. The coliseum currently has rest-room facilities too small for large crowds, dressing rooms too few for stage shows, and inadequate lighting and sound systems. These represent not only practical problems but also psychological ones: many event sponsors simply do not want to use an outdated facility.

A third problem with the coliseum is that there are not enough seats for many of the events. Most event sponsors need arena bleacher seating of around 4,000 or concert seating close to 6,000.

Staff estimates are that with elimination of these main problems. . . .

FIGURE 14–8. A feasibility-report section describing the problem

Determining the Scope of the Project.   Early in your feasibility study, you must consider the scope of your work. The *scope* of a feasibility study refers to the areas of the project whose feasibility you are going to study. Some common areas of feasibility of a project include the following:

Technical feasibility	Can it be done physically, technologically— regardless of the cost or desirability?
Economic feasibility	Can the project be done within certain financial limitations? Will the results be worth the expense?
Social feasibility	Will the project be acceptable or desirable to the community, the business, or the individual?
Administrative feasibility	Can the project be accomplished within the current laws? Can the approval for the project be obtained?

Your feasibility study may focus on all these issues, or it may focus on only one or two. In your project there may be other issues that you must study as well.

For some examples of how the scope of a feasibility study might be limited, consider the city bike-lanes project:

- One feasibility study might concern itself only with the *social feasibility*, in other words, citizens' interest in, desire for, or acceptance of bike lanes.
- Another report might concern itself only with the *economic feasibility*, in other words, whether the city can afford such a project.
- A feasibility study, or more likely a part of one, could also look into the *administrative feasibility* of bike lanes around the city, in other words, which zoning laws and other city ordinances might affect bike lanes or their design and layout.
- As for the *technical feasibility*, the bike lanes would certainly be possible technologically, but a feasibility report from this point of view would have to discuss technical details concerning the construction of the lanes.

STEP 4B.   On your worksheet explain the scope of your feasibility report: whether you are going to discuss the social, economic, technical, or administrative feasibility of the project or some combination of these aspects.

Identifying Solutions and Alternatives.   Once you've identified the problem or situation that your feasibility study will address, you must first determine whether the problem can be solved or the improvement can be made at all, and then identify which are the solutions or alternatives.

Some problems simply cannot be solved with our current knowledge and technology; some ideas for improvement simply cannot be accomplished by any technical means—regardless of the costs or benefits. For example, there may be no room anywhere in the small business for a computer or no one to operate it. The city streets and the traffic on them may make bike lanes a virtual impossibility. Unsuitable climate in a certain area may make farming a certain crop out of the question. Typical weather conditions in an area may preclude the use of wind-powered generators to produce electricity. If there is a question about the technological possibility of your project, you must prove that it can be done.

If you determine that there is no technologically feasible solution, you still must write the feasibility report to explain this conclusion. However, if you determine that the problem or situation can be handled, your job is to identify the different solutions or alternatives for solving the problem or making the improvement. As a small businessperson with too much paperwork, you might consider these solutions:

Hire additional clerical help.
Turn your paperwork over to an accountant.
Get a computer and word-processing and spreadsheet software.
Do nothing about the problem and just live with it.

If you were the owner of a larger company, the different alternatives for solving the paperwork problem might be these:

Make no changes in the current secretarial system.
Hire more secretaries and buy more typewriters.
Purchase some form of word-processing equipment.

In the bike-lanes project there are only two alternatives: to build the lanes or not to build them. However, if the decision is to build them, then the question is where to locate them. There might be many different alternatives for the layout and design of the lanes; for example:

Lanes on 4th, 6th, and 10th streets and on Baker, Dwyer Frontain, James, and Massey streets connecting areas A, B, D, and G
Lanes on 1st, 3d, 4th, 8th, and 9th streets and on Madison, Jefferson, Johnson, and Taft streets connecting areas A, B, C, D, and E.

Often, feasibility reports must cover several sets of alternatives. In the word-processing example, the company can

Purchase the equipment
Lease the equipment
Work out a time-sharing agreement.

In the same project the company must also choose a vendor of the word-processing equipment: for example, Wang, IBM, Apple, or Digital. When you identify the alternatives, analyze your project carefully for *all* the sets of possible alternatives about which you must make decisions.

You cannot safely recommend any plan unless you've compared all the reasonable alternatives. Remember that even though you may be convinced about the right course of action, others may not be as well-informed or convinced as you. You must investigate the other alternatives and present your readers with information proving that the other alternatives are not as good as yours. (See the model feasibility report for an example of sections in which solutions or alternatives are discussed.)

STEP 5B.   On your worksheet briefly list and describe the solutions or alternatives that you'll compare in your feasibility report.

Comparing the Solutions or Alternatives.   When you have identified the alternatives that might solve the problem or make the improvement, your next job is to compare those alternatives. (For more on writing comparisons, see Chapter 2.)

You do this analysis by identifying important points of comparison, such as these in the word-processor example:

Purchase costs: Which system is the least expensive?
Ease of operation: Which system is easiest to use?
Power: Which system has the highest potential for productivity?

The bike-lanes study might use these points of comparison:

Citizen approval: Would citizens gain more from bike lanes or some other civic improvements for the same money?
Placement of the bike-lane routes: Which system or network of bike lanes in the city going through which neighborhoods and on which streets would work best?
Financing options: Where will the money come from for this project: Loans? Operating funds? Citizen donations or fund-raising schemes?

Obviously, these points of comparison have a broad scope: they focus on the economic, technical, administrative, and social feasibility of their projects. However, if you were only concerned with the economic feasibility of the plan to purchase computers and word-processing software, the points of comparison might look like this:

> Purchase costs for the three alternatives
> Software costs for the three alternatives
> Maintenance-contract costs for the three alternatives
> Accessory costs (diskettes, ribbons, etc.) for the three alternatives

Once you've identified the points of comparison, your job is then to see how the alternatives stack up against each other on each point. This work in turn produces the information for the comparative section of your feasibility report (see the model feasibility report for an example).

STEP 6B.   On your worksheet, list the points of comparison (and criteria, if any) you'll use to compare the alternatives in your feasibility report.

Listing Conclusions.   When you compare the alternatives, you reach a number of conclusions: alternative *A* may be better in one respect than alternative *B*, but not in another. Your job now is to bring all those conclusions together—on a sheet of paper or in your mind—and decide which alternative is best overall. If the decision is difficult, you can use a chart called a scale (see Chapter 6 for discussion and examples), in which you add up points and choose the alternative with the most points.

In the conclusions section of a feasibility report, you list all the important conclusions reached during the comparative section. This repetition highlights the main points of the comparison and shows why the recommendation to be made in the next section is right.

When you prepare the conclusions section, remember a few things:

- Make sure each conclusion is a conclusion and not just a statement of a simple fact.
- Make sure that each conclusion is an important one that points directly toward the recommendation.
- Consolidate closely related conclusions in order to cut down on the number of conclusions.
- Make sure that the conclusions are in an appropriate or logical sequence.
- In parentheses after each conclusion, cite the page number in the discussion section where the conclusion is reached.
- Make sure that the last conclusion states the main decision or choice of alternative (but do not make the recommendation here).

The conclusions section is the logical skeleton or framework of the feasibility report. It shows the logic that led to the final decision and recommendation. If readers question certain conclusions, they can go to the part of the report where that conclusion is reached by using the page numbers in parentheses. Look at the example in Figure 14–9.

CONCLUSIONS

1. The use of the coliseum has been limited because the building is not adequately climate-controlled for many events during the hottest and coldest parts of the year (p. 7).
2. Many of the building's facilities and fixtures are old, outmoded, inadequate, or too small for the variety of events occurring there.
3. The coliseum has too few seats for many events that would otherwise be held there (p. 8).
4. The coliseum therefore needs substantial upgrading (p. 8).
5. With the elimination of the problems at the coliseum, use of the building is projected to grow 50 to 75 percent in a two-year period (p. 9).
6. With the addition of 2,000 seats, the return from operating revenue above operating expenses would be approximately $910,000 over a 10-year period (p. 9).
7. Costs to upgrade the facility vary from a low of $1,074,000 to a high of $1,406,000 (p. 10).
8. Available funds to finance the improvements total $864,000.
9. Additional funds to make up the remaining costs could be made available through the Special Events Funds. This however would reduce funding to promotional and arts agencies (p. 10).
10. Available funds for the complete improvement program are lacking and cannot be made up through cuts in funding for important cultural programs (p. 10).

FIGURE 14–9. Conclusions section in a feasibility report

Making the Recommendations.   The section in which the recommendations are made is usually quite short. If the discussion and conclusion sections that precede it are strong, the recommendations should come as no surprise and be quite convincing to the readers. An example appears in Figure 14–10. In this feasibility report the writers have been asked to evaluate the feasibility of major improvements to the city's coliseum; the answer is a qualified no, but they do offer specific, detailed recommendations on what to do instead.

Discussing the Potential Benefits.   In almost any feasibility report, you must present the potential benefits or advantages that would come from a project. In the small-business project, solving the paperwork problem might lead to these benefits:

More time to do more useful productive work
Clearer understanding of the business's position
Less chance for error or oversight
Less frustration and confusion

Recommendations

Since available funds and projected revenues over the life of the proposed coliseum improvement program are below the estimated project cost, we recommend that the scope of the project be narrowed. To do this, the following specific recommendations are offered:

1. Select an architect, either private or city, to review current plans for possible modifications.
2. Instruct the architect to determine specifically if a project that doubles current seating and adds HVAC as minimum requirements can be done for less than $1,000,000.
3. Finance the architect's study immediately from bed tax receipts.

The coliseum improvement project summarized here is not a final solution to Austin's coliseum/arena needs. It is a practical means to provide needed services for a five- to ten-year period. An interim solution such as this one can help ease the demand for public facilities without committing millions of dollars to a major construction project.

FIGURE 14–10.   Recommendations section in a feasibility report

In the bike-lanes project, these benefits might result:

Greater safety for bicyclists
Increased bicycling among citizens
Better general health among citizens
Less reliance on automobiles for transportation

Of course, these benefits might not come about, and that's why the feasibility study must be done. The study determines whether the benefits are worth the time, effort, and cost.

STEP 7B.   On your worksheet, list and briefly describe the potential benefits that would result from carrying out the project on which you are writing a feasibility report. (When you've done this step, go to the finishing section and continue.)

Introductions to Feasibility Reports.   Use the discussion of introductions in Chapter 4 to help you design the introduction to your feasibility report, and keep these suggestions in mind as well:

• Explain the purpose of the project.
• Explain the scope of the project.
• Discuss the problem, need, or idea for improvement.
• Provide background on the project.

- Provide administrative information.
- Indicate the audience level appropriate for the report.
- Discuss the importance of the recommendations.
- Outline the likely benefits coming from the plan.
- Overview the contents and organization of the report.

For an example see Figure 14–11.

Finishing Proposals and Feasibility Reports

If you've followed the steps to this point in your work on the proposal or feasibility report, you are ready now to make some final plans and start writing. The following steps take you through these final preparations to write the first draft, revise it, and put it in its final package. The following steps also direct you to the chapters of Parts I, II, and III. If you've already studied those chapters and have been through the steps there, you may only want to go back to them for a brief review.

STEP 8.   Use the following steps to write and complete your proposal or feasibility report.

INTRODUCTION

This is a report of a study, commissioned by the mayor's office, done to determine the feasibility of improvements to the City Coliseum. For some time now, people who operate or use the building have been aware that substantial upgrading to the 40-year-old structure is needed. The purpose of the study was to determine the specific improvements needed, to project the costs for various improvement schemes and the subsequent increases in revenues resulting from those improvements.

Problems with the coliseum involve seating capacity, climate control, inadequate rest rooms, dressing rooms, and stage facilities, as well as a generally outmoded, worn appearance. If the building were substantially improved, not only would operating revenue from its increased use result, but Austinites would have a more attractive, enjoyable facility in which to attend all types of civic events, and higher-quality performers and events could be handled there.

This report will (1) provide a detailed analysis of the problems of the coliseum as it is now, (2) describe five different improvement schemes, (3) project costs for each of these schemes and revenue increases resulting from them, (4) reach a set of conclusions from these studies, and (5) make recommendations about the best way to proceed. Appendices at the end of this report are concerned with mechanical and electrical engineers' comments on the selection of the air-conditioning equipment, summaries of related codes and ordinances, an acoustical report on the coliseum, and a detailed chart of cost and revenue projections.

FIGURE 14–11.   Introduction to a feasibility report

• *Plan your introductions and conclusions.* If you need some additional ideas on writing introductions and conclusions, read Chapter 4, do the steps there, and then return here for the next step.

• *Analyze your audience.* For direction on audience analysis, read Chapter 5, work the steps there, and then return here for the next step.

• *Design the graphic aids.* For help on graphic aids, read Chapter 6, work the steps there, and return here for the next step.

• *Use headings and lists.* For directions in planning headings and lists, read Chapter 6, do the steps, and return here for the next step.

• *Write the rough draft.* When you are ready to begin writing a rough draft of your report, read Chapter 10, and then return here for the next step.

• *List the conclusions, and write the recommendations.* For your feasibility report, list the most important conclusions you reach in the rough draft. (Return to the section on conclusions in this chapter, if necessary.)

• *Write the summaries.* If your proposal requires them, you are ready now to write the descriptive summary, informative summary, or both, to accompany your report. (Your feasibility report will require summaries; see the model at the end of this chapter. If you've not done so already, read the discussion and follow the steps in Chapter 4 on writing summaries.

• *Revise.* For help in revising your rough draft, read Chapter 10, follow the steps for revision there, and then return here for the next step.

• *Plan the additional textual aids.* During or after your revision work, you should also plan the additional textual aids that must be incorporated. These may include the following, depending on the type of report you are writing:

Title page	Pagination
List of figures	List of symbols and abbreviations
Letter of transmittal	Glossary
Table of contents	

For more on these elements, read Chapter 6, work the steps there, and then return here for the next step.

• *Proofread and do the final packaging.* When you are ready to type your report, proofread it, and put it in its final package (read Chapter 10 and follow the steps there).

EXERCISES

1. Review local newspapers for several days, and make a list of plans, problems, projects, or ideas for improvements that you see there for which proposals could be written. Sketch out on paper the purpose, content, and organization of the proposals, and explain the qualifications that the individual or organization making the proposals would need to have.

2. Schedule an interview with a city or county official (for example, someone in a city planning department) or that person's assistant, and ask that person about the proposals that are written or need to be written for projects that the city or county is involved in. Find out what contents and organization are expected in these proposals.

3. Review local newspapers or newspapers from large metropolitan areas for a week or so, and make a list of the problems, projects, or ideas for improvement that you see there for which feasibility reports might be written. Sketch out on paper the details about the purpose, content, and organization of these feasibility reports.

4. Schedule an interview with a city official or that official's assistant, as you did in exercise 2. Only in this case, ask that person about the feasibility reports that are written or need to be written. Ask about the content and organization of these reports.

Model 14–1. Managing Pine Timber *(proposal)*

Henry Sykes and Associates
Forestry Consultants
Route 5, Box 87
Cleveland, Texas

Phone: (515) 865–1002

17 October 19XX

Dr. Patrick Hughes Murray
Route 3, Box 127D
Cold Creek, Texas 78566

Dear Dr. Murray:

I enjoyed meeting you and your wife and having the chance to walk your property this past 15 September 19XX. I'm glad to see your interest in long-range forestry management; you have some good timber that will repay your care and attention. I am submitting this management proposal to you for your consideration and approval.

Proposal
I propose that Henry Sykes and Associates undertake the management of the pine timber on your property beginning with a series of short-term measures

that will bring the current timber into maximum growing potential and continuing with long-term measures that will realize maximum return on your investment in that timber.

Background

First, I'll review my comments on your property and the timber on it and then, second, some background on forestry practices.

Your Property.   From our brief tour of your property and two subsequent visits, I have found the following (a map of the property is provided in Figure 1):

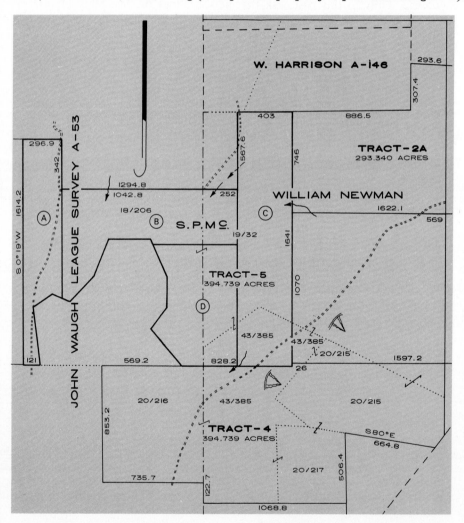

1. The land in general is highly suited for growing merchantable pine timber.
2. Much of the property, however, is covered with dense underbrush, probably the result of poor pulpwood-cutting practices in the past. This brush inhibits the growth of pine timber.

3. Much of the property is interspersed with many low-quality hardwood trees that take up productive acreage and also inhibit the growth of pine timber.

4. Of the mature pine timber, a substantial percentage (some 10 to 20 percent is a rough estimation until we can do the inventory) is poorly formed either because of overly dense growing conditions or because of the hard freeze of 1969. This lower-grade timber will not bring as good a sale as properly formed timber.

5. Many of the younger stands of pine are too densely grown together to allow for good growing conditions.

Forestry Management. Managing timber lands is essentially a matter of taking such measures that allow as much proper timber growth on as much of your land as possible. To achieve this maximum growth potential of timber on your land, forestry practices include determining the appropriate kind of timber for the property, thinning less desirable timber, clearing or burning underbrush, and replanting open areas in seedlings, among other things. Although clear-cutting is certainly one other tool of the forester, we try to avoid it as much as possible for environmental reasons.

Managed properly, sufficient acreages of timber can yield a good income, or certainly a good supplementary income. Forestry consultants are a vital part of management because of the training and experience that enables them to understand soil and climate conditions, growing characteristics of various types of timber, and the different grades of timber. Foresters are also skilled in the various techniques of control of a tract of timber such as marking and thinning trees, burning underbrush, and deadening unwanted timber. Foresters also know the timber industry and can guide property owners through its intricacies. Finally, foresters have a sensitivity to the local ecology of a forested area such that the management practices used do not harm the natural life on it.

Managing timberland thus takes some training, skill, experience, and continuity over the long cycles of timber production. My associates and I have demonstrated that we have these vital requirements to manage timber successfully, as our other clients will attest.

The Proposed Procedure
Here is the plan I am suggesting for the management of your timber. All phases but the last, you'll notice, are aimed at getting your timber into good shape.

Phase 1. We'll start with a thorough timber inventory which will give us proper records and ensure that you receive appropriate capital-gains treatment on any timber income produced.

Phase 2. In Area A (see in Figure 1 a map of your property, which I have divided into four areas), we will mark the timber to be thinned, and I will solicit bids for you. This thinning operation will get rid of poorly formed trees, allow better-quality trees to grow, and allow better access to logging equipment in the future. Specifically, this work will include

a. Designating the trees to cut
b. Determining the volume of trees in the sale
c. Soliciting timber bids
d. Assisting with the sale contract
e. Inspecting the sale while harvesting is in progress for compliance with the contract.

Phase 3.   Area B, as we discussed, is composed primarily of low-grade hardwoods. To gain the full growth potential of the site and to maximize income from the timber, I suggest controlling these hardwoods with chemical injections. A herbicide such as Tordon 101R, which is injected in each tree with a special hand tool, provides effective and economical control of unwanted hardwoods. An exception to this part of the plan should be those areas 66 feet along either side of all streams. The hardwoods in these areas should be retained for wildlife.

Phase 4.   After the injection work is complete, I suggest a prescribed burn to control smaller hardwoods and the dense underbrush that covers much of all four areas of the tract. A prescribed fire carefully managed and conducted when the wind, humidity, and temperatures are right can safely control hardwoods 2 inches in diameter and smaller.

An additional benefit of the burn is that it exposes the soil so that more seed can penetrate and germinate into young pine reproduction.

Phase 5.   Once the preceding phases are complete, Area D and any section within the other three areas that is moderately to poorly stocked with pine trees should be replanted in pine seedlings.

Phase 6.   Once all of the short-term work is complete, your forested property will be ready for long-term management consisting of thinnings and controlled burns as necessary and regular selective timber cuts every five to seven years.

I recommend timber inventories every 2 years beginning 3 years from the end of the short-term work just outlined.

Costs of the Proposed Work

As we discussed during our tour of your property, the costs of the work previously outlined will quickly be recovered in the selective timber cut. The specific costs are as follows:

Item	Cost
1. Timber inventory	$ 800
2. Controlled burn (at $3/acre × 450 acres)	1,350
3. Deadening low-quality hardwood	(no charge)
4. Marking pine for thinning (10% of proceeds)	8,000
5. Marking hardwood for cutting (10% of proceeds)	1,000
6. Supervision during the timber cut	750
7. Supervision of seedling planting (at $3/acre × 450 acres)	1,350
TOTAL	$13,250

Each of these amounts will be due as the specific phase is completed.

Costs for the long-term management work will be the same scale as just cited; our fees will be roughly the same for controlled burns, timber markings, and supervision of timber cuts, including the percentage from the regular timber cuttings.

Qualifications

To ensure that your forest work is done properly, I will personally perform or directly supervise the performance of all the proposed phases described thus far. My education and experience as a consulting forester are as follows:

Stephen F. Austin University
   Bachelor of Science in Forestry Science   1975
Texas Forestry Service   1975–1980
Cleveland Creosote   1978–1982
Private forestry work   1982–present

My associates and I have had substantial experience in all phases of forestry work:

controlled burns	selective marking
deadening of unwanted timber	replanting of seedlings
supervision of timber cuts	inventorying of timber

Currently I am managing forested tracts for 12 area property owners, any of whom will be glad to confirm the quality of my management work. If you wish, I'll supply you with their names, phone numbers, and addresses.

Feasibility of the Program
Although any forestry program is ultimately dependent on weather conditions and a number of other environmental factors, I can cite my work with my other 12 clients as good solid indication of the likelihood of the success of the program that I am proposing here. These other property owners have all seen timber incomes and increases in property values roughly along the lines that I projected. Assuming average annual rainfall and temperatures and no serious natural problems, I project a yield of $250 per acre in the first cut to thin the timber on the property and then a yield of $400 per acre once the property is brought to its maximum productive potential.

    I urge you to consider this proposed forestry management plan and to contact me as soon as you are convinced it is a sound one. As I mentioned in our last meeting, I suggest you contact the Texas Forestry Service and my other clients to confirm the soundness of this plan and the quality of my work. The timber inventory, as outlined in phase 1, could begin immediately on your acceptance of this proposal.

    If you have any questions about this plan or any modifications to request, don't hesitate to call me collect at the number indicated.

Sincerely,

Henry Sykes
Forestry Consultant

HAS/dam
encl.: map of property

Model 14—2. Conversion of a Heating System
(excerpt from a feasibility report)

1710 West 29th
Baldwin City, KS   66006
27 May 19XX

Ms. Jane Allen Mills, Director
Shiner National Forestry Service Facility
Shiner, KS   66606

Dear Director Mills:

Accompanying this letter is the report on the feasibility study I have just completed entitled Report on the Feasibility of Converting the Heating System of the Shiner Forestry Service Facility. It should give you a clear sense of how to proceed with the renovation of the facility's heating system.

The report analyzes the operation of the current heating system, in particular its fuel consumption and costs and the replacement costs that must soon be borne in its renovation. Two alternate heating systems are evaluated against the current system and against each other: a wood-fired heating system with thermal storage and a system without thermal storage. Construction, operation, and maintenance costs are all weighed against savings that these systems will generate.

I am confident that this report and its conclusions will answer the questions you originally presented to us for research. Please let me know if you have any questions about our work on this project or would like to review other alternatives.

Sincerely,

Patrick Hughes Murray

Encl.: Feasibility Report

Report on the

FEASIBILITY OF CONVERTING THE HEATING SYSTEM

of the

SHINER FORESTRY SERVICE FACILITY

Submitted to

The Director of the

Shiner Forestry Service Facility

by

Patrick Hughes Murray

Abstract

This document reports the results of a feasibility study aimed at determining the economic feasibility of converting the current forced-air, oil-fired heating system at the Shiner forestry facility to a system using wood as the primary fuel. Energy consumption and costs, operation and maintenance costs, replacement costs, and salvage value are used in determining the savings-to-investment ratios of the alternatives.

25 May 19XX

TABLE OF CONTENTS

List of Tables and Illustrations xx
Introduction xx
Factual Summary xx
Conclusions xx
Recommendations xx

APPENDICES

A. BACKGROUND ON THE SHINER FACILITY xx
    Energy Consumption xx
    Alternate Fuel Sources xx

B. THE EXISTING HEATING SYSTEM xx
    Fuel Consumption and Cost xx
    Energy Consumption and Cost xx
    Replacement Costs xx

C. THE PROPOSED WOOD-FIRED SYSTEM xx
    Design Basis xx
    System Description and Sketches xx
        Boiler System xx
        Heating, Ventilating, and Air Conditioning xx
        Sketches xx
    Investment Costs xx
    Operation and Maintenance Costs xx
    Fuel Consumption and Costs xx
    Sensitivity Analysis xx

BIBLIOGRAPHY xx

List of Tables and Illustrations

Tables

1. Costs of Alternate Fuels xx
2. Summary of Costs for the Existing System xx
3. Summary of Costs for the Proposed System xx
4. Life-Cycle Cost Analysis xx

Figures

1. The Wood-Fired Heating System xx

Report on the

Feasibility of Converting the Heating System of the
Shiner Forestry Service Facility

Introduction

This report presents the results of a feasibility study done to determine the merits of converting the Shiner National Forestry Service facility's forced-air, oil-fired heating system to a wood-fired system. For such a new system to be feasible, it should be operated by current facility personnel and have a savings-to-investment ratio significantly higher than that of the current heating system.

Conversion of energy systems with high energy demands, such as large industrial plants, poses few problems. However, where heating demand is less than 5 million Btu/hr (demands such as intermittent comfort heat for small commercial and industrial-process applications), the feasibility of using wood as a fuel is subject to many design, site, and fuel variations. In forestry facilities such as the one at Shiner, the range of peak demand is between 0.25 and 3.0 million Btu/hr.

In conjunction with our economic feasibility studies, we have kept in mind three important considerations:

--<u>Minimal combustion exhaust pollutants</u>. While some equipment may be legally exempt from air-quality standards by its size, all equipment recommended here meets current threshold air-quality standards in this state.

--<u>Optimum use of the energy available in the wood fuel</u>. In our work we have thoroughly investigated efficient heat exchangers, thermal storage to the level of demand-supply-combustion efficiency variations, and unique approaches in designing solid-fuel systems with interruptible use.

--<u>Retention of a low life-cycle cost for the heating system</u>. We have attempted to balance investments in equipment, operating costs, and maintenance costs in studying the feasibility of this plan.

This report compares the existing forced-air, oil-fired heating system to a wood-fired heating system without thermal storage and to a system with thermal storage. Criteria used in the study include energy consumption and costs, replacement costs, investment costs, operation and maintenance costs, and overall savings-to-investment ratios.

Factual Summary

The area in which the forestry service facility is located has had an annual average number of heating degree days of 4300° F. The kitchen–dining hall area has a total of 10,200 square feet, is open 95 hours per week, and serves about 1,500 meals daily.

The facility uses an average of 8,015 gallons of oil per year at a cost of $9,217 and an average of 470,000 kHw per year at a cost of $11,014. These consumption rates and costs represent a total heating demand (both furnace and water heater) of 684,302 Btu/hr.

Alternate fuels available to the facility are firewood at $7.14 per 10^6 Btu, pulpwood at \$3.43 per 10^6 Btu, and coal at \$3.23 per 10^6 Btu, while currently oil costs \$7.83 per 10^6 Btu and electricity, \$16.46 per 10^6 Btu.

To build a wood-fired heating system, the user must purchase a boiler, construct or convert a building to house it, purchase a bladesaw or chipper to process the wood, install multicyclone collectors to control emissions, and develop procedures for personnel who will operate the system. The system could also be equipped with a thermal storage to absorb and release heat during low and high demands, respectively.

Total investment costs for the wood-fired system with thermal storage are \$70,760, and \$56,520 without thermal storage. While wood costs for the system without thermal storage would be \$6,853, and \$7,710 with thermal storage, oil and electricity costs would be reduced to \$4,045 and \$2,023, respectively.

Net savings of the wood-fired system without thermal storage would be \$74,698 and with thermal storage, \$80,504. Reduction of energy costs in the system without thermal storage would be \$149,162 and \$167,785 in the system with thermal storage.

The savings-to-investment ratio of the wood-fired heating system without thermal storage is 2.55, whereas the ratio for the system with thermal storage is 2.32.

Conclusions

1. The proposed wood-fired system without thermal storage would result in a net life-cycle savings of \$74,698 over the existing system.
2. The proposed wood-fired system with thermal storage would result in a net life-cycle savings of \$80,504 over the existing system.
3. Reduction of energy costs would be \$149,162 if the wood-fired system without thermal storage were employed and \$167,785 if the wood-fired system with thermal storage were employed.
4. Savings in nonfuel and operation/maintenance costs would be \$26,212 for the system without thermal storage and \$26,213 with thermal storage.
5. Differential investment costs for the system without thermal storage are \$50,808 and \$68,684 for the system with thermal storage.
6. Differential salvage value for both wood-fired systems is 0 (zero).
7. The differential replacement costs of both of the wood-fired systems are \$2,616 in favor of the existing system.
8. The savings-to-investment ratio for the wood-fired system without thermal storage is 2.55, whereas the ratio for the system with thermal storage is 2.32.
9. The wood-fired heating without thermal storage is therefore the best choice economically over the existing heating system and over the wood-fired heating system with thermal storage.

Recommendations

Based on the feasibility study we have conducted over the past three months, I recommend the following:

1. Convert its existing forced-air, oil-fired heating system to a wood-fired heating system without thermal storage.
2. Contact engineers and contractors specialized in this kind of HVAC work.
3. Begin developing procedures for the acquisition, transport, cutting, storage, and feeding to the boiler of wood fuel as soon as possible.

APPENDICES

A. Background on the Shiner Facility

The Shiner Forestry Service facility is located in central Kansas 60 miles south of Gardner, Kansas. The average number of heating degree days is 4300° F (in 1980-4778° F and in 1979-4858° F). The annual precipitation was 36.5 inches in 1980 and 56.1 inches in 1979, which averages to 43.6 inches. The climate is cold in the winter and hot in the summer. The ground is covered with snow about 20 to 30 days per year. Roads are accessible on all but an average of 3 to 4 days during the winter.

The center consists of 14 buildings including dormitories, an administrative office, recreational facilities, a kitchen, and a dining hall. The center provides facilities for approximately 25 corps personnel.

The kitchen-dining hall building, for which the wood-fired heating system is being considered, has one full floor and half a basement. The total heated area is 10,200 square feet. The building is open from 5:00 A.M. to 7:30 P.M. Monday through Friday, serving three meals a day to approximately 300 people. On weekends, the building is open from 6:00 A.M. to 6:00 P.M., serving two meals and providing sack lunches for the evening. The whole center has only two maintenance employees who have no time for the operation of the wood-fired system under consideration. If a new person is employed for such an operation, the labor cost would be $9.00/hour. It is not likely that corps personnel would be able to assist in the operation and maintenance of the proposed heating system.

Energy Consumption

Oil consumption in 1979 was 8,500 gallons and in 1980 was 7,530 gallons. The average consumption is 8,015 gallons per year. The summer 1981 price for oil was $1.15 per gallon.

Electricity consumption during the period of July 1979 to June 1980 was 471,297 kWh at $0.562 per kWh. Part of this electricity is used to heat domestic water.

Alternate Fuel Sources

The wood species in the area are oak, hickory, ash, elm, locust, and maple. Although the center is located in the national forest, fuel sources are limited. There are no wastes from sawmills available to the center. The following possibilities exist for acquiring a wood supply:

1. The center could cut its own firewood. In this case, corps personnel can be used as "free" labor for loading and unloading of the wood. Cutting should be done by permanent personnel.
2. The center could buy pulpwood for $25 to $30 per cord, in lengths of 8 feet, and slash them to 4-foot lengths at the facility.
3. The center could contract out the whole task of firewood acquisition. The cost in this case would be approximately $100 per cord.

In addition to wood, coal is available at a cost of $63 per ton, plus a handling cost of $0.20 a mile. The costs for these alternative fuels are as follows:

TABLE 1. Costs of Alternate Fuels

Alternative Fuel	Cost per 10^6 Btu
Firewood $100/cord 14 × 10^6 Btu/cord	$ 7.14
Pulpwood $30/cord 14 × 10^6 Btu/cord (cutting and handling are estimated to be 2 hr/cord at $9/hr is 30 + 18 = $48/cord	$ 3.43
Coal $71/ton, delivered 11,000 Btu/lb, delivered	$ 3.23
In comparison, the present energy cost is: Oil	$ 7.83
Electricity	$16.46

B. The Existing Heating System

The building is heated with a forced-air heating system and an oil-fired furnace. It operates 24 hours a day, 7 days per week. The original furnace output is 800,000 Btu/hr. Several years of operating experience have shown that the maximum heating demand of the building is approximately 500,000 Btu/hr.

Domestic hot water is heated with two 80-gallon electric heaters with a total input of 54 kW (184,302 Btu/hr). Assuming a peak efficiency of 96 percent, the maximum output is estimated to be 176,930 Btu/hr.

To summarize:

Installed Output Capacity, Btu/hr		Estimated Maximum Demand, Btu/hr
Furnace	800,000	500,000
Water heater	184,302	184,302
TOTAL:	984,302	684,302

Fuel Consumption and Cost

Average annual figures for fuel consumption and costs are as follows:

Estimated oil consumption	8,015 gal/hr
Annual oil cost ($1.15 × 8,015)	$9,217/yr
Energy input (146,866 × 8,015)	1,177 × 10^6 Btu/yr
Annual average efficiency	0.55
Available heat (0.55 × 1,177 × 10^6)	647 × 10^6 Btu/yr

Energy Consumption and Cost

Domestic hot-water consumption is estimated from the number of meals served. Monday through Friday three meals are served for 300 people. Saturdays and Sundays two meals are served. This totals:

300 × (3 meals/day) × 260 days + 2 meals/day × 104 days × 2,030 Btu/meal = 602 × 10⁶ Btu/yr

$$300 \times (3 \text{ meals/day}) \times 260 \text{ days} + 2 \text{ meals/day} \times 104 \text{ days} \times 2{,}030 \text{ Btu/meal} = 602 \times 10^6 \text{ Btu/yr}$$

Assuming a water efficiency of 90 percent, the energy input is:

$$602 \times 10^6 / 0.9 = 668.9 \times 10^6 \text{ Btu/yr} = 195{,}986 \text{ Btu}$$

Electricity cost = \$0.562/kWh
Annual electricity cost = \$11,014

Replacement Costs

The oil furnace is 10 years old and should be replaced now, and on a 10-year schedule thereafter, at a 1981 cost of \$3,650. The electrical water heaters are 3 years old and should be replaced in years 7 and 17 at a 1981 cost of \$2,200. (See Table 2.)

TABLE 2.   Summary of Costs
for the Existing System

Annual Recurring Costs	1981 Costs
fuel oil	\$9,217
electricity	11,014

Nonrecurring Costs	1981 Costs
replacement, year 0	\$3,650
7	2,200
10	3,650
17	2,200

C. The Proposed Wood-Fired System

Design Basis

At this site, domestic water heating provides a basic load throughout the year. Two-thirds of the estimated maximum space-heating demand, therefore, has to be added to this amount in order to calculate the size of the boiler:

Component	Btu/hr
water heater	176,982
space heating	
2/3 × 500,000 =	333,300
TOTAL:	510,282

Based on this figure, the wood-fired boiler capacity should be selected to the closest standard size, i.e., 500,000 Btu/hr. Although a boiler of this size could supply 80 percent of the annual thermal demand, installation of a hot-water storage to absorb and release during low and high demand, respectively, would allow the boiler to supply as much as 90 percent of the annual demand. (No increase in thermal efficiency for wood boilers of this size can be expected.)

The cheapest source of wood fuel in the Shiner area is pulpwood, which is delivered in 8-foot lengths. This material must be cut into three pieces each by hired labor. Another possibility for processing this pulpwood is chipping, although a chipper is more expensive than a bladesaw that would be used in the other method of cutting. Chips would be more suitable for an automatic feeding system, but corps personnel would be available for manual boiler feeding, and for that reason, a manually fed system is recommended.

Although the building is currently heated with a warm-air furnace, the wood-fired system cannot be located within the existing building. The use of air as a heat-transfer medium, therefore, becomes impractical. Since the boiler system has to be located outside, the hot-water boiler becomes more practical.

Domestic water is currently heated with electricity and consumes approximately half of the annual heating energy. The water boiler can also provide heat for domestic water. This advantage can be achieved by installing an integrated hot-water-storage and heat-exchanger tank parallel to the space-heating system.

The new boiler offers an excellent opportunity to replace the existing incinerator to offset the environmental impacts caused by the entirely uncontrolled emissions of the wood-fired system.

The existing oil-fired capacity should be retained for backup and peaking for space heating. The existing electric hot-water heaters should also be retained as backup for domestic water requirements.

The wood-fired boiler will be subject to a particulate emission standard of 0.1 lb/10^6 Btu.

System Description and Sketches

Boiler System.   The existing incinerator site offers a favorable location for the new boiler building. The topography allows for easy unloading of pulpwood and for a two-level arrangement with roundwood storage on top and gravity feed to the boiler at the lower level. The boiler building will also provide space for the slashing of the wood to appropriate lengths. The storage and fuel feed systems are closer to allow simultaneous use of both wood and waste in the boiler.

Delivery trucks will dump 8-foot logs outside the building. From there they will be fed manually to a bladesaw, cut into 2.67-foot lengths, and stacked inside. The storage occupies one half of the upper level, with a capacity to store wood for 4 weeks of operation at the full load. Some floor area is reserved for solid waste. Both fuels are moved manually to the fuel chute, the top of which is near the floor level. The chute drops the fuel onto a grate in the boiler furnace. Some care must be exercised to retain a reasonable balance between the two fuels. Ash removal will be done manually.

The firing system has features of staged combustion, which will minimize the formation of nitrogen oxides but does require a forced-draft fan to control the air supply in order to avoid emissions of carbon monoxide or hydrocarbons.

A multicyclone collector is included to meet the particulate emission standard. The stack must be 50 percent higher than the tallest building in the Forest Service complex.

Heating, Ventilating, and Air-Conditioning (HVAC). The heating, ventilating, and air-conditioning system consists of a normal operating cycle and a backup operating cycle.

Normal Operation. Water heated by the coal-fired boiler is circulated in the pipe network to the heating coil, which is connected to the existing forced-air heating system and to the hot-water storage tank for heating the domestic hot water.
Water temperature in the network is kept constant within a thermostat control valve. The heating coil is provided with a two-way control valve and room thermostat. Operation of the oil-fired furnace will remain as it is.

Backup Operation. If the return water temperature in the network decreases below the lower set-point limit, the controller will start the oil-fired furnace, and when the temperature rises over the upper limit, the controller will stop the furnace. If the water temperature in the upper part of the storage tank is under the control point, electric resistance heating will be switched on.

Sketches. Figure 1 illustrates the proposed site of the wood-fired boiler (see Figure 1a) and provides a layout of the proposed wood-fired system (see Figure 1b.)

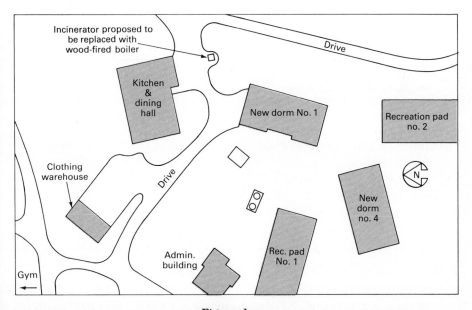

Figure 1a.

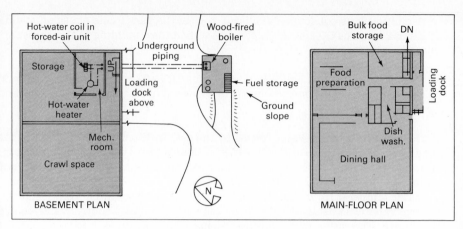

Figure 1b.

FIGURE 1.   The wood-fired heating system

Investment Costs

Costs of the proposed system depend on whether the thermal storage is incorporated in the operating cycle.

<u>Without Thermal Storage</u>.   Refer to Table 1 for the detailed cost estimate.

<u>With Thermal Storage</u>.   The estimated costs of the investment if thermal storage is included are as follows:

Item	Estimated Cost
Tank cost	
Required size = 2,075 gal	
Cost = 8,056 (0.2075).67 + (7,833) (1.17) (0.2075).62 =	\$ 6,270, installed
Instrumentation and controls	2,500
Piping	3,000
Direct costs w/o thermal storage	46,710
Total direct costs:	\$58,480
Indirect costs (21% of direct cost)	12,280
Fixed capital investment	\$70,760

. . .

Operation and Maintenance Costs

Approximately 250 man hours per year will be required to implement the new system. Thus, the 1981 cost for this annual labor is 250 × \$9.00 = \$2,250/year. Corps personnel will be responsible for preparing fuel and firing the boiler. This cost is assumed to be negligible.

Fuel Consumption and Cost

Again, the fuel cost varies depending on whether thermal storage is included in the plan.

Without Thermal Storage.   The costs of fuel consumption without thermal storage are as follows:

annual space-heating energy demand: 647×10^6 Btu/yr
annual water-heating energy demand: 602×10^6 Btu/yr
annual total heating energy demand: $1{,}249 \times 10^6$ Btu/yr

The wood-fired system will supply 80 percent of the space-heat and hot-water energy demand.

$$\text{heat from wood} = 0.8 \times 1{,}249 \times 10^6 \text{ Btu}$$

$$= 999.2 \times 10^6 \text{ Btu/yr}$$

Because the boiler has a thermal efficiency of 50 percent,

$$\text{fuel energy} = \frac{999.2 \times 10^6}{0.5} = 1{,}998 \times 10^6 \text{ Btu/yr}$$

The cost of the cheapest wood fuel is $3.43/10^6$ Btu, and it has a heating value of 14×10^6 Btu/cord.

$$\text{wood consumption} = \frac{1{,}998 \times 10^6}{14 \times 10^6} = 142.7 \text{ cord/yr}$$

$$\text{wood cost} = 1{,}998 \times \$3.43 = \$6{,}853/\text{yr}$$

Oil will supply the remaining 20 percent of the space-heating demand, or 129.4×10^6 Btu/yr.

$$\text{amount of oil} = \frac{129.4 \times 10^6}{0.55 \times 146{,}866} = 1{,}602 \text{ gal/yr}$$

$$\text{oil cost} = (1{,}602)(\$1.15) = \$1{,}842/\text{yr}$$

Electricity will supply the remaining 20 percent of the hot-water demand, or 120.4×10^6 Btu/yr.

$$\text{amount of electricity} = \frac{120.4 \times 10^6}{.90 \times 3{,}413} = 39{,}196 \text{ kWh/yr}$$

$$\text{electricity cost} = (39{,}196)(\$0.0562) = \$2{,}203$$

With thermal storage. Wood supplies 90 percent of the heat energy demand instead of the earlier 80 percent. Thus, wood fuel consumption is 9/8 of the consumption without storage, and oil consumption is only 1/2.

$$\text{amount of wood} = 9/8 \times 142.7 = 160.5 \text{ cords/yr}$$

$$\text{wood cost} = 9/8 \times \$6{,}853 = \$7{,}710/\text{yr}$$

$$\text{amount of oil} = 1/2 \times 1{,}602 = 801 \text{ gal/yr}$$

$$\text{oil cost} = 1/2 \times \$1{,}842 = \$921/\text{yr}$$

$$\text{amount of electricity} = 1/2 \times 39{,}196 = 19{,}598 \text{ kWh/yr}$$

$$\text{electricity cost} = 1/2 \times \$2{,}203 = \$1{,}102/\text{yr}$$

TABLE 3.   Summary of Costs for the Proposed System

Annual Recurring Costs	1981 Costs
Without storage	
Wood	$ 6,853
Oil	1,842
Electricity	2,203
Differential O & M cost	2,250
With storage	
Wood	$ 7,710
Oil	921
Electricity	1,102
Differential O & M cost	2,250
Nonrecurring Costs	**1981 Costs**
Initial investment (w/o thermal storage)	$56,520
Initial investment (w/ thermal storage)	70,760
Replacement, year 0	3,650
Replacement, year 15	3,650

TABLE 4.   Life-Cycle Cost Analysis

Net Life-Cycle Savings	
Existing system vs. new system without thermal storage:	
Net savings ($293,808 − 219,110)	$74,698
Existing system vs. new system with thermal storage:	
Net savings ($293,808 − 213,304)	$80,504
Savings-to-Investment Ratio (SIR)	
Existing system vs. new system without thermal storage:	
Reduction in energy costs	
($286,228 − 137,066)	$149,162
Differential nonfuel/O&M costs	26,212
Differential investment costs	50,808
Differential salvage value	0
Differential replacement costs	
($4,964 − 7,580)	−2,616
Savings-to-investment ratio	
(149,162 − 26,212) / [50,868 − 0 + (−2,616)]	2.55

TABLE 4. Life-Cycle Cost Analysis (cont.)

Existing system vs. new system with thermal storage:

Reduction in energy costs ($286,228 − 118,443)	$167,785
Differential nonfuel/O&M costs	26,213
Differential investment costs	63,684
Differential salvage value	0
Differential replacement costs ($4,964 − 7,580)	−2,616
Savings-to-investment ratio (167,785 − 26,213) / [63,684 − 0 + (−2,616)]	2.32

Sensitivity Analysis

Since the wood-fired system without thermal storage has the greater SIR, it is the most economical of the alternatives. The sensitivity of SIR for this alternative as a function of the following variables was tested and yielded these results:

Curve	Parameter	Variance
A	Cost estimate	−15% to 30%
B	Wood fuel cost	−15% to 50%
C	Diff. O & M cost	−10% to 50%

BIBLIOGRAPHY

1. Arola, Roger. Wood Waste for Energy Study Inventory Assessment and Economic Analysis. Washington, D.C.: Department of Energy, 1978.
2. Decision Maker's Guide to Wood Fuel for Small Industrial Users. SERI Report TR-8234-1, February 1980.
3. DeAngelis, D. G., Ruffin, D. S., and Reznik, R. B. Preliminary Characterization of Emissions from Wood-Fired Residential Combustion Equipment. Washington, D.C.: U.S. Environmental Protection Agency, Report No. EPA 600/7-80-040, March 1980.
4. Junge, D. C. Boilers Fired with Wood and Bark Residues. Corvallis, Ore.: Forest Research Lab, Oregon State Univ., Research Bulletin 17, 1975.

CHAPTER 15

Writing Popular Science Articles

Chapter Objectives
Types of Popular Science Articles
  How-To Articles
  Reviews
  Retrospectives
  Travelogs and Personal Accounts
Preparing to Write the Article
  Finding Ideas for Articles
  Finding and Analyzing the Right
    Magazine
  Other Preparations
Characteristics of Popular Science
    Articles
  Interest-Grabbing Titles
  Narrative Style
  Personalities and Dialogue
  Pacing and Density of
    Technical Detail
  Pervading Mood of Excitement
  Exploring the Potential of the Subject
  Attractive Graphics
Strategies for Openers
  A Question, Problem, or Mystery
  A Striking Fact or Statistic

Unusual or Humorous Phrasing of an
  Idea
An Opening Definition
An Interesting or Striking Quotation
An Introductory Anecdote
Prose-Poetry Openers
Attacking a Commonly Accepted Idea
Common Ground with the Reader
Ways to End Articles
  A Summarizing Quotation
  A Quotation with Supplementary
    Comment
  A Concluding Anecdote
  Prose-Poetry Endings
  A Striking or Important Fact or Idea
  Other Suggestions for Endings
Final Stages of Writing Popular
    Science Articles
Exercises
Model
  15.1 Geometrical Forms Known as
      Fractals Find Sense in Chaos
      (excerpt from a popular science
      article)

───────────── *Chapter Objectives* ─────────────

After you read this chapter, study the examples, work the steps, and do the practice writing, you should be able to:

- Describe the common types of popular science articles.
- List several strategies for finding ideas for articles.
- Describe the typical characteristics of popular science articles.
- Analyze a prospective magazine for its most important characteristics.
- Identify the common strategies to begin articles.
- Identify the common strategies to end articles.

At some point in your student or working career, you may decide that writing an article for a magazine or journal would be good for you professionally, financially rewarding, or just plain fun. Indeed, writing articles can be a valuable, stimulating, and enjoyable experience. If the idea of your actually publishing an article seems unlikely to you, follow the steps in this chapter: you may surprise yourself. Also, consider this observation:

> Many magazines seek science ideas. You need not be a scientist yourself to write in this field. Eager to perform a service, a housewife can discuss her quarrel with current food laws. A hotel clerk with a passion for toy rockets can do an article on the newest models. An alert tourist could do a piece about a passenger submarine he rode into the depths of the Mediterranean; as a fisherman you can describe new theories about marlin. I once spent two weeks at Marineland of the Pacific to report for a science magazine on experiments with dolphins. Another time, en route to report on preparations for the Summer Olympic Games, I proposed a piece about the electronic starting gear for various sports. My work was made easier by the technicians who liked to show off the latest inventions.
>
> The scientist or technologist is not expected to be a wizard with words; so the door swings open for the truly interested, organized apprentice writer. He does not require a Ph.D. in science. For instance, when conservation writer Michael Frome began, he had no special training in forestry science. His exposure of ruthless timber cutting and loggers' commercial excesses were widely cited. Frome also commands respect in such scientific areas as dam building, lake pollution, and the quenching of forest fires. [Curtis W. Casewit, Freelance Writing: Advice from the Pros (New York: Macmillan, 1974), 5.]

Types of Popular Science Articles

A great variety of articles on scientific and technical matters appears in such general-audience magazines as *Newsweek, Time, Esquire,* and *Atlantic Monthly.* These periodicals often feature articles on science and technology, and, in some cases, have special science and technology departments.

As indicated in Figure 15–1, a great many more periodicals exist to appeal to the specific technical interests of mass audiences. In magazines like these, the technical discussion is for general, nonspecialist readers who want to know what is going on in the world of science and technology around them and how to do certain

Omni	*Psychology Today*
Mechanix Illustrated	*Radio-Electronics*
Mother Earth News	*BYTE*
Discover	*Diver*
GEO	*Smithsonian*
Health	*Health Industry Today*
Farm and Forest	*Darkroom Techniques*
Craftswoman	*Dairy Goat Journal*
Gun World	*Homeowner: The How-To Magazine*
Interface Age	*Horse Illustrated*
Metalsmith	*Mushroom News*
New Shelter	*Skindiver*
Skydiving	*Video Games Player*
The Antiques Dealer	*Woodworker's Journal*
Telescope	*Today's OR Nurse*
Science 84	*Science Digest*
Organic Gardening	*1001 Home Ideas*
Technology Review	*Snowmobile Magazine*
Vegetarian Times	*National Geographic*

FIGURE 15–1. Examples of magazines featuring popular science articles

things. These magazines present such information to them in a way that they can understand. Figure 15–2 has some examples of article titles.

How-To-Articles

Notice in the list in Figure 15–2 that some of the articles explain how to build or fix things. A common type of article is this how-to article, which provides instructions on how to build, operate, maintain, or repair things. The difference between a how-to article and the kind of instructions discussed in Chapter 13 is that how-to articles are much lighter in tone; they try to entertain the reader as well as explain how to do something. If you intend to write a how-to article, merge some of the characteristics of articles you see in this chapter with the organizational principles you find in Chapter 13 on instruction writing.

Notice in Figure 15–3 how light and entertaining the excerpt from a how-to article is. Notice how the author of the article in the figure manages a nice, friendly, folksy tone. The author plays cheerleader for the do-it-yourselfer, emphasizes how easily the project can be done, and plays up the advantages and problem-solving qualities of the shredder. All of this makes the article fairly agreeable reading and a motivating piece, as a popular science article should be.

"New Parts for Damaged Brains," *Discover*, February 1984

"The Riddle of Sex: Why did it evolve? Why does it persist?" *Discover*, February 1984

"Build-It-Yourself Robot," *Omni*, January 1983

"Space Weapons Debate: Real Star Wars," *Omni*, November 1983

"Saturn Encounters: Voyager Eyes the Ringed Planet," *Omni*, November 1980

"The Delicate Architecture of Cement," *Science 82*, December 1982

"Who's Guilty? Lie Detectors Can Lie," *Science 82*, June 1982

"The Joy of Hacking: Computer Theft," *Science 82*, November 1982

"The New Proteins: Doing What Life's Molecules Can't," *Science 83*, December 1983

"One Step Behind a Killer: Clues to AIDS," *Science 83*, March 1983

"He and She: Different Brains?" *Science 82*, September 1982

"Pool Hall Physics," *Science 84*, March 1984

"A Wood Stove Catalytic Converter: You Can Build It," *Mother Earth News*, January/February 1983

"Greenhouse Cash Crops: Avoid Being a Peasant Under Glass," *Mother Earth News*, January/February 1983

"The $10-per-Square-Foot (Or Less) Home: Bringing It Below Budget," *Mother Earth News*, November/December 1983

"Marshall Price's Windplant: Power Production for $300," *Mother Earth News*, November/December 1983

"Small Business Basics: Getting a Grip on Your Bootstraps," *Mother Earth News*, March/April 1983

"Alternatives to the Five-Gallon Flush: Composting Toilets," *Mother Earth News*, March/April 1983

"Adapting an IBM Selectric for Use as a Computer Printer," *Radio Electronics*, February 1984

"Repairing and Adjusting Your VCR," *Radio Electronics*, February 1984

"Cable TV Descrambling: Techniques and Circuits," *Radio Electronics*, February 1984

"Energy Management Scaled Down for the Home," *Mechanix Illustrated*, February 1983

"Build Your Own Solar Water Heater," *Popular Mechanics*, January 1983

"A Brief Introduction to Electronic Music Synthesizers," *BYTE*, December 1982

"Design Techniques and Ideals for Computer Games," *BYTE*, December 1982

"Breaking the Jargon Barrier: Designing Computer Programs for the Humanist," *BYTE*, July 1982

"Better Software Manuals: Tips on Constructing a Good Manual," *BYTE*, May 1983

FIGURE 15–2. Examples of titles from popular science articles

Mom's homemade mower-with-mandibles can put a whole new twist on an old garden grind:

BUILD A COMMONSENSE COMPOST SHREDDER

Compost is one of the gardener's most versatile allies. This nutrient-rich humus not only is organic and free for the making but can serve equally well as a fertilizer, tilthbuilder, or biodegradable mulch for soil and weed control.

The hitch is, of course, that the decomposition process responsible for turning trash into treasure can take months. However, that long wait can be reduced to a matter of days if the organic feedback is properly prepared. And the key to that preparation procedure is shredding everything that goes into a compost heap. You see, by breaking up the material and increasing its exposed surface area, you can improve bacterial action, and ultimately contribute to the speed and quality of decomposition....

What you'll need is a working self-propelled rotary mower (the kind with the small power takeoff [PTO] shaft at the side of the engine); some sheet metal (the "skin" from an old washer or dryer would work fine); the chainwheel, chain, and guard from a junk bicycle; a small sprocket to fit the engine's PTO shaft; a 15-inch piece of ½-inch rod, two ¼-inch pipe floor flanges, a couple of ½-inch × 25-inch lengths of electrical metallic tubing, and some assorted fastening hardware. (If you just can't locate a good self-driven mower, a conventional rotary model will do, though you'll have to carefully hand-feed material into it when using the device.)

Start your project by looking over the mower and making certain there's enough room on its deck to allow you to add a feed chute at the front. If there appears to be a problem, try turning the engine 180° on its platform and remounting it. Once the correct position is established, cut a 4½-inch × 8½-inch opening in the top of the deck, centering it directly in front of the powerplant. Then, using the sheet metal, form a 16-inch-tall, wide-mouthed (11½ inch × 13 inch) tapered hopper, with a 3-inch shield at the top and some mounting lips at the bottom, using our illustration in Figure 15–3a as a guide.

FIGURE 15–3. Excerpt from a how-to article

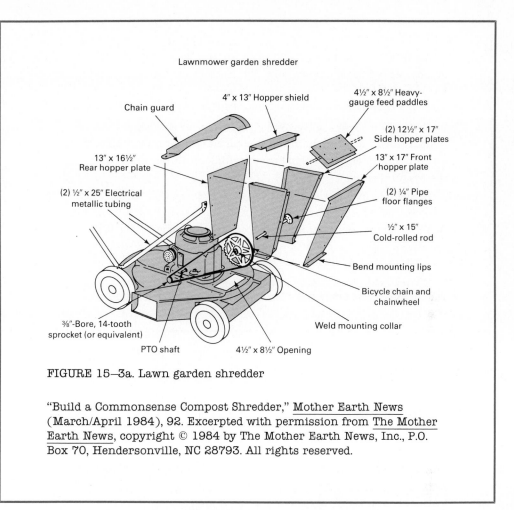

FIGURE 15—3a. Lawn garden shredder

"Build a Commonsense Compost Shredder," Mother Earth News (March/April 1984), 92. Excerpted with permission from The Mother Earth News, copyright © 1984 by The Mother Earth News, Inc., P.O. Box 70, Hendersonville, NC 28793. All rights reserved.

FIGURE 15—3.   (cont.)

Reviews

In the review you get to catch up on projects, innovations, research, big names, and other developments within a specific technical area. Such articles can be quite specialized, but they can also be for nonspecialist readers. The more popularized a review is—the more it is intended for nonspecialists—the more elements of the feature article it will contain. Consider the example in Figure 15—4. Reviews for general readers often contain profiles, details about researchers' personalities, their work environments, and dialogue.

An Israeli scientist is working on another way to relieve the symptoms [of the common cold]. Dr. Aharon Yerushalmi at the Weizmann Institute of Science has developed the "Rhinoterm," a machine that sends moist air heated to 107 degrees F into the nasal passages. The theory is that the viruses cannot survive at such a temperature; Dr. Yerushalmi makes no claim that all the viruses are killed but does say that using the machine for 30 minutes clears up the symptoms.

In the meantime, virologists continue their search for the unknown viruses that cause 40 percent of our colds. Pharmaceutical companies look for compounds that will work against all colds. So far it is all uphill. . . .

Richard L. Williams, "Looking for a Way to Beat the Common Cold," Smithsonian (December 1983), 55. Reprinted by permission.

FIGURE 15—4.   Excerpt from a popular science review article

Retrospectives

Another fairly common form of popular science article is the retrospective. In it, you get an account of an important person, invention, or event in the history of science and technology. Here are some examples of historical topics:

Einstein and the theory of relativity
The Curies and their work on radioactivity and radium
Neils Bohr and the quantum theory
Salk and the poliomyelitis vaccine
Watson and Crick and their discovery of the molecular structure of DNA
Mendel and his experimental work on heredity laws
Pasteur and his germ theory of infection
Brattain and Shockley and the invention of the transistor
The development of the integrated circuit
The development of ENIAC
Any space mission
Lindbergh's Atlantic crossing
Chichester's around-the-world solo sail
The first heart transplant
The first mechanical heart implant
The development of the atomic bomb
Alexander Bell and the telephone
The invention of the television

This type of article, however, must avoid the dry, textbookish tone; it must bring the excitement of the scientifically important moment to life. Figure 15–5 contains part of a historical retrospective.

Travelogs and Personal Accounts

Among popular science articles you'll also see accounts of journeys to scientifically or technologically interesting places. They may be interesting for their geology, botany, wildlife, or structures located there. Consider the following examples:

Golden Gate Bridge	Erie Canal
Astrodome	Brooklyn Bridge
World Trade Towers	Eiffel Tower
Epcot Center	Galápagos Islands
An oil refinery	A coal mine
A local dairy	The Everglades
Yellowstone National Park	Flint Hills National Park
A local beach	A local forest
A local lake	A local swamp
Death Valley	Grand Canyon
The Badlands	Mississippi River
Old Faithful (geyser)	The grasslands
A local integrated-circuit manufacturer	A hazardous chemical dump
	An automobile factory
Electronic publishing firm	A regional vineyard
Electric utility plant	A nuclear power plant

"I am become death, the destroyer of worlds." This passage from the sacred Hindu epic Bhagavad-Gita flashed into the mind of J. Robert Oppenheimer, director of the Los Alamos A-bomb laboratory, as he viewed the first nuclear explosion in the New Mexico desert on July 16 1945. Nearby, Enrico Fermi, the brilliant Italian-born physicist and Nobel laureate, coolly calculated the power of the weapon by dropping pieces of paper to measure the shock waves.

Within three weeks, the United States had dropped two atomic bombs on Japan, killing at least 110,000 people. In retrospect, many have questioned ...

Barton J. Bernstein, "Oppenheimer and the Radioactive-Poison Plan," Technology Review (May/June 1985), 15. Reprinted with permission from Technology Review, M.I.T. Alumni Association, copyright © 1985.

FIGURE 15–5. Excerpt from a retrospective popular science article

Writers of popular science articles also give accounts of experiences they've had that have an element of the scientific or technological to them. For example, if you experienced a tornado, hurricane, or some other natural phenomenon, you could tell about your experience of it but, at the same time, emphasize the scientific details. An example appears in Figure 15–6.

Preparing to Write the Article

Much of your work in getting ready to write a popular science article is no different from the preparatory work for reports described in Part III of this book. However, a few phases are special to article writing.

Finding Ideas for Articles

To begin finding an idea for an article, think of an interesting topic and find a magazine or two for which that idea and the resulting article are right. Use the ideas for topics in Chapter 8, which suggest looking into these areas for ideas:

Interests	Curiosities
Hobbies	Knowledge
Specialties	Skills
Work	Academic goals

STEP 1.   On your worksheet briefly describe the idea you have for a popular science article. Also, explain which type of article it will be. For additional ideas for article topics, see Chapter 8. (If you are thinking about collaborating with someone else on a popular science article, see "Collaborating on Technical Reports" in the Introduction for ideas and suggestions.)

Don't worry too much about the originality of your idea. If it interests you and you want to write about it, that should be all that matters. Usually, a writer's own special interest in a subject, writing style, point of view, and background all keep the article from duplicating some other. Still, to make sure that your idea is not too close to someone else's, check the appropriate indexes (usually *Readers Guide* and *Magazine Index*) back five to ten years to see what other writers have been doing with your topic. This search also helps locate magazines in which to publish your article.

STEP 2.   On your worksheet, list titles and bibliographic information on articles similar to yours published in the past 5 to 10 years. (For information on finding articles and using periodical indexes, see Chapter 9.)

Finding and Analyzing the Right Magazine

The next step is to locate and study *target* magazines, magazines that seem to be right for your article. Use this step to clarify the specific aspect of the subject you want to write about and the approach you want to take in writing it. Because your

For mycologist Roy Halling, this moment has been a long time coming. He has traveled by military transport, dugout canoe, turboprop helicopter, and high rubber boots to reach this mountain valley, 7,000 feet above the Venezuelan jungle. Head down, eyes alert, he has slogged for half a mile in the standing water hidden beneath the undergrowth, through an unlikely landscape where bright red, four-foot-high, carnivorous pitcher plants grow side by side with palm trees and the gray lichen known as reindeer moss.

Finally, triumphantly, he stands above a fallen tree trunk spanning a nameless, tea-dark stream. Planting his boots, he stretches out over the water, ignores an imposing, yellow-spiked bromeliad growing on the trunk, and plucks from beside it a nondescript brown mushroom slightly larger than a bottle cap. Later, inspecting his find, he grins like a new father. It is a Collybia mushroom, a member of the genus that is Halling's research specialty at the New York Botanical Garden. But it is a species with which he is totally unfamiliar.

The little fungus might seem a discovery only a field biologist could love, but there is more to it than that. On this mountain are plants and animals—including, perhaps, Halling's mushroom—that mankind has never encountered before. They are part of the very special flora and fauna of Venezuela's Cerro de la Neblina, the Mountain of the Mists, one of the most distinctive and scientifically compelling pieces of terrain on Earth. Sixty miles from the nearest settlement in the Amazonian jungle, this deep-green rumple of precipitous cliffs, hanging valleys, forested slopes, and cloud-draped ridges rises 9,000 feet above the lowlands at its base, forming the highest South American peak outside the Andes. Because of its isolation and its harsh, high-elevation conditions, the mountain provides a habitat entirely different from the vast rain forest around it. Here, living things shaped in another time survive in environments found today only in a scattering of similar spots in southern and eastern Venezuela.

Gary Blonston, "Mountain of the Mists," Science 85 (July/August 1985), 61. Reprinted by permission from the (July/August) issue of Science '85. Copyright © 1985 by the American Association for the Advancement of Science.

FIGURE 15—6.   Travelogs and personal accounts in popular science articles

local library may not subscribe to all of the magazines that might be right for your article, take a look at any of the following books or magazines that categorize and describe a wide range of magazines:

Writer's Market	*Magazine Industry*
Writer's Digest	*Encyclopedia of Associations*

The book *Writer's Market* categorizes magazines by type of subject covered and gives you addresses, descriptions of the kind of articles accepted, average payment to authors, tips, and other useful information. The magazine *Writer's Digest* is another useful resource to get to know: it contains practical advice from writers to other writers, discussions of new publishing markets, changes in copyright laws, evaluations of word-processing equipment, and most importantly, lists and descriptions of magazines soliciting articles from writers. If you look through several years' worth of back issues of *Writer's Digest,* you'll find an unexpected and sometimes amusing collection of articles that provide tips on writing for the various special-interest magazines—for example, how to write for horse magazines, sports magazines, antique magazines, farm magazines, medical and health magazines, muscle magazines. You'll find out how to write city guidebooks, craft articles, science stories, service articles, personal profiles, and on and on.

As mentioned in Chaper 8, trade and association literature is a huge field of periodical publishing that we do not normally see on the library shelves or on the magazine rack at the newsstand. Still, it represents a great opportunity for publishing. To find out about this area, investigate *Magazine Industry* and the *Encyclopedia of Associations. Magazine Industry* groups magazines by subject area and gives descriptions of the magazines. Although the *Encyclopedia of Associations* is not a periodicals index, it does list magazines and journals published by associations.

STEP 3.   Using the preceding suggestions, locate one or more target magazines that are right for your article idea. List these magazines on your worksheet.

When you locate target magazines suited to your article, your next step is to study them carefully. If necessary, write to the magazine for back issues. If the magazine provides its authors with a guide or some form of style sheet, write for that also and study it carefully. Most importantly, however, read several issues of the magazine carefully to get a feel for its particular style. Use these ideas to analyze a prospective magazine:

Average number of words per article	Average length of sentences and
Kinds of subjects presented in the	paragraphs
articles	Amount of scientific or technical
Use of "departments"	detail
The way scientific and technical	The general tone of the magazine
detail is handled	(light, serious, entertaining,
Amount and kinds of illustrations	scholarly, informal, humorous)
used	Typical format of the articles (use of
The type of reader likely to read the	headings, subtitles, abstracts, etc.)
magazine regularly	

The apparent viewpoint, slant, or
bias of the magazine

The amount of narrative, dialog,
and personality that are
commonly presented.

The typical way in which articles
begin, the strategy typically used

The typical way in which articles
close

STEP 4.   Using the criteria just listed, take notes on your worksheet about several
articles in your target magazine to get an idea of their typical characteristics.

Other Preparations

The steps involved in brainstorming, outlining, and information gathering for an
article are not much different from those in the other kinds of writing discussed in
this book.

1. Analyze the audience who will read your article; plan to make your article
   satisfy their interests or needs; translate difficult technical information so that
   they can understand it. Use the method for analyzing audiences and translating
   technical discussions in Chapter 5.
2. Develop as detailed an outline as you can for your article, through such means
   as exploratory reading or the invention checklist and other steps in Chapter 8.
3. Gather the necessary information, using library and nonlibrary sources as
   described in Chapter 9.
4. Read and take notes using a system like the one described in Chapter 10.
5. Use any of the feature-article strategies (discussed in the next section) that
   seem appropriate.

STEP 5.   If necessary, return to the discussion and steps for analyzing audiences
and translating technical subjects in Chapter 5; for brainstorming, narrowing, and
outlining in Chapter 8; for locating library and nonlibrary sources of information
in Chapter 9; and for note taking in Chapter 10.

Characteristics of Popular Science Articles

Articles appearing in popular magazines (magazines published for nonspecialist,
general-interest audiences) share a number of characteristics, usually associated with
the *feature article*. Examples can be found in the pullout section of the Sunday
paper or in *National Geographic, Esquire,* or *Ladies' Home Journal*. Many of the
characteristics of these feature articles can also be found in popular science articles.

Interest-Grabbing Titles

One of the first opportunities that you have to stimulate readers' interest in your
article is the title. Avoid dull, flat, textbookish titles, and at the same time, avoid
the other extreme, the overly cute, obnoxious, or confusing titles. Try for a title
that tells the reader what your article is about; has short, crisp phrasing of no more
than six to eight words; and has a certain memorable, ear- or eye-catching quality

about it. Review the example titles of published articles listed in Figure 15–2 as well as the ones in Figure 15–7. Consider including a subtitle, sometimes the length of a full sentence, to stimulate reader interest, to provide a more practical, concrete notion of what the article is about, or to summarize the content or state the main point of the article.

Narrative Style

Feature articles are commonly written as stories with plots, characters, and dialogue. In some popular science articles the writer builds the story around a visit with experts. In this kind of article you watch the writer gradually accumulate knowledge and gain a sense of admiration for those in the field. Textbook sorts of information about the subject are slipped in at intervals throughout the narrative in such a way that readers never become overwhelmed or bored.

In other popular science articles, the story traces the historical events, major discoveries, and the efforts of the major researchers working in that field. Sometimes, the plot of a feature article on science or technology develops like that of a detective story: the author establishes a mystery, creates and builds suspense, drops clues here and there, and entices the reader along to the end of the article where the secret will be revealed.

Personalities and Dialogue

Allied to the narrative style of feature articles on scientific and technical subjects is the presentation of personalities and dialogue. Dialogue breaks up the density of a piece of writing and gives you a sense of the personalities in the story. It also helps carry some of the scientific or technical discussion. This strategy gives a light, conversational feeling to such articles and, if done well, keeps the article from sounding textbookish. (The popular science article at the end of this chapter also contains plenty of dialogue and presentation of personalities.) Look at the example in Figure 15–8.

Pacing and Density of Technical Detail

Writers of popular science articles usually do not present too much hard technical information at any one point but spread out the technical detail evenly across the whole length of their articles.

As you prepare to write a popular science article, compare the writing styles of popular science magazines and textbooks in scientific and technical fields. To compare the amount and density of technical detail they contain, take a yellow marker and highlight the "hard-facts" areas, and estimate the percent of technical detail they contain. General-audience magazine articles contain a much lower percentage. Such rough estimates can give you an idea of what to strive for when you write an article for a specific magazine.

Usually textbooks must sacrifice the light, entertaining way of treating a subject to present as much information on technical subjects as possible. Textbook writing is undeniably less lively than the writing you find in most popular magazine articles;

"How Will the Universe End?—
Will it fall in upon itself in a Big Crunch, or fly away into the cold?"

Smithsonian, June 1983

"Rodent Gentry of the Jackson Laboratory—
To advance medical research, scientists are studying mice named
Streaker, Lurcher, and Hotfoot"

Smithsonian, May 1983

"The Revolutionary Microlaser Chip—
Created by Amnon Yariv at Caltech, it failed to interest U.S.
corporations—so Japan moved in"

Smithsonian, October 1983

"Trying to Predict Great Earthquakes—
When one hits, the loss of life and property can be tremendous, but
forecasting them is a shaky art"

Smithsonian, July 1983

"Looking for a Way to Beat the Common Cold—
Any one of more than 200 viruses can cause that unwelcome
sneezing, coughing and sniffing"

Smithsonian, December 1983

"Fractals Will Help to Make Order Out of Chaos—
Computer-generated abstract patterns provide a new way to
understand nature's irregular ones"

Smithsonian, December 1983

"New Tools for Medical Diagnosis—
Radiation, sound, magnetic fields and computers will be used to see
inside the human body"

Smithsonian, January 1984

FIGURE 15–7. Examples of titles and subtitles from
popular science articles

Jack St. Clair is an imposing figure, not fat but <u>big</u>: six feet six inches tall, wide shoulders, massive hands. Any hint of menace, though, is immediately dispelled by an easy smile that telegraphs a friendly, casual, unruffled personality. He spends a good deal of time alone with his thoughts, working through ideas ... As he treks through the meandering halls of Texas Instruments' Dallas headquarters-- walking with the wary, stooped gait of a man who has bumped his head too often on low ceilings--he greets everybody by name, from top management to messenger boys.... This man, who conceived and built the first integrated circuit, or semiconductor chip--along with the better known Robert Noyce, as the chip's coinventor--has an old-fashioned streak. He won't wear a digital watch....

T. R. Reid., "The Chip," <u>Science 85</u> (February 1985), 34. Reprinted by permission from the February issue of <u>Science '85</u>. Copyright © 1985 by the American Association for the Advancement of Science.

FIGURE 15–8.   **Presenting personality in popular science articles**

the purposes of these two genres of writing, however, are entirely different. In Figure 15–9 are two samples of passages with hard-fact areas shaded in. One, as you'll quickly see, is much more heavily ladened with facts.

Pervading Mood of Excitement

General-interest readers like popular science articles because they want to know about the important and exciting things that are going on in the world of science and technology. Popular science articles satisfy that curiosity especially when they convey the information with a sense of wonder, excitement, and importance. Try your best to inject excitement and energy into your article; make some sparks fly. Notice the undercurrent of excitement that runs through Figure 15–9 and through the model article at the end of this chapter.

Exploring the Potential of the Subject

An important ingredient of the popular science article is the discussion of the practical applications of the subject matter and an exploration of its possibilities. People want to know how new discoveries and new technologies or advances in current technologies will affect their lives and the world in general. In the model article much is made of the potential of fractals.

Not far away, in Covina, California, Jim Hill, a parts stocker for a car dealership, has assembled a robot Carroll estimates would have cost Rockwell $250,000 to build. "He's not even an engineer," says Carroll with admiration, "and he has done things that amaze aerospace scientists." The robot is humanoid in appearance. The eyes are a visual sensing system, the rotating head contains its brain (a Z80 microprocessor), and it has two robot arms with full arm movement, each capable of lifting about 10 pounds.

Hill has been working on robots for 15 years. He first tried to make a walking robot. "I got it to walk," he says, "but the movement took up too much of its power. In my second robot I've concentrated on its head." The scanning system is particularly elaborate, designed to allow the machine to recognize and manipulate objects. A scanning light beam in its eyes produces a three-dimensional picture in its head that lets it spot an object and determine how far away it is.

Hill's robot, affectionately known as Charlie, is already one of the most advanced hobbyist robots in the world, but Hill has far grander plans for it. The manipulators (hand grippers) have pressure sensors, but he wants to install light-sensors to provide feedback as the hand approaches an object. He also wants to hook up the hands to a solid-state video camera he has installed in Charlie's head. Then he'll knuckle down to more programming. "Once you build a robot, the whole thing comes down to programming," he says. "If you don't like programming, there is no point in beginning." Although voice recognition is still highly experimental, he wants Charlie to be completely responsive to the human voice. "I'm waiting for technology to catch up with me," says Hill....

Chris Lewis, a production manager for a laser manufacturer in Georgia, and his 16-year-old son Toby are perhaps typical of the vast majority of robot hobbyists. They got started in robotics when Toby received a Heathkit radio-controlled system for Christmas two years ago. They joined the fledgling Robotics Special Interest Group and decided to enter its first annual robotics competition.

The rules called for an inventor to maneuver a "mouse"—a small robot—through a maze as quickly as possible. The Lewises built a simple machine on a three-wheeled platform with a motor and drive

(continued)

FIGURE 15–9. Hard-fact areas in popular science articles: contrasting examples

system. Speed was controlled by an electrical throttle; turning was accomplished simply by isolating one wheel. "Literally all the thing could do was go forward, backward, turn left or turn right," says the elder Lewis, "but in the process we both learned a lot about electrical and electronic design."

Then Lewis bought an Apple. Toby got absorbed in programming, so for the second contest his father forged on alone. "I produced a design that was theoretically correct, but in paying attention to the electronics I neglected to consider power-to-weight ratio," he says ruefully. "I'd been doing my testing with no weight on the wheels, but when I came to run it in a facsimile of the maze, there wasn't enough power to drive it." Lewis is unfazed. "In fact, I derived most of the pleasure, most of the benefit, getting to that point. I was so elated at what I was learning about logic circuits and so on that I hadn't even considered the possibility of it not having enough power."

Tom Parrett, "The Rise of the Robot," Science Digest (April 1983), 75, 107. Reprinted by permission.

It is to study the problem of balance in its simplest form that one of us (Raibert) and his co-workers at Carnegie-Mellon University have built and demonstrated a machine that hops on its single leg and runs like a kangaroo, in a series of leaps. The device can be thought of as a computer-controlled pogo stick. We have been encouraged by the remarkable simplicity of the balancing algorithm. In its present form the machine is limited to movement in a single plane, so that it can tip over in only one direction.

The machine has two main parts: a body and a leg. The body provides the main structure and carries valves, sensors and electronics. The leg is a simple mechanism that not only changes length along its axis but also pivots with respect to the body at a hinge called the hip. The leg bounces on a spring with adjustable tension, much like a human leg with its springy muscles and tendons. The spring is an air cylinder in which pressures are controlled with sensors and valves. At the bottom of the leg is a small foot.

The pivoting motion of the leg is controlled by a second air-operated actuator that applies torques at the hip hinge. A simple on-off valve

FIGURE 15—9.   (cont.)

controls the leg spring, but control of the pivot angle of the leg requires a proportional servo-valve, that is, a feedback device that responds in proportion to the strength of the signal it receives. Because the moment of inertia of the leg is less than 10 percent of the body's moment of inertia the leg can pivot during flight without imparting much motion to the body. The tilt of the body is measured by a gyroscope, enabling the control computer to maintain the body in a level attitude. Other sensors measure the angle of the hip, the length of the leg, the air pressure in the leg spring, the angle between the leg and the ground, and the force of the leg's contact with the ground.

From "Machines That Walk," Marc H. Raibert and Ivan E. Sutherland. Copyright © 1983 by Scientific American, Inc. All rights reserved.

FIGURE 15—9. (cont.)

Attractive Graphics

Study the magazine in which you want to publish your article for the kinds and amounts of illustration it customarily uses. Are the illustrations heavily informative charts and tables? Or are they colorful photographs and drawings? Unless it is an instructional article, popular science articles make heavy use of eye-appealing graphics in order to make themselves more attractive to readers.

STEP 6.   On your worksheet, list and explain which of the characteristics of popular science articles (reviewed in the preceding section) you might use in your article. In particular, list any titles you are thinking about for your article.

Strategies for Openers

One of the toughest jobs in writing an article is to create an opening that grabs readers' attention, interest, or curiosity. An opener establishes the tone, mood, style, and pace for the rest of the article. Put off writing the opener until just the right idea or phrasing comes to you, and in the meantime, begin writing any part of the article with which you feel comfortable starting. However, if you are one of those writers who simply cannot write a single word until you've found just the right opener, here are some strategies to try.

From almost the time the first typewriter came into use, the skill of typing has intrigued experimental psychologists, and intrigues them even today, because the rate at which typists (even average ones) perform exceeds by far the rate that laboratory tests quite common in psychology would lead a psychologist to predict.... How is it possible? What have skilled typists learned that enables them to overcome what appear to be fundamental limitations?

From "The Skill of Typing," Timothy A. Salthouse. Scientific American, Inc. All rights reserved.

FIGURE 15—10. Question or mystery opener

A Question, Problem, or Mystery

A good way to get an article started, to hook the readers in, and to keep their interest is to present a question, problem, or mystery at the beginning. The rest of the article explores that puzzle or even solves it. Notice the approach taken in the excerpt in Figure 15–10.

A Striking Fact or Statistic

You can also use some startling piece of information to surprise your readers and make them want to read on, as in Figure 15–11.

In an awake human being the muscles of the body are continually contracting and relaxing. Strange as it may seem, as they do so they generate sound. Since this sound is not heard under ordinary conditions, you may be skeptical. If you are, put both thumbs gently in your ears and make a fist. You will hear a low rumble. The tighter you make the fist, the louder the sound will be. What you are hearing is the sound made by the muscles of the forearm as they contract.

From "Muscle Sounds," Gerald Oster. Scientific American, Inc. All rights reserved.

FIGURE 15—11. Striking-fact opener

There are so many new books about dying that there are now special shelves set aside for them in bookshops, along with the health-diet and home-repair paperbacks and the sex manuals. Some of them are so packed with detailed information and step-by-step instructions for performing the function that you'd think this was a new sort of skill which all of us are now required to learn. The strongest impression the casual reader gets, leafing through, is that proper dying has become an extraordinary, even an exotic experience, something only the specially trained get to do.

Lewis Thomas, "On Natural Death," The Medusa and the Snail (New York: Viking-Penguin, 1979), 102. Reprinted by permission.

FIGURE 15–12. Unusual or humorous opener

Unusual or Humorous Phrasing of an Idea

You can also get an article going with an opener phrased in an unusual or humorous way. The reader will get the feeling that your personality, wit, and writing style alone will make the article worth reading, as in Figure 15–12.

An Opening Definition

Occasionally articles begin with a definition that prepares readers for what's to come. Definition openers are often phrased in fresh, startling, humorous, or thought-provoking ways. Look at Figure 15–13, for example.

Cosmology is the science of the universe: its structure, its origin, and its final state. For as long as man could reason, he has wondered about this ultimate order. Yet the basic scientific discoveries in cosmology have been made only within the past 150 years.

Allan Sandage, "Inventing the Beginning," Science 84 (November 1984), 111. Reprinted by permission from the November issue of Science '84. Copyright © 1984 by the American Association for the Advancement of Science.

FIGURE 15–13. Definition opener

An Interesting or Striking Quotation

Some articles begin with interesting or striking quotations or quotations from important, well-known leaders or experts, as in Figure 15–14.

An Introductory Anecdote

You can begin your article with a brief story, perhaps a story about an individual with a problem. Such anecdotes build human interest, which is important in popular science articles. An example of an effective introductory anecdote appears in Figure 15–15.

Prose-Poetry Openers

Notice that some popular science articles begin with rather poetic-sounding descriptions and narratives. Such beginnings try to create a sense of wonder, beauty, or awe about the subject, as in Figure 15–16.

Attacking a Commonly Accepted Idea

Another well-used strategy for beginning articles is to set up a commonly accepted but mistaken idea and tear it down, an approach taken in the excerpt in Figure 15–17.

"The only way a scientist can start to understand something is to describe it, to measure it and name it." So wrote paleoanthropologist Donald Johnson in Lucy: The Beginnings of Humankind. Yet as a tool of science, measurement turns out to be as tricky as it is useful. Reality and its measurement are tied in so many knots that it is hard to untangle the axioms from the inferences. We imagine our yardsticks to be rigid, precise, and direct, while actually they are elastic, fuzzy, and inferential. Or as Nobel Prize winner physicist Werner Heisenberg cautioned: "We have to remember that what we observe is not nature herself, but nature exposed to our method of questioning."

K.C. Cole, "Beyond Measurement," Discover (October 1983), 68. Reprinted by permission.

FIGURE 15–14.   Interesting or striking quotation opener

Judy Weiss tucked her son Louie into his crib for a nap and tiptoed
out of the room, as she had done hundreds of times before. But this
time, she recalls, "I snuck around to the other door of his room and
crawled back in on my belly, so he wouldn't see me, and I slid
underneath the crib, right below his head, and started talking to him."
She called his name over and over, louder and louder; she chattered
desperately; she grabbed a toy and pounded the floor with it. But from
Louie, a lively eleven-month-old, nothing; no response, not the slightest
sign that he could hear her. "And I knew he had gone deaf." Doctors
confirmed Weiss's suspicion.... Powerful hearing aids did not seem to
help.... Then, when Louie was two ... Judy attended a lecture about
the cochlear implant—an electric device, surgically implanted in one
inner ear, that can restore limited hearing to the deaf. Activated by
sound, it bypasses the damaged hair cells and electrically stimulates
the auditory nerve. During the past eleven years, some 300 Americans—
including almost 70 children—have had such devices implanted.

Denise Grady, "Sounds Instead of Silence," Discover (October 1983),
54. Reprinted by permission.

FIGURE 15–15.   Anecdote opener

Common Ground with the Reader

One final strategy for openers is to touch upon some familiar chord within the
reader, to connect with some common feeling or experience that most readers have
had and can identify with, as in Figure 15–18.

STEP 7.   On your worksheet explain which of the openers (discussed in the preceding section) you think might work for your article. Also, explain the kind of
information these openers might contain.

Ways to End Articles

Articles end in a variety of ways. If the article is quite technical and scholarly, the
conclusion is much more of a mechanical thing than it is in articles for popular
audiences. (See Chapter 4 on conclusions for technical reports.) If the article is more
for nonspecialist, popular audiences, good endings are achieved in many different,
sometimes subtle and indefinable ways. Here are some often-used and often-com-
bined ways of finishing up articles.

A midday sun blazed down on the ripening cabernet sauvignon grapes as the vineyard's owner, Francisco Jose Ayala, trudged between the rows, inspecting his crop. It was a hot day in the San Joaquin Valley of California, and Ayala's boots kicked up little clouds of dust with each step.... The scion of a wealthy family from the Rioja wine growing region of Spain, Ayala early sought the discipline of monastic life and emerged a Dominican priest. In his late twenties, he left the church to become a scientist. Today, at 49, he is one of the world's foremost authorities on genetics and evolution, with eight books and more than 300 articles to his credit....

Kevin McKean, "Francisco Jose Ayala: Genetics, Grapes, and the Good Life," Discover (October 1983), 36. Reprinted by permission.

FIGURE 15–16. Prose-poetry opener

Most people associate fever with the harmful effects of infection. In fact, pharmaceutical advertisements often give the impression that a fever is the cause of an illness, rather than a symptom, and that suppression of the fever is an effective treatment of the underlying infection. We are told to treat fevers with antipyretics, drugs designed to return our body temperatures to normal, a treatment that has been an accepted part of medical practice at least since the ancient Romans began deriving aspirinlike salicylic acid from the bark of willow trees. That this body response, which has evolved over millions of years, might in fact be beneficial in killing infecting microorganisms is rarely implied in such advertisements.

Matthew J. Kluger, "The Importance of Being Feverish." With permission from Natural History, Vol. 85, No. 1; Copyright © the American Museum of Natural History, 1976.

FIGURE 15–17. An opener that attacks a commonly accepted idea

Everyone must have had at least one personal experience with a computer error by this time. Bank balances are suddenly reported to have jumped from $379 into the millions, appeals for charitable contributions are mailed over and over to people with crazy-sounding names at your address, department stores send the wrong bills, utility companies write that they're turning everything off, that sort of thing. If you manage to get in touch with someone and complain, you then get instantly typed, guilty letters from the same computer, saying, "Our computer was in error, and an adjustment is being made in your account."

These are supposed to be the sheerest, blindest accidents. Mistakes are not believed to be part of the normal behavior of a good machine....

Lewis Thomas, "To Err Is Human," The Medusa and the Snail (New York: Viking-Penguin, 1979), 36–37. Reprinted by permission.

FIGURE 15–18.   A common-ground opener

A Summarizing Quotation

If you can find a statement by a leader, a recognized expert, or an interesting individual that provides the right conclusion, use it to end an article. One example appears in Figure 15–19.

A Quotation with Supplementary Comment

Because some quotations cannot stand alone as the conclusion of an article, you must add information to make them meaningful, as in Figure 15–20.

A Concluding Anecdote

Articles often end with a brief anecdote just as they can begin with an anecdote. The concluding anecdote must give the right sense of finality. Figure 15–21 contains an example of this kind of closing from an article about a researcher's efforts to find cures for the common cold.

You can also introduce an anecdote at the beginning or in the body of an article and then finish up that anecdote in the conclusion. This strategy can provide a bit of suspense as well as continuity. In Figure 15–19, the article could be concluded by returning to Louie, the deaf boy, and showing how he is doing with his cochlear implant.

The real goal of their tests, says Gantz, is not so much to rank the [cochlear] implants in Consumer Reports fashion as to find a way of determining which one is best for each patient. People with severely damaged auditory nerves, for instance, could probably do no better with 22 channels than with one, but right now there is no reliable way to measure nerve damage.

Gantz has no doubts about the value of implants in general. "They will be widely used," he says. "You can't doubt that when you see the social isolation, the depression, that deafness brings to people—and then you see the elation when some hearing returns, even if they're never able to talk over the telephone. The cochlear implant is here to stay."

Denise Grady, "Sounds Instead of Silence," Discover (October 1983), 57. Reprinted by permission.

FIGURE 15—19.   Ending with a summarizing quotation

The years to come may see the further mechanization of medicine, but ironically, the high costs of the machinery may have strengthened an opposing trend as well. "I think we've begun to discover the less technological aspects of medicine," says Ronald Bayer of the Hastings Center, a think tank at Hastings-on-Hudson, New York. "One of the reasons for this trend is that we aren't able to afford all the high technology anymore." Thus the choices facing the health care system might ultimately help renew the human bond between the doctor and the patient.

Jack Fincher, "New Machines May Soon Replace the Doctor's Black Bag," Smithsonian (January 1984), 71. Reprinted with permission.

FIGURE 15—20.   Ending with a quotation and supplementary comment

Directly under Dr. Gwaltney's laboratory at Charlottesville is the University of Virginia's biomedical engineering headquarters where a professor in her 60's works. One day the woman came up to Gwaltney's lab and said, "Don't take affront, but I've been having a lot of colds this year after not having any for years past. I wonder, are you dumping virus in the drain of your sink?"

The doctor assured her that he never does, and asked her who was living in her house, knowing that she and her husband had no young children. "Well," she said, "this past year my daughter came to live with us with her four-year-old son, who's in nursery school."

"And that was it," said Dr. Gwaltney. "To get sick, you've got to be exposed."

Richard L. Williams, "Looking for a Way to Beat the Common Cold," Smithsonian (December 1983), 47. Reprinted with permission.

FIGURE 15–21. A concluding anecdote

Prose-Poetry Endings

Another common way to conclude an article is to use a prose-poetry narrative or description. Figure 15–22 contains an example.

A Striking or Important Fact or Idea

You can end articles by stating a striking fact or idea that reinforces the article's main point, an approach taken in the excerpt in Figure 15–23.

Other Suggestions for Endings

Still other ways to finish off articles include the following:

A call to action	A look to the future
A comparison to the past	The human side or element
An exception	A warning or caution
Implications	

Examples of some of these are shown in Chapter 4. Whichever strategy you use, keep conclusions for popular audiences short, and avoid repetitious summary and such well-worn phrases as "In conclusion." If you are not sure whether your article's conclusion works, ask a few friends to read it and find out what they think.

... at some distant time in the future, the Universe will probably be a cold, thin sea of radiation, with perhaps a few forlorn particles. Undaunted by this bleak prospect, Freeman Dyson argues that life could evolve away from flesh and blood—possibly into clouds of electrically charged particles—and outlast the stars and galaxies themselves while the Universe cools.

The great debate over whether the Universe is open or closed comes down to the question of whether it will all end in fire or in ice, whether everything will fall back in on itself only to repeat the cycle, or whether the last bits of matter and radiation will disappear into a darkness that expands forever.

This is, in a sense, the last, the ultimate, question of science. The cosmic switch has already been thrown; the answer, though unknown, is already ordained, and Man cannot influence the outcome. But simply to discover it would be a triumph of human intellect.

James S. Trefil, "How the Universe Will End," Smithsonian (July 1983), 84. Reprinted with permission.

FIGURE 15—22.   A prose-poetry ending

STEP 8.   On your worksheet explain which of the endings (reviewed in the preceding section) might work for your article, and explain the content of each.

Final Stages of Writing Popular Science Articles

If you've followed the steps to this point in preparing to write your article, you are ready now to make some final plans and start writing. The following steps direct you to the chapters of Parts I, II, and III. If you've already studied those chapters and have been through the steps there, you may only want to go back to them for a brief review.

STEP 9.   Follow these steps to write and complete your article:

• *Analyze the audience.* For an introduction to audience analysis, read Chapter 5, work the steps there, and then return here for the next step.

• *Design the graphic aids.* For direction on graphic aids, read Chapter 6, work the steps, and return here for the next step.

By 1986 the number of electronic functions incorporated into a wide range of products each year can be expected to be 100 times greater than it is today. The experience curve predicts that the cost per function will have declined by then to a twentieth of the 1976 cost, a reduction of 25 percent per year. At such prices electronic devices will be exploited even more widely, augmenting mail service, expanding the library and making its contents more accessible, providing entertainment, disseminating knowledge for educational purposes and performing many more of the routine tasks in the home and the office. It is in the exponential proliferation of products and services dependent on microelectronics that the real microelectronic revolution will be manifested.

From "Microelectronics," Robert N. Noyce. Copyright © September 1977 by Scientific American, Inc. All rights reserved.

FIGURE 15–23. Ending with a striking fact or idea

• *Use headings and lists.* For help on lists and headings, see Chapter 6, do the steps, and return here for the next step.

• *Write the rough draft.* If you've done the preceding steps, you should be ready to write a rough draft of your article. If you've not done so already, see the discussion and steps in Chapter 10, and then return here for the next step.

• *Revise.* For direction on revising your rough draft, read Chapter 10, and return here for the next step.

Writing Query Letters and Cover Letters

The query letter functions as a sort of scout, going ahead of the article to discover whether there is any potential interest in it. It describes the article and explains why the magazine's readers should be interested in it. It must be fairly precise about the article; you can't send out scattershot letters asking about interest in an article on, for example, solar energy devices. (See Chapter 11 for more on query letters.)

STEP 10. Use the steps for query letters in Chapter 11 to prepare and write your query or cover letter.

When you have a finished article ready to send to a magazine editor, write a cover letter and attach it to the front of the article. The cover letter, which is like the query letter, is important because busy editors can forget previous correspondence about the article. Here are some of the typical elements of the cover letter:

1. An announcement to the recipient about the subject of the letter—an article.
2. A reminder to the recipient of previous correspondence on the article.
3. A review or summary of the contents, purpose, and audience of the article.
4. A review of the reasons why you think readers of the magazine will find the article interesting.
5. Any special comments you want to make in defense of the article.
6. Description of any of the article's special graphics needs—for example, photographs or drawings you were not able to provide.
7. A closing in which you encourage the recipient to let you know as soon as possible about his or her decision on your article and in which you offer to discuss your article further.

An example of a cover letter appears in Figure 15–24.

3005 West 30th
Austin, Texas 78705
March 5, 19XX

Editor, <u>Smithsonian</u>
900 Jefferson Drive
Washington, DC 20560

Dear Sir:

I am delighted that you found my article, "Offshore Seismic Surveying," of interest and potentially publishable in your magazine. I've spent the past few weeks putting the finishing touches on it and have enclosed it with this letter for your consideration.

Of course the purpose of the article is to show people how we survey for oil out in the Gulf of Mexico. Your readers should find this energy-related topic of interest. But, as you'll notice when you read the article, I've incorporated plenty of description of cruising on the Gulf and some references to exotic ports of call in the Caribbean. I have tried to interweave into the technical discussion of how seismic surveying is

---

FIGURE 15–24. An example of a cover letter

done personal anecdotes of my own experiences on board, first, as an utter greenhorn, and then later, as an experienced hand watching a newcomer arrive on board.

As I mentioned, I think <u>Smithsonian</u> readers will find my article interesting because it is concerned with petroleum exploration and production, vital concerns for us all these days. The article also has a dash of the travelog, seagoing adventure, and personal drama mixed in, which should make it attractive to readers.

I've taped into my draft of the article photographs of the ship, our operations on board during surveys, some of the characters I worked with, and some of the ports of call where we stopped in the Caribbean. I've attached to the article several drawings in which I've attempted to sketch the seismic surveying process. These photos and drawings should give you an idea of what graphics the article will need.

I'll look forward to hearing from you soon on your reactions to the article.

Sincerely,

Scott A. Woodrow

Encl. Article, "Offshore Seismic Surveying"

FIGURE 15–24. (cont.)

Stages in the Publishing Process

When you type the final copy of your article, find out about the magazine's requirements: it may require double-spaced copies, multiple copies, or a self-addressed stamped envelope for return. In Figure 15–25 is an example of the kind of instructions to authors that some magazines and journals provide; this example actually appears in the journal itself.

Insert any illustrations you have as suggested in Chapter 6. For illustrations you cannot get, include an appendix entitled "Note on Illustrations Needed."

STEP 11.   Using the appropriate steps in Chapter 10, edit, revise, and do the final typing and proofreading of your article.

LAB ANIMAL accepts manuscripts on nearly all aspects of laboratory animal science and welcomes articles from individuals affiliated with laboratory and animal research facilties. While we publish some original research articles that are appropriate for our diverse readership, most of our editorial material deals with reviews of new animal models, breeds, or breeding practices; in vitro or mathematical/computer research models; lab animal care and nutrition; new ideas or techniques for biomedical or psychological research; short notes on. . . . If you are uncertain about the suitability of your topic, please submit a one-page abstract for preliminary consideration.

Reviewing and editing: LAB ANIMAL is a formally reviewed journal. All manuscripts are reviewed by the Editor, and most are further reviewed by several members of our Editorial Advisory Board or by qualified outside reviewers. . . . Reviewers' requests for major revisions are referred to the author(s) for comment and/or revision prior to final editing.

Manuscript style and length. Use an informal, narrative style rather than the standard scientific format. Case histories and anecdotal material should be included whenever possible. . . . Manuscripts should generally contain no more than 3000 words, which, including references and figure legends, equates to about 12 double-spaced typewritten pages. . . . Usual publication dates is 6 to 12 months after acceptance.

Reprinted with permission of LAB ANIMAL, Inc.

FIGURE 15–25. Example of instructions to authors provided by some periodicals

If you get your article accepted for publication, you may become involved in (1) reviewing the copy-edited pages of your article; (2) proofing the "galleys" of your article; and (3) doing a final check on the page proofs.

1. Some magazines will send your article to a professional copy-editor to get it into conformity with "house style" (such matters as the capitalization of certain words or personal pronouns in neutral situations), to correct grammatical errors and unclear or awkward sentences, and to mark the manuscript to show the typesetter how to print your manuscript. The marked-up manuscript will be sent back to you for your review and approval. See Appendix E for the kinds of marks and symbols copy editors use.
2. The next step is the galleys, which are long typeset pages. When you receive them, your job is to proofread and to make only minor stylistic changes.

3. A final step is the page proofs: these pages show you exactly how your article will look on the actual pages of the magazine. Any last-minute stylistic changes at this point are not allowed. The page proofs are your last chance to proof-read.

Thinking about Yourself as a Writer

Despite all these strategies, you may still have a hard time imagining yourself publishing an article. Keep in mind, however, that not all magazine writers are full-time employees with special training and special talent. Plenty of articles are written by free-lance writers not employed by any magazine. Plenty of people like you are out there writing articles about things they know about and are interested in: they enjoy it as a hobby and even make a bit of money from it. Writing and publishing an article can be exciting; you play many different roles.

First, you're a sleuth, prowling the libraries to discover several likely magazines for your article and then investigating them for clues about how to shape your article. Next, you're an intellectual and a scholar, learning the best that is known about your subject, making sure of that knowledge, and then putting it all on paper. Then, you're a writer banging away at the next draft of the article or scribbling away on a yellow pad (picture Ernest Hemingway, Agatha Christie, Stephen King, or whoever your favorite writer is). With a written article you become a salesperson, out there trying to sell people on what a great thing your article is. Toward the end of the process, you are living in constant excitement and anticipation, waiting for that letter or phone call about the fate of your article. Finally, you are the proud author of an article in a real magazine read by thousands of people, a recognized authority on something (even if it's only on some small aspect of, say, beekeeping), and a source of wonder and admiration to your friends and relatives.

If getting published is much easier than you had imagined, if ordinary people publish articles all the time, and if the publishing process can be so much fun—how can you pass up the chance?

EXERCISES

1. Make copies of several popular science articles you've enjoyed or would like to read, and label the strategies used in those articles: pay particular attention to the types of openers and endings used.
2. Select a popular science article and a technical report or textbook excerpt on the same topic, and compare them. Explain what details or techniques make the popular science article readable for general nonspecialist audiences.
3. Analyze the popular science article that you selected in exercise 2 in the following ways:
   a. The interest-grabbing qualities of the title (and subtitles)
   b. The techniques used to open the article
   c. The characteristics of the body of the article
   d. The effect of the graphic aids in attracting reader interest
   e. The strategy used to end the article

4. Using the popular science article and the technical report or textbook excerpt selected in exercise 2, or some other pair of articles, analyze for the amount and density of technical detail. Highlight the hard-fact areas, and estimate the percentage of technical discussion in each.

5. Locate a technical report (using the steps in Chapter 9 for finding government documents, if necessary), and think of ways you could transform some of the information in that report into a popular science article. Think of the openers, endings, and graphic aids you'd use.

6. Select a popular science magazine, and review several issues of it to determine the typical characteristics of articles published in that magazine. Use the suggestions in this chapter for analyzing articles.

Model 15–1.   Geometrical Forms Known as Fractals Find Sense in Chaos*
(excerpt from a popular science article)

Abstract patterns that were once called 'monsters' provide a new way to understand the order amid nature's irregular shapes

At ungodly hours of the morning or the evening, when the town's computers are freed from mundane activities, Palo Alto, California, hums. A simple two-story building which looks as though it should belong to a dentist rather than a computer company is no exception. Outside is parked a beat-up Volvo with paper coffee cups strewn across the back seat. Inside, computer scientist Bill Gosper sits in front of a terminal, eyes scanning the screen. Dressed in light-blue pants, a light-blue shirt and construction boots, he holds himself like an outlaw. He is lath-thin and ashen from the hours he keeps. But with fingers as long as heron wings, he plays the computer and it plays back.

Gosper is searching for an image that he made a few weeks earlier to please a friend. He finds it. It appears on the high-resolution color monitor, drawn in line by line. A white lightning bolt darts within an orange lightning bolt which darts within many more multihued lightning bolts. The jagged shape repeats itself with an eye-pleasing regularity at different scales. "This is a very simple fractal," he nearly apologizes, but he obviously enjoys its esthetics.

Fractals are not so hard to find across San Francisco Bay, in Marin County, where Loren Carpenter makes fractal images for Lucasfilm. The movie company that created the Star Wars saga is housed not in high-tech splendor but in an oak-paneled, lead-glass arts-and-crafts style building that immediately feels homey and familiar. Carpenter is a member of the staff for computer graphics projects (the first such unit within a movie company); but dressed in brown corduroys with the knees skidded out and a Run-for-the-Roses T-shirt, he just

*Source: Jeanne McDermott, "Fractals," Smithsonian (December 1983), 115–16. Reprinted with permission.

seems like an oversize kid. His specialty is coaxing imaginary landscapes out of mammoth computers. "We want the image to look indistinguishable from live action. It should look like someone went in these with a camera and made a movie," he explains.

Tall order. But Carpenter and his colleagues are perfecting the techniques that will bring realistic computer graphics to the movie screen. In a darkened room with several shelves of videotape machines, he demonstrates what is already possible. "Everything that you see in this animation is synthetic," he says with pride. The tape begins with hills of green polygons, cold artificial shapes that you instantly associate with a computer. Suddenly they erupt, forcing up a mountain range as craggy and majestic as the Rockies. Exhilarated, you fly through them, up and down steep cliffs scattered with ledges, covered with ice, until you land safely on an outcropping. "This is fractal, this is fractal, this fractal," Carpenter hurriedly explains, pointing to the most realistic images with the same delight that Gosper voiced.

Fractal? Close the dictionary. The word was coined only in 1975. But a sense is already building in fields as diverse as physics and ecology, pure mathematics and computer science, that fractals are changing the way we look at the world. "No one will be considered scientifically literate tomorrow who is not familiar with fractals," offers John Wheeler, professor of physics at the University of Texas at Austin.... "Fractals delineate a whole new way of thinking about structure and form," write Paul Davies, professor of physics at the University of Newcastle-upon-Tyne, England.

Fractals describe a new geometry of nature. They form a field of mathematics that may have a profound impact on how we view the world, not only in art and film but in many branches of science and technology, from astronomy to economics to predicting the weather. Euclid's lines, planes and spheres--the pure shapes that you probably studied in high school geometry--describe the world of built things. Fractals tackle the chancy intricacies of nature--bark patterns on oak trees, mud cracks in a dry riverbed, the profile of a brocoli spear. They are a family of irregular shapes with just enough regularity so that they can be mathematically described.

Fractals wriggle and wrinkle, meander and dawdle while remaining infinitely rich in detail. Magnify one again and again and more detail always emerges. Just a twig resembles a branch and a branch resembles a tree; each part of a fractal is like the whole.

That indeed is the definition of fractal, according to Benoit Mandelbrot, who coined the term. If you look at a circle, he explains, then look at it more and more closely, you will see a smaller and smaller segment of the curve and it will appear to become straighter and straighter. There is no new structure in a circle at higher magnifications. It simply looks more and more like a straight line. But imagine a shape in which increasing detail is revealed with increasing magnification, and the newly revealed structure looks the same as what you have seen at lower magnifications. This shape is a fractal.

Within the family of fractals are two clans. Geometric fractals, like Gosper's, repeat an identical pattern over and over at different scales. Random fractals, like Carpenter's landscapes, introduce some elements of chance. To get to the bottom of fractals, you must meet their "father" and champion, Benoit Mandelbrot. His colleagues describe Mandelbrot as a genius--eccentric, literary and contrary. He describes himself as a self-taught nonconformist. Whatever else, he is one mathematician who does not speak in dry, perfected balanced equations. Born in

Poland in 1924, Mandelbrot skipped most of college but did pass the entrance exam to the leading French science school, the Ecole Polytechnique. He then pursued a master's degree in aeronautics at the California Institute of Technology, and finally returned to the University of Paris where he got a doctorate in mathematics. While at the Ecole Polytechnique as a professor of mathematics, Mandelbrot accepted a position at IBM's Thomas J. Watson Research Center in Yorktown Heights, New York, where he is now an IBM Fellow and manager of a group working on fractals.

IBM's Research Center is only an hour from Manhattan but, set among rolling hills and large estates, it has the aura of a retreat. Indeed, it has been called the ivory tower of the corporate world, a university without teaching responsibilities. Mandelbrot's office--spartan, windowless, bare-walled--sits at the end of a hallway because he can't stand noise. Tall and formal in a pinstripe suit, he speaks with a strong Old World accent, urgency and wit.

Mandelbrot traces his work on fractals back 25 to 30 years, to a time when "science looked at things that were regular and smooth." He was intrigued by what are called chaotic phenomena. At IBM he turned his attention to a chaotic problem in data transmission by telephone. Every electrical signal is subject to random perturbations called noise. Usually, the noise is not so overpowering that it interferes with the signal's message. But under certain conditions the noise does interfere with the signal in destructive ways. Mandelbrot found a way to describe the chance fluctuations.

Defanging Mathematical Monsters

Mandelbrot's methods built on the ideas of several mathematicians who worked between 1875 and 1925 on shapes so strange that their colleagues labeled them "pathological" and "monsters." Scientists of the day were convinced that such shapes were mathematical abstractions with no relation to nature. Helge von Koch added even smaller triangles to the side of a large triangle to create an infinitely intricate snowflake curve.... Giuseppe Peano's curve writhed in contortions until it nearly filled a plane. Georg Cantor's shapes evaporated into mere dust particles while they repeated a pattern into infinity. Mandelbrot "defanged" or "exorcized" some of the monsters. He saw their similarities and called them "fractals" (from the Latin fractus: broken or fragmented).

While the turn-of-century mathematicians never thought their monsters bore any relation to reality, Mandelbrot believed that, on the contrary, they described nature much better than any ideal shapes. He set out to prove it. He scavenged problems that scientists had swept under the rugs of their disciplines, problems that did not fit conventional thinking. He characterized price jumps in the stock market, turbulence in the weather, the distribution of galaxies, the flooding of the Nile, even the length of coastlines. "The construction of this theory of chaotic behavior was itself chaotic," he observes.

In the late Sixties, a wider scientific community noticed Mandelbrot's work in a now classic paper called, "How long is the coast of Britain?" Mandelbrot answered: It depends. As the crow flies, the coast is one length. As the person walks, it stretches even longer. As the spider crawls, it stretches still longer. In essence, a coastline with all of its microscopic points and inlets is infinitely long. Mandelbrot suggested that it makes more sense to treat the coastline as a random fractal than as an approximation of a straight line.

Mandelbrot's first book on fractals appeared in 1975 in French. The turning point came when he started using computer graphics to illustrate fractals.

His book dazzled the eye with state-of-the-art computer images unlike any ever seen. Richard Voss, a physicist at IBM, created stunning landscapes, earthly and other-worldly, from Mandelbrot's ideas. "Without computer graphics, this work could have been completely disregarded," Mandelbrot acknowledges.

These images helped produce a change in the scientific world view. Until recently, scientists believed that the only shapes that were useful in science were those simple Euclidean shapes, lines, planes and spheres; all else was chaos. There was order and there was disorder. Now there is order (simple shapes), manageable chaos (fractals) and unmanageable chaos.

"The esthetic beauty came as a total surprise," Mandelbrot adds. "A premium. When people first come to work on this project, their first reaction to making the images is invariably a kind of intoxication."

For Doug McKenna, one of those drawn to Mandelbrot's circle at IBM, fractals crystallized a lifetime interest in mathematical designs. As a child, he painstakingly drew them by hand on graph paper with colored pens. In school he got interested in computers, in part because they meant automating the drawing process. But practical considerations, like pursuing a master's degree in electrical engineering at Yale, superseded his artistic inclinations.

After programming fractals at IBM for one year, McKenna is striking out on his own as a computer artist. With his reddish beard and his eyes made large by his glasses, a habit of precision and a quietly comic manner, McKenna probably comes as close as anyone to looking the part. Yet he has his doubts about the label. "What I am doing is not quite art and it is not new mathematics, but a synthesis. Computer art is a bad term. Most artists are afraid of computers except for a few who are discovering how wonderful they are," he says. "That's why I call it Mathemesthetics, I guess." Well aware of the sheer pleasure fractals evoke, he hopes to turn them into a variety of designs, from fabrics to architectural ornamentation to fine art.

McKenna has a library of "seed" shapes stored on the computer. He can take one out, glance at it on the monitor and then instruct the computer to repeat the pattern, with mechanically controlled ink pens that dance across a piece of paper. The results are pure abstract images that attract your gaze and attention. Some are "replicating tiles" or "reptiles" for short. Others are boldly colored mazes. "I should have been a hedge designer," McKenna laughs, "but I was born in the wrong century." He also works with ornate spiraling forms, creating "dragon curves" that would be worthy of St. George.

Loren Carpenter was working in computer graphics at the Boeing Company in Seattle when Mandelbrot's images inspired him to action. "I saw the picture of the mountain range and said, Hey, I've got to do this! But the methods Mandelbrot uses are totally unsuitable for animation, for making a picture where you stand in the landscape," Carpenter says. So Carpenter used his own techniques that allow the viewer to move around in the landscape, using mathematical shortcuts to produce many images quickly. Carpenter made an animated film to demonstrate this technique; it won him a job at Lucasfilm—and the irritation of Mandelbrot, who disdained these shortcuts.

Shortcuts or not, random fractals capture the texture of reality. In another three or four years, Carpenter expects computer graphics to replace some movie sets and models. The lure is making the impossible look real. "You can re-create the pyramids. Or a civilization from another planet. You could change colors, twist or deform shapes, do things that are completely fantastic," he says.

The true beauty of fractals is that they describe the pedestrian as well as the fantastic. But the practical uses of fractals have developed at a slower pace. "A lot of people say, 'Okay, so you have a new name for these things, you call them fractals. But what can you do with them?'" says Alan Norton, a former associate of Mandelbrot's who is now working on computer architectures at IBM. It is a question currently being asked by physicists and other scientists at many professional meetings. For a young idea still being translated into the dialects of each scientific discipline, the answer, Norton says, is: Quite a bit. The fractal dimension (a number expressing the complexity of a particular fractal form) may give scientists a way to describe a complex phenomenon with a single number.

Harold Hastings, a professor of mathematics at Hofstra University on Long Island, is enthusiastic about modeling the Okefenokee Swamp in Georgia with fractals. From aerial photographs, he has studied vegetation patterns and found that some key tree groups, like cypresses, are patchier and show a larger fractal dimension than others. In analyzing shapes that are hard to describe with any exactness—"patchy" ones, for example—using fractals may provide a more precise measure. Eventually, he hopes that slight and unexpected changes in the fractal dimension of key species can be used as an early-warning system for harmful disturbances like pollutants and acid rain.

Shaun Lovejoy, a meteorologist who works at Meterologie Nationale, the French national weather service in Paris, confirmed that clouds follow fractal patterns. Again, by analyzing satellite photographs he found similarities in the shape of many cloud types that formed over the Indian Ocean. From tiny pufflike clouds to an enormous mass that extended from Central Africa to Southern India, all exhibited the same fractal dimension. Prior to Mandelbrot's discovery of fractals, cloud shapes had not been candidates for mathematical analysis and meteorologists who theorize about the origin of weather ignored them. Lovejoy's work suggests that the atmosphere on a small-scale weather pattern near the Earth's surface resembles that on a large-scale pattern extending many miles away, an idea that runs counter to current theories.

The occurrence of earthquakes. The surfaces of metal fractures. The path a computer program takes when it scurries through its memory. The way our own neurons fire when we go searching through our memories. The wish list for fractal description grows. Time will tell if the fractal dimension becomes invaluable to scientists interested in building mathematical models of the world's working.

Whatever the purpose, fractals touch the imagination in a way that no other computer-generated image has. "They produce unprecedented visual effects. They are pure art, pure playthings," says Bill Gosper. But their images have changed the world of mathematics as well. Mandelbrot explains: "Imagine 100 years ago that singing was outlawed and a great science of analyzing scores arose. Now think that 100 years later someone looked at these scores and found that they were really much more beautiful and accessible when sung. Beautiful opera scores were appreciated by only a few but beautiful music was appreciated by everyone. I have done that for branches of mathematics." Who would disagree?

CHAPTER 16

Preparing and Delivering Oral Reports

Chapter Objectives
Functions of Oral Reports
Ideas for Oral Reports
Preparing Oral Reports
   Script Approach
   Outline Approach
   Cue-Card Approach
   Extemporaneous Approach
The Oral Delivery
   Rate of Delivery
   Enunciation
   Volume
   Pauses
   Eye Contact
   Posture and Gestures

Designing the Verbal and
   Visual Aids
   Verbal Signposts
   Visual Aids
Introductions and Conclusions to Oral
   Reports
Evaluating Oral Reports
Exercises
Model
   16–1. Report on Recycling to a
       Neighborhood Association (oral
       report excerpts)

———————————— *Chapter Objectives* ————————————

After you read this chapter, study the examples, and work the steps, you should be able to:

- Explain the different functions of oral reports.
- List the different ways to prepare for oral reports.
- List the common problem areas involving rate of delivery, enunciation, volume, pauses, eye contact, and posture.
- Explain the function of overviews and verbal headings in oral reports.
- Identify the different types of visual aids that can be used in oral reports.
- List several ways to begin and end oral reports.

In an oral report you present information through speech rather than through writing. As people advance in the business and professional worlds, most of them do more and more oral reporting as well as more and more writing. Effective oral reports are as important as written reports: both can be critical to the well-being and future of a community, to an organization, to a business, and of course to the individuals who do the oral reporting.

Functions of Oral Reports

Like written reports, oral reports inform, instruct, persuade, or combine some of these functions.

- An oral report can be primarily *informative*. For example, as a member of a committee involved in a project to relocate the plant, your job might be to give an oral report on the condition of the building and grounds at one of the sites proposed for purchase. Or, you might be required to go before the city council and report on the success of the new city-sponsored recycling project.

- An oral report can be primarily *instructional*. Your task might be to train new employees to use certain equipment or to perform certain routine tasks.

- An oral report can be primarily *persuasive*. You might want to convince members of local civic organizations to support a citywide recycling program. You might appear before the city council to persuade its members to reserve certain city-owned lands for park areas, softball and baseball parks, or community gardens.

Ideas for Oral Reports

Finding a topic for an oral report is not exactly like finding a topic for a written report. Still, you'll find the strategies for finding topics in Chapter 8 useful. Also, try the following suggestions.

- Most of the strategies in Chapter 8 start with a *technical subject*, for example, solar panels, microprocessors, drip irrigation, or laser surgery. For your oral report, think of a subject you'd be interested in talking about, but find a reason why an audience would want to hear your oral report. (See Chapter 5 on analyzing or inventing report situations.)

• You can find topics for oral reports or make more detailed plans for them by thinking about the *place* or the *situation* in which your oral report might naturally be given: at a neighborhood association? at the parent-teachers' association meeting? at a church meeting? at the gardening club? at a city council meeting? at a meeting of the board of directors or high-level executives of a company? Thinking about an oral report this way makes you focus on the audience, their reasons for listening to you, and their interests and background.

• Another way to find a topic is to think about the *purpose* of your talk. Is it to instruct (for example, to explain how to run a text-editing program on a computer), to persuade (to vote for or against a certain technically oriented bond issue), or simply to inform (to report on citizen participation in the new recycling program).

STEP 1.   On your worksheet describe the topic of your oral report, its purpose (information, instruction, or persuasion), and the situation (real or invented) in which you'll give your oral report. See Chapter 8 for topic ideas. (If you are thinking about collaborating with someone else on an oral report, see "Collaborating on Technical Reports" in the Introduction for ideas and suggestions. The discussion there focuses on written reports, but it is easily adaptable to oral reports.)

Preparing the Oral Report

Some of the steps in preparing for an oral report are practically the same as they are for a written report.

1. Analyze the background, needs, and interests of your listeners and identify any problems they may have with your report. (See Chapter 5 for more on audiences.)
2. Be prepared to translate your talk in nontechnical terms just as you would a written report. (See Chapter 5.)
3. Outline your talk and take notes in generally the same way explained in Chapters 8 and 10.
4. Gather information from library and nonlibrary sources in the same way as for a written report. (See Chapter 9.)

STEP 2.   If necessary, return to the discussion and steps for analyzing audiences and translating technical subjects in Chapter 5; for brainstorming, narrowing, and outlining in Chapter 8; for locating library and nonlibrary sources of information in Chapter 9; and for note taking in Chapter 10.

Preparing to give an oral report, however, is obviously quite different from preparing for a written report. If you've not done much oral reporting, you may be a little apprehensive about appearing before a group of people or about the length of your report, the way you'll present it, or your memory for all of the information.

That's why some form of rehearsal is necessary for oral-report preparation, just as rough drafts are necessary rehearsals for written reports. The less experienced you are at oral reporting, the more rehearsing you should probably do.

To reduce your concerns about nerves, memory lapses, and length or manner of presentation, consider one of the following methods.

Script Approach

If you lack experience as an oral reporter, you can get ready for an oral presentation by writing out a complete script of your talk. It may take more time, but it has a number of advantages.

- You can practice reading the script aloud in the manner you would present it to the group you must speak to; you can time your reading to see if it is an appropriate length. (Remember, however, to read it slowly.)
- Writing out the script forces you to think through all the details of the talk and to gather all the necessary information. It can show you unexpected gaps in your knowledge about the report subject.
- Writing the script gives you a chance to practice explaining more complicated matters in your report. This practice will enable you to explain things clearly and smoothly on the day of the oral report.

Once you have a script, you don't necessarily have to read it word for word during your talk.

- If you practice reading from your script, you'll increasingly be able to look away from it and explain the gist of the report. This will keep your talk fresh and enable you to make more eye contact with the audience. When you reach difficult parts, you can return to your script and read it word for word.
- You can type your script, double-spacing it and using the largest typestyle you can find to make the script easier to read.
- Also, you can use a felt-tip pen to highlight important areas of the script. You'd highlight important information that absolutely must be presented and the main topic phrases of each new section of the report. This will help you re-member not only to present the most important facts but also to plan the order in which topics are to be discussed.

Outline Approach

Another approach is to prepare an outline of what you want to cover. Such an outline might look like the one in Figure 16–1. Such an outline serves you in several ways. It keeps you from getting lost during the talk and from using up too much time on any one section of the report or on a digression; and it reminds you of the order in which to present the topics and ensures that you'll cover everything you had intended to cover.

If you practice with a script and get to know it well, you may end up not needing it and be able to rely on an outline instead. Or you can merge the script and outline and be able to refer to both during your talk.

Outline for Oral Report on Recycling
to a Neighborhood Association

I. Introduction
    A. Purpose of Talk
    B. Overview of Proposed Recycling Plan
    C. Overview of Talk

II. Current Solid Waste Generated
    A. Volumes
    B. Composition
    C. Recycling Value

III. Solid-Waste Disposal
    A. Methods Used
    B. Costs
    C. Problems

IV. Economic Potential of Recycling

V. Administrative Details
    A. Citizen Participation
    B. Personnel
    C. Facilities
    D. Publicity

VI. Other Communities with Recycling Programs

FIGURE 16–1.   Outline for an oral report

Cue-Card Approach

In the cue-card approach you write the topics and the most important facts and ideas for the oral report on index cards. Cue cards are much like the traditional notecards for written reports described in Chapter 10. Here are some suggestions for the preparation of cue cards:

- Limit information you put on each card; otherwise, the cue cards will be hard to read.
- Write the information on each cue card in large letters to make it easier to read.
- Generally, complete sentences are not necessary on the cue cards, just the essential information for quick reference.
- On each cue card, indicate where it belongs in the outline.

In Figure 16–2 are some examples of cue cards, some of which are used in the oral-report outline in Figure 16–1. If you use the outline approach, you may still need a few cue cards for the hard-to-remember statistics in your report, such as those in the examples in Figure 16–2.

```
┌─────────────────────────────────────────────────────────────┐
│ 1                                      IV. current recycl progs│
│                                                               │
│ 220 cities U.S. invld in source separ recycle program        │
└─────────────────────────────────────────────────────────────┘

┌─────────────────────────────────────────────────────────────┐
│ 2                                         IV. curr recycl progs│
│                                                               │
│ City of West Univ. Place, Tx                                  │
│ saves 1 acre landfill/ 3 yrs of oper thru recycl              │
└─────────────────────────────────────────────────────────────┘

┌─────────────────────────────────────────────────────────────┐
│ 3                                         IV. curr recycl progs│
│                                                               │
│ Grand Rapids, Mich                                            │
│ city recycl prog cost less < ½                                │
│ per ton than landfill                                         │
└─────────────────────────────────────────────────────────────┘

┌─────────────────────────────────────────────────────────────┐
│ 4                                         IV. curr recycl progs│
│                                                               │
│ Odessa, Tx--using ⅓ of its MSW for recyclg & composting       │
└─────────────────────────────────────────────────────────────┘

┌─────────────────────────────────────────────────────────────┐
│ 5                                         IV. curr recycl progs│
│                                                               │
│ Kent County, Mich--26% savings in landfill area expected      │
│    w/ 25% citizen particip in recycle prog                    │
└─────────────────────────────────────────────────────────────┘

┌─────────────────────────────────────────────────────────────┐
│ 6                                         IV. curr recycl progs│
│                                                               │
│ Santa Barbara, Cal.--93% return on investment in curbside     │
│    recycl prog                                                │
└─────────────────────────────────────────────────────────────┘

┌─────────────────────────────────────────────────────────────┐
│ 7                                         IV. curr recycl progs│
│                                                               │
│ Macon, Ga., Public Works Dept--curbside newsp recycl          │
│    program making profit with only 25% voluntary citizen      │
│    particip.                                                  │
└─────────────────────────────────────────────────────────────┘
```

FIGURE 16–2.   Example of cue cards for an oral report

Extemporaneous Approach

An extemporaneous delivery, in which such things as scripts, outlines, or cue cards are not used, can be the most personable, dynamic, and interesting of all methods of delivery; but it can also produce some of the greatest disasters in oral reporting.

We are used to seeing casual, glib, and entertaining speakers on TV and can fall into the trap of picturing ourselves in the same way. Oral-report day is not the time to discover that you're not the suave, polished crowd pleaser you'd thought you were or to discover that your mind goes blank in front of an audience. The methods of preparation for oral reports discussed here force you to think through all the details of a report and not to take your knowledge or your oral report style for granted.

If you are not careful, an extemporaneous delivery also tends to lose direction and organization: it is easy to spend too much time on one topic, to run out of time, simply to forget to discuss some topics altogether, or to get them out of order. If you intend to deliver your report extemporaneously, at least keep these suggestions in mind:

- Make a mental outline of your report.
- Estimate the amount of time for each part of your report.
- Be sure that you have all the necessary information.
- Know yourself: don't just assume things about your composure, personality, or ability to speak extemporaneously.
- Consider having some other resource (for example, a detailed written outline or cue cards) to fall back on.

STEP 3. On your worksheet explain which method or combination of methods you plan to use in preparing for your oral report and why you've chosen that method.

The Oral Delivery

When you actually deliver the report orally, you must of course speak at the right volume and rate and speak personably and confidently. You must find a way to be interesting and agreeable to listen to. If you are new to oral reporting, the finer touches may seem like too much to manage right at first. Instead, your whole attention may be focused on simply getting the information across to the audience clearly. To ensure this fundamental clarity, you can practice the following things.

Rate of Delivery

If you are likely to become a bit nervous or if you are worried about covering all of your material, you'll tend to speak too fast. Therefore, try to establish some imaginary metronome ticking away in front of you; set it at a tempo slower than that of your ordinary conversation, and practice speaking at that rate.

Enunciation

A slower rate of speaking also gives you more time to pronounce individual words clearly. To make sure that you enunciate clearly, practice pronouncing consonants more firmly than you'd ordinarily do. Some speakers "swallow" their consonants: they pronounce their bs, cs, ds, fs, gs, and so on very weakly and thus are hard to understand.

Volume

You should also make sure to deliver your oral report in a loud enough volume so that even those members of the audience at the back of the room can hear easily. Find out what volume is right for your voice and for the room in which you'll be speaking, and then practice speaking at that level.

Pauses

If you are new to oral reporting, you may be concerned about pauses in which you say nothing. This fear can cause you to speak in an increasingly rapid rate. Actually, nothing is wrong with occasional pauses; they give listeners time to absorb information; they can help to add emphasis to the next statement after the pause; and they can give listeners a chance to ask questions.

To cover up pauses, some inexperienced speakers use strings of "uh," "you know," and "okay." Such delaying tactics can become annoying. As opposed to saying "uh," say nothing at all! In the days before your oral report, practice avoiding use of "you know" and "uh," and notice how much other speakers use them.

Eye Contact

If you do not make occasional eye contact with your audience, your report will be much less effective. Avoid the head-down script-reading approach as much as possible. Either focus your eyes on the audience as a whole, or let your eyes dart around between three, four, or five pairs of eyes in the audience, and keep track of how these individuals respond to your talk.

Posture and Gestures

When you present an oral report, stand up straight. If a lectern is available, do not slouch over it. If you are so inclined and if it fits the situation, move around a bit and use hand gestures. Such movements can help to keep your audiences' attention focused on you. However, if you are highly demonstrative with your hands, practice keeping that habit under control before your report also.

STEP 4.   On your worksheet explain which of the aspects of oral delivery just discussed you plan to practice and why.

Designing the Verbal and Visual Aids

Another important difference between oral and written reports is that in oral reports you must use an equivalent of textual and graphics aids—that is, verbal and visual aids.

Verbal Signposts

In written reports, headings are critical: they break up the writing, guide readers, and indicate the subject matter of each section. In oral reports you use *overviews* and *verbal headings*—signals about your report's organization or about changes in topic.

Overviews.   In your opening remarks you should provide the audience with an overview of your report. For example, in an oral report on municipal recycling, you may plan to cover (1) the volume of municipal solid waste, (2) the costs and problems associated with current methods of disposal of it, (3) the economic potential of recycling that waste and the subsequent reduction of landfill needs, and (4) methods by which individual citizens can recycle. In your actual oral report, an overview of these topics might sound something like the example in Figure 16–3. Notice that in this overview:

- The subject matter of the report—the recycling of paper, glass and metals—is clearly indicated right away.

I'm happy to have this chance to discuss with you today a project my organization is promoting. The recycling of paper, glass, and metals in municipal solid waste is a project that can have great benefits for all of us and for our city in general. I hope that after my talk your organization will seriously consider putting its support behind the proposal to recycle on a city-wide basis when it comes before our city council.

To show you the potential recycling holds for our city and the relative ease with which it can be implemented, I want, first, to discuss the volume of waste this city produces and the problems and costs we face in disposing of that waste. Second, I want to present the economic returns of a recycling program and the reduction in landfill needs that can be realized from it. Finally, I want to discuss with you how relatively easy it is for a city like ours to begin a recycling program and for individual citizens to recycle their own paper, glass, and metals.

FIGURE 16–3.   Example of an overview from an oral report

- The purpose of the oral report—to win support for the recycling program—is also made clear.
- The introduction creates interest or curiosity: Just how much MSW does the city generate? How much can we save?
- The introduction also contains a cordial opening, a friendly, striking, or humorous comment to get the audience's attention and to break the ice.

Verbal Headings.   As you give your report, remind listeners of that overall organization established in the overview, and let them know when you've completed one section within the report and are moving to a new one. The signals, or verbal headings, indicate movement from one topic to the next:

> As you can see, our relatively average-size city produces a surprisingly large amount of solid waste. What is the cost of getting rid of it? I can tell you from the very beginning that it is not cheap. . . .

These two sentences move the listeners' attention from a consideration of the *volume* of municipal solid waste to a consideration of the *costs* of getting rid of it. Section-to-section transitions such as these do three essential things:

- They review, summarize, or echo the preceding topic.
- They indicate the topic of the next section.
- They specify the logic that connects these two sections.

Here is another example of verbal headings:

> Not only are the costs of getting rid of our garbage high, as I have shown, but it's getting harder and harder for city officials to find areas in which to get rid of it. These geographical problems involved in disposal. . . .

Here the review is *costs;* the preview of the next section is *areas in which to get rid of it*. The logic is additive: one idea is being added on to another. Here is a final example:

> We've seen how the various problems of getting rid of municipal solid waste are increasing, how much it costs us to get rid of it, and how great the economic potential of recycling is. I want to turn now to a discussion of how a citywide recycling project can be implemented. In particular, I want to focus on the widespread belief that recycling is more trouble than it's worth to both the city and to individual citizens. . . .

In this verbal heading, three of the preceding sections are echoed in order in the first sentence to underscore the logic of the presentation and build up to a strong finish.

STEP 5.   On your worksheet write an overview sentence for your oral report, and then write sentences for each verbal heading that you'll need when shifting from one section of your report to another.

Visual Aids

Visual aids, or "visuals," used in oral reports are the equivalent of graphic aids in written reports. They include overhead projections, large display charts, handouts to the audience, and other devices to help you convey your message easily and effectively. Good visuals are important in oral reports where detailed information, particularly statistics, must be presented.

Overhead Projection.   A popular way to present visuals in oral reports is overhead projection. (See Figure 16–4 for an illustration of an overhead projector.) Here are suggestions to keep in mind when you use this kind of visual aid:

- Make a photocopy of the information or illustration you want to project and then copy it onto a transparency using a heat transfer machine. Most copy shops have this kind of machine.
- If possible, type the information you want to show or find professionally drawn copies; photocopy these and then make transparencies of them.
- If you draw your transparencies or use color, use the special felt-tip pens that write on the slick surface of transparencies. (Also, use the colored pens to highlight areas of your visuals.)
- Beware of lettering or drawing that is too small. Make sure that the smallest details can be seen easily by your audience.

FIGURE 16–4.   Illustration of an overhead projector

- Also, make sure that an overhead projector will be available at the time of your oral report. Nothing is worse than planning an oral report around overhead projections and then not being able to use them at all.
- Make sure that the overhead projector works and that the bulb in the machine is not burned out. Consider locating a replacement bulb or actually having one in your pocket during your report.
- Make sure that the room in which you give your talk will permit overhead projection: there may be no screen available; the walls may not be appropriate to project images upon; or the plug for the projector may be located in an odd or inconvenient place.
- *Before* you begin your report, get your overhead projector in place, plugged in, positioned, focused, and adjusted. Have your transparencies in the right order with a sheet of blank paper behind each for quick and easy identification.

Poster-Size Displays.   You can also use large posters with the important information or illustrations drawn on them. If you use such displays, keep these suggestions in mind:

- Make sure your drawing or lettering is readable to the whole audience, not just to those in front.
- *Carefully* plan how you will fasten or hold up this kind of visual. It's very distracting to have this kind of visual continually falling down during a report.
- As with any kind of visual, refer to your displays and explain their significance.
- Do not try to display and discuss ordinary-size printed materials. No one can see the details of an 8½-by-11-inch sheet of paper (and passing such visuals around to the audience is not a solution to the problem either).

For an example of an effective display for a poster-size display, see Figure 16–5.

Objects for Display.   You can also use objects directly related to the subject of your report. If you are demonstrating how to use a mechanism, bring it and show how to use it, if possible. If the object, or part of it, is too small for the whole audience to see, you may need to choose some other kind of visual, for example, poster-size diagrams or drawings.

Handouts.   You can also hand out printed material to the audience—for example, an outline of your talk, application forms, lists of names and addresses, tables of statistical information, and brochures. When you do, plan how you'll use them during your talk and how you expect your audience to refer to them.

What kinds of information should you prepare visuals for? Any information in your report that may be hard to present orally or information that you don't want your audience to miss is a good candidate for visuals.

- Consider showing an outline of your talk; it reinforces the organization of your oral report in the minds of the listeners. For an example see Figure 16–6.

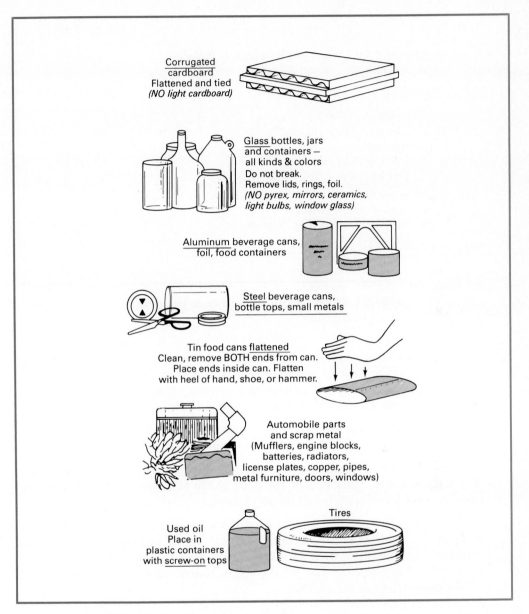

Corrugated cardboard
Flattened and tied
(NO light cardboard)

Glass bottles, jars and containers — all kinds & colors
Do not break.
Remove lids, rings, foil.
(NO pyrex, mirrors, ceramics, light bulbs, window glass)

Aluminum beverage cans, foil, food containers

Steel beverage cans, bottle tops, small metals

Tin food cans flattened
Clean, remove BOTH ends from can.
Place ends inside can. Flatten with heel of hand, shoe, or hammer.

Automobile parts and scrap metal
(Mufflers, engine blocks, batteries, radiators, license plates, copper, pipes, metal furniture, doors, windows)

Used oil
Place in plastic containers with screw-on tops

Tires

FIGURE 16–5.   Poster-size display

Reprinted by permission from Schocken Books, Inc. from
Recycling: How to Use Wastes in Home, Industry, and Society by
Jerome Goldstein. Copyright © by Schocken Books Inc.

• Consider preparing a visual that lists key terms you'll use; when each term comes up, simply turn and point to it. Such visuals emphasize main points and help listeners remember the terms. An example appears in Figure 16–7.

  I. Municipal Solid Waste (MSW) Currently Generated
     A. Volumes
     B. Composition
     C. Primary Producers
     D. Recycling Value
 II. Conventional MSW Disposal
     A. Methods
     B. Costs of Disposal
     C. Problems with Conventional Disposal
III. Overview of the Proposed Recycling Plan
     A. Administrative Details
     B. Benefits of a Recycling Program
     C. Citizens' Participation

FIGURE 16–6 Outline used as a visual aid in an oral report

• You'll need visuals any time you must present important statistical information: it's usually easier to look at large numbers than to hear them spoken. Also, you can present much more statistical information visually than you can orally. Figure 16–8 contains one example of a visual aid to convey statistical information.

• Illustrations of important objects, processes, or concepts in the report subject can be displayed through visuals. See the example in Figure 16–9.

• Any sequence of actions or events should be displayed by means of a flowchart. With each new step, you can turn and point to the new area of discussion on the flowchart. Look at Figure 16–10 for an example.

Two final suggestions about using visuals: always take time to discuss, explain, interpret, or highlight important details in oral reports because listeners do not automatically understand what the visual means; make sure you understand everything about your visuals so that you don't get embarrassed when you can't answer certain questions from the audience.

STEP 6.   Explain which visual aids you plan to use in your oral and what the content of those visuals will be.

Introductions and Conclusions to Oral Reports

Introductions and conclusions are quite important in oral reports. Introductions must set the right tone, attract the listeners' attention and interest, give them a clear sense of the subject matter and purpose of the report, and provide them with an

Recycling

Energy savings

Conservation of resources

Reduction of landfill needs

Financial savings

Maintaining Quality of Environment

Municipal Solid Waste (MSW)

Landfill disposal

Incineration

Ocean dumping

Recycling
  - Curbside pickup
  - Source separation
  - Voluntary participation

Figure 16–7.   Visual aids for key terms in oral reports

overview or plan of the topics to be covered. Conclusions must give listeners a sense of finality, a review of what has been discussed, and, sometimes, a final thought or two.

For introductions, see the excerpt from an oral report at the end of this chapter and the suggestions in Chapter 4. Most oral reports should have some combination of the following:

Lead-in
Reference to the situation of the oral report
Indication of the purpose of the report
Motivation for the listeners
Overview of the topics to be covered

RECYCLING COLLECTION STATISTICS

1983	Feb.	Mar.	Apr.	May	June	July	Aug.	Sept.
Tons collected	36.7	58	76.6	80.6	87.7	73.3	84.2	86.3
Percent participation, lowest (rainy day) to highest	11 25	10 32	15 43	13 46	19 35	19 44	16 52	20 34
Complaint calls	48	42	33	36	29	23	20	29

ENERGY SAVINGS THROUGH SAVINGS FROM RECYCLING

95%	recycled aluminum
74%	recycled steel
30%	recycled paper
25%	recycled glass

FIGURE 16—8. Visual aids for statistical information

The actual first words you say in an oral report are often the most difficult to find; here are some ideas that may work in various situations:

Tell something about yourself, your background, and your work.
Relate some recent news item to your report.
Tell about an event in your life that relates to your report.
Express appreciation for being invited to speak.
Explain why and how you are the one speaking on the topic.
Tell something interesting or amusing about a member of the audience.

For conclusions to oral reports, see the suggestions in Chapter 4. Whichever way you end your report, avoid trailing off into a mumble. In general, most oral reports conclude with some combination of the following:

Review of the main points
Emphasis of the main point
Invitation to the audience to ask questions or discuss
Final general thought related to the report topic

STEP 7.   On your worksheet write either an outline of your oral-report introduction or a rough-draft script of it. Do the same for your oral report's conclusion.

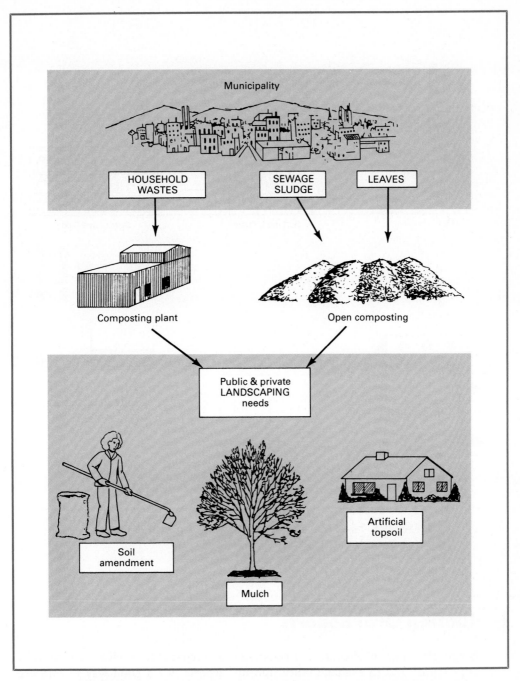

FIGURE 16—9. Visual aid of a drawing used in an oral report
Source: New York State Department of Engineering, Cornell University

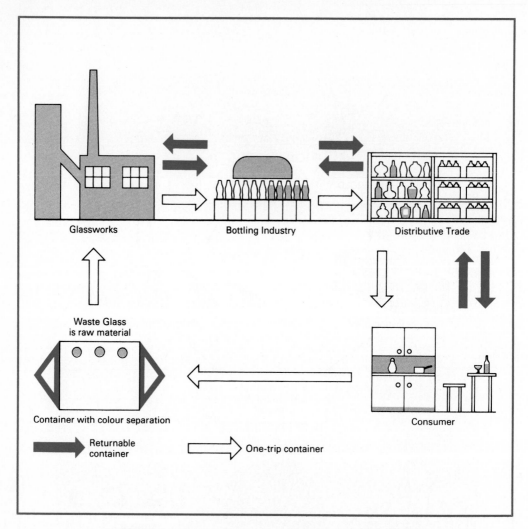

FIGURE 16–10.   Flowchart used in an oral report

Evaluating Oral Reports

If you give your oral report in a classroom, be prepared to receive evaluations of your report and to evaluate other students' reports. It's a good way to improve your oral-reporting skills. Fill out the model questionnaire in Figure 16–11 during or just after an oral report. Design your own questionnaire if you are concerned about particular aspects of your oral-report performance or if you think your particular oral report has unusual features that require different questions.

ORAL-REPORT EVALUATION

Student Reporter _____ Date _____

Evaluated by _____ Report Topic _____

Check the appropriate blank by each item to indicate your evaluation.
Leave blank any of the items below that do not apply.

	Strongly Agree 5	Agree 4	Undecided 3	Disagree 2	Strongly Disagree 1
Context of report realistic	—	—	—	—	—
Introduction gained interest	—	—	—	—	—
Introduction indicated purpose	—	—	—	—	—
Introduction indicated plan, overview	—	—	—	—	—
Spoke distinctly	—	—	—	—	—
Used appropriate gestures, eye contact, posture	—	—	—	—	—
Explained subject clearly	—	—	—	—	—
Used good examples	—	—	—	—	—
Used good illustrations	—	—	—	—	—
Explained/discussed illustrations	—	—	—	—	—
Report was well organized	—	—	—	—	—
Used "verbal headings" well	—	—	—	—	—

(continued)

FIGURE 16—11. Example of evaluation form for oral reports

Conclusion was effective	−	−	−	−	−
Use of script, notes, cue cards, outline, extemporaneous (circle one) was effective	−	−	−	−	−
Overall, report was interesting, informative, convincing (circle one)	−	−	−	−	−

OTHER COMMENTS/SUGGESTIONS:

FIGURE 16–11.   (cont.)

EXERCISES

1. Attend a meeting of some local organization such as the city council, PTA, school board, student government, or a church organization, and evaluate the oral reports you hear there in the following ways:
   - The appropriateness of the content and explanation to the audience's level of understanding
   - The function or purpose of the oral report
   - The method of delivery (cue card, outline, extemporaneous)
   - Problems in the style of delivery of the oral report
   - Use of verbal captions—or lack of it
   - Types of visual aids that are used (or could have been used) and their effectiveness during the report
   - Effectiveness of the introduction and conclusion
   - The response or responsiveness of the audience
2. Schedule an interview with someone in business, industry, or government and ask about the oral reports that person presents or hears: for example, how such oral reports are prepared and delivered, what problems typically occur in them, what visual aids are used, and how important these oral reports are.

3. Look at a list of technical topics, select two or three topics, and list oral reports that might reasonably be given involving each of these topics. Think about the purpose and the audience of each of those oral reports.

4. Think of a place, situation, or organization (city council, neighborhood association, PTA, a local business) in which oral reports are routinely given, and list three or four reports that might reasonably be presented there. Identify the subject, audience, and purpose.

5. Find a technical report or article and
   a. Design a situation in which an oral report using information from that report or article might reasonably be given.
   b. Define the audience and purpose of that oral report.
   c. Make an outline of that oral report (using information from the technical report or article).
   d. Describe the visual aids you'd use in the oral report.

Model 16–1:   Report on Recycling to a Neighborhood Association
(oral report excerpts)

NOTES

1. Thank group for invitation to neighborhood association meeting.
2. Introduce cospeaker.
3. Explain that if Austin recycling is to succeed, neighborhood associations will be key.
4. Austin Coalition for Recycling and city government need this sort of participation and involvement.

Valerie and I represent the Austin Coalition for Recycling, a group that was founded a couple of years ago, partly in response to rising utility bills and partly out of a concern for the environment and its resources. High utility bills not only hurt each of us in our pocketbooks but also hurt the quality of life of our city as a whole. We are all particularly proud of what a fine city we live in and what wonderful citizen involvement there is here in a whole range of civic activities— these things make our city special and ought to be the force that enables us to get a recycling program off the ground. And our group thinks that a recycling program will be a real contributor in keeping Austin the wonderful place that it is.

Valerie and I want to talk to you about what the proposed recycling plan is all about, how it can benefit our city in a variety of ways, and what you can do—if you believe it is a worthwhile project—to help get the plan going. Just stop me any time that you have a question or whenever; I get so carried away sometimes with the proposed plan that I stop making sense.

On the individual citizen level—that means each of us and our garbage cans every morning—recycling is not nearly the bother that it is often made out to be.

There seems to be the idea that recycling involves a lot of washing and scrubbing and delabeling of cans and jars and bottles. The proposed plan—and in fact the recycling programs that are working around America—do not require anything of the sort. In the proposed plan, you'll put your recyclables out once a week on the curb. You don't have to haul them across town or stomp or smash them; you simply sort your glass by color (green, brown, clear); you separate your aluminum from the other metal; and you bundle your newspaper up. You put all this stuff out on the curb one day a week, a big truck from the city comes by, dumps it into different barrels, and takes it away for processing and sale. If anything, recycling is simply a habit to grow into—sort of like taking out the garbage. And that's exactly what it is—taking out the garbage, but only in a slightly different way. Surveys done in other cities that have recycling programs have not uncovered any problems in citizen attitudes. Recycling does necessitate sorting and storing your recyclables, but the plan calls for the city to supply recyclers with specially marked plastic cans. You'll probably want to keep your recyclables out in the garage or somewhere out of the house but also out of the weather. Also, it's not necessary to put your recyclables out every week—in cities where programs are currently operating, many people save up their recyclables and put them out every month or so....

You can see from these figures that there is a tremendous economic potential in recycling for this city, not to mention the reduction of landfill use which causes all kinds of problems for us both financial and otherwise. But the question comes up—Is there any citizen interest in this plan? What's the likelihood of participation and involvement? Several months ago when the results of the Citizens Advisory Task Force's survey were released, I was elated to find such strong support and interest among our citizens. I had feared as I'm sure many others had that people would see recycling as too much trouble or impractical or some crazy environmentalist scheme, but in fact the survey proved otherwise. In the task force's canvassing of randomly selected households, 40 percent said that they had recycled informally in the past, 76 percent said they thought recycling was a worthwhile endeavor, and 86 percent said they were willing to participate in a recycling program....

We've looked at the proposed recycling plan from all the important angles—volume and value of MSW, benefits of recycling, the administrative plan, and citizen interest—but you may still be wondering whether it really works. Are there any successful recycling programs going on in the country? Recycling is not a new or a rare thing in America today. There are plenty of precedents and plenty of successful ongoing programs. Well over 220 cities in the United States are involved in some sort of recycling such as we are talking about tonight. One city, West University Place in Texas, saves an acre of landfill space every three years as a result of its recycling program. Another city, Odessa, Texas, is using a third of its MSW for recycling or composting. That's a third of its total solid waste not going into landfills or up the incinerator smokestack! Grand Rapids, Michigan's recycling program costs less than half as much per ton of waste than does its landfill operations. To put it simply, it costs that city less than half as much to recycle than it does to use conventional landfill disposal methods. If you've ever heard the complaints down at city council about the locations of proposed landfills or about operational ones, you'll understand that there are more than just financial reasons to get away from that method of disposal....

PART V

A Technical Writer's Handbook

Appendix **A.** **Common Systems for Documenting Reports**

Appendix **B.** **Basic Patterns and Elements of the Sentence**

Appendix **C.** **Basic Patterns and Elements of the Paragraph**

Appendix **D.** **Common Conventions in Standard Written English**

Appendix **E.** **Instructors' Correction Symbols and Copy Editors' Marks**

Appendix **F.** **Glossary of Terms Used in This Book**

Introduction

You can use the sections of this handbook for quick reference as you write and revise your technical reports and as you take technical-writing courses. Here are some of the specific ways you can use these appendixes:

Using the Appendices	Appendix
You need to know how to set up footnotes and bibliography for your report.	A
You're not sure about certain grammatical terms used in this book or by your instructor.	B
You need to know some of the basic concepts of paragraphing and the terms used to discuss paragraphs.	C
You need a review of some of the common grammar and usage errors, for example, subject-verb agreement or parallelism.	D
You're not sure whether to use numerals or written-out numbers, abbreviations or full words, or symbols or written-out terms.	D
You're not sure what your instructor or your editor means by certain comments, marks, or symbols on your reports.	E
You're not sure about the meaning of certain terms (other than grammatical ones) that are used in this book.	F

Common Systems for Documenting Reports

The Name-Year System
The Number System
The Works-Cited System
(MLA version)

Citing Government Documents and
Other Sources

A *documentation* system is the way you inform readers about how you got the information in your report. You must document the facts and ideas (as well as illustrations) you get from other writers; otherwise, it is plagiarism (as explained in Chapter 10.) You are probably familiar with footnotes and bibliographies, a common way to document reports, but a number of other systems are used as well. No matter whether you are writing in college, business, or government, you *must* document your information borrowing: to do so shows that you have done your homework and that you are a careful, thorough, reliable report writer; not to do so is considered plagiarism.

The main principle of documentation is actually to assist your readers in following up on interesting information that you've located: give your readers enough information so that they can find the source (book, article, report, person, videotape, etc.) on their own for further information.

Three of the most common systems—the name-year system, the number system, and the works-cited system—are presented here. Many other systems are only minor variations or combinations of the three shown here.

You should try to find out which system is preferred in your major, field, occupation, or profession and get used to it. There are several ways to find out which system is preferred:

- Ask instructors, librarians, or people in the field or profession.
- Model your documentation after the one you see in journal articles and reports published in your field or profession.
- Consult a reference book like Sheehy's *Guide to Reference Books:* look up your field or profession and find a subsection entitled style manuals, and then consult the book you find there for the right system to use.
- Find a guide to the literature in your field (again, using Sheehy's or the suggestions in Chapter 9), find the section on style manuals, and locate the book you need there.

There is not enough space in this book to list all of the details and variations for each of the three systems to be presented. Instead, some of the basic patterns can be shown; this should enable you to set up the documentation for most situations in your reports. If you do have sources you're not sure how to document—for example, multiple authors, second editions, or multiple volumes—go straight to the style manual in your field or profession. If you have trouble getting a specific style guide, use one of these readily available guides that give overviews of several documentation systems:

W. G. Campbell and S. V. Ballou. *Form and Style: Theses, Reports, Term Papers.* Boston: Houghton Mifflin, 1982.

James D. Lester. *Writing Research Papers.* Glenview, Ill.: Scott, Foresman, 1984.

Joseph Gibaldi and Walter S. Achtert. *MLA Handbook for Writers of Research Papers.* 2nd ed. New York: MLA, 1984.

The Name-Year System

In the name-year system you use the author's name and the year that that author's work was published to document your borrowing. The name and year references actually appear *in* the written text in parentheses. When it is important, the page number may also be cited. Because this system emphasizes names and years, it is useful to experts and scholars to whom certain names and dates in a field are significant. Look at this example:

Computerized Insulin Pumps

An implantable programmable insulin pump is now being developed at the Johns Hopkins Applied Physics Laboratory. The small computerized insulin pump will be placed in the patient surgically. The pump's insulin reservoir is refilled every few months by the injection of insulin through a membrane in the pump. This membrane will lie just under the skin. Radio waves will control the flow of the insulin. The physician's computer terminal will instruct the pump to deliver insulin on a certain schedule, and a small terminal belonging to the patient can signal any temporary change in the delivery pattern (Rosenthal, 1983).

These name, year, and occasionally page citations can be handled in several ways either inside or outside of parentheses in the text of the report:

• If the name appears in the text, only the year need appear in parentheses:

According to Garmon, however, other body fluid ions and compounds must be investigated before the device is used outside the laboratory (1982).

• If the page number is important to include, it can be placed within the parentheses also:

Other body fluid ions and compounds must be investigated before the device is used outside the laboratory (Garmon, 1982, p. 15).

• If the author has published two or more items in the same year and you make use of information from them, use lowercase letters just after the year to distinguish them:

Currently, only about 8,000 diabetics are using the insulin pump (Smith, 1983b).

• If no author's name is given, use the first word or two of the title of the article:

In the past 60 years, no major advances have been made in the prevention of long-term diabetic complications ("New," 1983).

- For an example of how to document borrowed illustrations, see Figure A–1.

In the name-year system, you include a list of references at the end of the report or paper, which gives the full bibliographic information on the sources cited in the text. Here is an excerpt from a list of references (which in various fields may be called "literature cited," "references," or "references cited"):

List of References

————. 1982. Fetus as organ donor. Science Digest *91*: 85.

Hollander, A. 1984. Diabetes management. Postgraduate Medicine *75*: 82–87.

Irsigler, K. 1982. Improvement of insulin therapy for diabetics through pump treatment. Diabetes Management in the 80's. New York, Praeger. 322p.

————. 1982. Prevention of allograft rejection by immunization with donor blood depleted of Ia-bearing cells. Science *217*: 157–58.

Rosenthal, E. 1983. Programs under the skin. Science Digest *91*: 38.

Smith, E. 1983a. Diabetes Research. Chicago. SRA. 253p.

————. 1983b. Problems with recent diabetes technology. Medical Technology Digest *14*: 15–18.

Notice the following details about the list of references:

- The items are alphabetically arranged with the author's last name first.
- The year of the publication of the item directly follows the author's name.
- Titles of articles are not enclosed in the traditional quotation marks; titles of journals, magazines, and books may or may not be underlined, depending on the field.
- The title of the journal in which an article appears may be abbreviated (although not in this example).
- For items involving journals or magazines, the volume number may be underlined and followed by a colon and the page numbers within which the article occurs.
- For books, the city of publication and name of the publisher *in that order* complete the citation.
- If there is no author name given, a blank line is typed in its place.

The Number System

In the number system, you generally use numbers to designate the source you are borrowing information from, although authors' names and page numbers can be included when they are important. Again, as with the name-year system, these references appear *in* the written text in parentheses.

Worldwide Fallout

In detonations greater than 100 kilotons, part of the fallout does not fall to the ground in the vicinity of the explosion but rises high into the troposphere and into the stratosphere, circulates around the earth, and then, over months or years, descends, contaminating the whole surface of the globe, although with doses of radiation far weaker than those delivered by the local fallout (6:12–21). Nuclear-fission products comprise some 300 radioactive isotopes, and though some of them decay to relatively harmless levels of radioactivity within a few hours, minutes, or even seconds, others persist to emit radiation for up to millions of years. The short-lived isotopes are the ones most responsible for the lethal effects of the local fallout, and the long-lived ones are responsible for the contamination of the earth by stratospheric fallout (6).

Notice that in some cases the source number can appear in parentheses by itself or in other cases it can appear with a colon and the page number from which the information has been taken. Although not shown in the preceding example, the author's name can appear in the parentheses if it is important to include it, in which case the source number appears within brackets to prevent confusion. (For an example of how to document borrowed illustrations, see Figure A–1.

In the number system, you include a list of the works cited, sometimes called "references" and other times called "works cited" or "literature cited," at the end of the report. In some cases, these lists are alphabetized and then numbered; in others, they are listed in the order in which they occur in the text. Here is an example of such a listing:

Literature Cited

1. Askew, George. "No Place to Hide." *International Wildlife* (September–October 1983), 44–48.
2. Durgens, Samuel. "Radiation Warfare Comes of Age." *Science News* (September 12, 1981), 169–72.
3. Ehrlich, Paul. "The Ecological Impact of Nuclear War." *Mother Earth* (September–October 1981), 142–50.
4. Gribben, John. "Nuclear Bombs Do Affect the Weather." *Analog VIII* (August 1982), 48–53.
5. Hopth, Clarence. "Nuclear Pulse: Ensuring the Delivery of the Doomsday Signal." *Science* (June 5, 1981), 1116–21.
6. Kosta, Tsipis. "Inside the Mushroom Cloud." *Bulletin of the Atomic Scientists* (February 1983), 23–28.
7. Richards, J. P. *Nuclear Warfare: Tactics and Realities.* New York: Schapiro, 1983.
8. Sartori, Leo. "Effects of Nuclear Weapons." *Physics Today* (March 1983), 32–41.

Notice the following details in the preceding list:

- The list is in alphabetical order by authors' last names; when no author's name is available, the title of the article or book is used in its place.
- Book, magazine, and journal titles are generally underlined; in most cases, journal titles are abbreviated.
- Titles of articles may be enclosed in quotation marks, underlined, or not treated in any special way at all, depending on the field.
- Depending on the field, the year of publication and the volume number may be underlined.
- In the number system, the date of publication appears just after the volume number if it is a journal and just after the publisher if it is a book.

The Works-Cited System (MLA Version)

In the MLA version of the works-cited system, you indicate where the borrowed information occurred in the original source with page numbers and, if necessary, authors' names in parentheses. Look at the example in Figure A–1.

Notice several things about Figure A–1's excerpt:

• When only the page number appears in parentheses, the author's name has appeared in the previous text.

The Device Used to Produce Nuclear Energy

The scientific principle for the production of nuclear fission is fairly simple, but putting the principle to work safely is somewhat more difficult. To produce nuclear energy to drive electrical generators, a complex device, called a nuclear reactor, is used. There are several different kinds of reactors in use: the boiling-water reactor (BWR), the pressurized water reactor (PWR), the high-temperature gas-cooled reactor (HTGR), and the liquid metal fast breeder reactor (LMFBR) (Dorf 220-228). Figure A–1a illustrates one of the most common nuclear reactors, the PWR.

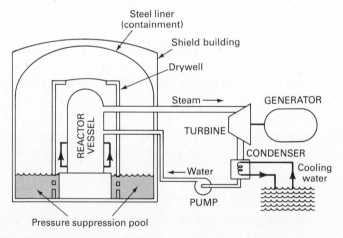

FIGURE A-1a.   Schematic diagram of a nuclear power plant

Source: R.V. Moore, Nuclear Power (London: Cambridge Univ. Press, 1971), 15. Reprinted with permission.

FIGURE A–1. Report excerpt using MLA works-cited system

A nuclear power plant (Fig. A—1a) for generating electricity
operates on the same principles as plants powered by fossil fuels:
heated water produces steam; steam drives a turbine that spins
a generator; and the generator produces electricity (Weaver 464). The
main difference is that instead of fossil fuel production of heat, as in
coal plants, the heat source for a nuclear power plant is the energy
released from the chain reaction of fissioning materials, mainly
uranium-235.

Fuels Used in Nuclear Reactors

Uranium is an element that is found widely in low concentrations
on land and in sea water (Dorf 223). Natural uranium consists of
about 99 percent uranium-238 and a trace of uranium-235 ("Nuclear"
511j). However, uranium-235 is the only readily fissionable isotope
of natural uranium. Since natural uranium contains only about
0.7 percent uranium-235, enrichment, according to Duderstadt, is
necessary (45).

FIGURE A—1.   (cont.)

- Notice that both the author's name and the page number appear in parentheses
  when the previous text does not indicate who the author is.
- Whenever there is a change of source—a new article, book, or report being
  used—the name of the new author appears, either in parentheses or in the text
  itself.
- When no author's name is available, the first distinguishing word or words of
  the title are used.

When the works-cited system is used, the full information on the books, reports,
and articles appears at the end of the paper under the title "Works Cited." Here is
an example:

Works Cited

Dorf, Richard C. *Energy, Resources and Policy.* Reading, Mass.: Smith and Smith, 1978.
Duderstadt, James C., and Chihird Kikuchi. *Nuclear Power: Technology on Trial.* Ann
    Arbor, Mich.: Univ. of Michigan Press, 1979.
Holdren, John, and Phillip Herrera. *Energy.* Washington, D.C.: Sierra Club, 1971.

Masche, George. *Systems Summary of a Westinghouse P.W.R. Nuclear Power Plant.* San Diego, Cal.: Westinghouse, 1971.

————. *Report on the Performance of a Westinghouse P.W.R. Nuclear Power Plant.* San Diego, Cal.: Westinghouse, 1972.

Moore, R. V. *Nuclear Power.* London: Cambridge Univ. Press, 1971.

"Nuclear Power." *Encyclopedia Americana.* Danbury, Conn.: America Corp., 1980.

Sunden, John, Director of Information Services, Energy Research, Inc. Personal Interview. Lawrence, Kansas. August 4, 1984.

Weaver, Kenneth F. "What About Nuclear Power?" *National Geographic* April 1979: 459–493.

Notice several things about this list of works cited:

- The items are alphabetically arranged by the author's last name.
- Titles of books, journals, and reports are underlined.
- For books, include the city of publication (and an abbreviation for the state if it is not a well-known city), the publisher, and the date of publication.
- When two separate works by the same author are cited, the second occurrence of the name is replaced by three hyphens.
- If no author name is available, the title of the article comes first and is alphabetized as if it were the author's name.

Citing Government Documents and Other Sources

In the following sections are shown some examples of how to document publications by the government and how to document unusual sources such as private letters, phone conversations, or interviews. Notice that the works-cited style of documentation is used in the following examples. To convert to some other style of documentation, simply rearrange the elements accordingly (for example, in the name-year system, bring the year number forward and place it just after the author's name).

When you encounter situations for which you cannot find a style model or rule to follow, just remember this important principle of documentation: give the readers enough information so that they can find the source (book, article, report, person, videotape, etc.) on their own.

Government Documents

A government document normally comes out of a branch of the U.S. government, a department, an administration, or an agency; it has many authors. You do not have to cite all of these agencies: make sure, however, to cite the department name (for example, "Department of Commerce") and the date. Usually, there are four, five, or more individuals who take credit for writing the document; their names are usually left off the citation of a government document. As for identifying numbers, there seems to be no clear rule; when in doubt, include them. GPO, the abbreviation for Government Printing Office, is used in such citations. Here are some examples:

U.S. Department of Commerce, National Bureau of Standards, *Investigation of the Kansas City Hyatt Regency Walkways Collapse.* NBSS 143. Washington, D.C.: GPO, May 1982.

U.S. Department of Commerce, Federal Energy Administration, *Economic Impact of Oil Resource Development on the Alaskan Economy, 1975–1985.* FE 1.2: Al 1975–85. Washington, D.C.: GPO, April 1976.

U.S. Department of Agriculture, Forest Service, *Wood-Fired Boiler Systems for Space Heating.* A13 13.84/2: 7180–2. Washington, D.C.: GPO, October 1982.

U.S. Environmental Protection Agency. *Evaluation of the Ames Solid Waste Recovery System. Part II: Performance of the Stoker-Fired Steam Generators.* EPA-600/7-79-229. Cincinnati, Ohio: Industrial Environmental Research Laboratory, October 1979.

Personal Correspondence and Interviews

When you cite interviews or correspondence (letters), you treat the interviewee or letter writer as the author:

Robert O. Doe, Manager, Technical Editing Division, Digicorp, Inc. Personal interview. Luckenbach, Tex. August 17, 1984.

Jeanne Frontaine, Technical Writer, Techtrans, Inc. Private correspondence. Kyoto, Japan. August 4, 1985.

Printed Sources Not in Published Form

The following examples obviously do not cover all the possibilities that exist among these kinds of sources, but when you face an unusual source, use these examples to design your own references. Also, please notice that these examples are set up in bibliography form.

Mimeographed Material

Ballester, Valerie. "Examples of Business Letters." Austin, Tex. 1984. (Mimeographed.)

Unpublished Paper

Murray, Alan David. "A Proposal for Internships in Technical Writing." (Unpublished paper.)

Microfilm

U.S. Department of Agriculture. *Report on Drip Irrigation Practices in Israel.* DOA 2.8/ NAA 6657:3. Washington, D.C.: GPO, April 1984. (Microfilm.)

Sources Not in Printed Form

Again, these examples do not cover all possibilities, but they should give you an idea what to do when you have an unusual source. Please notice that these examples are set up in works-cited form.

Movies and Television or Radio Programs

Energy: Choices for the Future. Washington, D.C.: PBS-TV, May 18, 1985.
All Things Considered. Austin, TX: KUT-FM. August 4, 1984.
Voyage Beyond Time. Unlimited Films, 1985.

Videotape

Staff of the Writing Lab. "Wordbusters." VHS-156. Austin, Tex.: University of Texas, Summer 1984.

Public Address or Lecture

Hughes, Patrick. "Technical Writing and the Liberal Arts Student." Lecture presented at the Society of Technical Writers Symposium. Luckenbach, Tex., May 25, 1985.

Recording on Record or Tape

Anderson, Laurie. "Big Science," in her recording *Big Science*. Warner Bros., 25077-1, 1984.

APPENDIX B

Basic Patterns and Elements of the Sentence

Basic Sentence Patterns
  Subject + Intransitive Verb
  Subject + Linking Verb + Subject
  Complement
  Subject + Transitive + Verb Direct
  Object
  Subject + Transitive + Verb Indirect
  Object + Direct Object
  Subject + Transitive Verb + Direct
  Object + Objective Complement
Passive Voice Construction
Sentence Types

Basic Parts of the Sentence
Parts of Speech and Other Sentence
  Elements
  Nouns and Pronouns
  Verbs
  Adjectives and Adverbs
  Conjunctions
  Phrases and Clauses

This section is a quick review of the fundamentals of the sentence. If you encounter unfamiliar terminology in this book or in your class, refer to this section for help. For more on sentence grammar, see *English Fundamentals* by Emery, Kierzek, and Lindblom, 8th ed. (Macmillan, 1986), for a thorough discussion of sentence grammar, along with exercises.

Basic Sentence Patterns

The basic sentence patterns and examples of each are shown in the following:

Subject (s) + Intransitive verb (vi)

Control rods remain inside the fuel assembly of the reactor.
The development of wind power practically ceased until the early 1970s.
All amplitude-modulation (AM) receivers work in the same way.
The cross member exposed to abnormal stress eventually broke.

Subject (sc) + Linking Verb (lv) + Subject Complement (sc)

The chain reaction is the basis of nuclear power.
The debate over nuclear power has often been bitter.
Windspeed seems to be highest during the middle of the day.
The silicon solar cell can be difficult and expensive to manufacture.

Subject (s) + Transitive Verb (vt) + Direct Object (do)

Silicon conducts electricity in an unusual way.
The antireflective coating on the silicon cell reduces reflection from 32 to 22 percent.
Prestressing of the concrete increases the load-carrying capacity of the members.

Subject (s) + Transitive Verb (vt) + Indirect Object (io) + Direct Object (do)

We are sending you the balance of the payment in this letter.
I am writing her about a number of problems that I have had with my Execucomp word processor.
The supervisor mailed the applicant a description of the job.
Austin, Texas, has recently built its citizens a system of bikelanes.

Subject (s) + Transitive Verb (vt) + Direct Object (do) + Objective Complement (oc)

The walls are usually painted black.
The plant shutdown left the entire area an economic disaster.

Passive Voice Construction

The passive voice reverses the subject and object and, in some cases, deletes the subject. (See Chapter 7 on problems with the weak use of the passive.)

Passive Voice	Active Voice
Saccharin is now permitted as an additive in food.	The FDA now permits saccharin as an additive in food.
This report is divided into three main sections.	I have divided this report into three main sections.
Windmills are classified as either lift or drag types.	Scientists classify windmills as either lift or drag types.
The remains of Troy were destroyed by later builders of the site.	Later builders on the site of Troy destroyed the remains of the citadel.
Some restaurant locations can be leased.	You can lease some restaurant locations.

Sentence Types

The sentence types are built from different combinations of independent (complete sentences) and dependent (noun, adjective, and adverb) clauses:

Simple Sentence: Contains only one independent clause.

To measure blood pressure, *a device known as a sphygmomanometer and a stethoscope are needed.*
There are basically two types of stethoscopes.
The sphygmomanometer is usually covered with cloth and has two rubber tubes attached to it.
One of the tubes is attached to the manometer part of the instrument indicating the pressure of the air within the cuff.

Compound Sentence: Contains two or more independent clauses.

In sphygmomanometers, too narrow a cuff can result in erroneously high readings, *and* too wide a cuff can result in erroneously low readings.
Some cuffs hook together; others wrap or snap into place.

Complex Sentence: Contains one or more dependent clause.

A part of the stethoscope is the cuff, a rubber bag *that can be filled with air.*
Inflate the cuff to about 40 mm Hg above the level *at which the radial pulse disappears.*
That point at which you stop hearing heart sounds through the stethoscope is the most reliable measure of diastolic pressure, *although it is usually somewhat above that found by intra-arterial measurements.*

Compound-Complex Sentence: Contains two or more independent clauses and at least one dependent clause.

The systolic pressure is the pressure of the blood as a result of the contraction of the ventricles, *and* the diastolic pressure is the pressure *when the ventricles are at rest.*

The upper two chambers of the heart, *which are called atria,* are thin-walled reservoirs; they readily distend to collect blood *that pours in from the veins between beats.*

Basic Parts of the Sentence

Here are some common terms for the basic parts of the sentence:

Subject (s): The noun, pronoun, or phrase or clause about which the sentence makes a statement.

Verb phrase (vp): A word or words expressing an action, event, or a state of existence.

Predicate (p): The rest of the sentence after the subject, including, for example, the main verb, subject complement, direct object, indirect object, or object complement.

Subject complement (sc): The noun, pronoun, adjective, phrase, or clause after a linking verb.

Direct object (do): A noun, pronoun, phrase, or clause acting as a noun that takes the action of the main verb.

Indirect Object (io): A noun, pronoun, phrase, or clause acting as a noun—that acts as object of an understood *to* or *for.*

Object complement (oc): A noun, adjective, phrase, or clause after a direct object that adds detail to the direct object.

Examples of these sentence parts occur in the sentences below:

The super**viser** found the program [to be] faulty. *(s, do, oc)*

The com**pany** considers the new com**puter** [to be] a major breakthrough. *(s, do, oc)*

The **deadening** of the sense of smell caused by H_2S *is* the *result* of the effects of H_2S on the olfactory nerves of the brain. Continuous **exposure** to toxic concentrations of H_2S *can be* **fatal.** *(s, sc, vp, sc)*

In the application letter, *tell* [to] the potential *employer* **that a resume accompanies the letter.** *(vp, io, do)*

The company **is designing** [for] senior **citizens** a new **walkway** to the park area. *(vp, io, do)*

Do not *send* [to] the personnel **office** a *resume* unless someone there specifically requests it. *(vp, io, do)*

Einstein's general *theory* of relativity *has been subjected* to many tests of validity over the years. *(s, vp)*

Although a majority of caffeine drinkers think of it as a stimulant, heavy *users* of caffeine *say* **the substance relaxes them.** *(s, do)*

Surrounding the secure landfill on all sides are impermeable barrier **walls.**
  ^p placed above *cure*

In a secure landfill, the *soil* on top and the *cover* **block storm water** intrusion into the landfill.

On Mariners 6 and 7, the two-axis scan *platforms* **provided much more capability and flexibility for the scientific payload than that of Mariner 4.**

Instruction in the source program **must be translated** into machine language.

The operating *system controls* the translation of the source program and *carries* out supervisory functions.

A 20-percent *fluctuation* in average global temperatuare **could reduce** biological activity, **shift** weather patterns, and *ruin* agriculture.

The pressure *is maintained* at about 2250 pounds per square inch to prevent steam from forming.

Parts of Speech and Other Sentence Elements

Nouns and Pronouns

A noun is the name of a person (Dr. Sanders), place (Lawrence, Kansas, factory, home), thing (scissors, saw, book), action (operation, irrigation), or idea (love, truth, beauty, intelligence). The nouns are italicized in the following examples.

The one *experiment* that has been given the most *attention* in the *debate* on *saccharin* is the 1977 Canadian *study* done on *rats.*

The *Calorie Control Council,* a *group* of Japanese and American *manufacturers* of *saccharin,* spent *$890,000* in the first three *months* of the 1977 *ban* on *saccharin* on *lobbying, advertisements,* and public *relations.*

A flat-plate *collector* located on a sloping *roof* heats *water* that circulates through a *coil* and is pumped back to the *collector.*

The *blades* start turning when the *windspeed* reaches 10 *mph,* and an *anemometer* is attached to the *shaft* to measure *windspeed.*

The multifuel *capacity* of the Stirling *engine* gives it a *versatility* not possible in the internal combustion *engine.*

The regenerative cooling *cycle* in the *engines* of the space *shuttle* is made up of high pressure *hydrogen* that flows in *tubes* connecting the *nozzle* and the combustion *chamber.*

A pronoun stands in the place of a noun. There are several types: personal pronouns, demonstrative and indefinite pronouns, and relative and interrogative pronouns. Pronouns have antecedents, a reference to a word they take the place of.

• *Personal pronouns.* Personal pronouns include nominative-case, objective-case, and possessive-case pronouns.

Nominative-case pronouns are used in the positions of subjects or subjective complements and include *I, we, you, he, she, it,* and *they.*

Objective-case pronouns are used as direct objects, indirect objects, and objects of prepositions and include *me, us, you, him, her, it,* and *them.*

Possessive-case pronouns show possession; they include *my, mine, our, ours, your, yours, his, her, hers, its, their,* and *theirs.*

• *Demonstrative and indefinite pronouns.* Demonstrative pronouns substitute for things being pointed out; they include *this, that, these,* and *those.* Indefinite pronouns substitute for unknown or unspecified things; they include *each, either, any, neither, anybody, some, every, somebody, everybody,* and *someone.*

• *Relative and interrogative pronouns.* Relative pronouns link dependent to independent clauses; they link to adjective or noun clauses to simple sentences. Relative pronouns include *who, when, which, whom, where, whether, whose, why,* and *that.* Interrogative pronouns include the same words, except for *whether* and *that,* and are used in question sentences. Here are some examples of these pronouns in use:

> The invention of the transistor in 1948 and the integrated circuit in 1964 were two events *that* formed the basis of the electronic calculator revolution.
> The form in *which* memory is presented to the software is sometimes called local address space.
> George Boole, *who* was a self-taught man, is famous for his pioneering efforts to express logical concepts in mathematical form.
> In 1855, Boole married Mary Everest, a niece of Sir George Everest, after *whom* Mount Everest was named.
> Lemaitre proposed *that* all the matter in the Universe was concentrated into *what* he termed the primeval atom, *whose* explosion scattered material into space to form galaxies, *which* have been flying outward ever since.
> *What* is the fundamental unit of storage in a computer?

Verbs

Traditionally, verbs are divided into four groups: active verbs, linking verbs, auxiliary verbs, and modals.

• *Active verbs.* Active verbs express some sort of action and can be subdivided into *intransitive* and *transitive* verbs. Intransitive verbs do not take direct objects while transitive verbs do, as these two sets of examples show:

Intransitive Verbs

> The rearrangement or division of a heavy nucleus *may take place* naturally (spontaneous fission) or under bombardment with neutrons.
> The probability of an accident leading to the melting of the fuel core *was estimated* to be one chance in 20,000 reactor-years of operation.
> The fuels used in ramjet engines *burn* in only a narrow range of fuel-air ratios.

Transitive Verbs

> The generation of electric energy by a nuclear power plant *requires* the use of heat to produce steam or to heat gases in order to drive turbogenerators.
> In an auxiliary relay, when the applied current or voltage *exceeds* a threshold value, the coil *activates* the armature, which either *closes* the open contacts or *opens* the closed contacts.

The solar power satellite *absorbs* the solar energy in geosynchronous orbit.
In the photovoltaic solar power system, solar cells *convert* the light energy into electricity.

• *Linking verbs.* A linking verb is any form of the verb *to be* without an action verb; it sets up something like an equal sign between the items it links. Here are some examples:

is	are
was	were
had been	would have been
was being	might have been
had to have been	will have been

A few linking verbs do not use *to be* but function like them:

That word-processing program *seems* adequate for our needs.
This calculus problem *looks* difficult.
Since the oil spill, the beach *has smelled* bad.
He quickly *grew* weary of computer games.

• *Auxiliary verbs.* Auxiliary verbs "help" the main part of the verb. Here are some italicized auxiliary verbs:

By 1967 about 500 U.S. citizens *had* received heart transplants.
Better immunosuppression management in transplant operations *has* yielded better results.
Researchers *have* found propranolol to be effective in the treatment of heartbeat irregularities.

• *Modals.* Modal verbs change the meaning of the verb in a variety of ways as illustrated in the following examples:

Cracks in the welding *can* only be detected by X-rays.
Liquid oxygen *could* have leaked into the turbine and caused the fire.
The light metal fast-breeder reactor *must* be operated under extreme safety precautions.

• Verbs are used together in a complex variety of tenses. In the following chart, keep in mind that *continuous* tenses are those that use *-ing* and *perfect* tenses are those that use some form of the auxiliary verb *have*.

Tense		*Verb Form*	
Simple Present	*works*	Present Continuous	*is working*
Simple Past	*worked*	Past Continuous	*was working*
Simple Future	*will work*	Future Continuous	*will be working*
		Present Perfect	*has worked*
		Past Perfect	*had worked*
		Future Perfect	*will have worked*
		Present Perfect Continuous	*has been working*
		Past Perfect Continuous	*had been working*
		Future Perfect Continuous	*will have been working*

Adjectives and Adverbs

An adjective provides more detail about a noun; that is, it modifies a noun. Adjectives occur just before the nouns they modify, or after a linking verb. An adverb provides more information about a verb, adjective, or another adverb; that is, it "qualifies" the verb, adjective, or adverb:

                        adj.   **adj.**   **adv.**

The armature is a *rectangular* ring about which *another* coil of wire is *tightly* wound.

          adv.   **adj.**   **adj.**

The generator is *often* used to convert *mechanical* energy into *electrical* energy.

      adj.   **adv.**   **adj.**   **adj.**

The *steel* pipes contain a *protective sacrificial* anode and are surrounded by *packing* material.

                adv.   **adj.**   **adj.**

The desk is made of an *especially corrosion-resistant industrial* steel.

Conjunctions

Conjunctions link words, phrases, and whole clauses to each other and are divided into coordinating, adverbial, and subordinating conjunctions. *Coordinating* conjunctions link words, phrases, and clauses. *Adverbial* conjunctions link two separate sentences, but require a semicolon or colon. *Subordinating* conjunctions combine separate sentences in a different way: they turn one of the sentences into an adverb clause. In the following list only the list of coordinating conjunctions is complete:

Coordinating Conjunctions	Subordinating Conjunctions	Adverbial Conjunctions
and	although	therefore
or	since	however
nor	because	in other words
but	when	thus
yet	while	then
for	if	otherwise
whereas	as if	nevertheless
	as	on the other hand

Here are some examples of these types of conjunctions:

Nuclear-powered artificial hearts proved to be complicated, bulky, *and* expensive.

In the 1960s artificial heart devices did not fit well *and* tended to obstruct the flow of venous blood into the right atrium.

The small clots that formed throughout the circulatory system used up so much of the clotting factor that uncontrolled bleeding from external *or* internal injury became a risk.

Current from the storage batteries can power lights, *but* the current for appliances must be modified within an inverter.

The Kedeco produces 1200 watts in 17 mph winds using a 16-foot rotor; *on the other hand,* the Dunlite produces 2000 watts in 25 mph winds.

The first artificial hearts were made of smooth silicone rubber which apparently caused excessive clotting and, *therefore,* uncontrolled bleeding. [This example does not contain two sentences; no semicolon, therefore, is needed.]

For short periods the fibers were beneficial; *however,* the eventual buildup of fibrin on the inner surface of the device would impair its function.

The atria of the heart contribute a negligible amount of energy; *in fact,* the total power output of the heart is only about 2.5 watts.

The heart undergoes two cardiac-cycle periods; a diastole, *when* blood enters the ventricles, and a systole, *when* the ventricles contract and blood is pumped out of the heart.

If the wire is broken, electrons will cease to flow and current is zero.

Phrases and Clauses

Phrases and clauses are groups of words that act as a unit and perform a single function within a sentence. A verbal phrase may have a partial subject or verb but not both; a clause has both a subject and a verb (but is not a complete sentence).

Prepositions Phrases.   A prepositional phrase, composed of a preposition and its object, shows relationships involving time, direction, or space:

An artificial heart was installed *in a human subject for the first time in 1969.*
The current leads *to the field coils* and *into an external circuit.*
Alternators are not compatible *with wind systems because of their high rpm requirements.*
The operation *of a wind generator* is based *upon Faraday's law of induced voltage,* which states that the voltage *between the ends of a loop of wire* is proportional *to the rate of change in the magnetic field lines within the loop.*

Appositives.   An appositive, a word or phrase that renames a noun or pronoun, adds information about a noun or pronoun but in a way different than do adjectives:

In 1972, Richard Nixon, *president of the United States,* approved the development of a reusable space vehicle, *the space shuttle.*
Broad principles about space flight were laid down by the Austrian astronautical pioneer, *Dr. Eugen Sanger.*
The external tank of the space shuttle's main engines is composed of two tanks—*a large hydrogen tank and a smaller oxygen tank.*
An upper air inversion, *a layer of stable air,* is usually present over large areas of the tradewinds as a hurricane develops.

Gerunds and Participial Phrases.   A gerund is a word ending in *-ing* or group of words introduced by an *-ing* word that plays the role of noun. A participial phrase is a word or words acting as an adjective and modifying a noun or pronoun. A participle is the *-ed* or *-ing* form of a verb:

gerund
In the iron-core type transformer, the *winding* is wrapped around an iron bar.

                                                           gerund phrase
Jarvik changed his artificial heart design in 1974 by *fitting his model with a highly flexible three-layer diaphragm made of smooth polyurethane.*

                                                          gerund phrase
The Jarvik-7 design in 1979 achieved a record time of *sustaining life in a calf for 221 days.*

                              gerund phrase
Reversing the rotation of the electrohydraulic heart pump reverses the direction of the hydraulic flow.

                                                        participial phrase
The Eagle uses a 6-pole, shunt-wound generator *designed to reach maximum power at 20 mph.*

                              participial phrase
Because of the design *created by Kwan Grett,* endothelial cells could grow on the fibrin

                              participial phrase
layer, *making the interior surface of the artificial heart similar to those of the natural heart.*

Adjective and Adverb Clauses.

An adjective clause functions as a single-word adjective does: both add more information to our understanding of a noun. Adjective clauses contain a relative pronoun, in some cases, a subject, a complete verb, and related phrases or clauses. An adverb clause functions as an adverb does by explaining the *how, when, where,* and *why* of the discussion. The adverb clause usually contains a subordinating conjunction, a subject, a complete verb, and related phrases or clauses.

                                                      adj. clause
Typically, one portable drilling rig, *which requires two tug boats to bring it to the site,* and several other boats are used in the exploratory drilling phase.

The company holds many patents on its wind energy systems, such as the flyball governor,
                         adj. clause
which varies the pitch of the blades in high winds, and the slow-speed generator *whose*
                         adj. clause
performance curve matches that of the propeller.

                                                              adj. clause
The idea of the artificial heart arose in part from the need to treat people *who cannot receive a donor heart.*

                                          adj. clause
Nose designed a "biolized" heart *in which the surfaces that came into contact with blood were made from natural tissues treated with chemical fixatives to make them tougher and immunologically inert.*

                              adj. clause
The regular CPR class *people are taking everywhere now* only lasts an evening.

                         adv. clause
Because the shortage in donor hearts is so severe, transplant surgery is limited to people with the best chances of surviving.

                    adv. clause
As long as the wind speed is sufficient, the electrical energy will be continuously generated.

         adv. clause   adv. clause
If an oil spill occurs away from shore, it is unlikely to affect many birds, *unless they are directly in a major migratory path at a migrating season.*

Noun Clauses.   A noun clause is a group of words used as a noun. Introduced by a relative pronoun, a noun clause can play any of the functions a noun plays: subject, direct object, object of preposition, subjective or objective complement. Here are examples of noun clauses, with their functions labeled:

direct object
Estimates indicate *that 20 million Americans owned hand-held calculators by 1974.*

object of preposition
Computer systems are often measured by *how much main memory their architectures allow and by how fast that memory can be accessed.*

direct object
Lematire proposed *that all matter in the universe was once concentrated into what he termed the primeval atom.* [In this sentence, "what he termed the primeval atom" is also a noun clause.]

object of preposition
The choice of furnace wall construction depends on *how sophisticated the gas-cleaning equipment to be used is* and on *whether a large amount of waste is to be recovered.*

direct object
Most microcomputers use *what are called flexible diskettes for program and data storage.*

subj. complement
The major disadvantage of sequential files is *that they are slow.*

APPENDIX C

Basic Patterns and Elements of the Paragraph

Topic Sentences
  Main-Point Topic Sentences
  Placeholder Topic Sentences
  Topic-Reference Sentences
  Listing Topic Sentences
Levels of Detail in Paragraphs
  Coordinate Detail
  Subordinate Detail
Types of Development in Paragraphs
Common Patterns of Paragraph
    Organization
  Spatial Organization
  Chronological Organization

Inductive Pattern of Organization
Deductive Pattern of Organization
Rhetorical Patterns of Organization
Coherence and Transitions in
    Paragraphs
Transitional Words and Phrases
Repetition of Important Words or
    Phrases
Combining, Paralleling, and
    Rephrasing Sentences
Rearrangement of Whole Sentences
Transitional Sentences
Transitional Paragraphs

Whereas Chapter 7 presents ways to revise paragraphs, this appendix shows you the basic patterns and elements of paragraphs. If you are unsure about some of the terms used to describe paragraphs, this appendix can help.

Topic Sentences

A topic sentence, usually one of the first two or three sentences of a paragraph, in some way indicates the main idea or point of that paragraph. Technical writing makes substantial use of topic sentences because they give a stronger sense of organization and clarity to complex discussions. They provide an overview, a look at the whole forest, before plunging into the individual details of the discussion. At least four types of topic sentences can be found in technical prose: the *main-point*, the *topic-reference*, the *placeholder*, and the *listing* topic sentence.

Main-Point Topic Sentences

A main-point topic sentence directly states the main assertion of the paragraph: for example, if the paragraph concludes that the company's new word-processing system requires a special employee available for training, troubleshooting, and programming, a main-point topic sentence would state that; the rest of the paragraph would prove that main point. In the example in Figure C–1, the topic sentence is underlined.

Einstein's general theory of relativity has been subjected to test after test over the years, and all confirm its validity. Although the deflection-of-light test has been carried out many times over the years, most recently at the 1980 eclipse, this type of measurement is now most accurately carried out in the radio part of the spectrum. The positions of the quasars in the sky can be observed very accurately with radio telescopes, and the bending of the radio waves as a quasar passes near the sun has been measured and found to agree with Einstein's prediction to better than 1 percent. The accuracy of the agreement is not only confirmation of Einstein's theory but also tends to rule out other alternative theories of gravitation that have been advanced from time to time since Einstein's work.

Reprinted from Invitation to Physics by Jay M. Pasachoff and Marc L. Kutner by permission of W. W. Norton & Company, Inc. Copyright © 1981 by Jay M. Pasachoff and Marc L. Kutner.

FIGURE C–1.   Main-point topic sentence

Placeholder Topic Sentences

The placeholder topic sentence stands in place of a direct statement of the main point. It hints that an assertion is coming but does not state it overtly. In the example in Figure C–2, the topic sentence (underlined) indicates that the relationship between the "burning rate" and the "characteristics of the system" is about to be explained.

Topic-Reference Sentences

A topic-reference sentence simply contains the word or phrase referring to the topic of the same paragraph. It alerts the reader to the focus of discussion in the new paragraph, as indicated by the underlined topic in Figure C–3.

Listing Topic Sentences

Another kind of topic sentence lists the main contents of the paragraph. It is an effective device because it gives an overview of what the paragraph or section will contain. In the example in Figure C–4, the listed items are underlined.

Levels of Detail in Paragraphs

Paragraphs in good technical writing are not just one sentence after another about the same topic but are carefully structured groups of sentences. One of the keys to the structure of paragraphs is how sentences can be *coordinate* or *subordinate* to each other.

Fires above horizontal liquid pools have been studied both experimentally and analytically to clarify the relationship between burning rate and the characteristics of the system. In small pools (up to 3 cm in diameter), burning is laminar and, unexplainedly, the burning rate per unit area decreases in approximate proportion as diameter increases. In a 3- to 5-cm diameter pool the flame is still laminar but regular oscillations occur. For diameters greater than 7 cm and less than 20 to 30 cm, a transition to turbulent burning takes place....

Reprinted from Walter R. Niessen, Combustion and Incineration Processes: Applications in Environmental Engineering, pp. 60–61, by courtesy of Marcel Dekker, Inc.

FIGURE C–2. Placeholder topic sentence

A ram-type feeding device is sometimes used for controlled feeding. With such a system, either the ram can clear the hopper at each stroke or an oversized hopper can be filled with refuse and the ram used to shear a horizontal section of refuse at selected intervals. The ram feeder provides an air seal at the feed to the furnace, an improvement over the bucket or front-end loader systems of batch feeding, which usually lets in undesirable quantities of cold air, as well as releasing occasional puffs of flames or hot gases while the charging gate is open. The inrush of cold air can be detrimental to the inside refractory walls of the furnace and can cause smoke evolution by cooling and quenching the burning process.

Walter R. Niessen, Combustion and Incineration Processes, 228.

FIGURE C–3.   The Topic-reference topic sentence

Coordinate Detail

If two sentences are coordinate to each other, they are at the same level of detail; if one sentence is subordinate to another, it is at a lower level of detail, more specific than the other. The paragraph in Figure C–5 appears with the sentences numbered according to the level of detail. The topic sentence indicates that features of the

Three types of buckets are in common use for handling municipal refuse: the clamshell bucket, the grapple bucket, and the orange peel bucket. The clamshell and grapple buckets can be equipped with teeth to assist in digging into the refuse for a full bucket. The orange peel bucket does not require teeth to grab the refuse, even for unusual or large pieces. However, with the orange peel, it is difficult to clean the floor of the receiving pit. . . .

Walter R. Niessen, Combustion and Incineration Processes, 226.

FIGURE C–4.   The listing topic sentence

FAS patient are about to be presented; each of the sentences that follow describes one of those features. Sentences 2 through 7 are coordinate to each other, but all subordinate to sentence 1. This paragraph can be called a coordinate paragraph because it is dominated by sentences that are coordinate to each other. (Normally, you'll find few paragraphs that are so purely coordinate as the one in Figure C–5.)

If you think about paragraphs this way, you can readily see how to add more detail and where to add it. For example, after sentence 5, if you were the writer, you might want to insert a new sentence defining the "piltrim."

Subordinate Detail

In Figure C–5, sentence 2 makes a comment about, elaborates upon, or adds more specific detail to sentence 1. Sentence 2 is therefore subordinate to sentence 1. Now, if a new sentence defining "epicanthic folds" were inserted at this point, it would be subordinate to sentence 2, adding detail to sentence 3 rather than sentence 1, as indicated in Figure C–6. By adding sentences like number 4 in Figure C–6, you go into greater detail and provide more information on a topic. In Figure C–7 is a paragraph with the subordinate and coordinate details labeled.

1. Although the faces of patients with FAS (fetal alcohol syndrome) are indeed quite distinctive, the individual features, or abnormalities, are subtle and not likely to be found in standard listings of malformations. 2. One quite noticeable feature is the shortness of the palpebral fissures, or longitudinal openings between the eyelids. 3. Another is the way in which the epicanthic folds sometimes cover the inner corner of the eye. 4. FAS victims also tend to have a low nasal bridge and a short upturned nose. 5. In the same area of the face, the piltrim tends to be smooth and indistinct. 6. As a result of the incomplete development of the maxilla, FAS patients tend to have a flattened profile and downslanting palpebral fissures. 7. Finally, the upper vermilion of the lips of FAS patients is thin and thus contributes additionally to the overall drawn-out appearance of the face of these patients.

FIGURE C–5. Paragraph with coordinate sentences

Sentence No.	Sentence	Level
1	While the faces of FAS patients are indeed quite distinctive, the individual features or abnormalities are subtle.	------
2	One quite noticeable feature is the shortness of the palpebral fissures, or longitudinal openings between the eyelids.	comments on no. 1
3	Another is the way in which the epicanthic folds sometimes cover the inner corner of the eye.	comments on no. 1
4	Epicanthic folds are the vertical folds of skin on either side of the nose.	comments on no. 3

FIGURE C–6.   Coordinate and subordinate sentences

1. Two main psychological actions of caffeine have been clarified through numerous studies.
2. The first is that caffeine does indeed act to   comments on no. 1
increase association of ideas. 3. The process of   comments on no. 2
thought formation is increased and new ideas
become abundant with small doses of caffeine.
4. A person is less likely to be at a loss for ideas   comments on no. 3
or words after ingesting one or two cups of
coffee. 5. The second main psychological action   comments on no. 1
of caffeine is the enhancement of immediate
intentional recall of information. 6. After ingest-   comments on no. 5
ing caffeine, people apparently find it easier to
organize incoming information and place it
in the memory banks. 7. Both of these psycho-   comments on nos. 1–6
logical effects combine to give the "pick-me-up"
feeling that relieves minor fatigue, an effect that
caffeine is famous for.

FIGURE C–7.   Paragraph with coordination and subordination illustrated

Think of paragraphs as having a gap or an empty slot between each sentence. In those slots, you can

- Insert one or more sentences that provide greater detail on a preceding sentence (as the definition of epicanthic folds in Figure C–6 does).
- Insert one or more sentences that add detail on the same level (for example, sentences that describe other facial features of the FAS patient in Figure C–5).

Types of Development in Paragraphs

When you insert coordinate and subordinate sentences into the slots between sentences, you are developing the paragraph more fully and, in some cases, supporting or proving the main point more convincingly. Different kinds of information are used to develop a paragraph; these include description, narration, process narration, definition, comparison, causal explanations, classifications, and examples. Use these different kinds of development as the report subject, purpose, or audience requires.

- *Description*. Chapter 2 explains that description means giving details about the size, shape, weight, height, color, texture, location, and other such details about a thing.
- *Narration*. Narration, as Chapter 1 explains, is the discussion of events that have occurred in the past.
- *Process Discussion*. Also covered in Chapter 1, a process discussion focuses on processes, an event or activity that occurs or is performed repeatedly.
- *Definition*. Definition, as explained in Chapter 3, is the discussion of the meaning of unfamiliar words or phrases or of words or phrases used in an unfamiliar way.
- *Comparison*. Comparison is simply the discussion of the similarities or differences between two or more things. As Chapter 2 explains, comparison can be informative (to help readers to understand) or evaluative (to enable people to make a decision or choice).
- *Causal Discussion*. When you discuss causes and effects, you explain any combination of the following: what cause or causes brought about the situation or problem; what effect or effects have occurred because of the situation or problem; what effect or effects may occur in the future because of the situation or problem. (See Chapter 1 for further discussion.)
- *Classification*. Explanation of types, classes, sorts, or kinds is often used in technical reports to provide background, as shown in Chapter 3.
- *Examples*. In technical writing, examples are often used to illustrate a point or make a complex discussion clearer.

Now, Figure C–8 contains a series of paragraphs in which most of these types of development occur.

Paragraph	Development Type
Full-floating decimal-point calculators are calculators that enable you to store values and perform computations in the calculator's own version of scientific notation.	definition
For example, a typical scientific calculator has full-floating decimal capability, which accepts 10 digits and allows exponents as small as -99 and as large as $+99$.	example
With this range, positive numbers as large as $9.999999999 \times 10^{99}$ and as small as 1.0×10^{-99} can be represented. Also, negative numbers can be represented over the same range of magnitudes. But no matter what the magnitude this calculator can store, it "thinks" of each as having 10 significant decimal digits.	cause-effect
For example, 123456789.0 is stored effectively as $1.234567890 \times 10^{8}$, whereas 0.00000001234567890, if properly entered, would be stored effectively as $1.234567890 \times 10^{-8}$.	example
Compared to this, a simple eight-digit calculator would display or store the numbers as 12345678 and 0.0000000, respectively--a loss of digits in both cases.	comparison
Hence, most full-floating decimal-point calculators with scientific-notation capability can operate over an extremely large range of values and can record 10 digits of presumed significance over the entire range.	cause-effect
There are two major construction techniques used in the making of aircraft; they are welded tubing and semimonocoque.	classification
Welded Tubing.　The welded tubing, sometimes called the truss type, is ordinarily used for	

(continued)

FIGURE C—8.　Three examples of paragraphs with development sentences labeled

small, fabric-covered aircraft. It is characterized   description
by small-diameter tubing arranged in much the
same way as that seen in an overhead crane. The
problem with this construction technique is   causal
that the whole assembly must be heat treated
after it is welded, an extra step that makes it
very expensive.

    Semimonocoque.   Semimonocoque is by far
the most widely used method of aircraft con-
struction today. It gets its strength in much the   comparison
same way as a soda straw does. In semimono-
coque, the skin, made of stamped and formed   description
sheets of aluminum alloy . . .

1.1 Background

On July 17, 1981, at approximately 7:05 p.m.,   narration
two suspended walkways within the atrium area
of the Hyatt Regency Hotel in Kansas City, Mo.,
collapsed, killing 111 people and injuring 188.
Two of the injured subsequently died. In terms   description
of loss of life and injuries, this was the most   comparison
devastating structural collapse ever to take place
in the United States.

On July 20, 1981, Senator Thomas F. Eagleton's   narration
office contacted the National Bureau of Standards
(NBS) and requested that technical assistance
be provided to the city of Kansas City. . . .

U.S. Department of Commerce and the National Bureau of Standards,
Investigation of the Kansas City Hyatt Regency Walkways Collapse
(Washington, D.C.: GPO, May 1982), 1.

FIGURE C–8.   (cont.)

Common Patterns of Paragraph Organization

Paragraphs can be organized spatially, temporally, inductively, deductively, and rhetorically.

Spatial Organization

If you are describing a thing or place, you must use some spatial pattern: for example, left-to-right; top-to-bottom; bottom-to-top; from a distance to close-up; from close-up to a distance; or from the outside to the inside. The example in Figure C–9 moves the focus closer and closer in on the subject.

Chronological Organization

One of the most familiar ways to organize paragraphs is according to time. Figure C–10 contains two passages: the first, a historical narrative; the second, a process discussion.

Inductive Pattern of Organization

An inductively organized paragraph usually has a conclusion, main generalization, main point, or topic sentence at the end. Inductive reasoning proceeds this way: the thinker consider the facts and concepts at hand and then draws a conclusion—or

---

DESCRIPTION OF THE PARTS

There are four main components that enable the mechanical pencil to function as it does. They are (1) the housing assembly, (2) the lead storage, (3) the eraser assembly, and (4) the lead guide.

Housing Assembly

The housing assembly contains the mechanical workings of the pencil. It is a 12-sided hollow cylinder made of black plastic. The length is 4.25 inches, and its outside diameter varies from 0.25 inches at the ends to 0.4 inches in the middle where it bulges slightly.

The housing assembly has some finer detail. For instance, there is a series of 11 rings cut into the barrel approximately 0.2 mm deep. These rings start 1.0 cm from the bottom of the housing and are 3 mm apart....

FIGURE C–9.   Paragraphs with spatial organization

In the later eighteenth century, the great French chemist, Antoine Lavoisier, began to use the sun for research purposes. Lavoisier used curved glass discs fastened together at their rims, with wine filling the space between, to focus the sun's rays enough to attain temperatures of about 3000° F. He used these high temperatures to discover the nature of carbon and platinum. Lavoisier also carried the science of the solar furnace forward by heating samples in a vacuum and in controlled atmospheres, using quartz containers. Unfortunately, Lavoisier lived during the French revolution and was beheaded because "the Republic has no need for scientists." With the lopping off of this pioneer's head, work with solar furnaces halted, and it was more than a hundred years before men again achieved elevated temperatures using the sun's rays.

U.S. Department of Energy, Introduction to Solar Heating and Cooling Design and Sizing (Washington, D.C.: GPO, August 1978), 9–10.

THE PRODUCTION OF ELECTRICITY

The main steps by which a pressurized water reactor converts water to steam in order to produce electricity are as follows: (1) circulating water to the primary system; (2) producing steam in the secondary system; (3) separating the steam; and (4) producing the electricity.

Circulating Water to the Primary System.   Coolant water from the steam generators is pumped toward the reactor core by coolant pumps. The water flows down the region between the reactor vessel wall and the lower core barrel and then upward through the core....

Producing Steam in the Secondary System.   The secondary system is composed of steam generators....

FIGURE C–10.   Organization by historical and process discussions

at least presents it that way. The inductive paragraph mirrors this pattern by presenting the facts and concepts first and the conclusion or generalization last. In Figure C–11, an example is discussed in order to illustrate a generality not stated until the final underlined paragraph.

8.3b TIME DILATION

... [A] simple way of measuring time [is] called the light clock. The clock has two mirrors facing each other, and a pulse of light travels back and forth between them. We think of each passage of the light pulse from one mirror to the other as one "tick" of the clock. How long is one tick?

The time for light to go from one mirror to the other is just the distance between the mirrors divided by the speed of light. (Remember, light travels at the same speed in all directions, so it doesn't matter if the light is going back and forth).

Now we put the clock in a rocketship moving at a constant speed. To an astronaut inside the rocket, the round trip of light appears just as we described above, since the clock is at rest in the rocket. The time kept by the clock as viewed by an observer at rest with respect to the clock is called the proper time of the clock. Thus, in this example, the proper time is the distance between the mirrors, divided by the speed of light.

Suppose the clock is mounted in the rocket so that the light pulse travels back and forth in a direction perpendicular to the path of the rocket's motion. How would the round trip of the light appear to an observer on a planet, say Mars, that the rocket happened to be passing? From the point of view of this observer, in the time it takes the light beam to go from one mirror to the other, the mirror has moved over slightly. The faster the rocket is going, the more it has moved. Thus, for each tick, the observer on the planet observes the light traveling farther than the astronaut observes it to travel. However, the speed of light is the same for both observers. Therefore, since the light travels a greater distance as seen by the Martian, the light pulse's trip between mirrors takes longer. The Martian sees time pass more slowly than the astronaut does.

From this example, we conclude that for the observer who sees the clock moving, each tick takes longer than for the observer who sees the clock at rest. Another way of saying this is that moving clocks appear to run slow. This phenomenon is called time dilation.

Invitation to Physics, 137–38.

FIGURE C–11. Paragraph with inductive organization

Deductive Pattern of Organization

A deductively organized paragraph is the reverse of the inductive paragraph. Its generalization, main point, or topic sentence is stated at the beginning of the paragraph rather than at the end, as indicated by the underlined sentences in Figure C–12.

Rhetorical Patterns of Organization

Many other patterns of organization could be listed: a good many of them, however, can be labeled rhetorical patterns. The word *rhetoric* has to do with the study and practice of how writing (or speaking) can be organized and expressed for maximum effectiveness upon a specific audience. Here are a few examples of rhetorical patterns:

Least to most controversial   Least to most important
Least to most familiar   Least to most believable
Least to most interesting   Least to most technical

Some of these orderings can be reversed: it may, for example, be a better idea to discuss more familiar things first and move slowly into less familiar ones, as in the example in Figure C–13.

Two factors contributed to the collapse: inadequacy of the original design for the box beam-hanger rod connection, which was identical for all three walkways, and a change in hanger rod arrangement during construction that essentially doubled the load on the box beam-hanger rod connections at the fourth floor walkway. As originally approved for construction, the contract drawings called for a set of continuous hanger rods that would attach to the roof framing and pass through the fourth floor box beams and on through the second floor box beams. As actually constructed, two sets of hanger rods were used, one set extending from the fourth floor box beams to the roof framing and another set from the second floor box beams to the fourth floor box beams.

Investigation of the Kansas City Hyatt Regency Walkways Collapse, A–98.

FIGURE C–12.   **Paragraph with deductive organization**

strongest impact

weak impact

no impact

Contrary to what many think, large-scale electric automobile use in the United States would not have the dramatic positive effect on the environment, economy, or the energy-resource problem. The most dramatic impact of such a large-scale conversion to electrical transportation would involve traffic noise. Electrical propulsion of automobiles is inherently quiet: some estimates hold that traffic noise would be decreased by nearly 50 percent if there were a significant shift to electrical automobiles. The petroleum saved by such vehicles, on the other hand, would be taken back by the increased demand for electricity needed to recharge so many of these same vehicles. Still, in the best of combinations, a maximum of 10 percent in savings in petroleum could be gained after some 20 to 30 years of conversion to this kind of transportation. Less dramatic still would be the impact on air quality. Although electrical autos themselves do not pollute the air, the plants that produce the electricity needed to recharge them do. With the increased number of such plants required, no net reduction in emissions would result.

FIGURE C–13. Paragraph with rhetorical organization

Coherence and Transitions in Paragraphs

Coherence in writing enables readers to follow the discussion easily. A paragraph that lacks coherence does not seem to flow smoothly; reading it can be difficult and confusing. Transitional devices are those words, phrases, or arrangements within and between paragraphs that give a piece of writing coherence.

In some cases, usually in writing on rather simple subject matter, the transitions can be implied or understood: in other words, there are no identifiable transitional words or phrases to be seen, except for repetition of keys words or phrases. For example, look at Figure C–14. Notice that there are no words or phrases such as

Mariner 6 ... weighed about 380 kg (840 lb) ..., considerably more than [its] predecessor. The two-axis scan platform provided considerably more capability and flexibility for the scientific payload than that of Mariner 4, and the solar panels and antennas were larger. (See Figure C–14a.) The eight electronics bays in the base of [the] spacecraft were no larger than those of Mariner 4, owing to improved packaging and wide use of integrated circuitry. Although there were 40 percent fewer electronic parts in Mariner 6 ..., integrated circuitry more than doubled the number of equivalent discrete parts flown on Mariner 4.

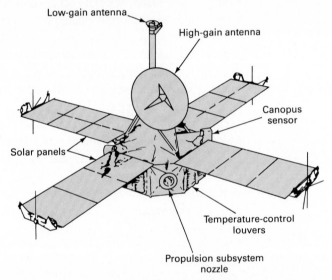

FIGURE C–14a.   Spacecraft configuration for Mariner 6
Mariner-Mars 1969: A Preliminary Report, NASA SP-225, 14–15.

FIGURE C–14.   Implied transitions

"on the other hand" or "in comparison" to lead the reader along through this paragraph. Still the paragraph reads clearly.

Discussion of more complicated subject matter, however, requires transitions to lead readers from one sentence to the next, from one paragraph or section to another, or from one idea to another. In Figure C–15 are two versions of a paragraph, one without transitions, the other with transitions. The paragraph without transitions would normally be described as incoherent or lacking transitions. The

Paragraph without Transitions

I-45 North has become one of the most congested freeways in the state and will only become worse. Major residential growth has occurred, and traffic to the Intercontinental Airport has expanded. Daily traffic is expected to increase at annual rates of 6 to 12 percent for the remainder of the century. There is new office development in the corridor area. An additional 4 million square feet has been built in one year. Corridor traffic volumes have increased. Growth rates have been 3 to 10 percent in the 1970s.

Paragraph with Transitions

I-45 North has become one of the most congested freeways in the state and will only become worse. Two causes of that congestion are the major residential growth occurring around the I-45 corridor and the expanded traffic to the Intercontinental Airport. Another contributing factor has been the additional office space, some 4 million square feet built just this year, in the corridor area. With these added sources of traffic, daily use of the highway is expected to increase at annual rates of 6 to 12 percent for the remainder of the century. This growth is significantly above the 3 to 10 percent rate experienced during the 1970s.

FIGURE C–15.   Revising paragraphs for coherence

revision of it uses several of these techniques (to be explained in the following sections):

- Transitional words or phrases can be inserted to show the reader the way.
- Key words or phrases in the subject matter can be repeated at important moments in the discussion to keep the reader from getting lost.
- Sentences can be phrased for parallelism, combined, or rearranged in such a way to create a smoother flow in the reading.
- Whole groups of sentences within paragraphs can be rearranged to create better coherence.
- Sentences at the beginning and end of paragraphs can be written so that they lead readers smoothly from one paragraph or group of paragraphs to the next.
- Whole paragraphs, usually rather short ones, can be used to reinforce the connection of one set of ideas or paragraphs to the next.

Transitional Words and Phrases

Quite a large group of words and phrases show readers the connections between ideas, sentences, and even paragraphs. These words and phrases indicate the logic that hooks two sentences together: for example, "I have just been paid;"—therefore—"I can go to the movies tonight." *Therefore* in this sentence could act as the transition providing the link between the two sentences. Transitional words and phrases can be divided into types according to the kind of logic that they indicate.

• Additive: one idea can be added to another; information can simply be added to other information within a paragraph. Additive transitional words and phrases include *and, moreover, as well as, too, in addition to, furthermore, also,* and *additionally.*

• Narrative: one idea can follow, precede, or occur simultaneously with another. Narrative transitional words and phrases include *then, next, after, before, since, subsequently, following, later, as soon as, as, when, while, during, until,* and *once.*

• Contrastive: two ideas can be compared to each other to show differences or similarities. Contrastive transitional words and phrases in this category include *but, on the other hand, unlike, as opposed to, than, although, though, instead,* and *similarly.*

• Alternative: two ideas can act as alternatives or substitutes for each other. Alternative transitional words and phrases in this category include *either, or, nor, on the other hand, however, neither,* and *otherwise.*

• Causal: one idea can be the cause or the result (effect, consequence, etc.) of another. Causal transitional words and phrases in this category include *thus, then, unless, subsequently, therefore, because, consequently, as a result, if, in order to/ that, for,* and *so.*

• Illustrative: one idea can be an example or an illustration of another. Illustrative transitional words and phrases in this category include *for example, for instance, to illustrate,* and *as an example.*

• Repetitive: for the sake of clarity, an idea can be restated or repeated using other, perhaps more familiar, words. Repetitive transitional words and phrases in this category include *in other words, in short, that is, stated simply,* and *to put it another way.*

Repetition of Important Words or Phrases

Coherence can often be achieved by repeating important words or phrases related to the subject matter under discussion. Notice the underlined words and phrases used for repetition in the passage in Figure C–16.

Combining, Paralleling, and Rephrasing Sentences

Sentences within paragraphs can be rephrased in at least three ways to create more smoothly reading prose.

• One way is to *combine* sentences so that the connection between ideas—the flow of ideas—is emphasized. See the example in Figure C–17.

• A sense of order or coherence can also be achieved by phrasing key sentences in such a way that they *parallel* or echo each other. Notice the similar phrasing in the passage in Figure C–18.

The cpu memory unit is commonly called the internal memory of the computing system. On older machines this memory usually consisted of magnetic cores, but new machines utilize metal oxide semiconductors. Although these devices allow for the rapid retrieval of the information stored in them, they are rather expensive. Consequently, most computing systems also incorporate components that serve as auxiliary or external memory. Common forms of this memory are the magnetic discs and magnetic tapes. These media provide relatively inexpensive storage for large files of information, but the rate of transfer of information to and from the cpu is considerably slower than for internal memory.

Larry Nyhoff and Sanford Leestma, Problem Solving with FORTRAN 77 (New York: Macmillan, 1983), 12.

FIGURE C–16. Repetition of important words and phrases for coherence

• One final way to achieve coherence is to *rephrase* sentences so that an important word or group of words occurs at the right time in those sentences. For example, if you locate a word at the end of one sentence, coherence can be strengthened if it occurs near the beginning of the next sentence, as has been done in Figure C–19. The sentences are like runners in a relay race; the batons, which one hands to the next, are the words *steam generator, heat exchanger,* and *tubes:*

Rearrangement of Whole Sentences

Paragraphs can also seem incoherent if sentences are not properly grouped within them. For example, if you have a paragraph that discusses the materials something is made of and the way it operates, you'd not want to mix those two subtopics. In the two versions of a passage in Figure C–20, the sentences in the second are grouped more appropriately. In the revised version, discussion of office and residential growth (italicized sentences) is mixed with discussion of other causes of the traffic congestion. In the problem paragraph in Figure C–21, descriptive and process sentences (italicized) are mixed.

Paragraph with Coherence Problems

The basic component of the photovoltaic cell is a nearly pure single-crystal silicon wafer. It is approximately 1 mm thick and 25 mm long. Silicon is a semiconductor. It conducts electricity better than glass. It does not conduct as well as copper though. One section of the wafer contains an abundance of electrons. These can also be called negatively charged carriers. This side of the wafer is called the "n-side." The other region is a thin top layer. It is approximately 25 micrometers thick. It contains an abundance of holes. These are called positively charged carriers. This area is the "p-side." The interface between these two parts is an electrical connection. It is called the "p-n junction." Thin wires serve as electrical contacts. They are attached to the front and back of the photovoltaic cell. The cell is coated with an antireflective material. It minimizes the percent of light reflected from the surface of the cell. It therefore maximizes the percent of light absorbed. The entire cell is encapsulated in a protective skin.

Revision

The basic component of the photovoltaic cell is a nearly pure single-crystal silicon wafer, approximately 1 mm thick and 25 mm long. Silicon is called a semiconductor because it conducts electricity better than glass but not as well as copper. One section of the wafer, containing an abundance of electrons, or negatively charged carriers, is called the "n-side." The other section, the "p-side," is a thin top layer approximately 25 micrometers thick containing an abundance of holes known as positively charged carriers. The interface between these parts is an electrical connection known as the "p-n junction." Thin wires serve as electrical contacts and are attached to the front and back of the cell. The cell is coated with an antireflective material to minimize the percent of light reflected from the cell's surface and therefore to maximize the percent of light absorbed. The entire cell is encapsulated in a protective skin.

FIGURE C–17. Paragraph revised by combining sentences

Transitional Sentences

One of the most important ways to achieve coherence is the transitional sentence, which leads readers from one paragraph or section to another. The transitional sentence does three important things:

- It summarizes, reviews, or echoes the main idea or topic of the preceding discussion.
- It introduces or previews the discussion of the next paragraph or section.
- It indicates the connection between the two, in other words, the logic that holds them together, with transitional words such as those previously discussed.

In the passages in Figure C–22, transitional sentences are italicized, and the review and the preview are listed below each.

Well Requirements

Many government regulations have been placed on injection wells in order to assure protection of all underground water reservoirs containing usable water. These requirements provide a strong barrier between the disposal liquids and the freshwater zone. The barrier consists of three concentric strings of pipe, two cement sheaths, and a sealed and monitored annulus, or ring of space around the injection tubing. The surface casing *must extend* below the freshwater zones and be cemented from the bottom to the surface. The next string of casing *must extend* to the disposal formation and is also cemented from the bottom to the surface. The third string of pipe, the injection tubing, *must extend* to the bottom of the casing and the annulus sealed with an appropriate packer.

FIGURE C–18.   Parallel phrasing for paragraph coherence

In a pressurized nuclear reactor, the primary coolant, after passing through the core and absorbing heat, proceeds to a secondary system consisting of a *steam generator*. In this *steam generator,* the primary coolant flows through hundreds of small stainless-steel tubes that act as *heat exchangers*. These *heat exchanger* tubes are surrounded by the water of the secondary system, which is heated by the primary coolant in the *tubes*. Outside these *tubes*, wet steam from the secondary coolant is then formed.

FIGURE C–19.   Sentence rephrasing for coherence

Transitional Paragraphs

Whole paragraphs, usually rather short ones, can be used to guide readers from one section of a report to the next. In Figure C–23, the preceding paragraphs have discussed applications of silicon micromechanical devices and the advantages of using them. The transitional paragraph introduces the discussion of the purification of silica and the manufacturing properties inherent in silica.

The introductory paragraphs of sections within reports are essentially transitional paragraphs. See Chapter 4 on section introductions.

Problem Paragraph

I-45 North has become one of the most congested freeways in the state and will only become worse. *Major residential growth has occurred,* and traffic to the Intercontinental Airport has increased. Daily traffic is expected to increase at annual rates of 6 to 12 percent for the remainder of the century. *There is new office development in the corridor area. An additional 4 million square feet has been built in one year.* Corridor traffic volumes have increased. Growth rates have been 3 to 10 percent in the 1970s.

Revision

I-45 North has become one of the most congested freeways in the state and will only become worse. Two causes of that congestion are the major residential growth occurring around the I-45 corridor and the increased traffic to the Intercontinental Airport. Another contributing factor has been the additional office space, some 4 million square feet built just this year, in the corridor area. With these added sources of traffic, daily use of the highway is expected to increase at annual rates of 6 to 12 percent for the remainder of the century. This growth is significantly above the 3 to 10 percent rate experienced during the 1970s.

FIGURE C–20. Coherence through regrouping of sentences

Problem Paragraph

The function of the combustion chamber of the space shuttle's main engines is to mix hydrogen and nitrogen under very high pressures. The combustion chamber is located at the top of the nozzle. Its inner wall is made of a specially developed copper alloy called Narloy. Narloy was developed by Rocketdyne, a division of Rockwell International, which was the prime contractor of the space shuttle. This alloy has characteristics of high strength, easy machinability, and high thermal conductivity. *As the hydrogen and oxygen enter the combustion chamber, a large flow rate and rapid mixing occur because of the high pressures. In the ensuing combustion, the amount of hydrogen and oxygen that actually interact chemically is 99 percent.*

FIGURE C–21. Revision through regrouping sentences

Revision

One of the most important components of the space shuttle's main engines is the combustion chamber. It is located at the top of the nozzle. Its inner wall is made of a specially developed copper alloy called Narloy. Narloy was developed by Rocketdyne, a division of Rockwell International, which was the prime contractor of the space shuttle. This alloy has characteristics of high strength, easy machinability, and high thermal conductivity. With this alloy in its construction, the combustion chamber can carry out its main function of mixing hydrogen and oxygen under very high pressures. As the hydrogen and oxygen enter the combustion chamber, a large flow rate and rapid mixing occur because of the high pressures. In the ensuing combustion, the amount of hydrogen and oxygen that actually interact chemically is 99 percent.

FIGURE C–21. (cont.)

The mechanical properties of single-crystal silicon show great potential for building strong, reliable, and durable mechanical components. Any material capable of absorbing the same stresses as steel but more than three times as light has great promise in mechanical device structures.

To gain the advantages of the properties of single-crystal silicon, a process known as micromachining, in which micromechanical devices are fabricated, must be used. This process begins with photolithography. . . .

Review: "properties" and   Preview: "process of
   "advantages"   micromachining"

The 1.125-inch parallel tubing in the DM 1036 solar collector is a plus in that mineral deposits do not become a problem for at least ten years. The headers on the tubing are inaccessible for repair, a design feature that can cause problems if the collector develops a leak. The DM 1036 is sold by Demarco Solar, Inc.

The Grumman 300/400 series collector differs from the DM 1036 in that a grid of circulating tubes on the plate is made of only 0.375-inch outside-diameter tubing. The Grumman is also designed so that. . . .

Review: "DM 1036"   Preview: "Grumman 300/400"

(continued)

FIGURE C–22. Examples of transitional sentences

In general, the major disadvantage of the insulin-infusion pump is not its technical acceptability but its physical acceptability. Patients must wear a heavy, bulky, and unattractive machine—a machine that is a constant reminder to diabetics of their disease.

Many of the problems of the insulin-infusion pump will undoubtedly be overcome in the coming years as researchers develop smaller, more versatile, more efficient, and more independent devices. Specifically, great promise lies in the computerized, implantable pump with a glucose sensor. . . .

Review: "problems with insulin-   **Preview:** new, improved
     infusion pumps"   "devices"

FIGURE C–22.   (cont.)

III. MANUFACTURING SINGLE-CRYSTAL SILICON

To create the micromechanical devices described in the previous section and to derive their benefits, the designer and the technologist must understand the mechanical properties of silicon. The silicon used to make micromechanical devices and electronic devices must be single crystal. Single-crystal silicon possesses certain qualities that make it the perfect material to use in manufacturing such devices. To obtain single-crystal silicon, one must first purify silica and then understand the manufacturing properties of the resulting single-crystal silicon.

FIGURE C–23.   Example of a transitional paragraph

Common Conventions in Standard Written English

Structural Problems
  Fragments
  Run-ons and Comma Splices
  Parallelism
  Modifier Problems
Usage Problems
  Principal Parts of Verbs
  Agreement
  Pronoun Case
  Adjectives and Adverbs
  Glossary of Other Usage Problems
Graphics Problems
  Commas
  Semicolons
  Colons
  Dashes
  Hyphens
  Apostrophes
  Quotation Marks, Brackets, and
    Ellipsis Points
  Underlining and Italics
  Parentheses
  Capital Letters

Diction: The Use of Words
  Precision with the Meaning of Words
  Concrete and Abstract Words
  Formal and Informal (Slang) Words
  Neutral and Slanted Words
  Clichés
Spelling
  Homonyms
  Doubled Internal Consonants
  Internal Syllables or Letters
  Words with Endings Such as -ance
    and -able
  Words Ending in -sede, -ceed, and
    -cede
  The Silent -e Rule
  Words Ending in -ie and -ei
  Doubling Consonants
  Words Ending in -y
**Handling Numbers, Abbreviations,
    and Symbols**
  Numbers in Technical Prose
  Abbreviations in Technical Prose
  Special Symbols in Technical Prose

This appendix covers the most common conventions—or rules—concerning grammar, usage, and punctuation. It also discusses how to handle numbers, abbreviations, and symbols in technical writing. The discussion in this appendix of the various problems or errors uses the terminology explained in Appendix B. If any terms, such as *object complement* or *antecedent*, are unfamiliar to you, go to that appendix.

Structural Problems

Problems with fragments, run-ons, comma splices, parallelism, and modifiers are structural because they involve the way in which whole clauses and phrases are arranged within sentences.

Fragments

A fragment is an incomplete sentence: it lacks a complete subject or complete verb, or it has another word attached that makes it incomplete. A fragment sounds incomplete if you simply read it out loud by itself. In these examples, the fragments are italicized:

Fragments

Mary appeared at the committee meeting last week. *And made a convincing presentation of her ideas about the new product.*

The committee considered her ideas for a new marketing strategy quite powerful. *The best ideas that they had heard in years.*

In a proposal you must include a number of sections. *For example, a discussion of your personnel and their qualifications, your expectations concerning the schedule of the project, and a cost breakdown.*

The research team has completely reorganized the workload. *Making sure that members work in areas of their own expertise and that no member is assigned proportionately too much work.*

She spent a full month evaluating his computer-based instructional materials. *Which she eventually sent to her supervisor with the strongest of recommendations.*

The corporation wants to begin a new marketing push in educational software. *Although the more conservative executives of the firm are skeptical.*

To correct fragments, you can attach the fragment to the preceding sentence, attach it to the following sentence, or rephrase it so that it reads as a complete sentence itself, as in the following revisions:

Revisions

Mary appeared at the committee meeting last week and made a convincing presentation of her ideas about the new product.

The committee considered her ideas for a new marketing strategy quite powerful, the best ideas that they had heard in years.

In a proposal you must include a number of sections: for example, a discussion of your personnel and their qualifications, your expectations concerning the schedule of the project, and a cost breakdown.

The research team has completely reorganized the workload. They made sure that members work in areas of their own expertise and that no member is assigned proportionately too much work.

She spent a full month evaluating his computer-based instructional materials. Eventually, she sent the evaluation to her supervisor with the strongest of recommendations.

Although the more conservative executives of the firm are skeptical, the corporation wants to begin a new marketing push in educational software.

Run-ons and Comma Splices

The terms *run-on, comma splice,* and *fused sentence* all refer to the same kind of problem: two complete sentences joined incorrectly. This type of sentence problem often occurs when an adverbial conjunction (*therefore* and *then,* for example) is used as if it were a coordinating conjunction (see Appendix B on these two terms). In these examples, the point where the run-on or comma splice occurs is italicized:

Run-ons and Comma Splices

Sometimes, books do not have the most complete *information, it is* a good idea then to look for articles in specialized periodicals.

Most of the hours I've earned toward my associate's degree do not *transfer, however, I do have* at least some hours the university will accept.

The opposite is true of stronger types of stainless *steel, they* tend to be more susceptible to rust.

Some people were highly educated *professionals, others* were from small villages in underdeveloped countries.

This report presents the data we found concerning the cost of the water treatment *project, then it* presents comparative data from other similar projects.

Most of this firm's contracts have been with major metropolitan *hospitals, included* among them is Memorial East in Luckenbach.

To correct run-ons and comma splices, you can delete the comma and insert a period, delete the comma and insert a semicolon, or rephrase one of the two sentences so that it is a *dependent* rather than an *independent* clause (see Appendix B for definitions):

Revisions

Sometimes, books do not have the most complete information; it is a good idea then to look for articles in specialized periodicals.

Most of the hours I've earned toward my associate's degree do not transfer. However, I do have at least some hours the university will accept.

The opposite is true of stronger types of stainless steel: they tend to be more susceptible to rust.

Some people were highly educated professionals, while others were from small villages in underdeveloped countries.

This report first presents the data we found concerning the cost of the water-treatment project and then comparative data from other similar projects.

Most of this firm's contracts have been with major metropolitan hospitals, included among which is Memorial East in Luckenbach.

Parallelism

A *lack* of parallelism in sentences means that different kinds of clauses and phrases are mixed in a series incorrectly. In these examples, the nonparallel parts are italicized:

Sentences Lacking Parallelism

The report discusses *how telescopes work, what types are available, mounts, accessories, and techniques for beginning star gazers.*

Customers often call the showroom *to inquire about pricing, what items are available, and to place orders.*

While the dialysis solution remains in the peritoneal cavity, the dialysis is achieved, a process that includes *the removal of nitrogenous wastes and correcting electrolyte imbalances and fluid overloads.*

This report is intended for people *with some electronics background but have little or no knowledge of geophysical prospecting.*

To correct nonparallel sentences, you must identify the part (or parts) of the sentence that are not parallel to the others, and then rephrase it so that it is like the others (the key words that make the revisions parallel are italicized), as in the following examples:

Revisions

The report discusses *how* telescopes work; *what* types of telescopes, mounts, and accessories are available; and *how* to begin your hobby as a star gazer.

Customers often call the showroom *to* inquire about the price and availability of certain items and *to* place orders.

While the dialysis solution remains in the peritoneal cavity, the dialysis is achieved, a process that includes the *removal* of nitrogenous wastes and the *correction* of electrolyte imbalances and fluid overloads.

This report is intended for people with some electronics *background* but with little or no *knowledge* of geophysical prospecting.

Modifier Problems

Modifier problems occur when the word or phrase that a modifier is supposed to modify is unclear or absent, or when the modifier is located in the wrong place within the sentence. A modifier is any element—a word, phrase, or clause—that adds information to a noun or pronoun in a sentence. Modifier problems are usually divided into two groups: misplaced modifiers and dangling modifiers.

Misplaced Modifiers

They found out that the walkways had collapsed *on the late evening news.* (Was that before or after the sports news?)

The committee *nearly* spent a hundred hours investigating the accident. (Did they spend even a minute?)

The supervisor said *after the initial planning* the in-depth study would begin. (Just when did she say that, and when will the study begin?)

Dangling Modifiers

Having damaged the previous one, a new fuse was installed in the car. (Who damaged that fuse?)

After receiving the new dumb waiter, household chores became so much easier in the old mansion. (Who received the dumb waiter?)

Using a grant from the Urban Mass Transportation Administration, a contraflow lane was designed for I-45 North. (Who used that money?)

Pointing out the productivity and health problems plaguing U.S. workers, aerobic fitness programs may become much more common in American industry, according to the spokeswoman. (Who pointed that out?)

To correct misplaced-modifier problems, you can usually relocate the misplaced modifier (the word or phrase). To correct dangling modifiers, you can rephrase the dangling modifier, or rephrase the rest of the sentence that it modifies.

Revisions

On the late evening news we heard that the walkways had collapsed.
The committee spent nearly a hundred hours investigating the accident.
The supervisor said that the in-depth study would begin after the initial planning.

Because the previous fuse had been damaged, a new one had to be installed.
or
Having damaged the previous one, I had to install a new fuse in my car.
After we received the dumb waiter, it was immediately installed.
or
After receiving the dumb waiter, we immediately installed it.
When the Urban Mass Transportation Administration granted funds to the city, planners began designing a contraflow lane for I-45 North.
or
Using a grant from the Urban Mass Transportation Administration, city planners designed a contraflow lane for I-45 North.
Because of the productivity and health problems plaguing U.S. workers, aerobic fitness programs may become much more common in American industry, according to the spokeswoman.
or
Pointing out the productivity and health problems plaguing U.S. workers, the spokeswoman said that aerobic fitness programs may become much more common in American industry.

One particularly effective way to correct dangling modifiers is to create a *summary appositive,* that is, a noun or pronoun summarizing what was just said followed by an adjective clause:

Dangling-Modifier Problems	Summary-Appositive Revisions
Stars that were formed relatively recently should have higher concentrations of heavy elements than do the older stars, *which is confirmed by observation.*	Stars that were formed relatively recently should have higher concentrations of heavy elements than do the older stars, *a prediction* that is confirmed by observation.
Most astronomers now believe that the energy of quasars comes from giant black holes in the cores of the quasars, *which fits the growing belief that black holes are present in the cores of many galaxies, our own included.*	Most astronomers now believe that the energy of quasars comes from giant black holes in the cores of quasars, *a theory* that fits the growing belief that black holes are present in the cores of many galaxies, our own included.

Usage Problems

Problems with principal parts of verbs, subject-verb agreement, pronoun-reference agreement, pronoun case, and adjectives and adverbs can be called usage problems in that they are based on the conventions English-speaking people have adopted over the years. A convention is simply an agreement or understanding people have concerning, for example, when to use *who* as opposed to *whom* or when to use a singular verb as opposed to a plural verb.

Principal Parts of Verbs

Considering the complex nature of English verb forms, it's not hard to see why the principal parts of verbs are occasionally confused. Here are some examples:

Problems with Principal Parts

The water in the bottom of the tank was *froze.*
The wrench was *laying* on the bench in the toolshed.
The patient may have *throwed* a clot.
The committee has finally *wrote* the report.
She *laid* down to take a short nap.
Another hurricane has *raised* in the Gulf of Mexico.

If you were not sure of the correct form of the verb in cases like these, you could look them up in the dictionary. Here's what you'd see under *throw:*

[1]throw \\^{1}thrō\ vb threw \\^{1}thrü\; thrown \\^{1}thrōn\; throw·ing [ME *thrawen, throwen* to cause to twist, throw, fr. OE *thrāwen* to cause to twist or turn; akin to OHG *drāen*

to turn, L *terere* to rub, Gk *tribein* to rub, *tetrainein* to bore, pier] vt (14c) 1 a: to propel through the air by a forward motion of the hand and arm (∼ a baseball) . . .

Reprinted from *Webster's Ninth New Collegiate Dictionary* by permission from Merriam-Webster, Inc. © Copyright 1984.

Here are examples of other principal parts of verbs:

Present	Past	Past Participle
work	worked	worked
study	studied	studied
drive	drove	driven
dig	dug	dug
burst	burst	burst
drag	dragged	dragged
drug	drugged	drugged
lay	laid	laid
lie	lay	lain
set	set	set
sit	sat	sat
raise	raised	raised
rise	rose	risen

Several pairs of verbs, however, present special problems because they sound so much alike and because their definitions are rather similar. These include *lay* and *lie, set* and *sit,* and *raise* and *rise.* Study the following contrasting examples to see the difference, or consult your dictionary:

The operator *lays* the manual on the table. (present tense)
The shop manual *lies* on the table in the corner. (present tense)
The shop manual *lay* on the table all yesterday. (past tense)
She *sets* the video camera in an inconspicuous place. (present tense)
The operator *sits* by the machine, watching the gauges. (present tense)
The additional light *raises* the temperature substantially. (present tense)
The temperature *rises* dramatically when the lights are on. (present tense)

Agreement

There are three kinds of agreement problems to watch for: *subject-verb, pronoun-reference,* and *verb-tense* agreement. Agreement means that if the subject is plural, the verb should be plural; if the reference is singular, the pronoun should be singular; if one verb is in the present tense, the next one referring to the same situation should be in the present tense.

Subject-Verb Agreement.   With subject-verb agreement problems, either a singular subject is matched with a plural verb, or vice versa. (Remember that many singular verbs end in -s.) Sometimes it's hard to spot the true subject, particularly in these cases:

- When several words come between the subject and verb:

Agreement Problems	Revisions
The *communications* between the programmer and the rest of the company *tends* to be rather informal.	The *communications* between the programmer and the rest of the company *tend* to be rather informal.
The *purpose* of the monorails *have* changed from one of carrying food to one of carrying people to work in crowded urban areas.	The *purpose* of the monorails *has* changed from one of carrying food to one of carrying people to work in crowded urban areas.
The *shortage* of available infants and the *availability* of children with special needs *has* changed the focus of adoption for many parents.	The *shortage* of available infants and the *availability* of children with special needs *have* changed the focus of adoption for many parents.

- When there are two or more subjects joined by *and* or *or*:

Agreement Problems	Revisions
In the computer's memory *is* stored the *program* and the *data* to be manipulated by that program.	In the computer's memory *are* stored the *program* and the *data* to be manipulated by that program.
Either *BASIC* or *Pascal are* the high-level computer language you should take first.	Either *BASIC* or *Pascal is* the high-level computer language you should take first.
Skyrocketing *charges* for data preparation, the *need* to keep pace with rapidly increasing amounts of data, and *requirements* for fast system response *has* led to a search for more efficient input devices.	Skyrocketing *charges* for data preparation, the *need* to keep pace with rapidly increasing amounts of data, and *requirements* for fast system response *have* led to a search for more efficient input devices.
The magnetic-ink character-recognition *device* and the optical character-recognition *device is* two important advances in the preparation of batch input.	The magnetic-ink character-recognition *device* and the optical character-recognition *device are* two important advances in the preparation of batch input.

- When the normal subject-verb order is inverted:

Agreement Problems	Revisions
In the computer's memory *is* stored the *program* and the *data* to be manipulated by that program.	In the computer's memory *are* stored the *program* and the *data* to be manipulated by that program.
Introduced in 1968 by the Computer Machine Corporation *was* the *concept* of key-to-disk processing and the *concept* of shared processing.	Introduced in 1968 by the Computer Machine Corporation *were* the *concept* of key-to-disk processing and the *concept* of shared processing.
Equivalent to more than 3,000 punched cards *are* the single *diskette*, first introduced in 1972.	Equivalent to more than 3,000 punched cards *is* the single *diskette*, first introduced in 1972.
Through the center of the core *runs* several sense *wires*.	Through the center of the core *run* several sense *wires*.

• When the subject is a word like *each, every, none, either, neither, no one*, and *nobody*, especially when followed by a plural object of a preposition:

Agreement Problems	Revisions
Each of the steps in the process *are* treated in a separate chapter of this report.	*Each* of the steps in the process *is* treated in a separate chapter of this report.
Neither of the two high-level languages *offer* a facility for designing your own variables.	*Neither* of the two high-level languages *offers* a facility for designing your own variables.

• When the subject is a phrase or clause acting as a unit:

Agreement Problems	Revisions
Printing 54,000 characters per 60 seconds were considered a high speed for printers at one time.	*Printing 54,000 chararacters per 60 seconds* was considered a high speed for printers at one time.
Reversing the direction of currents through the wires change the magnetic state of the core.	*Reversing the direction of currents through the wires* changes the magnetic state of the core.
What is truly amazing about bits cells in integrated circuits are that 30 cells lined up side by side are about as wide as a human hair.	*What is truly amazing about bits cells in integrated circuits* is that 30 cells lined up side by side are about as wide as a human hair.

Pronoun-Reference Agreement.   When a pronoun and its reference (or antecedent) do not agree, one is plural and the other is singular. This problem also includes situations where the reference of the pronoun is vague or unclear: you wonder, "they who?" or "it what?"

Pronoun-Reference Problems

NASA hoped that by using production tooling rather than by making each tool individually, *they* could save time and money.

If an energy-efficient system can be developed, electrical *vehicles* could become as popular as *its* conventional counterpart.

Currently, *Houston* has $328.2 million in *their* 1984–85 budget to help fund a new form of mass transportation.

Aerobic fitness programs help to improve *an employee*'s physical condition by strengthening *their* circulatory, muscular, and respiratory systems.

American *industry* should implement aerobic fitness *programs* for the betterment of *their* employees even if there is some opposition to *it* at first.

To correct pronoun-reference problems, you either change the pronoun according to its reference or you change the reference according to the pronoun.

Revisions

NASA hoped that by using production tooling rather than by making each tool individually, *it* could save time and money.

If an energy-efficient system can be developed, electrical *vehicles* could become as popular as *their* conventional counterpart.

Currently, *Houston* has $328.2 million in *its* 1984–85 budget to help fund a new form of mass transportation.

Aerobic fitness programs help to improve *an employee*'s physical condition by strengthening *his* circulatory, muscular, and respiratory systems.

American *industry* should implement aerobic fitness *programs* for the betterment of *its* employees even if there is some opposition to *them* at first.

Another pronoun problem occurs when pronouns like *it, this, that,* or *which* have no clear reference:

Problem Pronouns	Revisions
Eventually, Faraday discovered that a change in magnetism could create an electrical current, *which* modern power supplies depend on.	Eventually, Faraday discovered that a change in magnetism could create an electrical current, *a principle* that modern power supplies depend on.
Since light has much higher frequencies than do radio waves, much more information can be carried by a light beam than by a radio wave, *which* enables it to carry many more	Since light has much higher frequencies than radio waves, much more information can be carried by a light beam than by a radio wave. *This capability* enables it to carry many

Problem Pronouns	Revisions
telephone conversations and television channels.	more telephone conversations and television channels.
Lasers have been used to study the reaction by which nitric oxide (NO) and ozone (O_3) make nitrogen dioxide (NO_2) and molecular oxygen (O_2). *This* is important in the production of smog from automobile exhausts.	Lasers have been used to study the reaction by which nitric oxide (NO) and ozone (O_3) make nitrogen dioxide (NO_2) and molecular oxygen (O_2), *a process* that is important in the production of smog from automobile exhausts.
Lasers have also been used to study the reaction by which nitric oxide and ozone make nitrogen dioxide (NO_2) and molecular oxygen. *It* plays an important role in the chemistry of the ozone layer that surrounds the earth and protects us from the sun's harmful ultraviolet radiation.	Lasers have also been used to study the reaction by which nitric oxide and ozone make nitrogen dioxide (NO_2) and molecular oxygen. *This process* plays an important role in the chemistry of the ozone layer that surrounds the earth and protects us from the sun's harmful ultraviolet radiation.

One final pronoun problem involves shifting between such pronouns as *he, they,* and *you* as well as nouns:

Pronoun Shift Problems	Revisions
The installation *crew* should make sure that the incinerator discharge duct is 100 percent tight. Discharge gases may be in the neighborhood of 1400° F, and duct leakage could lead to fires. *You* should also install a fan and ducting to the incinerator to prevent loss of heat by the fumes.	The installation *crew* should make sure that the incinerator discharge duct is 100 percent tight. Discharge gases may be in the neighborhood of 1400° F, and duct leakage could lead to fires. *The crew* should also install a fan and ducting to the incinerator to prevent loss of heat by the fumes.
In areas where below-freezing temperatures are encountered, *one* should install steam or electric tracer lines for air or fuel lines to prevent freezing or entrained water. *You* should also protect control valves from freezing.	In areas where below-freezing temperatures are encountered, *the crew* should install steam or electric tracer lines for air or fuel lines to prevent freezing or entrained water. *They* should also protect control valves from freezing.

Verb-Tense Agreement. Shifting between the different verb tenses at the wrong time is also an agreement problem. Remember that tense shifting is not incorrect in its own right, but when you start out discussing an event in the past and then shift to the present for no reason, it is. Here is an example:

Problems with Tense Shifting	*Tense*
On July 17, 1981, at approximately 7:05 P.M., two suspended walkways within the atrium area of the Hyatt Regency Hotel in Kansas City, Mo., *collapsed,* killing 111 people and injuring 188. Two of the injured subsequently *die.* In terms of loss of life and injuries, this *is* the most devastating structural collapse ever to take place in the United States.	past present present
At the time of the collapse, the hotel *had been* in service for approximately one year. The Hyatt Regency *consisted* of three main sections: a forty-story tower section, a function block, and a connecting atrium area. The atrium *was* a large open area approximately 117 ft (36 m) by 145 ft (44 m) in plan and 50 ft (15 m) high. Three suspended walkways *spanned* the atrium at the second-, third-, and fourth-floor levels. These walkways *connect* the tower section and the function block. The third-floor walkway *is* independently suspended from the atrium roof trusses while the second-floor walkway *was* suspended from the fourth-floor walkway, which in turn *was* suspended from the roof framing.	past perfect past past past present present past past
Senator Thomas F. Eagleton's office *has contacted* the National Bureau of Standards and *has requested* that technical assistance be provided to the city of Kansas City. Accordingly, two NBS structural research engineers *will be arriving* on July 21 and *will meet* with Mayor Richard L. Berkeley and other city officials.	present perf. present perf. future contin. future

In this example, the writer forgets to stay in the past tense to discuss the accident. Also a tense problem occurs in the discussion of the parts of the hotel: the original design of the walkways must be discussed in the past tense, because after the collapse the parts are no longer the same. Now, here's the revision:

Tense Shifts Revised	*Tense*
On July 17, 1981, at approximately 7:05 P.M., two suspended walkways within the atrium area of the Hyatt Regency Hotel in Kansas City, Mo., *collapsed,* killing 111 people and injuring 188. Two of the injured subsequently *died.* In terms of loss of life and injuries, this *was* the most devastating structural collapse ever to take place in the United States.	past past past
At the time of the collapse, the hotel *had been* in service for approximately one year. The Hyatt Regency *consists* of three main sections: a forty-story tower section, a function block, and a connecting atrium area. The atrium *is* a large open area approximately 117 ft (36 m) by 145 ft (44 m) in plan and 50 ft (15 m) high. Three suspended walkways *spanned* the atrium at the second-, third-, and fourth-floor levels. These walkways *connected* the tower section and the function block. The third-floor walkway *was* independently suspended from the atrium roof trusses while	past perfect present present past past past

Tense Shifts Revised	Tense
the second-floor walkway *was* suspended from the fourth-floor walkway, which in turn *was* suspended from the roof framing.	past past
Senator Thomas F. Eagleton's office *has contacted* the National Bureau of Standards and *has requested* that technical assistance be provided to the city of Kansas City. Accordingly, two NBS structural research engineers *will be arriving* on July 21 and *will meet* with Mayor Richard L. Berkeley and other city officials.	present perf. present perf. future contin. future

Pronoun Case

Pronoun-case problems occur when you use the wrong case of a pronoun: for example, *I* as opposed to *me*, or *who* as opposed to *whom* (for more on the cases of pronouns, see Appendix B):

Problems in Pronoun Case

Ms. Ohlen sent Mr. Steen and *I* the final report on the investigation of the accident.

Just between you and *I*, writing documentation for novice computer users is difficult.

The perception of pain is a first-line mechanism in a human being that enables *he* or *she* to respond quickly to potentially dangerous stimuli.

The supervisor then recommended that Mr. Ramirez and *me* write a report summarizing our observations at the site of the accident.

Us technical writers work closely with engineers on almost every detail of our technical publications.

All of *we* technical writers have met to plan the documentation for the new computer system.

Simplifying the sentence by deleting the words that have no bearing on the choice of the pronoun can help you select the right pronoun:

Revisions

Ms. Ohlen sent M̶r̶.̶ S̶t̶e̶e̶n̶ a̶n̶d̶ *me* the final report on the investigation of the accident.

Just between y̶o̶u̶ a̶n̶d̶ *me*, writing documentation for novice computer users is difficult.

The perception of pain is a first-line mechanism in a human being that enables *him* or *her* to respond quickly to potentially dangerous stimuli.

The supervisor then recommended that M̶r̶.̶ R̶a̶m̶i̶r̶e̶z̶ a̶n̶d̶ *I* write a report summarizing our observations at the site of the accident.

We t̶e̶c̶h̶n̶i̶c̶a̶l̶ w̶r̶i̶t̶e̶r̶s̶ work closely with engineers on almost every detail of our technical publications.

All of *us* t̶e̶c̶h̶n̶i̶c̶a̶l̶ w̶r̶i̶t̶e̶r̶s̶ have met to plan the documentation for the new computer system.

Pronoun-case problems involving *than* or *as* must be handled differently; you must rebuild the sentence following the pronoun:

Few graduates of that program have as much technical-writing training and experience as *we*. (. . . as *we* have.)

Understanding the architecture of the new system has been more difficult for Trinh than *her*. (. . . than for *her*.)

The new property taxes have hit residents of the northwestern part of the city harder than *us*. (. . . than they have hit *us*.)

The pronouns *who* and *whom* function the same way that other pronouns do: *who* is the nominative pronoun (for subjects or subject complements); *whom* is the objective pronoun (for direct objects, indirect objects, and objects of prepositions). To determine which pronoun to use, try this technique:

1. If the sentence is not a question, strike out all the words up to the *who* or *whom*:

   ~~It was the NBS engineers~~ *whom* Senator Eagleton's office contacted on 17 July.

   ~~It was the NBS engineers~~ *who* performed the tests on the walkways.

   ~~Send a copy of the report to~~ *who*ever wants one.

   ~~No one is sure~~ *who* will be the next mayor.

   ~~It was the NBS engineers to~~ *whom* Senator Eagleton's office made the request for technical assistance.

2. Now, make the remaining words into a complete sentence, juggling some of the words if necessary:

   Senator Eagleton's office contacted *the NBS* engineers.

   The NBS engineers performed the tests on the walkways.

   Who wants one?

   Who will be the next mayor?

   Senator Eagleton's office made the request for the technical assistance to *the NBS engineers*.

3. If it sounds right to substitute a nominative-case pronoun (I, he, she, they, we), use *who*. If it sounds right to substitute an objective-case pronoun (me, him, her, us, them), use *whom*:

   Senator Eagleton's office contacted *them*. → *(whom)*

   He wants one? → *(who)*

   She will be the next mayor? → *(who)*

   Senator Eagleton's office made the request for the technical assistance to *them*. → *(whom)*

Adjectives and Adverbs

Another usage problem involves knowing when to use an adjective as opposed to an adverb. Use an adjective when the word modifies a noun ("a *blue* car" or "a *portable* computer"). Use an adverb when the word modifies a verb, adjective, or another adverb ("reading *rapidly*," "a *well*-used television," or "reading *extremely* rapidly"). Usually, you can tell whether to use an adjective if the word answers the question *what? which?* or *which kind?* You can tell whether to use an adverb if the word answers the question *when? where? why?*, or *how?* Here are some examples of correct use of adjectives and adverbs:

Adjective-Adverb Use

Afterburner designs vary according to how *well* they achieve the goal of raising all the fumes to the required temperature for the required combustion residence time. (*How* do they achieve the goal? It modifies a verb.)

Contact of a waste stream with a catalyst bed allows oxidation reactions to occur *rapidly* in the temperature range of 700° to 900° F. (*How* does it occur? It modifies a verb.)

The relationship between Valles Marineris and the chaotic terrain northeastward is not understood *well*. (*How* is it understood? It modifies a verb.)

Impact craters appear most *frequently* on smooth areas of the canyon floor. (*When* or *how* do they appear? It modifies a verb.)

The rigid outer shell of the Earth (lithosphere) is divided into plates that move *laterally* with respect to one another. (*How* do they move in relation to each other? It modifies a verb.)

The fractures on Mars's surface are arrayed *unevenly* and are concentrated in *intensely* fractured zones called fossae. (*How* are they arrayed, and *how* are they fractured? The first modifies a verb; the second, an adjective.)

A special problem occurs when certain verbs such as *seem, appear, taste, turn, grow,* and *remain* are used as if they were linking verbs:

The geological history of Mars seems quite *different* [not *differently*] from that of Earth's.

By the 1970s our dependence on foreign oil had become *enormous* [not *enormously*].

The price of oil has remained *constant* [not *constantly*] for the past few years.

Details in the user's manual should be kept *simple* [not *simply*] at first.

Local citizens claim that the water from the desalination process does not taste *bad* [not *badly*].

As for adverbs used to strengthen adjectives or other adverbs, notice in the following examples that comparative adjectives are never used together (for example, *more denser*). Some adjectives add *-er* or *-est;* others use *more* or *most.* If you're not sure which to use, check your dictionary.

Incorrect Versions	*Revised Versions*
The streaks may be *more lighter* or *darker* than the surroundings.	The streaks may be *lighter* or *darker* than the surroundings.
A *more dense* atmosphere and a higher temperature are required for the existence of liquid water on the Martian surface.	A *denser* atmosphere and a higher temperature are required for the existence of liquid water on the Martian surface.
The Chryse outflow channels, and similar ones elsewhere on the planet, provide evidence of enormous floods on Mars—*more greater* than any known on Earth.	The Chryse outflow channels, and similar ones elsewhere on the planet, provide evidence of enormous floods on Mars—*greater* than any known on Earth.
Hawaiian volcanoes are among the *most largest* on Earth.	Hawaiian volcanoes are among the *largest* on Earth.
The snow is *powderier* in the mountains of Montana.	The snow is *more powdery* in the mountains of Montana.

Glossary of Other Usage Problems

Here is a miscellany of other common usage problems. *Nonstandard* means that a word or phrase is not considered correct in standard written English.

- *ain't.* A nonstandard usage for *is not, isn't, are not,* or *aren't.*
- *alot, lots.* A misspelling of "a lot"; a weak, vague, loose, conversational indicator of amount or quantity.
- *among, between. Among* is used for locations among three or more people, things, or for locations that are vague and unspecified; *between* is used for locations involving only two people or things or for locations involving two or more people or things when the relationship is fairly precise:

> We were standing *among* a half dozen friends when the crash occurred.
> Pinpointing the cause of the walkways collapse comes down to a choice *between* the design of the walkways, the quality of the construction work, and the materials used in the construction.
> The lawyer is standing *between* the contractor and the architect.
> The answer to the question concerning the walkways collapse was eventually found *among* the fragments of the wreckage.

- *few, less. Few* is used with nouns that can be changed from plural to singular, often called "countable" nouns (for example, dollar or woman); *less* is used with nouns that are not pluralized (for example, water, money).

> *Fewer* customers are shopping at this store; therefore we are making *less* money.

- *many, much. Many* and *much* are used the same way that *few* and *less* are, respectively.
- *as, like. As* is used as a subordinating conjunction to connect dependent to independent clauses when comparisons are made; *like* is a preposition used to make comparisons between nouns, pronouns, or phrases:

> The box beam-hanger rod arrangement was not constructed *as* it should have been.
> The actual construction of the box beam-hanger rod arrangement was *like* the blueprint specifications of it.

- *awful, awfully.* Nonstandard versions of such words as *very, quite,* or *much.*
- *being as, being that, being as how.* Wordy, awkward constructions for *because, in that,* or *since.*
- *could of, should of,* etc. Nonstandard sound-alike versions of *could have, should have,* etc.
- *different from, different than.* Words, phrases, or dependent clauses follow "different from"; independent clauses follow "different than":

The box beam-hanger rod arrangement was different *from* what NBS engineers had expected to find.

The box beam-hanger rod arrangement in the actual construction was different *from* its design specifications.

The box beam-hanger rod arrangement was different *than* the NBS engineers had expected.

• *farther, further. Farther* is used with geographical or physical distances, whereas *further* is used with chronological, nonmeasurable, or conceptual distances:

Is Jupiter *farther* from Earth than Mars?

Is Los Angeles *farther* from Kansas City than New York?

An independent, thinking computer is much *further* away from becoming a reality than many people envision.

The computer industry has come *further* in the last two decades than anyone could have imagined.

• *fine, great, neat, really, terrific.* All conversational speech words that add little or no meaning to technical prose.

• *irregardless.* A double negative form of *regardless;* use *regardless* instead.

• *is when, is where.* An awkward construction that often causes unclear, wordy writing especially when the preceding word is being defined:

Wordy Version	*Revised Versions*
The box beam-hanger rod arrangement *is where* the problem was in the KC Hyatt Regency walkway collapse.	In the KC Hyatt Regency walkway collapse, the problem occurred in the box beam-hanger rod arrangement.
Angina pectoris *is when* a person experiences chest pain caused by occlusion of the coronary arteries, resulting in an insufficient supply of oxygen to the heart muscle.	Angina pectoris occurs when [or is a condition in which] a person experiences chest pain caused by occlusion of the coronary arteries, resulting in an insufficient supply of oxygen to the heart muscle.

• *kind of, sort of.* Loose conversational ways of writing *rather, somewhat, almost,* or *nearly.*

• *off of.* A nonstandard construction for *off.*

• *okay.* A loose, conversational way of indicating something is adequate.

• *reason is because, reason is due to, reason is owing to, reason is on account of.* Redundant ways of writing "reason is that." These constructions can also be eliminated by using action verbs.

Wordy Version	Revised Version
The *reason* that the KC Hyatt Regency walkways collapsed *was due to the fact that* the original design had been altered during construction.	The KC Hyatt Regency walkways collapsed because the original design had been altered during construction.

- *suppose to, use to.* Incorrectly spelled versions of *supposed to* and *used to.*
- *sure and, try and.* Loose, slangy versions of *be sure to* and *try to.*
- *this here, that there,* etc. Nonstandard versions of *this, that,* etc.
- *where . . . at.* A nonstandard and unnecessary use of *at*:

The repairman wondered where the thermostat was *át.*

- *-wise.* A wordy, awkward construction that can be rephrased in any of a number of ways:

Problem Sentences	Revisions
Design-wise, the walkways were more than adequate for the loads they were subjected to.	The walkways were designed to be more than adequate for the loads they were subjected to.
The NBS engineers discovered crucial differences blueprint-wise in the collapsed walkways.	The NBS engineers discovered crucial differences between the blueprints of the collapsed walkways and their actual construction.

Graphics Problems

Problems with the different kinds of punctuation and with capital letters are graphics problems: they have to do with writing signals that indicate how to read sentences. Commas, semicolons, colons, dashes, hyphens, parentheses, quotation marks, and apostrophes all tell readers when to pause or stop and how to read certain words or groups of words. Similarly, capital letters show readers how to understand certain words.

Commas

Surprisingly few rules concern the use of commas. Learn how commas are used structurally within sentences; then you can start bending those rules to achieve the clarity or effect that you want.

- Use a comma between two sentences joined by a coordinating conjunction (*and, or, nor, but, yet, for, whereas*), except when the two sentences are very short. (In the second set of examples that follow, commas are not needed because they are compound predicates, not compound sentences. Long compound predicates, however, can use commas.)

Compound Sentences

The tank is made of aluminum, *but* the outer surface is protected by a spray-on foam.

By the mid-1970s, the free-spending ways of the Apollo Program were gone, *and* NASA now had to grapple with large technical challenges on a limited budget.

It first appeared that Hurricane Betsy would reach the eastern United States, *but* a looping path took her around the tip of Florida and into the Gulf instead.

Gamma rays produce few pairs but they travel farther. (short sentences)

One grate turns at 50 mph but the others turn at 15 mph. (short sentences)

Compound Predicates

Offspring exposed to significant amounts of alcohol in utero are much more active than controls *and* sometimes seem to fly around the room.

Plastic parts are not weldable *and* must be repaired by other methods.

The observation and measurement of such small frequency shifts require excellent radar frequency-stability characteristics that are not usually found in conventional radar, *but* can be added without a drastic increase in equipment costs. (long predicates)

Pulse Doppler radar effectively samples the backscattered signal at the radar repetition rate, *and* can therefore provide unambiguous Doppler frequency observations only in the frequency range allowed by the sampling rate. (long predicates)

The manganese dioxide used in batteries is usually obtained from natural ore (mainly from Gabon, Greece, and Mexico), *but* can be a synthetic product prepared by chemical precipitation or by electrolytic methods. (long predicates)

• Use a comma after any longer introductory element (prepositional phrase or adverb clause) and after introductory participial phrases.

When an atom acquires enough energy to leave its orbit, the atom is positively charged.

As for the energy required to produce plastic automobile parts, the automakers view the additional cost as justified by the savings in petroleum by a lighter car during its lifetime.

Since the high-pressure turbopumps rotate at speeds of 30,000 rpm, the weight distribution on the turbine blades must be balanced with great accuracy.

Because there is no belt of doldrums in the Atlantic south of the equator, hurricanes do not usually occur there.

Between 40 and 50 degrees west and just south of 10 degrees north in the western end of the doldrums belt, calms do occur with frequency, and hurricanes originate there with great frequency.

In 1831 Michael Faraday discovered that if a magnet was moved in the vicinity of a coil, a current could be induced in the coil. (short introductory phrase)

Using this concept Faraday arrived at a relation between the changing flux and the induced electromagnetic field. (short introductory phrase)

• Use commas with nonrestrictive phrases or clauses; do not use commas with restrictive phrases or clauses. (If you can delete the phrase or clause without changing the meaning of the sentence, it is a nonrestrictive element, not essential to the meaning of the sentence):

Restrictive Elements: No Commas

A turbopump is essentially a pump *that is turned by the action of a turbine that shares a common shaft with the pump.*

Eighty percent of the work *done by the heart* is carried out by the left ventricle, which pumps blood into the arteries *serving the organs and the tissues.*

A drop of water almost flattens out *when it is placed on a glass plate.*

In one study, 11 percent of the offspring *whose mothers consumed two to four drinks per day* showed partial features of fetal alcohol syndrome (FAS), while 19 percent of those *whose mothers consumed four or more drinks per day* showed FAS features.

Nonrestrictive Elements: Commas Needed

Eighty percent of the work done by the heart is carried out by the left ventricle, *which pumps blood into the arteries serving the organs and the tissues.*

The test produced a speed in the high-pressure hydrogen turbopump of 7000 rpm, *which is 19 percent of design speed.*

The Coriolis force, *caused by the rotation of the earth,* always acts at right angles to the pressure gradient in the northern hemisphere.

The bulky equipment, *although placed on a rolling cart,* must always remain within 6 feet of the heart-transplant patient.

The formation of hurricane, *a type of atmospheric vortex,* involves the combined effect of pressure and circular wind.

Researchers also found that heavy drinkers—*women drinking at least 1.6 ounces of absolute alcohol during pregnancy*—have infants averaging 59 grams less than the infants of lighter drinkers.

When added to liquids, detergent materials decrease the contact angle, *thereby decreasing the wettability.*

When waterproofing material is added to a fabric, it increases the contact angle, *making the fabric water-repellant.*

Molecules may also have some degree of ordered as well as disordered motion, *in which case the total energy is the sum of the mechanical and thermal energies.*

• Do not break up the main sentence pattern with a single comma; use pairs of commas as shown in the preceding examples (the *x*s in the following examples show where commas are likely to be incorrectly placed):

Decreasing the radar operating frequency thus *x* increases the effective velocity coverage for the same sampling rate.

It can be assumed that *x* precipitation particles move with the air in their environment and are therefore good tracers for air motion.

The separator between the black mix and the zinc electrode *x* consists of a paper barrier coated with cereal or methyl cellulose.

That European refuse incineration costs are substantially lower than U.S. costs *x* is particularly evident when income from by-product recovery and salvage operations is included.

- Use commas in any series of three or more items (although the comma before the *and* is considered optional, use it to ensure clarity).

> *Instrument panels, bumper components, door liners, seat covers, and grille panels* are the most common parts produced directly by automakers.
>
> *A 12-ounce can of beer, a 5-ounce glass of wine, and a mixed drink with 1.5 ounces of 80-proof liquor* all contain approximately the same amount of alcohol.
>
> The development years involved *designing the components for the space shuttle's engines, testing the original designs, and retesting the redesigned components.*
>
> In humans, the period of rapid brain development *begins at midpregnancy, peaks in the third trimester, and ends by the postnatal year.*

With adjectives in a series before a noun, use commas if changing the order of the adjectives does not cause the sentence to sound strange, if you can add an *and* between items in the series without causing the sentence to sound strange, or if you think commas help the clarity of the sentence:

> The space shuttle uses *high-pressure liquid, hydrogen-oxygen* engines mounted on the aft section.
>
> Each door is held shut with an *adjustable, spring-loaded* door latch.
>
> As each rank passes through the wash chamber, the dishes get a *thorough soil-stripping* wash and a *final, automatic, hot-water* rinse.

- Use commas to prevent the possibility of misreading (think about how you could read the following sentences *without* the commas):

> Before, solar energy devices had not attracted much interest.
>
> Once outside, the astronauts began repairing the damaged communications satellite.
>
> Having finished sanding, Mr. Waley then applied the first coat of paint.
>
> With the temperature over 90°, eight of the machines malfunctioned.
>
> Instead of cooling off, the engines continued to overheat.
>
> While closely watching, Alfredo saw a shooting star burst across the sky.

- Use commas in dates and addresses as shown in these examples:

> More information can be obtained from AT&T, 1 Speldwill Avenue, Morristown, New Jersey 07960.
>
> They wrote to Framingham, Massachusetts, where several computer and software companies are located.
>
> On July 10, 1985, the Office Applications conference began.
>
> They attended the National Computer Conference in May 1985 to see the latest in computerized graphics equipment.

Semicolons

A semicolon is a stronger kind of punctuation, indicating a longer pause than a comma, but a shorter one than a period. Semicolons are used when there is no coordinating conjunction between two complete sentences, when there is a coordinating conjunction but commas in the complete sentences, and when there is a series with other commas in the items in that series.

• Use a semicolon between two complete sentences closely related in meaning but lacking a coordinating conjunction (here, the semicolon indicates less than a full stop):

"Plaque-fissuring" refers to the formation of an opening from the lumen to the intima; it leads to an intraintimal thrombus containing not just red cells but mainly fibrin and platelets.

In 1940 philanthropy accounted for 24 percent of the total operating budget of nonprofit hospitals in New York City; in 1948 it had dropped to 17 percent.

Gray mold is one of the most important fungal diseases in Italian viticulture; its growth causes serious production losses and adversely affects wine quality.

• Use a semicolon when you want to join two sentences with an adverbial conjunction (no semicolon is needed if the adverbial conjunction occurs within an individual sentence):

Dolomitization of limestones may be fully selective; *for example*, the cores of the Silurian reefs of Illinois, Indiana, and Wisconsin are dolomite, whereas the reef flank material may be only partially dolomitic.

Precipitation has the form of a "distributed" target; *that is*, there are numerous independent scatterers distributed in space.

The total load on any electrical power system is seldom constant; *rather*, it varies widely with hourly, weekly, monthly, and annual changes in the requirements of the area served.

The voltage of an electrical generator varies with the load and power factor; *consequently*, some form of regulating equipment is required to maintain a reasonably constant and predetermined potential at distribution stations or load centers.

Computer simulations of modeled systems or components are very successful at testing known forces; *however*, this type of testing does not give accurate performance data on the unexpected forces.

The engine failure, *however*, led to a major review of hardware performance. (only one complete sentence)

Complete velocity determination, *therefore*, requires the use of at least three systems. (only one complete sentence)

• Use a semicolon between two complete sentences that are joined by a coordinating conjunction but that have other commas:

Injury caused by pollutants can easily be mistaken for injury caused by other stresses; or, just the opposite, injury symptoms from adverse temperature or moisture relations may resemble, and can be incorrectly attributed to, air pollutants.

Possible research areas announced recently have included genetics, fermentation microbiology, and immobilized biocatalysts; but environmental biotechnology, such as metal recovery and waste recycling, is also included.

A typical membrane potential of about one-tenth of a volt sounds relatively small; but, because it occurs across a membrane that is only about 10 nanometers thick, it represents an enormous voltage gradient of about 10 million volts per meter.

• Use a semicolon to connect two sentences, the second of which is elliptical (that is, when words are understood and can be omitted):

The day was July 17, 1981; the time, 7:05 P.M.
Transistors are fabricated by monolithic processes; resistors and capacitors, by deposition of semiconductor material on a ceramic substrate.

• Use semicolons to punctuate a series that has commas within some of the items:

The heart undergoes two cardiac-cycle periods: diastole, when blood enters the ventricles; and systole, when the ventricles contract and blood is pumped out.
An organization may be functional, with responsibility assigned on the basis of buying, selling, promotion, distribution, and other tasks; production-oriented, with production managers for each product category and brand managers for each individual brand in addition to functional categories; or market-oriented, with managers assigned on the basis of geographical markets and customer types in addition to functional categories.
Electric-power substations are used for some or all of the following purposes: connection of generators with transmission or distribution lines, and of loads to each other; transformation of power from one voltage level to another; interconnection of alternate sources of power; and detection of faults, monitoring and recording of information, power measurement, and remote communication.
Carl Sagan, in his book *The Dragons of Eden*, compresses the entire fifteen-billion-year history of the universe into a single year to show how short and how recent human history is: recorded human history occupies only the last ten seconds of the year; the history of the general-purpose computer, the last three-tenths of a second of that year; the history of the electronic computer and of the microprocessor, the last one eight-hundredths and the last eleven one-thousandths of a second of that year, respectively.

Colons

Although they look rather similar, semicolons and colons have quite different functions.

• Use a colon to join a list of items to the end of a complete sentence.

The main engines of the space shuttle consist of six main components: the external tank, the low-pressure turbopump, the high-pressure turbopumps, the preburners, the combustion chamber, and the nozzle.
Hurricane size is expressed in four ways: the strength of the maximum winds, the diameter of the hurricane-force winds, the diameter of the gale-force winds, and the overall size of the cyclone circulation.
To make a metal dashboard, three steps are required: (1) the metal must be stamped; (2) the texture must be stamped into the metal; and (3) the part must be painted.

• If the list is part of the sentence rather than tacked on to the end, don't use a colon. To illustrate this rule, here are different versions of the preceding sentences:

The main engines of the space shuttle consist of the external tank, the low-pressure turbopump, the high-pressure turbopumps, the preburners, the combustion chamber, and the nozzle.

Hurricane size is expressed in the strength of the maximum winds, the diameter of the hurricane-force winds, the diameter of the gale-force winds, and the overall size of the cyclone circulation.

To make a metal dashboard, (1) the metal must be stamped, (2) the texture must be stamped into the metal, and (3) the part must be painted.

• Use a colon between two sentences when the first sentence introduces or prepares the reader for the second:

The grades of the students in the caffeine research project told a dramatic story: the higher the caffeine intake, the lower the grades, both for semester and overall grade point average.

In general, shelf life increases as the cell size of the battery becomes smaller: with well-constructed cells, shelf lives of three years with a No. 6 telephone cell and ten years with a penlight cell are possible.

The line-of-sight in a communication satellite can be a problem: communication satellites can see the earth's surface only between about 83° north latitude and 83° south latitude.

Many of the new applications of microcomputers are "interactive": there is frequent interaction between the computer and one or more users.

• Use a colon to join a quotation to a complete sentence that introduces that quotation:

John Evelyn, who wrote one of the first treatises in 1661 on air-pollution problems caused by coal smoke, provided an early account of the impact of this smoke on plant health: "These agents are in nature able to make the particles of bodies stick together by very strong attractions. And it is the business of experimental philosophy to find them out."

H. G. Wells had this observation to make about the earlier and the more recent physics: "The atoms of our fathers seemed by contrast like a game of marbles abandoned in the corner of a muddy playground on a wet day."

• Do *not* use colons to interrupt a complete sentence (the *x*s show incorrect placement):

The typical Doppler velocity sensor consists of **x** a transistor, an antenna, and a receiver. Three significant types of generating plants are **x** hydroelectric, fossil-fuel-electric, and nuclear-electric.

Dashes

Just as the semicolon is another kind of period indicating a shorter pause between complete sentences, the dash is another kind of comma used within sentences. To make a dash with a regular typewriter, type two hyphens, leaving no space between the dash and the words before or after it. Remember that dashes are always used in pairs unless the phrase comes at the end of a sentence. Also, do not use dashes to connect two complete sentences.

• Use a dash to indicate a sudden shift in thought, for example, when a short complete sentence interrupts a sentence:

> For one moment in every 137 moments—a moment being a very short time—you find a particle of light in the vicinity of an electron.
>
> Imagine a set of millions of different universes—a "world ensemble" was Brandon Carter's phrase—possessing between them every conceivable combination of starting conditions and strengths of forces.
>
> The evidence soon shifted strongly—though not decisively—in favor of an "open universe."
>
> A filter that has the inverse performance of that of a low-pass filter—that is, one that stops low frequencies but passes high ones—is called a high-pass filter.

• Use dashes to set off a series containing commas of its own:

> A control group of patients was studied in whom there was a clear noncardiac cause of sudden death that was either natural—such as intracerebral hemorrhage, dissecting aneurysm, or pulmonary emboli—or unnatural, involving trauma or suicide.
>
> A 10-week lecture program on fundamental aspects of biotechnology—current applications, microbiology, genetics of industrial organisms, and biochemical engineering—will be followed by a 9-month period of research training.
>
> The xanthine derivatives—caffeine, theophylline, and theobromine—occur naturally in coffee beans, tea leaves, kola nuts, and cocoa beans.

• Use a dash when the final phrase or clause summarizes the contents of the sentence, especially if the main part is a list:

> Dust blown free from desert soils or wastelands, ash and gases spewed from volcanoes or rising from burning forests, even pleasantly odoriferous organic vapors released from forest trees and other plants together with pollens and spores, and the fresh aroma of the sea near the coasts—all contribute to the character of the natural air.
>
> Reading, watching TV, listening to the radio or the stereo, playing any kind of game, or using a personal computer—all are information pursuits.

• Use dashes to place emphasis on interrupting phrases:

> A young neurosurgeon starting out in an independent practice faces a prospective outlay of $150,000 per year in office rent, liability coverage, and other expenses—before seeing the first patient.
>
> Donaldson advocates examining the cash flows of the company under the most adverse conditions—that is, in his definition, under recession conditions.
>
> Much as with health effects, measurement of air pollution on plant life and on ecosystems is difficult—particularly at the lower levels of pollution.

• Use dashes to attach explanatory phrases or clauses to the ends of sentences:

Eventually, Michael Faraday discovered that a change in magnetism could create an electric current—the principle of electrical generation on which modern power supplies depend.

In fact, antimatter is so perfectly opposite to matter that if matching particles and anti-particles come together, they simply cancel out—annihilating each other and disappearing from the universe.

Already, machine builders from different laboratories around the world are beginning seriously to discuss a "World Machine"—an accelerator so big that even the United States cannot afford it.

The temperature of a black hole formed by a collapse of a heavy star is very low—less than a millionth of a degree above absolute cold.

Hyphens

Hyphens are mainly used when two or more words act as a single unit within a sentence. Knowing when to hyphenate two words can be tricky in that our language is changing so much in this area. For example, *data base* started out as two separate words, but with increasing use, it has been hyphenated, *data-base*, and, among some publications, is now even written solid, *database*. Although it cannot keep up with changes in hyphenation, the dictionary is a good place to look when you have a question on whether words are separate, hyphenated, or solid.

• Use hyphens for written-out compound numbers from twenty-one to ninety-nine and for fractions.

twenty-one 100-meter pipes	a billion-billionth of a second
one-half of the output	two-thirds of the total

• Use hyphens in certain compound-adjective situations:

—If one of the words of the compound adjective is a preposition:

below-average rainfall	warm-up period
built-in scale	on-board timer
start-up costs	pay-off period
in-service accuracy	written-out number

—If one of the words in the compound adjective is a noun:

low-cost pesticide	three-phase circuit
sea-floor spreading	first-order gradient
triple-vessel coronary disease	main-sequence stars
670-km seismic discontinuity	flat-cell battery
carbon-14 isotope tracer	energy-volume ratio
quantitative-skills test	ocean-surface temperature
coronary-bypass surgery	watt-hour meter
large-scale changes	hurricane-force winds
third-party payers	deep-well injections
ten-month period	five-year grant
	256-kilobyte memory

—If the second word of the compound adjective is an adjective modifying the
first (particularly if the second word ends in *-ed*, *-ing*, or some similar form):

drought-producing system	water-repellent fabric
coffee-flavored ice cream	nutrient-rich waters
government-sponsored programs	corrosion-resistant metal
pressure-induced melting	water-soluble reactants
spring-balanced doors	salt-free diet
health-related costs	caffeine-containing substances

• Use hyphens on certain compound nouns (see your dictionary when in doubt):

a half-length	a light-year
the by-product	a read-out
the half-life	the start-up

• Use hyphens with series compound adjectives:

base-, intermediate-, and peak-load service
resistance- and submerged-arc furnace
second- and third-degree burns
radiation-mutated and -altered molecules

• Use hyphens with some of the common prefixes such as *self-* and *mid-* (see
your dictionary when in doubt).
• Use hyphens with adjectives made up of three or more words:

over-the-counter drugs	debt-to-equity ratio
signal-to-noise ratio	twenty-seven-year-old physicist
double-declining-balance method	off-and-on switch
	cost-per-unit limitation

Apostrophes

Apostrophes are used to show possession, to form contractions, and sometimes to
indicate plurals of letters, numbers, or words.

• Singular words not ending in *-s* use *'s* to show possession:

Earth's shadow	the fish's ear
the Moon's orbit	India's population
this company's profits	the family's car

• Singular nouns ending in *-s* add *'s* to show possession:

Mars's shadow	Venus's orbit
James's calculator	tennis's popularity

• Plural words ending in *-s* add an apostrophe to show possession:

these companies' employees	planets' orbits
these species' niches	these countries' population
southern states' capitals	these computers' capabilities

- Plural words not ending in -s add an 's to show possession:

women's rights	men's rights
children's education	geese's honking

- Possessive pronouns never use apostrophes:

This book is yours.
This CRT is theirs, not ours.

- Use apostrophes to make contractions with *not*, *is*, and other words:

The mail hasn't arrived yet.
The battery doesn't work anymore.
They aren't registered to vote.
He's going to the Olympics this year.
Sheila's taking the train.
She's learning Pascal.
They'll handle the artwork.

Quotation Marks, Brackets, and Ellipsis Points

Because they are so often used together, quotation marks, brackets, and ellipsis points are all discussed together in this section.

Quotation Marks.   Here are the standard rules for using quotation marks:

- Use quotation marks to set off direct quotations but not indirect quotations:

"If I have seen farther," Isaac Newton once said, "it was because I was standing on the shoulders of giants."
As distinguished physicist Robert W. Wilson, the former director of the Fermi National Accelerator Laboratory, said when asked by a U.S. senator to state what the physicist's laboratory was contributing to national security, "It has nothing to do directly with defending our country except to help make it worth defending."
"The only existing things are atoms and empty space; all else is mere opinion," wrote Democritus, the Greek philosopher in the fifth century B.C.
The commission on the Three Mile Island accident concluded that most of the radiation was contained in the plant and that the radiation that was released will "have a negligible effect on the physical health of the individuals."
The report holds that nuclear power is cheaper than conventional sources of power: "The fuel cost for a nuclear reactor is 15.8 mills per kilowatt hour compared to 13.7 mills per kilowat hour for a coal-fired power plant."
Aristotle states that the earth is in the center of the universe.
Hubble announced that the spirals always showed redshifts and that the farther the galaxies were from us, the larger their redshifts.

- Use quotation marks for titles of magazine articles, speeches, television or radio programs, poems, songs, or chapters of books:

We read Martin Luther King, Jr.'s speech, "I Have a Dream."
She has been reading an article entitled "What Kind of a Programmer Are You?" published
in *Datamation* in March 1977.
They listen to "All Things Considered," a news program on NPR radio stations.
Last night, he spent four hours reading and thinking about Yeats's eight-line poem entitled
"The Magi."
Scrapers are discussed in Chapter 5, "Transporting Materials," because of their close
affinity with tractor operations.

• Use quotation marks to set off unusual or highly individualized phrases, nick-
names, or brief quoted material (but use such marks sparingly with phrases, even
when used in an ironic sense):

The additional carbon dioxide in the atmosphere will increase the "greenhouse effect."
Few could remain aloof from the "naked charm" of an understanding of the broader
scheme of the universe.
Critics sneered about the "expensive toys" that were being built at the Fermi labs.
Devices called "heat exchangers" can provide ventilation without losing all the indoor
heat of a building.
Some scientists believe that the "life force" is simply electricity.

• When a direct quotation contains a quotation of its own, use single quotation
marks for the quotation-within-a-quotation:

Derman emphasizes Mrazek's belief that "the PLA [Programmable Logic Array] is going
the 'way of the dinosaur and the dodo bird' and will eventually become a museum piece."

• Punctuate quotations as if the quotation marks were not there.

—Periods and commas go on the inside of closing quotation marks:

"Custom chips in ten weeks for $10,000 are not far off," with improved design and layout
aids, says Jim Meyer of Silicon Systems in Santa Ana, California.
"We're seeing a trend toward general-purpose architectures and general-purpose designs,"
he explains, "but not a general-purpose chip."

—Semicolons and colons go on the outside of quotation marks:

According to one expert, "The PLA may soon be on its way out"; the microprocessor is
pushing it out of existence.
In Mrazek's view, "The PLA can simplify many traditional ROM applications": one
example he cites is code conversion.

—Placement of question marks and exclamation marks depends on whether they
are part of the quoted statement or part of the statement that contains the
quotation.

> Do you understand what is meant by the phrase "Programmable Array Logic"?
> She asked, "Do you understand what is meant by the phrase 'Programmable Array Logic'?"

Brackets.   Brackets are similar to parentheses but have a special and much more limited use.

• Use brackets when you want to insert explanatory material of your own in a direct quotation:

> As Wallace Hansen and Edwin Eckel wrote in their U.S. Geological Survey report on the quake.

> > One of the greatest tectonic events of our time occurred in Southern Alaska late in the afternoon of March 27, 1964 [the Alaskan earthquake whose shocks had a magnitude of 8.3–8.7 and lasted 1–7 minutes]. Beneath the leaden sky, the chill of evening was just settling over the Alaskan countryside. . . .

• Use brackets around words or letters inserted into a direct quotation to make it read as clear, standard English:

> Andre Vaucroux described the surprising new technology of the microcomputer in the May 1975 *Scientific American* this way:

> > [A] major conceptual advance in 1971 . . . [occurred] when Intel Corporation, which had undertaken to develop a calculator chip, chose to design it as a more versatile, programmable, single-chip microprocessor.

The words *A* and *occurred* are not in the original; the deletions (marked by the three dots, or ellipsis points) and the brackets enable you to present a shorter quotation.

• Use a bracketed "[*sic*]" within a direct quotation if the quotation contains an error, misspelling, or strange usage; this way you indicate the error is not yours:

> A credit bureau mailed letters throughout Massachusetts and New Hampshire bearing this chilling message:

> > We have a credit file that contains all or part of the following information about you . . . your employment, your income, your martial [*sic*] status, credit references, your payment on bills, mortgages, liens, and your history in paying them. . . .

Martial of course refers to military matters, whereas *marital* refers to matters relating to marriage.

Ellipsis Marks.   Use ellipsis marks, three dots (. . .), to indicate where you've omitted words from a quotation:

> Weizenbaum suggests that "since we do not . . . have any way of making computers wise, we ought not to give computers tasks that demand wisdom."

Before 1820, several orders of the Surgeon General of the United States directed that weather observations were to be taken by the Post Surgeons to provide data that could be used in answering questions about the effect of climate on the health of troops in remote outposts, on "medical topography . . . prevalent regional complaints . . . change of climate . . . cultivation of soil . . . [and] density of population" (U.S. Weather Bureau, 1955, p. 2).

John R. Mather, *Climatology: Fundamentals and Applications* (New York: McGraw-Hill, 1974), 3–4. Reprinted with permission.

Underlining and Italics

Underlining and italics are used to indicate different treatments of words, for example, titles of books. Use underlining if you have no way to create italics.

• Italicize the titles of books, magazines, journals, newspapers, plays, long poems, long musical works, movies, and technical reports; names of specific water, air, or space vehicles; and species' scientific names.

In their book *Search for Charm*, Gaillard, Lee, and Rosner had written that convincing evidence for charmed particles would come from observations of short tracks.

"This is the tune of our catch, played by the picture of Nobody," complains Trinculo in Shakespeare's play *The Tempest*.

She had been reading an article entitled "Beyond Plate Tectonics" in *Scientific American* magazine.

The same fossil flora, known as *Glossopteris*, has been found in sediments deposited close to the ice in Antarctica, South America, India, and Australia.

Possibly the first coral collected from the Galápagos for scientific study was a specimen found by Darwin during the *Beagle*'s sojourn in the islands in 1835.

Viking I and *Viking II*, two U.S. spacecraft, landed on Mars in 1976.

We read reviews of *Chorus Line,* a Broadway musical, in the *New York Times* and the *Washington Post.*

Computers have not yet reached the point of long-range, deliberative behavior exhibited by HAL, the power-mad computer in the film *2001: A Space Odyssey.*

The NBS has just submitted its findings on the accident in a report entitled *Investigation of the Kansas City Hyatt Regency Walkways Collapse.*

• Italicize foreign words or phrases, except when commonly used:

Einstein's theory of gravity, known as general relativity, is a *tour de force.*

The word *digital* is derived from the Latin *digitus,* which means "finger."

The chairman does not want to upset the status quo.

The *ancien regime* in the English department has recently carried out a veritable *jihad* against some of its own members.

• Italicize words, letters, or numbers when discussed *as* such:

It is difficult to remember how many *c*s and *s*s there are in words like *necessary.*

To a dyslexic, a *35* may appear as a *53.*

• Italicize words or phrases to show emphasis (but only sparingly) or to indicate that the italicized term is being defined:

> To produce a system that will be readily accepted by novice computer users, you must keep in mind that the interface with users has to *appear* simple, even if it takes greater complexity in the computer or software itself.
>
> *Chemelectrics* concerns itself with the conversion of chemical energy into electrical current.

Parentheses

Like dashes, parentheses are another form of comma, except that the words that they enclose are much less essential.

• Use parentheses to enclose nonessential information you want to include anyway:

> It follows that there will be an incentive to seek investment with faster paybacks (shorter economic lines) and that industry will become less capital intensive.
>
> Because suppliers of capital to the firm (investors and creditors) tend to be risk-averse, the acceptance of a project that changes the risk complexion of a firm may cause it to change its required rates of return for investing or extending credit.
>
> The specifications for velocity accuracy are around a quarter of a percent of ground speed (and 0.2 knots or 0.1 m/s when hovering).
>
> Since the need for increasing velocity coverage would otherwise require an increase of the pulse repetition rate (which reduces the radar maximim range), it is advantageous to use the longest possible wavelength.
>
> The cost of a design is now based on how efficiently circuits (and not necessarily the components within them) are used.

• Use parentheses to set up an abbreviation that you will use throughout the rest of a report:

> Classically, a computer system is composed of software plus three basic hardware types of subsystems: the input-output units, the memory, and the central processing unit (CPU).
>
> On the horizontal axis is plotted earnings before interest and taxes (EBIT); and on the vertical axis, earnings per share (EPS).

• Use parentheses to enclose a whole sentence either as part of another sentence or separate from it. Notice in these examples how the capitalization and punctuation differ:

> Batteries stored at 4° C (sealed polyurethane bags should be used to prevent condensation with subsequent corrosion of the terminals and metal jacket or degradation of the paper jacket) have their shelf life increased two or three times.
>
> All tetrapods and most fish have three semicircular canals (the jawless fish have only one or two), one lying in each of the three planes of space.

The sending end of the system consists of a battery and a telegraph key. One side of the
   battery is connected to the ground. (The wire from the negative side of the battery is
   connected to a conducting rod that is driven into the ground.)

• Use parentheses to enclose numbers or letters that introduce items in a list:

The company may finance with (a) all common stock, (b) all debt at 15 percent interest,
   or (c) all preferred stock with a 9 percent dividend.
Research on heat has evolved under three categories: (1) thermodynamics, (2) the kinetic
   theory of gases, and (3) statistical mechanics.

Capital Letters

Capital letters are used primarily for proper nouns: the specific name or title of
someone or something. Capitalization practices can vary; find a style guide for your
field (see Chapter 9) to make sure when to use capital letters.

• Use capital letters for names of people, races, cities, regions, counties, states,
nations, languages, and other such proper names.

Samuel Morse invented the coding system called the Morse code.
The Early Bird satellite was launched by Intelsat, a consortium of many Western countries
   including the United States, France, the United Kingdom, and Germany.
Among Muslims, Ramadan commemorates the first revelation of the Koran and is cele-
   brated by fasting.
The population of Quebec is largely French speaking.
The Middle East, culturally speaking, refers to those lands in that part of the world that
   are predominantly Islamic in culture.
The Midwest includes Ohio, Indiana, Illinois, Michigan, Wisconsin, Minnesota, Iowa,
   Missouri, Kansas, and Nebraska.
The Rhine River rises in the Swiss Alps, flows north through Switzerland, Liechenstein,
   Austria, West Germany, France, and the Netherlands, and empties into the North Sea.
In her sophomore semester, Gilda took English, French, astronomy, biology, and geology;
   next semester, she's thinking about taking a special course entitled "Key Concepts in
   the History of Science."

• Use capital letters for points of the compass only when they refer to well-
established regions but not when they simply refer to a direction of travel.

In the 1970s and 1980s, the major population and economic growth regions of the United
   States have been the South and the Southwest.
The dam is located southwest of the city.
Oil imports from South America have been decreasing recently.
Drive ten miles north from Baldwin City, Kansas, and you'll be in Lawrence.

• Use capital letters for titles of offices when the title precedes the name of an
officeholder (this includes the first letter of *president* when it occurs alone and refers
to the office of the U.S. president and not to a particular officeholder):

The first electronic computer was assembled in the years 1940 to 1942 by Professor John V. Atanasoff and Clifford Berry, a student, at Iowa State University.
A professor and a student assembled the first electronic computer in the years 1940 to 1942.
The President holds the power of veto over any legislation passed by the Congress.
Last week, mayors from several nearby cities met to discuss an integrated system of health care.

• Use capitals for titles of works such as novels, speeches, paintings and sculpture, except for the articles and prepositions within those titles:

One of the primary journals for the publication of original research in physics is the *Physics Review*.
Her technical-writing students frequently review back issues of *Scientific American* for ideas on technical reports.
The Department of Energy has recently published a directory of manufacturers and suppliers of solar heating and cooling equipment entitled *Catalog of Solar Heating and Cooling Products*.
On May 21, 1927, Lindbergh landed the *Spirit of St. Louis* in Paris, ending the first solo flight across the Atlantic.
The sinking of the *Lusitania* in 1915 swayed American opinion toward entry into World War I.

• Use capital letters for academic subjects when they are part of a specific course title or when they are derived from the name of a person, country, or language. (This rule is often ignored in application letters and resumes to achieve emphasis; see Chapter 11.)

She took a course in world history entitled "The Shaping of Western Thought" at Baker University in Kansas.
They consider Chemistry 301 a hard course even though they are chemistry majors.
This semester Marjorie intends to take French, physics, and finance.

• Use capital letters for the days of the week, the months, special days, and holidays but not for the seasons:

On Monday, July 24, 1978, they celebrated her birthday at a local restaurant.
Last fall they spent Thanksgiving in Denmark.
In the United States, national independence day is July the Fourth; in Mexico, it is called *Cinco de Mayo*.

• Use capital letters for religions, religious groups, historical events, periods of history, or historical documents:

The telegraph played an important role during the Civil War.
The term *Protestantism* is used to distinguish this faith from the other major Christian faiths: Roman Catholicism and Eastern Orthodoxy.

At the Casablanca Conference, the Allies agreed to continue the war until the unconditional surrender of the Axis power.

The Allies landed on Normandy Beach on July 6, 1944, a day known as D-Day.

The Great Depression in the United States was supposedly precipitated by the stockmarket crash of 1929.

Under compulsion by English barons and the church, King John signed the Magna Carta in 1215.

• Use capital letters for organization names as well as their products:

In the late 1950s the U.S. Department of Defense initiated a number of projects, such as Project Courier, which finally resulted in the Initial Defense Communications Satellite Program (IDCSP).

The IDCSP satellites were launched by the U.S. Air Force in 1966.

Saudia Arabia has its own air force and its own integrated defense system.

After the FCC's 1971 adoption of a limited "open skies" policy, three domestic carriers initiated operations during 1974: American Satellite Corporation, a subsidiary of Fairchild Industries, Inc.; Americom of RCA; and Western Union.

On March 24, 1980, Pennsylvania Governor Richard Thornburgh asked the Union of Concerned Scientists to make an independent evaluation of the krypton problem at the Three Mile Island nuclear power plant.

Recently, Apple Corporation introduced its Macintosh to compete with IBM's Personal Computer.

• Use capital letters for references to most numbered or lettered items (figure, chapter, room, building, etc.):

In Figure 3 is shown a simple telegraph arrangement.

Unfortunately, this small amount of krypton is uniformly mixed with the roughly 2 million cubic feet of air in the sealed Three Mile Island Unit 2 reactor containment building.

In this book, Chapter 5 discusses different types of audiences and techniques for translating technical discussions for the less-specialized audiences.

In this book, Part I discusses the basic patterns of technical writing.

• Use capital letters for objects that have individualized names:

The first operational communications satellite, *Early Bird,* was launched in 1965.

Until the *Challenger* space shuttle, expendable launch vehicles such as the Thor Delta, Alpha-Centaur, and Titan were used for launching space communications satellites.

The Golden Gate Bridge was opened in 1937 and is one of the most extraordinary bridges in the world.

• Use capital letters for the earth, sun, moon, and universe when they are discussed with other celestial bodies or systems:

The Sun is 1.4 million km from Earth.

The theory that the Universe is constantly expanding is based on the observation of redshifts.

• Acronyms (abbreviations) of organizations, systems, objects, etc., are normally capitalized, although a few, such as ac and dc are not (when in doubt, check your dictionary) :

In 1969, an experiment at SLAC (Stanford Linear Accelerator) shattered electrons with protons.
In 1977 and 1978, NASA launched the first two High-Energy Astronomy Observation (HEAO) satellites to study black holes.

Diction: The Use of Words

Problems with diction normally mean that a writer has gotten the meaning of certain words wrong: for example, if a writer explains that Cuba grows much sugar cane and sends this "import" all over the world.

Precision with the Meanings of Words

The confusion over the meaning of "import" and "export" in the preceding example has to do with the precise denotative meanings of words: the dictionary meanings. Such problems often occur when the right word and the wrong word sound similar. Here are some examples of imprecise or inaccurate diction:

Sentences with Diction Problems

I'll be happy to *redeem* any costs you may incur. [reimburse]
Cuba is the world's largest producer of sugar cane, and thus the crop is that country's largest *import*. [export]
Japan has almost no domestic oil resources, and thus it must *export* all its oil. [import]
The Stanford radio interferometer is composed of five 60-foot diameter *convex* dishes. [concave]
With increasing economic problems at home, the United States has become a great deal *more* liberal in its foreign aid. [less]
The *Viking I* and *II* missions were perfect in their *descent* from Cape Kennedy. [ascent]
Payment into this company's retirement plan is not *compulsive;* you may choose this plan, that of some other agency, or none at all. [compulsory]
Mr. Watson is a *compulsory* risk-taker; he seems incapable of passing up speculative projects where the stakes and the potential gains are high. [compulsive]
The city council views the commission's report as entirely *factitious;* the members see the report as a huge misrepresentation of the facts in favor of real estate developers. [fictitious]

Concrete and Abstract Words

Another common diction problem involves using words that are too abstract or general, when more specific ones are needed to convey the message. With problems like these, the reader needs more information but does not get it:

Overly General Diction

This past summer in the evening hours, structures within a Kansas City area building malfunctioned, resulting in significant death and injury to inhabitants. At the time of the malfunction, the building had been in service for some number of months. The building consists of several component structures: a relatively tall tower section, a function block, and another section as well. This area of the building is quite large. In the malfunction, some of the structures within this latter area experienced severe problems. Most of the people killed or injured were in the general vicinity.

Obviously, this passage tells you little or nothing; it contains almost no details on the accident. Here is a revision with much more concrete, specific diction:

Revision

On 17 July 1981, at approximately 7:05 P.M., two suspended walkways within the atrium section of the Hyatt Regency Hotel in Kansas City, Mo., collapsed, killing 111 people and injuring 188. At the time of the collapse, the hotel had been in service for 13 months. The Hyatt Regency consists of three main sections: a 40-story tower section, a function block, and a connecting atrium area. The atrium is a large open area approximately 117 ft by 145 ft in plan and 50 ft high. In the collapse, the second- and fourth-floor walkways fell to the atrium floor, with the fourth-floor walkway coming to rest on top of the second. Most of those killed or injured were either on the atrium first-floor level or on the second-floor walkway.

Formal and Informal (Slang) Words

Diction problems can also occur when the writer forgets, mistakes, or overdoes the level of formality in a writing situation. For example, a letter between long-time business associates can be quite informal; between a job seeker and a potential employer, rather formal; a job seeker trying to project himself as "just plain folks" may interject too much of the conversational or humorous; a business associate trying to sound serious, businesslike, or official may end up sounding pompous, stuffy, and rigidly impersonal. Here are two examples:

Overly Formal Diction

At your request, this office has investigated the possibility of contracting offshore fishing facilities for the annual EGF (Employees Gone Fishin') Event. Weekend Mariners, Inc., agrees to furnish a 60-foot craft with pilot, crew, and fishing guide for $2,500 per 24-hour period. No guarantees are extended regarding fishing success. The firm does, however, agree to reschedule in the event of inclement weather at no cost to EGF participants. Inspection of the firm's facilities, contact with its personnel, and discussion of its services all indicate that an adequate outing will be obtained. Employees will undoubtedly gain significant enjoyment from this excursion, as they have in the past; they anticipate its occurrence this year with enthusiasm. If these arrangements are found suitable, this office will begin making final plans and scheduling for the event upon notification.

Overly Informal Diction

This company's benefits program—the goodies, for short—is noncontributory. That's a big word; it means you don't have to pay a red cent for them. The company takes care of the whole thing for you, and that's what's really great about this place. This benefits package is constantly being eyeballed by the pros in the business to make sure that it hangs in there with other companies' programs and to make sure that other companies and organizations don't beat us out. Let's face it, once we've got you, we're going to try to hang on to you! A historical chart of the improvements that the guys and gals in the benefits shop have gotten for us over the years is provided over there on the other side of the page—just in case you're not taking our word for it. If you have any questions about these plans, hey, just give us a holler and we'll do our darndest to give it to you as straight as we can.

Revisions

As you suggested the other day, I have looked into what sorts of offshore fishing arrangements can be made for our annual EGF Event. I did locate a company called Weekend Mariners, Inc. It furnishes a 60-foot boat with pilot, crew, and guide for $2,500 per full day. Surprisingly enough, they will reschedule at no cost to us if the weather is bad on our weekend. As you might guess, however, they don't guarantee we'll catch anything.

I went down there and took a look at their facilities and met their people; I think they'll do just fine for us. Everybody around here is looking forward to this year's event. If it's anything like last year's, I know I'll have a great time (although by the time we all get back, I may be a bit worse for wear . . . again).

If you think these arrangements are okay, let me know, and I'll go ahead and schedule us.

The benefits program of this company is noncontributory: the company pays the full cost. The program is constantly being reexamined and compared with those of other organizations to make sure that it remains the leader. The goal of the company is to keep its employees satisfied with their work and their company; a benefits program is naturally one means of doing so. To the right is a chart showing the history of the improvements that have been made to this program by our benefits division. If you have any questions about any of these plans, contact the people in charge of benefits at your location.

Neutral and Slanted Words

Another kind of diction problem occurs when writers use slanted or biased words rather than neutral and objective ones when the situation calls for objectivity. One favorite slanting trick is to put quotation marks around certain words to indicate skepticism. In these examples, the highly emotional slanted diction is italicized:

Slanted Diction

Much of the debate on the *"energy crisis"* has been carried out on *absurdly* emotional grounds.

Part of this may result from the fact that the *fools* who are called *"rational scientists"* cannot agree on what the important facts are.

One *ridiculous* fear that the *misguided* public has of fission reactors is that a malfunction might cause a chain reaction to get out of hand and cause an atomic-bomb-type explosion.

In *frightening, nightmarish abdication of its responsibility*, the commission concluded that the radiation released in the accident will have only *"negligible"* effect on human beings.

Clichés

A cliché is a set phrase used over and over to the point that most people groan or wince when they hear it or read it. For some, the phrase "bottom line" has become a cliché. A decade ago, some people were getting tired of other people telling them that they knew where they were "coming from." And why does the last item in every series have to be introduced with the infamous "last but not least"? Clichés can be used for humor or for the folksy touch, but they must be used carefully. Here is just a brief listing of clichés:

right on the nose
better late than never
foot loose and fancy free
in a nutshell
the long and the short of it
snug as a bug in a rug
cute as a bug
crack of dawn
spreading like wildfire
eyeball it
over the hill
like a bat out of hell
a snowball's chance in hell
nipped in the bud
down to brass tacks
get on the horn
loud and clear
armed to the teeth
up the creek without a paddle
hung up (on)
too much
out of sight
give me a break
lay off
smooth sailing
fat as a pig
wouldn't touch it with a ten-foot pole
loose as a goose
dry as a bone
the bottom line

one night's stand
come hell or high water
at the drop of a hat
like a bull in a china shop
the rat race
with it
out of it
on a roll
in the ball park
off the beaten track
in the groove
down and out
over and out
no stone unturned
straight shooter
throw your hat in the ring
freaked out
far out
black as night
off/on my back
blind as a bat
rolling in the aisles
flat as a pancake
it's all downhill from here
behind the 8-ball
hot potato
can of worms
rotten egg/bad apple/black sheep
last but not least

Of course, some of these clichés add spice to our language. Delivered the right way orally, they can be a barrel of laughs, but in writing, where your facial expression and the tone of your voice are absent, they usually just don't come off at all!

Spelling

The following sections review some of the most common areas of spelling problems.

Homonyms

For some writers, their main spelling problem is similar-sounding words, for example, *principle* and *principal* or *affect* and *effect*. Here is a list of these commonly confused homonyms, with examples of their correct use.

accept, except

The construction firm *accepted* the offer to build the bridge.
Everything has been finished *except* for the paint job.

advice, advise

The construction firm ignored the engineer's *advice*.
The engineer *advised* the firm to use single-suspension walkways.

affect, effect

The increased oil prices have *affected* our economy drastically.
The *effect* of the increased oil prices has been devastating on our economy.

cite, site, sight

The consulting engineer *cited* a paragraph from the building code.
At the construction *site*, the workers carefully erected the scaffolding.
The collapse of the walkways was a terrible *sight*.

complement, compliment

The colors that have been selected for the room do not *complement* each other.
The programmer has received many *compliments* on her new system.

counsel, council, consul

He *counseled* her to get a degree in technical communications.
There was lengthy debate on the tax proposal at city *council* last night.
She was appointed *consul* to the embassy in Beirut.

its, it's

The car has lost one of *its* headlights.
It's time to go home; *it's* getting late.

lose, loose

Your car *loses* power when it is out of tune.
I have some *loose* change in my pocket.
Don't let Mamie get *loose!*

personal, personnel

They plan to take out a *personal* loan to build the deck.
Send your application to the *personnel* office.
The CEO wants to have a *personal* chat with all of this company's *personnel*.

principal, principle

The *principal* component of the solar panel is the collector.
Explain to me the *principle* of convection.

stationary, stationery

The derrick may not remain *stationary* during the gale-force winds.
Use company *stationery* for company business purposes only.

than, then

My utility bill is higher this month *than* it was last month.
The hurricane reached the Texas coast; *then* it plunged right into the heart of Houston.

their, there, they're

Their calculus course is much harder than ours.
Over *there* on the table is your calculus book.
They're not taking calculus this semester.

to, too, two

Are they going *to* pave the street today?
It is still *too* rainy to pave the street.
Two hours ago the sky was clear.

whose, who's

Whose technical-writing book is this?
There is the woman *whose* technical report won top honors.
Do you know *who's* in charge around here?
He's a man *who's* not afraid of criticism.

your, you're

Your technical-writing book is on the table.
You're going to have to review Part 1 before writing that report.

Doubled Internal Consonants

Many words double internal consonants whereas others do not: for example, *rec-ommend*, *accommodate*, and *committee*. Try memorizing these in contrasting pairs (*recommend* and *accommodate*, for example).

Internal Syllables or Letters

Many words have short, practically unpronounced internal syllables that are easily omitted or misspelled: for example, *athletics*, *category*, *disastrous*, *optimistic*, *privilege*, and *desperate*. Perhaps the only way to learn these is to repeat them several times, emphasizing the internal syllable: for example, sound out ben–EH–fi–cial, bound–AH–ries, cat–EH–go–ry.

Words with Endings Such as -ance and -able

Another source of spelling difficulties is words with similar-sounding endings: *ex-travagant*, *occurrence*, *compatible*, *irresistible*, and *performance*.

Words Ending in -sede, -ceed, and -cede

Still another group of confusingly spelled words is that group ending in *-sede*, *-ceed*, and *-cede*: for example, *precede, proceed, exceed, supersede*. Again, the best thing to do is memorize them or look them up.

The groups of words just discussed are by no means all of the possibilities. You may have trouble with words ending in *-or* and *-er* or those ending in *-ary, -ery*, and *-ory*. Make your own lists of such word groups that give you problems in spelling.

The Silent -e Rule

When words end in a silent *-e* (for example, *write*), you drop the *-e* when adding a suffix (*write + ing = writing*), except when the suffix begins with a consonant (*excite + ment = excitement*).

The Rule for -ie and -ei

Use *i* before *e* except after *c* in words in which the sound is a long *e* (as in *feet*) in words such as *piece, receive*, and *fiend*. There are exceptions to this rule: *leisure, either, weird*, and *seize*.

Doubling Consonants

When you add a suffix to a word ending in a consonant, make sure you know whether to double the final consonant: *drag* becomes *dragged*, but *equip* becomes *equipment*.

Words Ending in -y

When adding a suffix to a word ending in *-y*, make sure whether to change the *y* to *i*: *enjoy* becomes *enjoys*, but *try* becomes *tries*.

Handling Numbers, Abbreviations, and Symbols

Generally, you see more numbers, abbreviations, and symbols in technical writing than in other kinds of writing; but scientific, technical, and business fields have rather carefully defined rules on handling them. The following sections provide you with the standard guidelines, but see style guides in your own field as well.

Numbers in Technical Prose

Whether to use numbers (2, 5, 16, etc.) or words for numbers (two, five, sixteen, etc.) is often a source of confusion. Here are some general principles: numerals are thought to distract the reader and disrupt the easy flow of reading; reading large numbers written out in words is much more difficult than when they are written as numerals; readers are much more likely to notice and remember numerals in prose than written-out numbers; and numerals in written text suggest greater precision or exactness.

When to Use Numerals.   Use numerals according to the following rules.

- Use numerals for any number higher than ten in technical prose.

Some 19 million tons of sulphur dioxide are discharged from U.S. sources alone each year, and another 14 million tons from Canada.

It was not until after December 1952, when 4,000 people died in London from air pollution in just a few days, that real gains in pollution-control legislation were made.

The U.S. Army's standard airborne Doppler navigator weighs 28 lb (12.7 kg), requires 89 W of power, and operates at 13.325-GHz frequency.

All vitrain of the European classification, if more than 14 micrometers thick, has been regarded as anthraxylon.

In 1971, 11 countries accounted for about 91 percent of world production of coal.

The Department of the Interior has just published a report that reviews 65 different coal gasification processes.

- Use numerals for any number under ten if the audience has a specific interest in or need for statistical information, as in the following situations:

  - If the number represents a unit of measurement
  - If the number represents a specific item or unit number
  - If the number is part of a hyphenated compound
  - If the number stands for a specific value
  - If one or more numbers in a series is above ten

Here are some examples of these various situations that call for use of numerals:

Combustion turbines total about 8% of the total installed capability of U.S. utility systems and supply less than 3% of the total energy generated.

Internal-combustion engines in small power plants account for about 1% of the total power-system generating capability of the United States.

The water-cement ratio will generally range from 4 gal of water per sack of cement to about 9 gal per sack.

The problem is located in piston number 6.

The signal occurs in 6-second intervals.

The order is for 6-, 8-, and 12-foot two-by-fours.

Use Code 3 if a system shutdown occurs.

- Try not to mix numerals and written numbers in the same sentence, except when two different numbers occur next to each other.

Mined coals commonly contain between 5 and 15 percent mineral matter.

The above illustration shows a 20-unit coaxial cable with 9 working coaxial pairs and 2 standby coaxials, which automatically switch in if the electronics of the regular circuits fail.

There are 59 different species of the coffee shrub, but only 4 are of commercial importance.

• Use numerals when the number is expressed in decimals. Be sure, however, to include a zero before the decimal point of a number less than one in order to prevent readers from misreading the period (unless your writing includes probability statistics, in which case the zero preceding the decimal point is standardly omitted).

> Most grinds of coffee contain particles ranging in size from 0.023 to 0.055 inches in diameter.
>
> Using carrier frequencies between 0.535 MHz and 1.605 MHz in the United States, AM broadcasting stations sprang up all over the country beginning in the 1910s.

• Use numerals when a whole number is accompanied by a fraction (and handle integer-fraction combinations as shown in the following example):

> As a base from which to work, 2.5 to 3 gal of water are needed for each sack of cement for complete hydration and maximum strength.

• Use numerals for one of a pair of numbers that occur side by side:

> The order for twelve 30-foot beams was placed yesterday.
> The order was for thirty 15-gallon tubs.
> They used six 8-pound sacks of nails.

• Use a combination of numerals and words to refer to large numbers in the millions. If the number is exact to the last digit, however, use only numerals.

> The microprocesors of the 1970s and 1980s operated under the control of clocks running at 1 to 5 MHz, that is, 1 to 5 million counts per second.
> Your eye has a bandwidth of 370 trillion Hz, the visible spectrum.
> Transmission rates on ETHERNET range from 1 to 10 megabits per second (0.125 to 1.25 million bytes per second).
> In 1978, the satellite carriers' revenues were about $88 million, and by 1986 they are expected to reach $800 million.
> Most communications satellites are in geostationary orbit: at an altitude of 22,300 miles over the surface of the earth and at a distance of 26,260 miles from the center of the earth (the earth's radius being 3,960 miles).

• Use numerals for percentages.

> Aggregates constitute about 70 percent of a concrete mix.
> Uniform compaction of 95% or better of standard AASHO densities is recommended.

• Use numerals for any number (e.g., dates, addresses, times of the day, ZIP codes, phone numbers, page numbers, or chapter numbers) that will read more easily, clearly, or noticeably when expressed in numerals than in words.

IBM-Austin is located at 11200 Burnet Rd., Austin, Texas 78758.
For information call (512) 555-8800.
In this book, Chapter 5 discusses the different audiences for technical prose and the translation techniques for communicating effectively with less-specialized audiences.

When to Use Spelled-Out Numbers.   Use spelled-out numbers (for example, two, five, eight) according to the following rules.

• Use spelled-out numbers for numbers lower than eleven, unless the readers are specifically interested in the statistical information.

The wheels of the four-wheel tractor give it increased speed over the Crawler, but because of the weight distribution over four wheels rather than over two wheels or tracks, this vehicle has less traction.
Hundreds of thousands of people will have purchased microcomputers by the end of 1980. Tens of millions of them will have bought them by the end of the century.
There are two telephones in service today for every three people in the United States.
In 1965, Dr. Gordon Moore announced his "law" that the complexity of a chip would double every year for ten years.
The typical stand-alone microcomputer system consists of seven physical components.

• Try to spell out the numbers *zero* and *one* whenever possible in that these two numbers can easily be misread when written as numerals.

If you are using page-zero addressing, use a RAM for memory page zero.
Primary fuel cells are those through which reactants are passed only one time.
Before being recharged, a zinc-carbon battery must have a working voltage not less than one volt.

• Spell out fractions when they occur by themselves without whole numbers in technical prose.

Japan has roughly one-third of the U.S. production of dry batteries.
The radial fractures are so extensive that they are the dominant structural element over half of Mars's surface.
A nanosecond is one-billionth of a second.

• Spell out one or the other of two sets of numbers that occur next to each other in the same sentence.

Inside the UP are three 16-bit registers.
Data from the frequency counter take the form of sixteen 7-bit ASCII words.

• Use a combination of words and numerals for numbers that are in the millions but that are not exact.

Sales of batteries have increased from $510 million on the average during 1957 to 1959 to $867 million in 1966 and are projected to exceed $1.8 billion in 1980.
The speed of light is roughly 300 million meters per second.

• Spell out numbers that begin sentences (but if it is a large number, rephrase the sentence so that the number no longer begins the sentence):

One hundred fifty-three representatives of different software-development companies showed up at the meeting.
At the meeting, 153 representatives of different software-development companies showed up.

Abbreviations in Technical Prose

In general, any abbreviation in a passage of writing can be distracting to the reader, especially those abbreviations containing periods. Here are the standard rules to use for abbreviations; consult style manuals or guides in the specific situations in which you are writing to make sure your abbreviations conform with those standards (see Chapter 9 on finding style manuals).

• Use abbreviations when the text contains much discussion of sizes, lengths, distances, weights, and other measurements.
• Use abbreviations when the abbreviation is easier to recognize or more familiar than its spelled-out counterpart (for example, "radar" or "laser" as opposed to "radio detection and ranging" or "light amplification by stimulated emission of radiation" and "ac" or "dc" as opposed to "alternating current" or "direct current").
• Use abbreviations in tables and figures, especially when there is not room to spell out the words.
• Use standard, commonly accepted abbreviations: "gal" instead of "gl" for gallons and "mm" instead of "mt" for meter, for example. Consult general or specialized dictionaries for lists of these commonly accepted abbreviations. Here are some examples:

High-resolution displays use larger video bandwidths, up to 30 MHz or more.
Most touch-sensitive displays use a matrix of either LED/photodiodes or transparent capacitor arrays to detect a physical touch.
The part of the memory that is easily alterable by the operator consists of RAM chips.
A satellite in geostationary orbit looks at the earth with a cone angle of 17.3° corresponding to an arc of 18,080 km along the equator.
The arc from 53° W to 139° W will cover 48 states (excluding Alaska and Hawaii) and is said to provide conus coverage.
Fairchild Industries, Inc., was an early participant in commercial satellites.
The voice was compressed from the usual 64-kb/s pulse code modulation (PCM) to 32 kb/s per channel by near-instantaneous companding (a modified PCM technique).
Terrestrial microwave radio communications require repeaters spaced every 20 to 40 mi from each other.

Over a period of several days the spacecraft is tracked from the ground and positioned on station (i.e., in the preassigned orbital spot) in order to commence operations.

A velocity increment of approximately 155 ft/s per year is required to correct drift problems in satellites.

The ancient batterylike objects made by the Parthians in 250 B.C. were thin sheets of copper soldered into a cylinder 1.125 cm long and 2.6 cm in diameter.

The standard electrodes are the normal and the 0.1 normal (N) calomel electrodes in which the system is Hg/KCl solution saturated with HgCl.

Such batteries contain 4400 cc of water in which NaOH is dissolved.

Water pressure in the heat recovery loop can be as much as 25 psig.

• If your report contains many abbreviations or, more importantly, abbreviations with which readers may not be familiar, create a list of abbreviations and place it just after the list of figures. (See Chapter 6 for information on constructing lists of abbreviations.)

• For unusual or unfamiliar abbreviations, write out the abbreviation in full and then show the abbreviation in parentheses just after it. Thereafter, you can use the abbreviation by itself. Here is an example in which this technique is used:

The absolute system of electrical units is derived from fundamental mechanical units of length, mass, and time and by principles of electromagnetism, with permeability of space taken as unity in the centimeter-gram-second (cgs) units or as 10^{-7} in the corresponding meta-kilogram-second-ampere units (mksa).

• Try to use the abbreviations that are standard in your field, profession, occupation, or major. To find out what these standard abbreviations are, see Chapter 9 on finding style guides in your fields.

• As for the punctuation of abbreviations, the traditional rule has been this: use periods after abbreviations that spell a word (for example, "bar." for barometric, "no." for number, or "in." for inch). You'll notice, however, in most technical prose the period is scarcely used after abbreviations at all.

• Abbreviations of organization names usually do not use periods or spacing. Here are some examples:

AEC   NASA   NCAA

• Use abbreviations for measurements *only* if they are preceded by numerals that express exact quantities. Here are a few contrasting examples:

While this recipe does not specify how many ounces of milk to use, yours requires exactly 2.5 oz.

Our cargo is many pounds over the weight allowance. The attendant says that our freight weighs 653 lbs.

• Some abbreviations change to indicate plurals:

Henry chose Plan No. 1, but Alan chose Plan Nos. 2 and 4.

• Spell out the word, instead of abbreviating it, if no numbers or exact numbers are associated with it:

> We need several extra pounds of nails.
> A gallon of gas is more than enough to mow the lawn.
> A meter is just a few inches longer than a yard.

Special Symbols in Technical Prose

Every scientific and technical field has its own special set of special symbols, just as it has its own special vocabulary (jargon). When you write in such fields, you are obligated to use the symbols accepted in those fields. Obviously, this book cannot list all of the symbols for every profession, science, or technology. However, you can use a guide to your field (see Chapter 9 or see *Webster's*) to locate lists of such symbols.

Instructors' Correction Symbols and Copy Editors' Marks

Your technical reports and articles can be marked in one or a combination of two ways: (a) a copy editor can make corrections and mark your report so that typesetters or printers can set it up for producing the final copy; and (b) your instructor can use symbols and abbreviations to indicate errors or problems but not actually correct those errors.

This appendix contains a quick-reference listing of marks used by copy editors and instructors. The correction symbols are accompanied by references to chapters and appendixes of this book.

Instructors' Correction Symbols and Abbreviations

The following is a list of symbols and abbreviations commonly used by instructors to mark students' technical reports.

Abbreviation	Problem	Explanation	Reference
abbrev	abbreviations	An abbreviation is used incorrectly or should be used.	App. D
apost	apostrophes	An apostrophe is used incorrectly or is missing.	App. D
adj	adjectives	An incorrect form of an adjective is used, or an adjective is used incorrectly in place of an adverb.	App. D

Abbreviation	Problem	Explanation	Reference
adv	adverbs	An adverb is used incorrectly or is in an incorrect form.	App. D
A/voice	lack of active voice	Sentence needs to be rephrased with active-voice verbs.	App. D Ch. 7
art	articles	Articles (*the, a, an*) are used incorrectly.	————
aud	audience	The discussion is not suited to its audience: too technical, too simplistic, or just not relevant to the audience's concerns.	Ch. 5
awk	awkward phrasing	Sentence(s) need to be rephrased to read more clearly or simply.	Ch. 7
CS	comma splice or fused sentence	Two sentences are joined by a comma or dash instead of a period or semicolon.	App. D
cap	capital letters	Capital letters should or should not used.	App. D
caption	captions	Something is wrong with the captions: lacking, not phrased well, etc.	Ch. 6
cliché	clichés	Phrasing is clichéd, hackneyed, trite.	App. D
col	colons	A colon should or should not be used.	App. D
D	diction	Level, tone, or style of diction is inappropriate.	App. D
DM	dangling modifier	A phrase either lacks the right word to modify or appears to modify the wrong word(s).	App. D
dash	dashes	A dash or dashes should or should not be used.	App. D
frag	fragments	A sentence is incomplete: it lacks a complete subject or verb (or both); either attach the fragment to the preceding sentence or	App. D

Abbreviation	Problem	Explanation	Reference
		rephrase the subject or verb to make it complete.	
hyph	hyphens	A hyphen should or should not be used.	App. D
idiom	idiomatic English	This sentence is not phrased in idiomatic English.	———
ital	italics or underlining	A word or phrase should or should not be italicized or underlined.	App. D
logic	logic problem	A problem with the logic of this passage; for example, the conclusion does not follow from the facts.	———
MM	misplaced modifier	A word or short phrase (for example, prepositional phrase) appears to modify the wrong word; relocate the modifier so that it modifies the right word.	App. D
num	numbers	Either numbers should be presented as numerals or written out as words.	App. D
paral	lack of parallelism	A series of two or more words, phrases or clauses are not worded in a grammatically similar way; rephrase the odd word, phrase, or clause so that it is similar to the others.	App. D
p ref	pronoun reference	A pronoun either lacks an antecedent (or referent) or does not agree with its antecedent in number, gender, or person; change the pronoun or its antecedent so that they agree, or supply an appropriate antecedent.	App. D
p case	pronoun case	The wrong case (nominative, objective, possessive) is used (for example, *who* not *whom*, or *me* not *I*).	App. D

Abbreviation	Problem	Explanation	Reference
punct	punctuation	Comma(s) should or should not be used.	App. D
pass	weak use of the passive voice	The passive voice is used ineffectively; rephrase so that the active voice appears.	Ch. 7 App. D
¶	paragraph-break problems	Paragraph break needed (or not needed if it appears with "no").	Ch. 7
¶ coh	paragraph coherence	Paragraph(s) lack flow, continuity; better transitions are needed.	Ch. 7 App. C
¶ dev	paragraph development	Paragraph(s) lack development (for example, detail, examples, comparisons, definitions); add more specific information.	Ch. 7 App. C
¶ org	paragraph organization	The information as presented in the paragraph(s) is disorganized.	Ch. 7 App. C
¶ trans	paragraph transitions	Transitions between or within paragraphs are weak; need to be stronger.	Ch. 7 App. C
quot	quotations	Problems with quoted matter in this passage: lack of quotation marks, punctuation is incorrect, attribution lacking, or no documentation.	App. D
rep	repetition	Too much repetition of a word or phrasing; rephrase for variety.	———
sp	spelling	One or more words are misspelled in this passage.	App. D
s-v	subject-verb agreement problem	A subject and verb do not agree; change either the subject or the verb to its singular or plural form.	App. D
subord	faulty subordination	This passage reads in a choppy way; combine	App. B

Abbreviation	Problem	Explanation	Reference
		some of the sentences for smoother-flowing reading.	
SC	semicolon problems	A semicolon should or should not be used.	App. D
TS	topic sentence	This paragraph needs a topic sentence or a stronger one.	Ch. 7 App. C
tense	inappropriate tense shifts	This passage contains inappropriate shifts between tenses (for example, present, past, future).	App. D
uncl (or) ?	unclear discussion	Something about this passage is unclear or difficult to read or follow.	Ch. 5
vag	vagueness	The discussion in this passage is vague, unclear: more specific information needed (get to the point!).	Ch. 5 Ch. 7
verb	problem with the form of a verb	Problem with the form of a verb (for example, *brung* not *brought*, or *laying* not *lying*). Check dictionary for correct forms.	App. D
w	wordiness	Passage contains unnecessary or redundant words; rephrase more succinctly and concisely.	Ch. 7
ww	wrong word	Incorrect word used: check the dictionary for its accepted meaning.	App. D

Copy Editors' Marks

A list of copy editors' marks is shown on pp. 778–779. Each of the marks is accompanied by a before-and-after version of a report excerpt with that mark in it. Copy editors' marks are made at the point of the addition, deletion, or other change. If the spacing does not allow for the marks, a caret (∧) is used to indicate where the mark, letter, or word is to be inserted. The change is written in the margin and is followed by a slash (/).

Indicating Punctuation and Other Graphics Changes

Mark	Explanation	Examples Corrected Original	Revision
ℓ	Delete this element (mark, letter, word, or words).	toϕday	today
⌃ /	Insert a comma at this point.	small⌃inexpensive car	small, expensive car
⊙	Insert a period at this point.	the end⊙ A new...	the end. A new...
⌃⌄	Insert a colon at this point.	tools⌄a hammer, a saw	tools: a hammer, a saw
⌃;/	Insert a semicolon at this point.	;/the end⌄ then they...	the end, then they...
=	Insert a hyphen at this point.	computer=controlled motor	computer-controlled motor
⌄'	Inset an apostrophe here.	a writers handbook	a writer's handbook
⌄"	Insert quotation marks at these points.	it"carves"an image	it ''carves'' an image
(/)	Insert parentheses at these points.	12 ounces ⌃525 ml⌃	12 ounces (525 ml)
(stet)	Retain the letters or words above these dots. (With this symbol you'll see a ''stet'' with a circle around it in the margin).	(stet)the 15 mm wire	the 15 mm wire
___	Underline or italicize these	the Columbia space-shuttle	the Columbia space-shuttle
≡	Capitalize this letter. (Often the abbreviation ''caps'' will appear in the margin to the left or right of this symbol).	Austin community college	Austin Community College
⫽	Lowercase this letter (often the abbreviation ''lc'' will accompany this symbol).	a standard Xransducer	a standard transducer

Indicating Spacing and Alignment Changes in a Manuscript

Mark	Explanation	Examples Corrected Original	Revision
ℓ	Delete this element (mark, letter, letters, word, or words).	it's yield is ...	its yield is ...
⌒	Close up the space between these two elements.	poly crystalline material	polycrystalline material
∼	Transpose these two letters.	its yeild strength	its yield strength
¶	Make a paragraph here. (If this symbol is in the margin, look for a caret in the text to show at what point to make the break).	¶ the end. Considering...	the end. Considering...

Indicating Punctuation and Other Graphics Changes

Indicating Spacing and Alignment Changes in a Manuscript (cont)

		Examples	
Mark	Explanation	Corrected Original	Revision
(no ¶)	Make a curved line between paragraphs that should be run together. (Often the abbreviation "no ¶" appears in the margin beside this line.)	the end. (no ¶) e Also, the . . .	the end. Also, the . . .
#	Add space here. Can be used to indicate either a letter space or a line space.	# anew system	a new system
#		# one line. Another line . . .	one line. Another line . . .
⌐⌐⌐	Transpose these words.	new the system	the new system
⌐⌐	Move these elements up on the page.		
⌐⌐	Move these elements down on the page.		
]	Move this material to the right.	(see composite example that follows)	
[	Move this material to the left.		
‖	Align these elements properly.		

III. MANUFACTURING SINGLE-CYRSTAL SILICON

    In general, the advantages of using silicon to fabricate micro
[devices are as follows:

    1. Precision batch-fabrication techniques similar to those used
       in making microelectronics can be used, thus making the mass-
       production of micromechanical devices inexpensive.

    2. Silicon is strong material, with a yield strength 40 percent
    2. greater than that of steel.

 3. The shapes that can be formed can be quite complex.

    Development of Silicon Micromechanical Devices

    Silicon micromechanical devices consist mainly of snsors and
miniature structures. A sensor is a device . . .

Purification if Silica. The process of purifying silican begins with . . .

APPENDIX F

Glossary of Terms Used in This Book

The following glossary contains definitions of terms used in this book to discuss techniques and components of technical writing. Explanations of grammar terms, which are not covered in this glossary, can be found in Appendix B and D. (See Index for specific page references.)

abstract. See *informative summary*.

adjustment letter. A business letter written in response to a complaint letter either granting or denying the compensation requested by the writer of the claim letter.

afterword. The kind of conclusion (last paragraph or section of a report) that neither reaches conclusions based on the previous discussion nor summarizes the previous discussion but discusses a related topic in a more general way.

application letter. The kind of business letter that you write to a potential employer when you apply for a job. It highlights your best qualifications for the job.

attribution of a quotation. An important part of any direct quotation in which you provide information about the person who made the statement that you are quoting. Attribution usually means stating the author's name, the title of the book, article, report, or other source from which the quotation comes, and, sometimes, a brief comment on the author, the quotation, or both.

audience. The group of readers for whom a written report is intended, or the group of listeners to whom you'll present an oral report. The most important way in which report audiences vary is the knowledge about the report subject that they already possess: that knowledge can include education, training, skills, and capabilities. See the specific types of audiences: *experts, executives, technicians,* and *nonspecialists.*

basis of classification.   The principle by which you divide a collection of related things into classes; for example, computers are often divided into microcomputers and minicomputers and mainframe computers, with memory size as the basis of the classification.

bibliographic information.   Publishing information about a book: the author's name, the title of the book, the city in which it was published, the company that published it, and the year in which it was published. (Some fields require additional information such as edition number; for these special requirements, see the style guide in the appropriate field.)

bibliography.   The list of books, reports, articles, and other information resources you've used to write a report or article. A complete bibliography includes both information sources you've used directly in a report as well as those you've gained general background knowledge from. In certain documentation systems the bibliography is called a list of references or literature cited.

bibliography card.   An index card on which you copy bibliographical information about an information source (book, article, report, etc.) that you might use in gathering information for a report.

block combination.   The kind of combination of basic report components in which one section containing a type of writing follows another end to end. For example, a section of description might be followed by a section of process narration. Compare with *sentence combination* and *frame combination*.

block quotation.   An indented direct quotation of five or more lines that is separated from the regular text by blank lines.

business correspondence.   Letters and memos written in the business and professional world.

caption.   A term used to refer to the titles of figures and tables in a report. For example, "Figure 33. Example of an informative summary" is a caption.

causal discussion.   A basic report component in which causes and effects are discussed. This kind of writing also includes discussions of problems and solutions. See *report component,* or other specific examples such as *description, process discussion, comparison,* and *classification.*

cause-effect discussion.   See *causal discussion.*

characteristics.   Another set of elements, along with parts, by which things can be described. For example, a computer can be described by its memory capacity, its processing speed, its cost, or other characteristics; or it can be described by its display device, disk drive, fixed disk, keyboard, and other parts.

classification.   A basic report component in which classes, types, or kinds are discussed. See *report component,* or other specific examples such as *description, process discussion, comparison,* and *causal discussion.*

comparison.   A basic report component in which points of comparison and criteria are the main focus of the discussion. See *report component,* or other specific examples such as *description, process discussion,* and *causal discussion.*

compartmentalization in business letters.   A writing technique important in business letters in which each paragraph has a separate content or purpose, even if it is only a sentence long.

complaint letter.   A type of business letter written to complain about problems with a product or service and to request some form of compensation. See also *adjustment letter.*

conceptual diagram.   A drawing used to represent ideas and concepts or relationships between them. A conceptual diagram does not depict physical things but ideas and concepts: for example, using circles, squares, and arrows to represent the writer's relationship to the technical subject matter, the audience, and the report.

conclusion.   A term referring to the final paragraph or section of a report or article. There are actually three kinds of conclusions, often combined into individual final sections: the summary, the true conclusion, and the afterword.

coordination or coordinate elements.   A term referring to the kind of relationship between sentence or paragraph elements in which the elements are at the same level of detail: for example, two words or phrases joined by *and,* or two sentences in a paragraph that describe a separate part of a mechanism. Contrast with *subordination.*

criteria.   Certain standards or requirements people use when they compare things in order to make a choice. Criteria typically have maximum or minimum values, for example, a cost no greater than $3,000 or a memory capacity no less than 256K bytes. See also *points of comparison.*

data sheet.   A term also used to refer to the resume. See *resume.*

decimal system for outlines and headings.   A system of numbering outline items and headings in the text in which numbers and decimals are used to indicate the organization. For example, the first subsection of section 1 would be section 1.1; the first subsection of section 1.1 would be section 1.1.1.

definition.   The explanation of the meaning of an unfamiliar word or phrase, or one used in an unfamiliar way. Also, a basic report component in which various kinds of writing are used to provide an extended explanation of the meaning of a word or phrase. See also *report component,* or other specific examples such as *description, comparison,* and *process* and *causal* discussions.

description.   A basic report component in which the physical details of things are explained. For example, the weight, height, color, materials used in construction, and other details of a solar collector. See also *report component,* or other specific examples such as *process* and *causal* discussions, *comparison,* and *classification.*

descriptive summary.   That kind of summary that briefly outlines the contents and purpose of a report but that gives none of the actual details of the report. Contrast with *informative summary.*

division.   A term commonly used to refer to the breaking up of a collection of things into classes or types. See *classification.* Compare with *true classification.*

documentation.   The system you use to show your readers where you found your information. Documentation systems give readers such information as authors' names, book or article titles, city of publication, publisher, year of publication, magazine title, and page numbers. A report with borrowed information but without documentation is a plagiarized report. See *plagiarism.*

elaboration of an outline.   A phase in the creation of an outline in which you add detail to the first sketchy outline. For example, you might elaborate an outline with only five items by creating three, four, or five subdivisions under each of those original five items.

ellipsis.   A term referring to the deletion of unnecessary or unimportant words from a direct quotation. Long quotations are often trimmed down to a more appropriate size by use of ellipsis points. Deletions are marked by three dots ... (ellipsis points).

evaluative comparison.   The kind of comparison used to make a decision or select from a set of alternatives. Contrast with *informative comparison.*

executive audience.   That type of report audience that needs technical information in order to make business decisions but does not necessarily have a technical background. See *audience,* and other examples of audience such as *expert, technician,* and *nonspecialist* audiences.

expert audience.   That type of report audience that has in-depth knowledge about a technical subject. This audience is typically involved in the design, development, research, and theory surrounding technology. See *audience,* and other examples of audiences such as *expert, technician,* and *nonspecialist* audiences.

exploratory draft.   A rough draft of a report that you write in order to see where the gaps in your knowledge about the report topic are and what information you need to gather. Used most often by writers who are already fairly familiar with their report subject.

extended definition, classification, comparison,   etc. Any discussion that is a paragraph or more in length. This term contrasts with sentence-length definitions, classification, comparison, and other kinds of writing.

feasibility report.   The type of report that investigates whether a plan (to purchase, build, or repair something, for example) is practicable (whether it can be done with current technology) and practical (whether it is advantageous economically and socially). Often called a recommendation report, this kind of report presents information, conclusions, and recommendations concerning a proposed plan of action.

feature article.   The kind of magazine article generally intended for nonspecialist audiences and written in a light, entertaining manner. Satisfies people's interest in or curiosity about things. See also *popular science article.*

final packaging.   That phase in the preparation of a report in which you do the final typing job, tape in the illustrations, photocopy the whole report, bind it, and attach the cover letter.

flowchart.   A diagram of the relationships between components of a system and, in some cases, the flow of information between them. A typical example is the organizational chart of a business depicting the interrelationships of manufacturing, development, accounting, personnel, and the chief executive officer.

font.   A specific style of type or print, for example, gothic, roman, pica, or elite. In certain typewriters you can choose the type style you prefer simply by changing the typing element.

formal sentence definition.   A sentence that defines a word or phrase by indicating the class to which it belongs and explaining the characteristics that distinguish it from other members of that class.

frame combination.   The type of combination of basic report components in which one kind of writing sets up a frame around another. For example, an introductory classification sentence that precedes a descriptive discussion of the classes. Contrast with *block combination* and *sentence combination*.

free-floating quotation.   A writing problem in which a direct quotation is presented within a report or article without attribution, that is, without any explanation as to the author or source of the quotation other than simple documentation such as a footnote or parenthetical reference. See *attribution of a quotation*.

government documents.   Information in the form of articles, pamphlets, reports, and books published and distributed by the government. Although the U.S. government is the largest publisher in the world, state and local governments also publish much literature. A large portion of government documents is in the form of technical reports.

graphic aids.   Those graphic devices that present illustrations of things, concepts, or numbers. See also *textual aids*.

guide to literature of a field.   A useful kind of reference book that helps you find specialized information sources for a specific field or profession, for example, specialized dictionaries and encyclopedias in the field of electronics. Also useful for locating other information about a field or profession such as important organization names and addresses.

handbook.   A type of reference book that presents in a condensed manner as much of the basic knowledge of a field as possible. Similar to a specialized encyclopedia except that the content is arranged in chapters rather than small alphabetized discussions of terms.

heading.   The title of an individual section within a report that indicates the subject matter and purpose of that section. Techniques such as position on the page, capitalization, and underlining are used to make first-level, second-level, and even lower-level headings.

informational report.   That class of reports that presents information to readers who have a specific need for it or interest in it but that does not provide instructions or recommend any action. For specific examples, see *technical-background report*, *progress report*, and *primary-research report*. Contrast with *feasibility report* and *instructions*.

informative comparison.   The kind of comparison that is done to help readers understand a technical subject. Such writing often uses comparison to familiar things to facilitate understanding. Contrast with *evaluative comparison*.

informative summary.   That kind of summary, often called an abstract, that presents the most important concepts, facts, conclusions, and recommendations of a report or article. Contrast with *descriptive summary*.

inquiry letter.   The kind of business letter that you write when you need information. See the two types, *solicited inquiry letter* and *unsolicited inquiry letter*.

in-sentence list.   A useful textual aid for making lists within sentences clearer by separating the items in those lists with parenthetical numbers or letters. For example, such elements as (a) words, (b) phrases, and (c) clauses can be presented with in-sentence listing. This device makes reading easier, emphasizes main points, and promotes better recall of information. See also *vertical lists*.

instructions.   That type of document in which explanation of how to construct, operate, repair, or perform something is provided.

invention.   A phase in preparing to write in which you identify the topics and subtopics that you may need to discuss. Synonymous with brainstorming. Contrast with *narrowing*.

keywords.   Those words or phrases that indicate the subject areas of reports, articles, and books and that are used to index those documents.

kind of writing.   See *report component*.

layman audience.   See *nonspecialist audience*.

legend.   Brief comments or descriptions accompanying a caption to a graphic aid that provide additional detail to that graphic aid or explain how to read it.

line drawing.   An illustration using only solid black-and-white lines or drawings, in contrast to a photograph, for example.

list or listing.   See *vertical list* and *in-sentence list*.

memorandum.   The kind of business correspondence that is used regularly within an organization or business. Memos have the characteristic headings of "TO," "FROM," and "SUBJECT."

narrowing.   The phase in planning a report in which you decide which topics related to the report subject to discuss and how to discuss them (generally or specifically, technically or nontechnically). Narrowing decisions are based on the report-writing situation: the purpose of the report and the needs and background of the report audience.

nonspecialist audience.   That type of audience that has no background in the subject of a report or article but that is interested in it or curious about it. Writers have to use translating techniques to enable these readers to understand. See *translation*, or other types of audiences—*experts, technicians*, and *executives*.

one-item outline entry.   A problem in outlining in which there is a Roman numeral *I* but no corresponding Roman numeral *II*, an *A* but no *B*, or a *1* but no *2*. In outlines there must be at least two items in every section or division.

overnominalization.   A writing problem in which too many nouns are jammed together in phrases, and the result is unclear, difficult reading. This problem is often corrected by transforming some of the nouns into verbs and rephrasing the sentence and by turning some of the nouns into dependent clauses or verbal phrases.

overview.   A technique used in introductions to both written and oral reports in which the main topics of discussion are listed. Overviews give readers and listeners a sense of what will be discussed and the order in which topics will be discussed.

paragraph coherence.   That quality of a paragraph that enables readers to follow the flow of ideas easily. Coherence is achieved through transitional devices and good organization.

paragraph development.   Discussion used to explain the topic or main point of a paragraph as completely as necessary. The tools for paragraph development include such kinds of writing as definition, description, comparison, classification, and examples.

paragraph organization.   The orderly arrangement of the units of discussion (points, ideas, etc.) within a paragraph.

paragraph topic.   The specific subject matter of a paragraph. A report may concern itself with solar devices for the average homeowner, but an individual paragraph might describe a solar cooling system used by an individual homeowner in the Southwest. See also *topic sentence.*

parallelism.   A grammatical term referring to similarity of phrasing in headings, lists, or outlines. A group of related outline items, for example, should have parallel phrasing; that is, they should be phrased in generally the same way.

passive voice.   A type of sentence phrasing in which the active agent of the sentence either comes after the main verb and after the prepositions *by* or *for* or is deleted from the sentence altogether. For example, the active-voice sentence, "The technician checked the gauges," in the passive voice would be "The gauges were checked by the technician" or "The gauges were checked." Misuse of the passive voice leads to unclear, wordy, impersonal writing.

periodical.   Any publication that comes out periodically, for example, a magazine, newspaper, or journal.

periodical index.   A reference book that enables you to find articles on a specific subject, for example, laser surgery or solar energy, in magazines or journals. See also *specialized periodical index.*

plagiarism.   The unethical, and in some cases, illegal use of other people's ideas and writing without proper documentation. Using other people's ideas or writing as if they were one's own.

point-by-point comparison.   That kind of comparison in which two or more things are compared one detail or feature at a time. For example, discussion of the costs of microwave ovens A, B, and C in paragraph 1, the special features of the three microwave ovens in paragraph 2, and so on. Contrast with *whole-to-whole comparison.*

points of comparison.   The specific aspects, features, or details by which you compare two or more things, for example, the costs, memory capacity, display screen, keyboard, and reliability of several computers.

popular science article.   An article on some aspect of modern technology and science written for nonspecialist readers. Primarily intended for nonspecialist readers who are interested in or curious about new technology but who have no direct professional or business need for such information. See also *feature article.*

preview element (in transitions).   An element of a transition, particularly of the transitional sentence, in which the discussion to follow is indicated. Provides a brief introductory glimpse of the next topic or subtopic of discussion. See *transitions* and *transitional sentence.* Contrast with *review element.*

primary-research report.   An informational report that presents the results of an experiment, survey, or other original information-gathering project. Contrast with *technical-background report.*

principle of classification.   The basis upon which a collection of things is put into separate and distinct categories. Computers can be categorized with such principles of classification as cost, memory capacity, or expandability, but not by more than one principle at a time. See *classification.*

process.   An event or action that is repeatable or repeated, for example, a natural process, a routine, or a set procedure. Any set of recurring actions or events in the natural world, in mechanisms, or in human society. Examples of processes include the formation of hurricanes, the operation of a computer, the gestation of human embryos, the election of a president, the raising of children, the gaining of an education, and the writing of a technical report. See also *step.*

process discussion.   A communication, either written or oral, in which a process is explained or discussed.

process narration.   See *process discussion.*

progress report.   A type of report that you write in order to update a customer, client, or associate on the progress you have made on a project.

proposal.   The kind of document you write in order to offer to do work (usually a fairly large project) for some individual or organization. Proposals typically explain such things as how you plan to carry out the project, what your background is, and what you plan to charge.

query letter.   A business letter you send to prospective publishers concerning an idea you have for an article or book. The letter describes the idea and explains its value.

reference book.   A tool used for finding information or for finding books, articles, or reports that have the information you are seeking. Reference books such as dictionaries, encyclopedias, and handbooks are tools for finding information; reference books such as periodical indexes are tools for finding the books, articles, or reports that have the information you seek.

report.   A communication, either written or oral, that contains information on a specific subject matter intended for a specific audience that has specific needs for or interests in that information.

report component.   A term used in a special sense in this book to refer to one of the common kinds of writing found in technical reports. Report components are characterized by unique contents, organizational patterns, or both. For specific examples, see *description, process discussion, causal discussion, classification,* and *comparison.*

report situation.   The specific set of circumstances that create the demand for a report, for example, a supervisor's orders or an organization's need for information.

report topic.   The specific focus of the discussion in a report as opposed to the general subject it concerns itself with: for example, a report on the subject of lasers that focuses specifically on the topic of uses of lasers in brain surgery. Contrast with *subject*.

resume.   A one-, two- or three-page summary of an individual's education, work experience, and other background relevant to a job application. Resumes are summaries of people's work qualifications that enable prospective employers to select new employees. See also *application letter*.

retrospective popular science articles.   The type of popular science article that recounts an event important in the history of science and technology or the work of an important scientist or engineer.

review popular science article.   The type of popular science article that covers recent work done on certain projects or in certain research areas, for example, the latest advances in insulin devices for diabetics.

review element (in transitions).   An element of a transition, particularly of the transitional sentence, in which the preceding discussion is indicated or summarized in a few words. Provides a brief recap of what has just been discussed. See *transitions* and *transitional sentence*. Contrast with *preview element*.

revision.   That phase in article or report writing in which you analyze the clarity, organization, and content and make corrections, improvements, or other changes in order to produce a better article or report.

rhetoric.   The art and skill of communicating in the most effective way possible. Using the techniques, strategies, and skills of communication to accomplish the purpose of the communication in the most effective way possible.

rhetorical organization.   A category of organizational patterns whose main concern is impact or influence on the reader. In contrast to spatial or chronological patterns, rhetorical patterns organize topics from least to most important, most to least convincing, or least to most controversial, for example.

running quotation.   A direct quotation that is a grammatical part of another sentence. A useful technique for trimming the length of direct quotations and avoiding the problem of free-floating quotations. Contrast with *block quotation*.

scale for comparison.   A kind of table used to present comparative information. Columns of numbers in comparison scales make the job of understanding the details and making a decision based on them easier. See also *weighted scale*.

scope.   The amount of information to be covered in a report, more specifically, which topics will be covered and how much detail will be provided on each topic. Often an element of introductions where the writer previews what he or she will and will not cover in the report. See also *narrowing*.

section.   A major division of a report made up of several paragraphs, similar to chapters in a book. Sections in reports are often marked by headings.

section introduction.   The paragraph or two that introduces the discussion contained in an individual section of a report. Section introductions have many of the same elements of whole-report introductions. Contrast with *whole-report introduction*.

sentence combination.   The kind of combination in which individual sentences of different kinds of writing are inserted into basic report components, for example, descriptive sentences scattered through an extended process narration. Contrast with *block combination* and *frame combination*.

solicited inquiry letter.   The type of inquiry letter in which the recipient has sought the inquiry in some way, for example, through advertisements or invitations to write for more information. Compare with *unsolicited inquiry letter*.

specialized periodical index.   A kind of reference book that enables you to find magazine or journal articles on specific subjects in specific fields, for example, computers, medicine, or agriculture. Most fields and professions have one or more specialized periodical indexes for articles specific to their interests.

step.   A group of related events or actions that occur or are performed in a process, for example, the information-gathering phase in writing a report. See also *process*.

style guide or manual.   A book published by a specific field or profession (for example, psychology, nursing, mathematics, engineering) that shows you how to handle footnotes, bibliographies, references, numbers, abbreviations, capitalizations, and other special problems in books, reports, and articles in that field.

subject.   A term that refers to the more general subject matter about which a report or article concerns itself; for example, the subject of a report on a new design for solar collectors might be energy or solar energy. Contrast this term with *topic,* the term referring to the specific subject matter of a report.

subject heading.   A word or phrase you use to find titles of books in the card catalog or other indexing source in a library: for example, you'd probably find books on the medical applications of lasers under the subject headings "lasers" and "medicine" in a library's card catalog.

subordination or subordinate elements.   A term referring to the kind of relationship between sentence or paragraph elements in which the elements are at different levels of detail. For example, dependent clauses are subordinate elements in sentences; sentences that comment on preceding sentences in paragraphs are subordinate elements in paragraphs. Contrast with *coordination*.

substep.   Groups of related events or actions that occur within a single step of a process. For example, in the information-gathering step in writing reports, there is the substep of finding books. See *step*.

summary.   Often called an abstract, a report element in which the important facts or contents of a report are summarized. See definitions of the two types of summaries, *descriptive summary* and *informative summary*.

summary table.   A table that combines numbers and words to present the main facts of a discussion, most often an extended comparison. In the comparison of several products, for example, some of the summarized information is typically numbers (costs, memory size, speed of operation) and words (brief indications such as "good," "fair," "medium," and "large"). Summary tables present the most important facts of a discussion so that they can be viewed and considered on a single page.

supplementary section.   Sections of other kinds of writing used in basic report components, for example, a paragraph explaining the process by which a machine operates when the rest of the report is descriptive.

supplementary sentence. Sentences of other kinds of writing used within basic report components, for example, a process sentence used in a description.

technical-background report. The type of informational report that presents information on a technical subject and that is built primarily from sources found in the library.

technical writing. The type of writing that involves practical written business and professional communication. The communication of technical information through writing. For specific examples, see *informational report, feasibility report, proposal, instructions,* and *popular science article.*

technician audience. That type of audience typically involved in construction, operation, repair, and maintenance but not necessarily in design, development, theory, and research. This audience's knowledge tends to be practical rather than theoretical. See *audience,* and other examples of audiences such as *expert* and *nonspecialist* audiences.

textual aids. Devices that help readers find their way around in a report or article: for example, page numbers, headings, tables of contents, lists of figures, and in-sentence and vertical lists. See also *graphic aids.*

topic. A specific portion of a subject that is discussed either in a report, in a section, or in a paragraph. See *paragraph topic, report topic,* and *topic sentence.*

topic sentence. A sentence that identifies the main topic of discussion or the purpose of a paragraph.

trade and association literature. Literature, usually periodicals, published by businesses, groups of businesses, and professional associations concerning their own interests. This literature is not generally available to the public. For example, beekeepers have their trade magazines; intensive-care nurses have their professional journals.

transitional sentence. A sentence that shows readers the relationship between the preceding thought (expressed in a section, paragraph, or portion of a paragraph) and the next. Contains a review, preview, and transition.

transitional words and phrases. Those words or phrases used in writing to indicate the logic or connection between ideas: for example, *therefore, and, on the other hand,* and *however.*

transitions. Devices or techniques used in writing to guide readers through the discussion, from idea to idea or point to point. For such devices see *transitional words and phrases, topic sentence, transitional sentence,* and *overview.*

translation. A term used in a special sense in this book to refer to the explanation of complex, technical subject matter for nonspecialist readers. Those writing techniques that help people who are just beginning to learn about a technical subject understand more easily.

true classification. A term referring to the locating of a thing in its proper class or type, for example, a new computer in one of the common categories of computers (microcomputer, minicomputer, mainframe). See *classification.* Contrast with *division.*

unit of discussion.   A portion of a paragraph that discusses one discrete idea or topic. Usually made up of only a few sentences. Used to analyze and evaluate the organization and coherence of paragraphs.

unsolicited inquiry letter.   The type of inquiry letter in which the recipient has not sought inquiries, as opposed to advertisers who invite further inquiries. Usually written to experts as a way of getting help or information on a subject. Compare with *solicited inquiry letter*.

verbal headings.   In oral reports, those words or statements that alert listeners to a change of subtopics in the oral report. A transitional device to help listeners follow an oral report. Compare with *heading*.

vertical list.   A textual-aid device in which a series of items (words, phrases, or whole sentences) is presented in a vertical column on the page rather than in regular paragraph format. This device makes reading easier, emphasizes main points, and promotes better recall of information. See also *in-sentence list*.

visual aids.   In oral reports, those illustrations, flip charts, objects for display, overhead projections, slides, handouts, and other devices used to present or emphasize information to the listeners. Compare with *graphic aids*.

vita.   The term often used in colleges and universities to refer to resumes. See *resume*.

weighted scale.   A kind of table used for comparing things in which different values have been assigned to different points of comparison. In comparing different computers, you might want to weight such things as cost, memory size, and reliability more heavily than color of the metallic cover of the system unit and display. See also *scale for comparison*.

whole-report introduction.   The paragraph or section that introduces an entire report. Contrast with *section introduction*.

whole-to-whole comparison.   That kind of comparison in which each object being compared is discussed separately. For example, all the comparative details about microwave oven A in one paragraph, all the details about microwave oven B in the next paragraph, and so on. Contrast with *point-by-point comparison*.

yearbook.   A type of reference book appearing yearly that summarizes the important events, activities, or developments of that year. There are general yearbooks covering a wide range of fields and specialized yearbooks covering individual fields.

Index

A

Abbreviations (in writing), 770–772
Abstract. *See* Informational summary; Descriptive summary
Adjective-Adverb problem, 738–739
Adjustment letter, 447–450
  example, 450
  steps for writing, 449
Adverbial conjunction, 698
Afterword, 180–184. *See also* Conclusion (final section)
Agreement problems, 731–737
Alternate block letter, 450, 476
Apostrophe, rules for, 751–752
Application letter, 454–459
  examples, 455–457
  follow-up letter to, 460
  steps for writing, 458–459
Applied Science and Technology Index, 373–374
Article. *See* Popular science article
Articles, finding, 372–376
Atlases, finding, 380
Attribution of a quotation, 401–403
Audience, 5, 205–216, 331, 426–427
  analysis chart for, 215–216
  analysis techniques, 205–216
  types, 207
Awkward phrasing, 310–312

B

Basis of classification. *See* Principle of classification
Bibliography card, 368, 371, 373, 379, 383, 397
Bindings (covers) for reports, 436
Block letter, 453, 460, 476
Block quotation, 402–403
Books, finding, 369–372
Brainstorming. *See* Invention
Business correspondence
  importance of, 444–445
  positioning on the page, 488
  tips on writing style, 479–486
Business correspondence, components of, 473–475
  complimentary close, 474
  end notations, 475
  envelope format, 476
  following-page format, 475
  heading, 473
  inside address, 473
  salutation, 473
  signature block, 475
  subject, reference line, 473
Business correspondence, format
  alternate block letter, 450
  block letter, 454, 460
  memorandum, 477–479

Business correspondence, format *(cont.)*
    semiblock letter, 446, 448
    simplified letter, 451–452
Business letters, types of
    application, 454–459
    complaint and adjustment, 447–450
    inquiry, 445–447
    order, 449–452
    query, 452–454

C

Capitalization, rules, 757–760
Card catalog (libraries), 370
Causal discussion, 45–58
    defined, 45–47
    model of, 69–71
    paragraph-length example, 56
    topics, 64
    types of, 46–49
Cause-effect discussion. *See* Causal
    discussion
Characteristics (in descriptions), 79–80
Checklist of invention questions, 332–334
Classification, 136–147
    defined, 136–138
    model of, 158–161
    paragraph-length example, 146
    principle of, 139–140
    topics, 152–153
    true classification, 136–138
Clauses and phrases. *See* Phrases and
    clauses
Cliches, 763
Coherence, in paragraphs, 288–295,
    715–724
Collaborative writing, 19–22, 30, 46, 74,
    86, 117, 138, 492, 543, 582, 628,
    659
    example schedule for, 22
    how to organize for, 20–21
Colon, rules for, 747–748
Comma, rules for, 742–745
Comma splice, 727–728
Commerce Business Daily, 584
Comparison, 86–100
    criteria, 90, 171
    defined, 86–87
    evaluative, 88–89
    informative, 86–88

model of, 108–114
    paragraph-length example, 98
    point-by-point, 91–92
    points of comparison, 90
    topics, 105
    transitions used in, 92–94
    whole-to-whole, 90–91
Compartmentalization (business letters),
    482
Complaint letter, 447–450
    example, 448
    steps for writing, 447–449
Complimentary close, 474
Computerized information retrieval,
    386–387
Conceptual diagram, 248, 252
Conclusion (final section), 175–184
    afterwords, 180–184
    conclusions, 178–180
    recommendations, 180–184
    summaries, 175–178
Coordinating conjunctions, 698
Coordination or coordinate elements,
    705–708
Copy editors' marks, 777–779
Correction symbols, 773–779
Cover label, 273, 436
Cover letter (articles), 647–679
Criteria, 90, 171

D

Dangling modifiers participles, 728–730
Dashes, rules for, 748–750
Data sheet. *See* Resume
Decimal system, outlines and headings,
    262–263
Deductive organization, 714
Definition, 116–136
    checklist, 120
    defined, 116–117
    extended definitions, 116–124
    formal sentence definition, 124–126
    model, 154–157
    organization, 121–124
    paragraph-length extended, 131, 134
    topics, 150
description, 73–76
    defined, 73–75
    model, 106–108

organization by characteristics, 79–80
organization by parts, 79–80
paragraph-length example, 76, 84
sources of information, 80–82
topics, 103–104
types, 74–75
Descriptive summary, 184–185
Development, paragraphs, 295–299,
 708–710
Diction, word choice, 760–764
Documentation systems, 682–690
 defined, 682
 for graphic aids, 686
 MLA system, 686–688
 name-year system, 683–684
 number system, 684–685
 plagiarism, 412, 682
 unusual sources, 688–690
 works-cited (MLA version) system,
  686–688

E

Elaboration (outlines), 344–347
Ellipsis, 754–755
Employment letter. *See* Application letter
End notations (letters), 475
Envelope format (letters), 476
Evaluative comparison, 88–89. *See also*
 Comparison
Examples and models (report types and
  components)
 causal discussion, 56, 69–71
 classification, 158–161, 146
 comparison, 98, 108–114
 description, 76, 84, 106–108
 extended definition, 131, 134, 154–157
 feasibility report, 606–619
 instructions, 573–579
 minutes of meetings, 521–522
 oral report, 677–678
 popular science article, 652–656
 primary research report, 528–531
 process discussion, 42, 65–69
 progress report, 525–527
 proposal, 601–605
 technical-background report, 532–540
 site-inspection report, 515–517
 survey results, 520
 work estimates, 518–519

Examples and models (subject matter of)
 acid rain, 15, 35, 49, 267, 315
 agriculture, 5, 29, 33, 46, 89, 246, 252,
  326, 503–504, 506–509, 528–531,
  568–570, 624–625
 Alzheimer's disease, 121–124, 134–135,
  511
 artificial heart, 73, 221–222
 astronomy, 7, 13, 33, 39, 80, 81, 137,
  370, 375
 automotive mechanics, 6, 29, 33, 47,
  98–99, 106–108, 118, 121–122, 182,
  271, 296–298, 511, 561–562, 565
 aviation, 8, 263–264, 448, 709–710
 blood-pressure reading, 65–69
 cocombustion of municipal solid waste
  (MSW), 170–171, 213, 328,
  339–341, 343–347, 349–356
 community and civic problems or
  projects, 13, 16, 79, 80, 165,
  208–210, 325, 326, 330, 388–393,
  591–593, 597–599, 717
 computerized speech recognition, 30,
  40, 188–189, 223, 269
 computers, 3, 4, 5, 13, 82, 87–88,
  91–93, 129, 132, 209, 223, 272,
  525–527, 719
 consumer issues, 12, 30, 95, 105, 106,
  253, 328, 448, 480, 520, 548, 551,
  554, 573–577, 577–579, 624–625
 desalination process and technologies,
  32–33, 178, 221, 326, 496, 512
 diabetes, 5, 13, 34, 35, 325, 446, 683
 drip irrigation, 89, 118
 electrical vehicles, 213, 715
 electronic publishing, 9
 electronics, 53, 76, 121, 126, 140, 146,
  225, 261, 274, 290–293, 460,
  471–472, 720
 engineering, 6, 13, 30, 46, 127, 174,
  191, 211, 225, 262, 298
 environmental issues, 6, 15, 35, 47, 49,
  51, 52, 56, 57, 79, 119, 123,
  128–129, 169, 172, 183–184, 224,
  258, 267, 284, 293–294, 315
 fiber optics, 30, 285
 forestry, 173, 601–605, 606–619, 621
 fractals, 13, 652–656
 general business, 118, 168, 185, 241,
  327, 515–519, 450–451, 478–479,
  500

Examples and models *(cont.)*
   genetics, 42, 44, 154, 227–228, 642
   greenhouse effect, 47, 51–52, 56–57,
     128–129, 169, 183–184, 284
   geology, 10–11, 55, 176–177, 198, 328
   hazardous wastes, 119, 258, 293–294
   honey bee dance language, 192–193
   Jupiter, 7, 137
   lab technology, 12, 30, 35, 66–69, 139,
     147, 164, 168, 176, 268, 299, 328,
     331, 446, 511, 549, 558–560, 563
   lasers, 8, 9, 30, 186, 229–230, 232,
     233–234, 313–315, 325
   Mars, 80, 81
   medical, 50, 52, 73, 121–124, 125,
     130–131, 134–135, 139, 147,
     218–219, 220, 221–222, 229, 242,
     282–285, 286–288, 300–303,
     317–319, 327, 511, 641, 646, 683,
     706–708
   meteorology, 30, 33, 46, 140, 284, 328,
     357–358
   neonatal care, 453
   nuclear power, 5, 11, 38, 81, 108–111,
     143–144, 197, 209, 293–294,
     339–340, 375–376, 398–416, 419,
     532–540, 686–688
   nuclear warfare, 40, 41, 69, 71, 627,
     684
   nursing, 5, 14, 65–69, 157, 259, 268,
     326, 327, 378, 446, 453, 511, 570,
     586–590
   oil spills, 6, 79, 123, 172, 224
   petroleum industry, 6, 79, 166–167,
     169, 174, 176–177, 187, 190, 257,
     420–425
   photography, 31, 39, 326, 327
   recycling, 13, 165, 326, 328, 492,
     661–662, 665–666, 669–670,
     671–673, 677–678
   robots, 13, 30, 80, 84–85, 158–161,
     179–180, 181, 226–227, 635–637
   sickle cell disease, 15, 118, 154–157,
     164, 227–228
   solar power, 26, 35, 49, 74, 77–79,
     179, 194–196, 239, 240, 289–290,
     326, 367
   space flight, 13, 33, 36, 264–266, 338,
     717, 722–723
   telescopes, 253

   wind power, 89, 111–118, 325,
     335–339, 341–342
Examples (business correspondence)
   adjustment letter, 450
   application letter, 455–457
   complaint letter, 448
   cover letter, 648–649
   follow-up letter (to application letters),
     460
   inquiry letter, 392–393, 446
   memoranda, 478–479
   order letter, 450, 451
   query letter, 453
Executive audience, 207. *See also*
   Audience
Exercises on
   graphic aids, 275
   outlining, 357–358
   paragraph coherence, 314–317
   paragraph development, 317–318
   paragraph organization, 314–317
   sentence style, 319
   textual aids, 278
Expert audience, 207. *See also* Audience
Expletives, problems with, 309–310
Exploratory draft, 417
Extended definition. *See* Definition

F

Feasibility report, 326, 590–599
   ideas, 591–592
   model, 606–619
   phases in a feasibility study, 592–598
   typical parts, 592–598
Feature article. *See* Popular science article
Field-trip report, 515–517, 519
Final packaging, 430–436
   binding, 435–436
   cover label, 436
   hired typists, 432–433
   photocopying, 435
   taping illustrations, 434
   typing tips, 431–433
   word processing, 433
Final section. *See* Conclusion (final
   section)
Finding government documents, 380–383
Finding report topics, 326–330
Flowchart, 248–250, 441–442, 673–674

Following-page format (letters), 475
Follow-up letter, 460. *See also* Application letter
Font, 431–432
Formal sentence definition, 124–126
Fragments, 726–727
Free-floating quotation, 400–403

G

Glossaries (in reports), 273
Government documents, 380–383, 390–391
  documenting, 688–690
Grammar and usage problems, 312–314, 726–772
  handbook for, 725–772
  how to study for, 312–314
Graphic aids, 237–256
  documenting borrowed, 686
  function, 237
  informal tables, 242
  incorporating into reports, 256, 434
  for key concepts, 248
  for numbers, 239
  for physical things, 238
  pie charts, 244
  planning and developing, 251–256
  summary table, 251–253
  weighted scales, 243
  for words, 251
Guide to literature of a field, 377

H

Handbook (specific fields), 379–380
Heading (letters), 473
Headings, 257–266
  common system, 257–258
  decimal system, 262–263
  guidelines, 258–262
Homonyms, 764
How-to popular science article, 622–625
Human perspective, 231–232. *See also* Translation
Hyphens, rules for, 750–751

I

Indexes, periodical, 372–376
Inductive organization, 711
Informational report, 491–540
  defined, 325–326, 491–492
  field-trip report, 515–519
  minutes of meetings, 521–522
  progress report, 493–499
  primary research report, 499–506
  survey results, 519–520
  technical-background report, 506–514
  work estimate, 514–519
Informative comparison, 86–87. *See also* Comparison
Informative summary (abstract), 186–199
  defined, 186
  developing, 193–199
  examples, 189, 192–193
  keywords, 190
In-other-words technique. *See* Translation
Inquiry letter, 445–447
  examples, 392–393, 446
  steps for writing, 445–447
In-sentence list, 270–272
Inside address (letters), 473
Instructions, 30–32, 326, 542–579
  complex, 547–553
  critical parts, 567
  critical points, 567
  elements of, 544–547
  ideas for, 543–544
  illustrations, 564–569
  models, 573–579
  simple, 547
  supplementary sections, 557–564
  task-oriented, 548
  testing, 572
  tool-oriented, 550
  types of steps, 553–557
Instructors' marks, 773–777
Interest groups, 383–386
Introductions, 163–175
  elements, 163–171
  for sections, 171–175
  for whole reports, 163–171
Inventing report situations and audiences, 212–213
Invention (brainstorming), 331–336
Invention questions checklist, 332–334

Inventorying paragraph organization, 285–288

J

Job letter. *See* Application letter

K

Keywords, 190–193
Kind of writing. *See* Report component

L

Layman audience. *See* Nonspecialist audience
Length
  of paragraphs, 299–303
  of sentences, 312
Libraries, using, 368–387
  finding articles, 372–376
  finding books, 369–372
  finding government documents, 380–383
  finding guides to field-specific literature, 377
  finding periodical indexes, 372–378
  finding reference works, 376–380
  finding reports, 380–383
  finding style guides, 377
  finding subject headings, 368–369
  finding trade and association literature, 383–386
  overview of sources, 364–367
Library of Congress Subject Headings (LCSH), 368–369
Line drawing, 238, 248
List of abbreviations, 277
List of figures, 270
List or listing, 270–272

M

Memorandum, 477–479
  examples, 478–479
  format, 447
  on report topic, 359–360

  similarities to business letters and reports, 477
Minutes of meetings, 521–522
Miscellaneous usage problems, 740–742
Misplaced modifiers, 728–730
MLA system (documentation), 686–688
Models. *See* Examples and models
Modifier problems, 728–730

N

Name-year system (documentation), 683–684
Narrowing (topics), 336–338
Nonlibrary sources of information, 388–393
Nonspecialist audience, 207. *See also* Audience
Notecard
  compared to rough draft, 420–425
  examples, 399, 401, 404, 409–411, 413–414
  information on, 398
Note-taking process, 396–417
  other systems, 417–418
  paraphrasing sources, 404–407
  quoting sources, 400–404, 752–755
  by the source, 417–419
  summarizing sources, 407–412
  traditional system, 396–417
  updating the outline, 412–415
Numbers or words, 766–770
Number system (documentation), 684–685

O

One-item outline entry, 352–354
Oral reports, 658–678
  delivery problems, 663–664
  evaluation form, 675–676
  excerpts, 677–678
  functions, 658
  ideas, 658–659
  overviews, 665–666
  verbal aids, 665–666
  verbal headings, 666
  visual aids, 667–674
  ways to prepare, 659–663

Organization, of paragraphs, 285–288
Organization of this book. *See* Using this book
Outlining, 338–356
  common patterns, 339–344
  elaborating, 344–347
  finishing, 347–356
  typical problems, 343–344, 347–356
  updating, 412–415
Overnominalization, 304–305
Overview (introductions), 166
Overview (report types), 325–326

P

Pagination (reports), 272–273
Paragraph coherence, 715–724
Paragraph development, 708–710
Paragraph organization, 711–715
Paragraph revision, 280–304
  coherence, 288–295
  development, 295–299
  length, 299–303
  organization, 285–288
  topic sentence, 282–285
Paragraph structure, 704–708
Parallelism, 728
Paraphrasing, 404–407
Parentheses, rules for, 756–757
Part-by-part description, 79–80
Parts of speech, 695–701
Parts of the sentence, 694–695
Passive-voice problems, 309
Periodicals, finding, 372–378
Periodical index, finding, 372–378
Phrases and clauses
  adjective clause, 700
  adverb clause, 700
  appositive, 699
  gerund, 699–700
  noun clause, 701
  participial phrase, 699–700
  predicate, 694
  preposition phrase, 699
  verb phrase, 694
Plagiarism, 412, 682
Point-by-point comparison, 91–92
Points of comparison, 90

Popular science article, 13, 621–656
  characteristics, 631–637
  conclusions, 641–646
  cover letter, 647–649
  how-to articles, 622–625
  ideas, 626–628
  instructions to authors, 650
  locating and analyzing magazines, 628–631
  openers, 637–641
  query letter, 452–454
  retrospectives, 626–627
  reviews, 625–626
  travelogues, 626–627
Predication problems, 310
Preview transition, 175–177
Primary research report, 499–506
  defined, 499–500
  ideas, 500–502
  model, 528–531
  parts of, 502–505
Principle of classification, 139–140
Principle parts of verbs, 730–731
Process
  component of report, 29–30
  concept in this book, 9–10
  of writing reports, 440–442
process discussion, 29–45
  defined, 29–30
  models, 65–69
  paragraph-length example, 42
  topics, 62–63
  types, 30–35
Process narration. *See* Process discussion
Progress report, 493–499
  defined, 493
  formats, 493–494
  ideas, 493
  information-gathering strategy, 496–498
  model, 525–527
  organization, 494–495
Pronouns, problems with, 734–738
Proposal, 582–590
  defined, 581
  ideas, 582–583
  model, 601–605
  parts, 584–590
  types, 583–584
Punctuation, rules for, 742–757

Q

Query letter, 452–454
  example, 453
  steps for writing, 454
Questionnaires, 390
Quotation, 400–404
  guidelines for, 401–404
  rules for, 400–404, 752–755

R

Readers of reports. *See* audience
Redundant phrasing, 305–306
Redundant words and phrases (list), 306
Reference books, finding, 376–378
Report component
  causal discussion, 45–58
  classification, 136–147
  comparison, 86–100
  definition, 116–136
  description, 73–86
  process discussion, 29–45
Report situation
  defined, 6–7, 211
  inventing, 212–213
Report topic
  how to find, 326–330
  list of possibilities, 328
  memorandum on, 359–360
Report-topic memo, 359–360
Report types, overview, 325–326
Research strategy, 362–368
Resume, 459–472
  designing format, 462–470
  examples, 471–472
  gathering information, 459–462
  sketch, 463
  steps in preparing, 472
Retrospective popular science articles,
  626–627
Review popular science articles, 625–626
Review transition, 175–177
Revision, 280–314, 425–430
  defined, 280–281, 425–429
  of business correspondence, 479–486
  overview of the process, 281, 425–429
  for paragraph coherence, 288–295

  for paragraph development, 295–299
  for paragraph length, 299–303
  for paragraph organization, 285–288
  planning a strategy for, 426–430
  problem-spotting tips, 429–430, 434
  for sentence style, 304–314
  specific problem categories, 426–430
  for topic sentences, 282–285
Rhetoric, 714
Rhetorical organization, 714
Rhetorical questions, 225–227. *See also*
  translation
Rough drafts, 420–425
  preparations for, 418–419
  and related notecards, 420–422
Running quotation, 401–403
Run-on problem, 727–728

S

Salutation (letters), 473
Scales (comparison), 242–243
Scope (of report), 325–326
Section introduction, 171–175
Semiblock letter, 446, 448, 476
Semicolons, rules for, 745–747
Sentence patterns, 692–694
Sentence style problems, 304–315
  awkward phrasing, 310–312
  expletive problems, 309–310
  grammar, usage, and punctuation
    problems, 312–314
  overnominalization, 304–305
  passive-voice problems, 309
  predication problems, 310
  redundant phrasing, 305–306
  sentence length, 312
  weak *be* verbs, 308
  weak pronouns, 307–308
Sheehy's *Guide to Reference Books*,
  376–377
Signature block (letters), 475
Simplified letter, 451–452, 476
Site-inspection report, 515–519
Situation, of reports, 6–7, 211–213
Solicited inquiry letter, 445
Specialized periodical index, 372–376,
  378

Spelling problems, 764–766
Step, 18, 37
Style guide or manual, 377
Subject guide, 377. *See also* Guide to the literature of a field
Subject heading, 367–368
Subject, reference line (letters), 473
Subject-verb agreement, 731–733
Subordinating conjunctions, 698
Subordination or subordinate elements, 705–708
Substep, 41
Summaries (in note taking), 407–412
Summary (abstract-type). *See* Informational summary; Descriptive summary
Summary (final section), 175–178. *See also* Conclusion (final section)
Summary table, 251–253
Surveys, 390
Survey-results reports, 519–520
Symbols, in writing, 772

T

Table of contents (of reports), 188, 268–269
Task-oriented instructions, 548
Team report-writing. *See* Collaborative writing
Technical article. *See* Popular science article; Primary-research report
Technical-background report, 506–514
  defined, 506–510
  ideas, 328
  model, 532–540
Technical reports, overview, 325–326
Technical writing
  defined, 2–11
  importance, 2, 15–16
  skills needed, 14–15
  writers, 12–13
Technician audience, 207. *See also* Audience
Tense-shift problem, 735–757
Textual aids, 257–275
Thomas Register, 96, 384–385
Title page (reports), 273–274
Titles (reports), 267
Tool-oriented instructions, 550

Topic list, for reports, 328
Topic-proposal memo, 359–360
Topics, for
  causal discussion, 63–64
  classification, 152–153
  comparison, 105
  definition, 150
  description, 103–104
  extended definition, 150
  feasibility reports, 582–583, 591–592
  instructions, 543–544
  oral reports, 658–659
  primary research reports, 499–501
  process discussion, 62–63
  progress reports, 493
  proposals, 582–583
  popular science articles, 622–628
  technical-background reports, 328
Topic sentence, 282–285, 703–704
  defined, 282, 703
  examples, 282–285, 703–705
  revising for, 283–284
  types, 285, 703–704
Trade and association literature
  finding, 383–386
Transitional devices, 288–295, 715–728
Transitional paragraph, 721, 724
Transitional sentence, 175–177
Transitional words and phrases, 717–718
Transitions, 715–728
  defined, 715–717
  specific techniques, 288–295, 717–728
Translation, 205–206
  defined, 205–206
  specific techniques for, 216–234
Travelogue popular science article, 627–628. *See also* Popular science article
True classification, 136–138. *See also* Classification
Typing reports, 431–433

U

Unit of discussion, 285–286
Unusual sources, documenting, 688–690
Unsolicited inquiry letter, 445
Using this book, 16–19
  filling out worksheets, 26

Using this book *(cont.)*
    flowchart for using this book, 441–442
    how to use Part I chapters, 24–25
    how to use Part II chapters, 202–203
    how to use Part III chapters, 322–323
    how to use Part IV chapters, 440–442
    how to use Part V appendices, 680
    organization of the main parts, 16–17
    planning reports with Part I, 35, 49,
       75–79, 89, 117–118, 138–139
    process approach, 19
    steps (blue-lettered), 18
    worksheets, 18, 25–27

V

Verbal headings (oral reports), 661
Verbs, problems with, 730–733
Vertical list, 270–272
Visual aid (oral reports), 667–674
Vita. *See* Resume

W

Weak *be* verb problems, 308
Weak pronoun problems, 307–308
Weighted scale, 243
Whole-report introduction, 163–171
Whole-to-Whole comparison, 90–91. *See also* Comparison
Word choice (diction), 760–764
Words or numbers, 766–770
Work-cited system (documentation), 686–688
Work-estimate reports, 514, 518–519
Worksheets, 18, 25–27
    example of, 26
    filling out, 25–27

Y

Yearbook, 365, 378–379